PRICE GUIDE TO ANTIQUE
AND CLASSIC CAMERAS
Sixth Edition
1987-1988

Edited by James M. McKeown
and Joan C. McKeown

Sixth Edition on press. Published June 1, 1987

European Distributors:
Hove Foto Books
Hove, East Sussex, U.K.

Library of Congress Catalog Card Number: 87-070880

ISBN 0-931838-09-6 (PAPER)
ISBN 0-931838-10-X (CLOTH)

EDITORS
James M. McKeown
Joan C. McKeown

ASSISTANT EDITOR
LeeAnne Byers

**HISTORICAL AND
TECHNICAL CONSULTANTS**
Roger Adams
Ron Anger
Bob Barlow
William P. Carroll
Don Chatterton
Peter Dechert
Dr. Arthur Evans
Matthew Isenberg
Robert Johnson
Alan Kattelle
KEH Camera Brokers
Mike Kessler
Mead Kibbey
Dr. Rudolf Kingslake
George Kirkman
Helmut Kummer
Eaton S. Lothrop, Jr.
Steve Lyons
Thurman F. Naylor
Richard Paine
Mr. Poster
Michael Pritchard
Jack & Debbie Quigley
Cynthia A. Repinski
Robert Rotoloni
Dr. Burton Rubin
Richard Sanford
Jerry Smith
Bob Sperling
Frank Storey
Jim Stewart
Jay Tepper
Paul-Henry van Hasbroeck
Allen Weiner

OTHER CONTRIBUTORS
Dennis Allaman
Sig Bloom
Peter Boots
Robert Byers
Bob Campbell
Barney Copeland
John Courtis
John S. Craig
Ray D'Addario
Alton H. Donor
RoBerta Etter
Ken Hough
Wesley Jost
Mike Kudla
Mike McCabe
Tom McKeown
Tim McNally
Parker Pen Co.
Pilecki's Camera Exchange
Bill Savage
Harry Smith
Vintage Cameras Ltd.
Gene Vogel
Gerry Vogel
Marge Vogel
Gene Whitman
Dick Whitstone
Duane Williams
British Journal Photographic
    Almanac

PRICE RESEARCH STAFF
Jeremy Byers
David Vogel
Denise Vogel
Tom Vogel, Sr.
Tom Vogel, Jr.

ON THE COVER

FRONT COVER - *Bower X Model II (burgundy)*
Revere Eye Matic EE 127
Kiddie Camera, Clown
Deyrolle Scenographe
Gerschel Le Mosaic
Mamiyaflex II
Hunter Gilbert
Yamato Pax Golden View

BACK COVER - *Anthony & Scovill Stereo Solograph*
Shelcore Clicker Bear "Squeez-a-Mal"
Asahiflex I
Hermagis Micromegas
EKC Gift Kodak No. 1A with Gift box
United Optical Instruments Merlin (green)
Bell & Howell Two Twenty
Rolleicord bank
Kalart Press camera
Bochod (Voskho)
Foster Swiftshot (Made in Australia)
K.S.K. Corona

DEDICATION

To DAVIDA COPELAND
1923-1986
Whose untiring efforts
helped to shape not only the
Chicago Photographic Collectors Society
but the entire field of camera collecting.

McKeown's Law:

The price of an antique camera is entirely dependent upon the moods of the buyer and seller at the time of the transaction.

CONTENTS

ACKNOWLEDGEMENTS

This book has grown tremendously since its first edition fourteen years ago, not only in the number of cameras included, but also in the amount and accuracy of the information on each. Obviously this has not been the work of a single individual. This current edition has benefitted greatly from the knowledge and research of many authorities in specialized areas of the camera collecting field. The depth of information in these specialty areas would not have been possible without their generous sharing, for while the job of editing this guide requires a broad interest in the field, this wide interest is necessarily shallow overall.

A totally new section in this edition is ACCESSORIES, virtually all of which was contributed by *Fred Waterman*, a camera collector since 1972. His current interests center around novel cameras with unusual devices or appearance, and the accessories of photography such as meters, exposure guides, darkroom equipment, etc. He welcomes correspondence from collectors with similar interests and is actively seeking to expand his collection of accessories. Write to him at: 1704 Valencia Dr.; Rockford, IL 61108.

The basis for the movie camera section was information supplied by *Wes Lambert* on the early 35mm and professional cameras. For this edition, a large amount of new material was provided by *Alan Kattelle*. Alan provided information and photos for many unusual cameras and virtually all of the projectors included in this edition. Cine enthusiasts are welcomed to contact Alan at: 50 Old County Rd.; Hudson, MA 01749. Also see his ad on page 662.

The section on Minolta is primarily the work of *Jack & Debbie Quigley* of Quigley Photographic Services. They provided dates and technical information as well as photographs for nearly every Minolta model up to about 1965. The Quigleys are well known authorities on Minolta. Debbie runs the mail order end of their business and teaches photography. Jack takes time from his career in commercial photography, camera repair and custom crafting to write the "Minolta Mania" column for Shutterbug.

The Zeiss-Ikon section is the work of *Mead Kibbey*. Mead is widely recognized as one of the world's leading authorities on Zeiss-Ikon.

Peter Dechert is responsible for the Canon section. Dr. Dechert is well known as a leading authority in the field of Canon rangefinder cameras, and author of the book *Canon Rangefinder Cameras* published by Hove Foto Books.

Bob Rotoloni, who literally wrote the book on Nikon, was the major contributor for that section. His book, *Nikon Rangefinder Cameras*, is published by Hove Foto Books.

Paul-Henry van Hasbroeck contributed historical information and photographs for the Leica section. Paul-Henry is the author of several books on Leica cameras, including *Leica: A History Illustrating Every Model and Accessory*.

Art Evans supplied information for the Franke & Heidecke (Rollei) section. His book, *Collectors Guide to Rollei Cameras*, is published by Centennial Photo Service.

Dick Paine was kind enough to let us use material from his book, *Graflex, The All American Cameras*. Further help in the Graflex area was provided by *Roger Adams*, who is currently working on a book on the subject.

Jim Stewart provided help in several areas, of which the Alpa section is only the most obvious. Many other details and bits of information provided by Mr. Stewart are scattered throughout the book, in areas including 35mm and subminiature cameras. He may be contacted at 201-361-0114.

Bill Carroll made numerous additions throughout the guide. His particular interests are early shutters, small format rollfilm cameras, mechanically complex cameras (built-in motor drives or other unusual features), camera look-alikes (flasks, compacts, etc.), and non-photo-electric exposure determining devices. Contact him at 8500 La Entrada, Whittier, CA 90605, (213)-693-8421.

Mike Kessler is particularly interested in unusual 1880-1890's disguised or detective cameras and Simon Wing cameras. He may be reached at 25749 Anchor Circle, San Juan Capistrano, CA 92675, (714)-661-3320.

George Kirkman provided information on many early stereo cameras. He will field questions on (or buy) stereo cameras (1900-1940) and would appreciate hearing from you at: P.O. Box 24468, Los Angeles, CA 90024, (213)-208-6148.

The Western Photographic Collectors Association volunteered to respond to any questions on collectible cameras. If they don't have the answers, they will find someone who does. Write: WPCA, P.O. Box 4294, Whittier, CA 90607. Please include a self-addressed, stamped envelope.

In addition to the historian/collectors, we are indebted to another group of friends who are the market specialists. These are primarily dealers or very active collectors who review the price data from a viewpoint based on extensive experience in the general market or specialized areas thereof. While the majority of the prices in this book are derived from our database of worldwide sales records, it is of critical importance that these figures be reviewed for possible errors. We communicate regularly with many of the top dealers and collectors in the field to constantly verify our statistics.

Jay Tepper has always been willing to help in this area. Jay and his wife Bobby publish a monthly list and regularly purchase large numbers of cameras worldwide to maintain their extensive inventory. He may be contacted at 313 N. Quaker Lane, West Hartford, CT 06119 U.S.A. Tel: 203-233-2851.

Don Chatterton is a specialist in the Leica field, and we greatly appreciate his help with the nuances of Leica pricing. He actively buys and sells Leica cameras. See his display advertisement in the back of this book or call 805-682-3540.

Bob Barlow helped eliminate some of the confusion among the various Contax-type cameras made in post-war East Germany. Bob specializes in East German Contax cameras, and welcomes the exchange of information and/or equipment. Contact him at P.O. Box 76, Livingston, NJ 07039.

Ron Anger contributed to the Ernemann section from the market and historical viewpoints.

Subminiature camera collecting has its specialists who were also very cooperative, including *Bob Johnson, Don Sellers, Jim Stewart, and Jay Tepper.*

Allen Weiner was called upon for his respected opinion on relatively unusual cameras for which there are always inadequate sales figures to make a good average. Allen & Hilary Weiner are well established and respected dealers who are always interested in buying entire collections or fine individual items. They may be contacted at 80 Central Park West, New York City 10023. Tel: 212-787-8357.

Thurman F. (Jack) Naylor of Cameras & Images International Inc. has always been generous in sharing his knowledge in both the historical and pricing areas. Certainly one of the world's leading collectors, Jack keeps abreast of the latest price trends on significant cameras, and has also been thoroughly cooperative in providing needed information on many of the rare items from his collection.

9

Camera manufacturers are in business to sell cameras, not to provide historical information to those of us who live with one foot in the past. In spite of the sometimes cold push toward productivity so prevalent in today's world, there are a few camera manufacturers who took time from their schedules to provide us with information and/or photographs. Included are *Agfa-Gevaert, Eastman Kodak Co., Ernst Leitz GmbH, Victor Hasselblad Aktiebolag, VEB Pentacon, Robot Foto & Electronic GmbH, Rollei-Werk, Ehrenreich Photo Optical Industries, and Durst S.A.* We would like to thank them for the help they have provided.

Numerous other people and organizations have helped, and unfortunately they can not all be listed here. Even the list of contributors at the front of the book is not nearly complete. This book has become a depository for useful information, and we are often approached by collectors at camera shows who fill in bits and pieces of information gleaned from new purchases and discoveries. We receive many letters and postcards with contributions of historical, technical, or pricing information. All of this is greatly appreciated. While we have tried to list the major contributors, I am sure that there are omissions, and I would like to thank especially those whose contributions are going temporarily without recognition.

I would like to thank all the people who helped me recover from a serious injury and put me back on my feet again in time to finish this book. Special thanks to Dr. Ramon Rodriguez-Rivas, whose presence was always reassuring, and who took time to answer my many questions. But most of all, I appreciate the care and companionship of Richard and Norma Rodriguez who adopted me and kept my spirits up. They are indeed special people.

FOR FURTHER INFORMATION:
We receive many inquiries and requests for further information, far more than we can possibly answer. We do not give opinions or appraisals on items not included in this book. We realize that many cameras are not included in this book, and caution you that omission does not indicate rarity. We have excluded at least 30,000 cameras for various reasons to keep this book to a reasonable size and price. Some of the excluded cameras include: most cameras produced since the 1960's, which are generaly more usable than collectible; most 126 and 110 cameras which were produced in such large numbers that they are common and inexpensive; and many early cameras which rarely are seen for sale. We have selected about 6,000 cameras which are representative of the field of camera collecting, and for which we can determine typical selling prices.

Requests for further information will be considered only if a self-addressed, stamped envelope is enclosed with the inquiry. There is often a delay of several months in answering such inquiries due to our backlog of mail.

SAVE 20% ON EVERY NEW BOOK WE PUBLISH
We can't control the cost of paper and printing, but we can hold down your cost for the next edition of this book. Each time we go to press, we need cash to buy over 10 tons of paper, not to mention all the associated supplies and services. By ordering your book a month in advance you help us tremendously. Not only does it help us with our printing costs, but it gives us time to get your mailing label and package ready so we can ship your book within hours of the time it leaves the bindery. In return for your early order, we give you a 20% discount.

Where else can you get a 20% per month return on your investment? But we can't offer you this special price if we don't know who you are. We promise to offer you a discount on every new book we publish, plus first day shipping if you will just send your name and address on a postcard or letter to:
Centennial Photo
Pre-Pub Club
Rt. 3 Box 1125
Grantsburg, WI 54840

INTRODUCTION

The first edition of *Price Guide to Antique & Classic Still Cameras* was published in 1974, shortly after the camera collecting hobby came out of the closet. Since that time, this guide has been the single most complete and accurate reference guide to cameras in the entire field. The first edition included 1000 cameras. This Sixth Edition now includes over six times that number. Not only has it been expanded to include more camera models, but we have made every effort to expand the information given for the individual cameras, providing dates and historical information wherever possible. We have also added over 500 new photographs to make a total of 2000 cameras illustrated. Each new edition of this guide has made significant improvements over the last, and with your support we hope to continue this tradition.

WHERE ARE PRICES GOING?

In order to understand the current and future prices of collectible cameras, it helps to know some of the history. The general trends of prices showed ascending patterns through 1981 and a leveling off about 1982-83 with some items beginning to drop. In 1983 and 1984, camera prices dropped considerably, especially in reference to the American Dollar, which is our basis. Partially this was due to the general softening of the market and of course a good portion of the loss was due to the rapid rise in the value of the dollar compared to other currencies. The rate of decline slowed in 1985, and by 1986 had stabilized and some items had begun to recover. By late 1986 and early 1987, the relative strength of British, German, and Japanese currencies against the Dollar had strengthened the market, since shopping for classic cameras in the U.S. was a little like shopping in a discount store. Prices in the U.S. began to firm up for many of the better collectibles.

Extremely rare, important, and unique cameras in the higher price ranges (over $10,000) had experienced the least depression in the 1983-85 period. The small number of collectors active in that segment of the market are not generally as susceptible to short-term fluctuations in the economy. Price fluctuations in that range are generally more related to currency exchange rates than buying fads. Prices in the $3,000-10,000 range had softened as we entered the 1983-1984 period as the collectors who purchase cameras in that range tightened the purse-strings. This is an area of the market which is still limited to a rather small group of collectors. Since the cameras in that range are few, and those who seek them are few, the entire market can be affected by a much smaller number of people. While individual cameras suffer greatly from the supply and demand syndrome, this area of the market is remaining quite stable overall and many changes in price figures are due only to currency fluctuation.

During the 1983-85 slump, the most drastically affected by the softened market were the low and medium priced cameras in less than perfect condition. As camera sales slowed, collectors were able to be more selective in their purchases. From a wider selection of offerings, they were able to purchase those items in better condition and pass up anything which showed heavy signs of use or abuse. And so while some of the prices of cameras did not drop as much as one would have expected, the toll was paid by the models in lesser condition to maintain the prices of those in better shape. In the stabilized market of 1987, we find that cameras in imperfect condition have not rebounded.

It should be emphasized that these are generalities, and that each camera must be individually considered. Obviously a low-priced camera which is rare will not suffer like a common one, and some types of cameras will be affected more than others by these conditions.

One phenomenon which has been noted by many dealers is the continual fluctuation within the market. Some have compared it to the stock market and insist that the only ones who know the value of a camera are those who are in the market daily. There is a certain element of truth in this. Those who are in the market as a daily way of life can spot a chance to pick up a few percentage points by trading or buying the right camera at the right time. To the normal collector, however, this is not of great importance, since these fluctuations are both up and down. The long range graph for any particular camera is generally quite steady. As a matter of fact, from an investment standpoint, cameras have been a relatively stable investment. Our statistics show that over the broad range of collectible cameras, the appreciation rate is surprisingly similar. From the perspective of seventeen years of keeping records of the values of collectible cameras, we find that the most rapid changes in values are usually due to the "fad factor" or readjustment of priorities among collectors.

WELCOME BACK, COLLECTORS! BON VOYAGE, SPECULATORS!

When camera collecting was experiencing a boom in the late 1970's, speculators began buying heavily and indiscriminately, which fanned the flames of inflation and drove prices to the breaking point. Some collectors left the field as they saw the commercial aspect of collecting overshadow the historians and hobbyists who truly appreciated the cameras and not just their price tags. The major slump of 1982-83 was a cloud with a silver lining. Many speculators left the field, and new collectors joined our ranks. While prices may not be as high as they once peaked, the field is stronger and more stable than it was a few years ago.

ADVICE TO NEW COLLECTORS

Our advice to collectors would depend entirely on your motives for collecting. If you are concerned with collecting as an investment, you should concentrate on the more rare and unusual camera models, which will naturally require more capital and expertise. If you are collecting primarily for the enjoyment of it, you should follow the dictates of your interest and budget. Many of the lower-priced cameras offer an inexpensive hobby, and often this is a good place to start. Most collectors start out with a general interest which often becomes more defined and specialized as they continue in collecting. If you are dealing in cameras to make a profit, you must maintain close contact with the market, and remain within your area of expertise. By following the market closely, you can make a profit from its ordinary fluctuations, and by knowing your customers' interests.

All prices in this edition have been updated. They are as current as possible, and data has been weighted toward the most recent figures. However, we have also retained the stabilizing influence of the 10 year price record of each camera to prevent the "overshooting" which can occur in a less researched effort. Our prices tend to follow the long-term trends more accurately in the same way that a viscous-damped compass maintains a smooth heading.

The information and data in this edition is based on hundreds of thousands of verifiable sales, trades, offers, and auction bids. It lists cameras from over 1000 manufacturers. It contains thousands of little bits and pieces of photographic history and trivia, many of which are not to be found in other reference works. It is a reference work -- a research report. The prices do not tell you what I think the camera is worth, but they tell you what a lot of former owners and present owners thought it was worth at the moment of truth. That is the essence of "McKeown's Law" which states: **"The price of an antique camera is entirely dependent upon the moods of the buyer and seller at the time of the transaction."**

Several corollaries have been added to this general philosophy of collecting.
1. **"If you pass up the chance to buy a camera you really want, you will never have that chance again."**
2. **"If you buy a camera because you know you will never have the chance again, a better example of the same camera will be offered to you a week later for a much lower price."**
3. **"The intrinsic value of an antique or classic camera is directly proportional to the owner's certainty that someone else wants it."** -*Dan Adams*
These observations should always be taken into account when applying McKeown's Law.

INSTRUCTIONS FOR USE OF THIS GUIDE:

All cameras are listed by manufacturer, and manufacturers are listed in alphabetical order. A few cameras are listed by model name if we were not sure of the manufacturer. Generally, we have listed the cameras under each manufacturer in alphabetical order, but occasionally we have grouped them by type, size, or date of introduction or other sequence appropriate to the situation.

Photos appear immediately above the listing which describes them. In a few cases, the photographs have been positioned nearby and identified with a caption.

We have used different type faces to make the guide easier to follow. The pattern is as follows:

MANUFACTURER NAME (all caps)
Historical notes or comments on the manufacturer.
Camera Name - Description of camera and current value data. *Special notes regarding camera or price.*

CAMERA NAME - If the camera model name is in all caps, it is a separate listing, not related to the previous manufacturer. We use this style usually when the manufacturer is unknown.

CONDITION OF CAMERAS
Two recent trends in describing condition should be noted. The first is a rather alarming number of people who consistently describe the condition while looking through rose-colored glasses. One dealer, speaking of his printed ads, recently said to me: "If I don't put it down as Excellent, I can't sell it." Personally, I disagree with that policy and attitude. In the short term, he may sell a few overrated cameras, but eventually will lose his entire business. I once bought by mail from another dealer a camera which was described as "excellent". It was not only less than excellent, but had parts missing. That was my first and last mail transaction with that dealer. I know of many other people who have had the same type of experience with the same dealer. In order to maintain any stability in the collecting field, we would recommend that buyers insist on a return privilege for any items purchased unseen by mail or phone. Any reputable dealer will allow this, but some individuals may not. If you find a dealer or collector who consistently exaggerates condition, we would recommend that you confront him with the problem or perhaps stop dealing with him. There are various sets of standards in use, but none that should allow a dented, scratched or non-functioning camera to be described as "excellent".

The second trend in describing condition is a reaction against the earlier system of misleading word descriptions in which a camera described as "good" really means it is "poor" and a camera described as "very good" is really only "fair". The more recent approach is to separately describe the cosmetic and functional attributes of the camera. We feel strongly that the field should adopt a universally accepted standard which would allow for this flexibility. A camera in mint cosmetic condition, but not functioning may be perfectly acceptable to a collector who will put it on the shelf. On the other hand, a user may not care much about the appearance as long as it works. We strongly support such a system, and recommend that it be implemented on a world-wide scale with the cooperation of pricing guides, collector publications and societies, auction houses and dealers.

In an effort to establish an international standard for describing condition, we are proposing the following scale. We have purposely used a combination of a number and a letter to avoid any confusion with other grading systems already in use. Condition of a camera should be given as a single digit followed by a letter. The number represents cosmetic condition and the letter gives functional condition.

GRADE---COSMETIC CONDITION
0 - New merchandise, never sold. In original box, with warranties.
1 - AS NEW. Never used. Same as new, but not warrantied. With box or original packaging.
2 - No signs of wear. If it had a box, you wouldn't be able to tell it from new.
3 - Very minimal signs of wear.
4 - Signs of light use, but not misuse. No other cosmetic damage.
5 - Complete, but showing signs of normal use or age.
6 - Complete, but showing signs of heavy use. Well used.
7 - Restorable. Some refinshing neccessary. Minor parts may be broken or missing.
8 - Restorable. Refinishing required. May be missing some parts.
9 - For parts only, or major restoration if a rare camera.

GRADE---FUNCTIONAL CONDITION
A - AS NEW. Everything in perfect working order, with factory and/or warranty.
B - AS NEW. Everything in perfect working order, but not warrantied by factory. Seller fully guaranties functioning.
C - Everything working. Recently professionally cleaned, lubed, overhauled and fully guaraniteed.
D - Everything working. Recently professionally cleaned, or overhauled, but no longer under warranty.
E - Everything working. Major functions have recently been professionally tested.
F - Not recently cleaned, lubed, or overhauled. Fully functioning, but accuracy of shutter or meter not guaranteed.
G - Fully fuctioning. Shutter speeds and/or meter probably not accurate. Needs adjusting or cleaning only.
H - Usable but not fully. Shutter may stick on slow speeds. Meter may not work.
J - NOT USABLE without repair or cleaning. Shutter, meter, film advance may be stuck, jammed, or broken.
K - Probably not repairable.

In this system, an average camera would be rated as 5F. A camera rated as 3G would mean cosmetically showing minimal signs of wear, but with questionable accuracy of meter or shutter. Thus a very specific description of condition fits in a small amount of space, and eliminates the problems which have been associated with word or letter descriptions which do not allow distinctions between cosmetic and functional condition. To be even more specific, users may wish to expand the cosmetic grade by using a second digit. Thus "56B" would mean cosmetic condition somewhere between grade 5 and 6, guaranteed to be functioning properly.

Sometimes collectors are more lenient in applying these standards to older and more rare cameras, and more strict in applying them to newer or more common models. This is somewhat self-defeating. If you describe a camera as "very good condition considering its age", you are adding a personal judgement that old cameras should be judged by a different set of standards. Even though most cameras of that age may show some signs of age, the fact that it is old does nothing to improve its condition.

COMPARISON WITH OTHER GRADING SYSTEMS:
The following table compares the Cosmetic portion of the condition grading system with some of the common word or letter descriptions currently in use. These comparisons are approximate and are provided only to help users move to the new system more easily. The last column in the table shows in general terms how condition will affect prices. However, these are only approximations. Condition affects price differently on various types and ages of cameras. The suggested allowances on the next page are given as percentages of the listed price.

Any missing or loose parts should be specifically noted. Use of a (-) after a condition number or letter means that it meets the standard except for minor condition AS DESCRIBED in adjoining comment. Use of a (+) means it exceeds this condition standard, but doesn't qualify for next higher rating.

McKeown	SA	Cornwall	Percent of listed price
0	N	-	150-200%
1	LN	-	130-150%
2	M	A	120-140%
3	M-	AB	115-130%
4	E+	B	110-120%
5	E	C	95-115%
6	VG	CD	80-110%
7	G	D	55-85%
8	F	E	30-60%
9	P	-	10-30%

INTERPRETATION OF PRICE FIGURES:

All price figures are in United States Dollars. Prices apply to cameras in condition range 5 to 6 according to the standards previously set forth. This is the most common condition in which cameras are found and collected, and makes the most useful standard. To determine the value of a particular camera, the user of this guide should consider any variation from this condition when assessing it and vary his value estimate accordingly.

The lower priced items in this guide and on the market tend to be slightly over-priced, simply because the cost and bother of advertising, selling, and shipping an $5.00 item is not much different from the same costs and efforts to sell an item valued for hundreds or thousands of dollars. The middle priced items show the most accurate and prices. They are the most commonly traded; they are in large supply; and thus the market is very stable. The higher priced cameras of any particular style, brand, or age tend to be the most volatile, because there is both limited supply and limited demand.

EXCHANGE RATES

The prices in this guide represent prices in the U.S.A. market. There are definite variations from these figures in the foreign markets. Some cameras are more common in one country than another. Collectors' interests are different in various parts of the world, and "trends" or "fads" affect different markets at different times. However, none of the world's markets are closed to outside influence, and the fluctuations have a tendency to level off on a world wide scale. A higher price in one country will tend to draw more cameras to that area and the world price rises until that demand eventually becomes satisfied, usually between the earlier norm and the "fad" high. Keeping this general background in mind, the following chart will prove useful to people dealing across national boundaries. The following figures are for the U.S. Dollar values of the indicated currencies as of March 26, 1987. Multiplying these factors* times the U.S. Dollar price gives the value in the foreign currencies.

CURRENCY	EXCHANGE RATE	MULTIPLCATION FACTOR *
Australian $	.6953	1.4382
Canadian $	.7639	1.3091
British £	1.6013	.6245
French Franc	.1642	6.0910
German DM	.5470	1.8280
Japanese Yen	.006691	149.45

CUSTOMIZE YOUR GUIDE:

You will notice that the index section can be easily found by the black at the edge of the page. If there is a particular manufacturer which you reference often, we suggest marking that section as follows. Open the book on each side of the section to be marked, then use a PERMANENT, WATERPROOF marking pen to rub along the EDGE of the pages to be marked. You may mark several manufacturers or sections by making your edge marks in different places or by the use of different colors.

ACCURAFLEX - 1950's TLR. 2¼x2¼" on 120 rollfilm. Accurar Anastigmat f3.5/80mm lens. Accurapid 1-300,B,ST sync shutter. Semi-automatic film transport. Original price was $60 in 1957. Current value: $20-30.

ACMA (Australasian Camera Manufacturers; Australia)

Sportshot Senior Twenty - Bakelite box camera, trapezoidal shape, for either 620 or 120 film. Made in black, brown, maroon, grey, and green. Folding frame finder on top. $15-25.

ACRO - c1940. Brown bakelite minicam for 16 exposures on 127 rollfilm. Identical to Photo Master. $4-8.

ACRO SCIENTIFIC PRODUCTS CO. (Chicago)

Acro Model R - Black plastic and metal camera for 16 exp. on 127 rollfilm. Built-in rangefinder & extinction meter. Similar in style to the Detrola. Wollensak f3.5 lens in Alphax shutter. $25-35.

ADAMS & CO. (London)
Aidex - c1928. Folding single-lens reflex, made in sizes for 2½x3½ or 3¼x4¼" plates. Self-capping FP shutter T,B, 3-1000. Ross Xpres f3.5 lens. $300-350.

Challenge - c1892. Half-plate mahogany tailboard-style camera, with Dallmeyer landscape lens. $400-500.

Club - c1890's-1930's. Folding mahogany field camera, 6½x8½". Ross Symmetrical lens with wheel stops or Rapid Rectilinear lens with iris diaphragm are typical lenses. Thornton-Pickard roller-blind shutter. $125-175.

De Luxe - c1898. A deluxe variation of the earlier Adams Hand Camera for 3¼x4¼" plates. Spanish mahogany with sealskin covering. Double extension bellows with rack and pinion focusing. $350-500.

Hand Camera - c1891-96. Leather covered hand camera in 3¼x4¼" or 4x5" sizes. Has detachable 12-plate magazine. Rising, shifting front, double swing back. Ross Rapid Symmetrical f8 lens, Iris T,I shutter. Rare. $350-500.

Hat Detective Camera - c1892-96. The camera fits into a bowler-style hat. ¼-plate is secured in a strut folding mechanism inside the hat. Bayonet mount f11 Rapid Rectilinear lens and T,I between-the-lens shutter are in the crown of the hat. Hat had to be removed from the head to be used. Advertised as a "secret Camera that defies detection". Made from Jekeli & Horner's patent of the Chapeau Photographique;

Adams had sole rights in Great Britain. Extremely rare. No known sales, but it would command a very high price, easily over $10,000.

Ideal - c1892-95. Magazine box camera taking 12 plates, 3¼x4¼". Falling-plate mechanism. Rapid Rectilinear f8/5½" lens. Shutter 1-100. $25-40.

Idento - c1905. Folding camera with side panels supporting the lensboard, similar to the Shew Xit. Ross Homocentric or Zeiss Protar f6.3/5" lens. Between-the-lens ½-100, T shutter. Leather covered. Made in 5 sizes 2½x3½" to ½-plate. $200-300.

Minex - 1910's-1930's. Single lens reflex cameras similar to the Graflex, made in various sizes. $150-200.

Minex Stereoscopic Reflex Deluxe - A deluxe stereo version of the Minex, with brown leather bellows & focusing hood. With a Ross Xpres f4.5 lens, one of these sold at auction in mid-1982 for $8600.

Minex Tropical - c1930's. 2½x3½, 3¼x4¼, 4x5, 4¾x6½" sizes. Teakwood SLR with brass binding. With film holders, lens, and crocodile leather case. $2000-3000.

Royal - c1890's. Compact folding field camera made in half-plate and full-plate sizes. Very similar to the Club, but a less expensive and somewhat heavier model. $75-125.

Vesta - Folding bed and strut cameras. Ross Xpres f4.5 lens. Several versions:
Focal Plane Vesta - c1912. For 9x12cm plates. $200-300.
Vesta Model A - Basic model without FP shutter. For 9x12cm plates. $70-100.
Rollfilm Vesta - c1930's. Compound 1-200,T,B shutter. Takes 6.5x9cm plates and 6x9cm on 120 rollfilm. $200-300.

Tropical Hand Camera - Teakwood box camera with brass trim. Thornton-Pickard roller-blind shutter concealed behind front door, which must be opened for use. Rack and pinion focus, tilting front. Hinged door at top rear for changing plates. $800-1000.

Videx - c1909. SLR, usually found in the 3¼x4¼" size. $125-175. The 4¼x6½" size is less common. $150-250.

Yale Nos. 1, 2 - c1895. Detective magazine camera for 12 plates, 3¼x4¼". Internal bellows focusing. Adams Patent Shutter ½-100. No. 1 has Rapid Rectilinear f8 lens; No. 2 has Cooke f6.5/5" lens. $150-200.

Yale Stereo Detective No. 5 - c1902. Leather covered body, and leather plate changing bag. Zeiss 7½" lenses. Internal bellows with rack focusing. $450-550.

ADAMS & WESTLAKE CO. (Chicago)

Adlake Cameras - c1897. Manual plate changing box cameras for 12 plates. 3¼x4¼" & 4x5" sizes. $35-50.

ADINA - Folding 6x9cm rollfilm camera. Rodenstock Trinar f6.3/105mm lens. Adina or Compur shutter. $15-20.

ADOX KAMERAWERK (Wiesbaden)
Adox, Adox II, Adox III - c1936-50. 35mm

cameras with extensible front. Made by Wirgin; styled like the Wirgin Edinex. $25-35.

Juka - c1950. A postwar version of the Junka-Werke "Junka" camera for 3x4cm on special rollfilm. Achromat f8/45mm lens. Single speed shutter. $50-75.

Adox 66 - c1950. Bakelite box camera for 6x6cm on 120. $15-20.

Adox 300 - c1958. The first German 35mm camera with interchangeable magazine backs. Large film advance & shutter cocking lever concentric with lens. BIM. Steinheil Cassar or Schneider Xenar f2.8/45mm lens. Synchro-Compur to 500. Originally supplied with 3 magazines in 1957. $100-125.

Adrette - c1939. 35mm camera with extensible front. Identical to the Wirgin Edinex. Front focus Steinheil Cassar f3.5/50mm, Schneider Radionar f2.9/50mm, or Xenon f2/50mm lens in Prontor, Prontor II, or Compur shutter. $25-40.

Adrette II - c1939. Same as the Adrette, but with helical focus. Prontor II, Compur, or Compur Rapid shutter. $30-50.

Blitz - c1950. Bakelite box camera for 6x6cm on 120 film. Styled like the Adox 66. f6.3/75mm lens. $15-25.

Golf - c1950's. Folding camera, 6x6cm. Adoxar or Cassar f6.3 lens in Pronto or Vario shutter. Rangefinder model: $20-25. Simple model without rangefinder: $10-20.

Golf IA Rapid - c1963-65. Simple, boxy 35mm camera for rapid cassettes. Adoxon f2.8/45mm in Prontor to 125. $5-8.

Golf IIA - c1964. Similar, but with built-in selenium meter above lens. Prontor-Matic shutter to 125. $8-12.

Golf IIIA - c1960's. Coupled light meter. Radionar L f2.8/45mm in Prontor 500LK. $5-10.

Polomat - c1962. Rigid body 35mm camera with BIM. f2.8 lens. Pronto LK shutter 15-250. $10-15.

Sport - c1950. Folding dual-format rollfilm cameras for 6x9 or 4.5x6cm on 120 film. Steinheil Cassar f6.3 or Radionar f4.5 lens. Vario shutter. Optical or folding viewfinder models. Common. $12-15.

AFIOM (Italy)
Kristall - c1955. Leica copy. Elionar f3.5/5cm lens. $225-275.

Wega II, IIa - c1950. Leica copies which accept Leica screw-mount lenses. CRF. Synchronized FP shutter to 1000. Trixar f3.5/50mm. $225-275.

AGFA KAMERAWERKE (Munich)

Established in 1867. "Aktien Gesellschaft fuer Analin-Fabrikation" was formed in 1873. AGFA is an abbreviation of the original name. Rietzschel merged with Agfa in 1925, at which time the Rietzschel name was no longer used on cameras and the first Agfa cameras were produced. Agfa's USA operations joined forces with Ansco in 1928 to form Agfa-Ansco, which eventually became GAF. Agfa also continued operations in Germany both in the production of cameras and films. After the war, Agfa abandoned its Wolfen factories, and in 1952 founded "Agfa Kamerawerk AG" in Munich and "Agfa AG fuer Photofabrikation" in Leverkusen. These merged in 1957 to become Agfa AG, which soon acquired Leonar-Werke, Mimosa, Perutz Photowerke, and others before merging with Gevaert of Belgium in 1964.

Agfaflex - c1959. SLR cameras. Prontor 1-300. Models I-IV. Apotar or Solinar f2.8 lens. $50-65. Model V with f2 lens: $60-85.

Ambi-Silette - c1957. 35mm. Solinar f2.8/50mm lens in Synchro-Compur to 500. Interchangeable lenses include f4/35mm Ambion, f4/90mm, and 135mm. With normal lens: $40-50. Extra lenses: $30-50.

Ambiflex - c1959. SLR. Coupled meter. Interchangeable prism & WL finders. Color Solinar f2.8/50mm in Prontor Reflex 1-300. $60-90.

Automatic 66 - c1956. Horizontally styled folding camera for 6x6cm on 120 rollfilm. CRF. Fully automatic metering with manual override. Helical focusing. Color Solinar f3.5/75mm in Prontor-SL shutter. $350-550.

Billy (O,I,II,III,Record,etc.) - A series of folding rollfilm cameras produced from 1929-1960, usually encountered in 6x9cm size with f4.5 Apotar or Solinar or f6.3 Agnar or Igestar. Shutters include Automat and Prontor. A few of the better models: $16-22. Most models: $8-12.

Billy I Luxus - c1930's. Igestar f8.8/100 in Billy 25-100 shutter. $60-90.

Billy-Clack - c1935-38. Strut-type folding rollfilm cameras similar in appearance to the Jiffy Kodak cameras. Two sizes. One takes 16 exp. 4.5x6cm on 120, the other takes 6x9cm. $20-30.

Billy Compur - c1935-38. Like the Billy, but with Compur shutter and f4.5 or f3.9 Solinar or f4.5 Apotar. $20-35.

Billy Optima - c1930's. 7.5x10.5cm. Solinar f4.5/120mm in Compur 1-250. $50-75.

Box cameras - misc. sizes, styles including B-2, I, 45, 50, 54, and Special. $5-10. *(Illustrated top of next page.)*

Box 44 - c1932-40. Box camera for 6x9cm on 120 film. Leatherette covering on

Agfa Box I

cardboard body and metal front plate. For some reason, these have sold on recent auctions in the $15-25 range.

Cadet B-2 - c1939. Made by Agfa-Ansco in Binghamton, New York. After 1943, sold under the Ansco Cadet name. Metal box camera. $1-5.

Captain - 6x9cm art-deco folding camera. Captain lens in Agfa T,l shutter. $8-12.

Chief - c1940. Metal eye-level box camera. Similar to the Pioneer, but with zone focus and built-in finder. $4-8.

Clack - c1954-59. Metal eye-level box camera with reptile-grained covering. Takes 6x9cm on 120 film. Common. $1-5.

Click I - c1958-1965. Simple plastic eye-level box camera for 6x6cm on 120 film. Meniscus lens. Single speed shutter. Common. $1-5.
Click II - c1959-65. Similar to Click I, but

with zone-focusing f8.8 Achromat. Common. $3-6.

Clipper PD-16 - c1938. Metal bodied camera with extensible rectangular front section. Made in U.S.A. Takes 16 exp. on 616 film. Single speed shutter & meniscus lens. $1-5.

Clipper Special - c1939. Like the Clipper, but with f6.3 Anastigmat and 25-100 shutter. Optical finder. $4-7.

Colorflex I, II - Same as Agfaflex I and II. (Agfaflex was the name used in the U.S.A.)

Flexilette - c1960. 35mm TLR. Unusual design has viewing lens above taking lens in a round front panel. Color Apotar f2.8/45mm in Prontor 1-500. $75-115.

Folding Rollfilm cameras - Common models for 116 and 120 films. $8-12.

Iso Rapid I, IF, IC - c1965-70's. Compact cameras resembling the 126 cartridge type, but for Rapid 35mm cassettes. I has hot shoe. IF has AG-1 flash. IC has flashcube socket. $1-5.

Isoflash Rapid - c1965. Similar to the Iso

Rapid IF. Isoflash Rapid C uses flashcubes. $1-5.

Isola - c1955. Simple eye-level camera for 6x6cm on 120 film. Telescoping front. Agnar f6.3 lens in Singlo shutter. $3-5.

Isola I - c1957-59. Similar, but with Meniscus lens in single speed shutter. "Agfa Isola I" on shutter face. $3-5.

Isola II - c1956-59. 2¼x2¼". Agnar f6.3/75mm in Singlo 2 shutter B,30,100. $3-5.

Isolar - c1927-35. 9x12cm folding plate camera. Metal body, ground glass back. Double extension bellows. Solinear f4.5/135mm. Dial Compur to 200. $30-45.

Isolar Luxus - Deluxe version of above with brown bellows and brown leather covering. Unusual. $150-200.

Isolette I & II - Folding rollfilm cameras for 6x6cm & 4.5x6cm on 120 film. Original model 1939-1949 with Igestar f6.3 in Vario. Model I c1952-1957 with f4.5 Agnar in Vario or Pronto. Model II c1948-1950 has f4.5 Agnar or Apotar or f3.5 or 4.5 Solinar in Vario, Pronto, Prontor-S, Compur, Synchro-Compur. $10-18.

Isolette III - c1952. Non-cpld rangefinder. f4.5 Apotar or f3.5 Solinar in Pronto, Prontor, SV, SVS, or Synchro-Compur. $30-45.

Isolette V - c1953. Similar to Isolette I and II. Agnar f4.5/85mm in Vario or Pronto. $12-18.

Isolette L - 1957-60. 6x6cm or 4.5x6cm on 120 film. Apotar f4.5/85mm in Pronto. BIM. $50-65.

Isolette Super - c1954. Folding camera for 6x6cm on 120 film. Coupled rangefinder. Solinar f3.5/75mm. Synchro-Compur MXV

shutter to 500. Not often seen. $100-125.

Isoly - c1960-67. Inexpensive eye-level cameras for 16 exposures 4x4cm on 120 film. Models include:
Isoly (I) - Achromat f8 in B,30-100 shutter. $5-10.
Isoly IIa - Color-Agnar f5.6. $6-10.
Isoly III - Apotar f3.9. $8-12.
Isoly IIIa - Apotar f3.5. $10-15.

Isoly-Mat - c1961. Like Isoly, but with built-in automatic meter with selenium cell below lens. Color Agnar f5.6/55mm. $12-15.

Isorette - c1938-39. Horizontally styled folding-bed camera for 6x6cm on 120 rollfilm. Models include: Igestar f6.3/85mm in Vario or Pronto; Apotar f4.5 in Prontor II or Compur; Solinar f4.5 in Compur Rapid. $40-55.

Karat - *A long-lived series of cameras for 24x36mm exposures on 35mm film in Karat-cassettes, the original design which eventually led to the international standard "Rapid Cassette" system. The pre-WWII models, officially named by their lens aperture, all have the same body style with tapered ends and with the viewfinder protruding from the slightly rounded top.*
Karat 6.3 - 1938-1940. Igestar f6.3 in Automat shutter. $25-40.

Karat 3.5 - 1938-1940. Solinar f3.5 in Compur Rapid shutter. $35-45.
Karat 4.5 - 1939-1950. Oppar f4.5 in Pronto shutter. $20-25.

Karat - *Postwar models have a new body style with beveled ends and viewfinder incorporated with rangefinder in the top housing.*
Karat 12 - Solinar f3.5 or Xenar f2.8 lens in Compur-Rapid shutter (1948). Apotar f3.5 in Prontor-S (1948-1950). $35-45.
Karat 36 - (also called Karomat 36) Xenar f2.8/Compur Rapid or Xenon f2/Synchro-Compur (1949). Heligon or Xenon f2/Synchro-Compur (1950). Solinar or Soligon f2.8/Synchro-Compur (1952). $40-55.
Karat IV - 1950-56. Identifiable by the equally sized and spaced finder windows on the front. Prontor SV or SVS. Solinar f2.8

AGFA (cont.)

(1950). Solagon f2 or Apotar f3.5 (1955-56). With f2 lens: $75-95. Others: $40-60.

Karomat - c1951. Also called Karat 36. f2.8 Xenar or f2 Xenon. $40-55.

Major - Folding bed camera for 6x9cm exposures on 120 film. $10-15.

Memo (full frame) - c1939. Horizontally styled folding bed camera for 24x36mm exposures on 35mm Agfa Rapid cassettes. Rapid advance lever on back. Made in U.S.A. Agfa Memar f3.5, 4.5, or 5.6 lens. $25-40.

Memo (half-frame) - Similar to the above, this single-frame (18x24mm) model was added in 1940. $35-50.

Moto-Rapid C - 1965. Spring-motor driven camera for 24x24mm on Agfa-Rapid 35mm cassette film. Color Isomar f8 in Parator shutter. $20-35.

Motor-Kamera - c1951. Unusual 35mm camera for remote control use. Agfa Color Telinear f3.4/90mm. Large electric motor built on to front of camera and externally coupled to the advance knob. (A rather clumsy arrangement when compared with modern mass-marketed autowinders.) $300-400.

Nitor - 1927-30. 6x9cm on plates, pack, or rollfilm. Helostar f6.3/Pronto or Linear f4.5/Compur to 250. $25-40.

Opal Luxus - c1925-26. 6.5x9cm folding bed camera for plates. Double extension brown bellows; brown leather covering. Rietzschel Solinear f4.5/105mm in Compur. $225-250.

Optima - A series of 35mm cameras. The original model, 1959-1963, has left-hand shutter release, Color Apotar f3.9 lens in Compur. Claimed to be the first fully automatic camera in the world. Model I, 1960-1964, has Color Agnar f2.8/45mm

in Prontorlux. Right-hand release. Mod. IA c1962 has an advance lever on top and removable back. Model II 1960-1964. IIS 1961-1966 is like the II but with CRF. Model III (1960) has meter and IIIS (1960) includes meter & CRF. Prices range from $15-25 for the simpler models to $35-45 for a nice IIIS.

Optima Parat - c1960. Metered half-frame 35mm camera. Color Solinar f2.8/30mm in Compur. $20-40.

Optima Rapid 125C - c1967. Simple camera for 16 exposures 24x24mm with Agfa-Rapid cassettes. Fully automatic exposures controlled by selenium meter. Apotar f2.8/35mm in Paratic shutter. $3-7.

Optima Reflex - c1963-1966. 35mm TLR with eye-level pentaprism, meter, matched Color Apotar f2.8/45mm lenses. An unusual design, and not commonly found. $75-125.

Paramat - c1960. Like the Parat but with meter. $20-30.

Parat, Parat I - c1960. 18x24mm (half-frame). Color Apotar f2.8/30mm. $15-25.

PD-16 - This was Agfa's number for the same size film as Kodak 116. Several of the Agfa cameras use this number in their name, but they are listed by their key word (Clipper, Plenax, etc.)

Pioneer - c1940. Metal & plastic eye-level box camera with tapered ends in both PD-16 and PB-20 sizes. Made in the USA by Agfa-Ansco. After 1943, sold as "Ansco" Pioneer. Very common. $2-5.

Plate cameras - 6x9cm with f4.5/105mm and 9x12cm with f4.5/135mm Double Anastigmat or Solinar lenses. Compur shutters. $20-40.

Plenax - c1935. Folding rollfilm cameras made in U.S.A. Models PD-16 and PB-20. Antar, Tripar, or Hypar lens. $8-12.

Preis-Box - c1932. Box camera which originally sold for 4 marks. Meniscus lens, simple shutter. $7-12.

Record I - c1952. Folding-bed rollfilm camera with self-erecting front. Agnar f6.3 or f4.5 in Pronto. $10-20.

Record II - c1954. Agnar f4.5 in Pronto; Apotar f4.5 in Prontor S or SV. $15-25.

Schul-Praemie Box - Originally given out as a school premium in Germany, which accounts for the inscribed title. A blue metal and plastic box for 6x9cm rollfilm. $25-35.

Selecta - c1960. 35mm rangefinder camera with automatic metering. Color Apotar f2.8/45. Prontor-Matic P shutter. $9-13.

Selecta-Flex - c1964. Pentaprism 35mm SLR. Interchangeable f2.8 Solinar or f2 Solagon. $45-60.

Selecta-M - c1965. Fully automatic motor camera for 24x36mm. Shutter regulated by BIM. Solinar f2.8/45mm in Compur 30-500. $100-175.

Shurflash, Shurshot - Made in USA by Agfa-Ansco. Common box cameras. $4-8.

Silette - A series of 35mm cameras introduced in 1956 and ranging from the simple viewfinder model to the metered rangefinder models. Common.
Silette (I) - $5-15.
Silette II - $5-15.
Silette L - $10-20.
Silette LK - $20-25.
Silette SL - $20-25.
Silette SLE - $15-20.
Super Silette - $20-25.
Super Silette L - $25-30. *(illustrated)*
Super Silette LK - $25-30.

Silette Rapid - c1965. Similar to the normal Silette but for rapid cassettes. All have Color Agnar f2.8/45mm lens.
Silette Rapid I - Prontor 30-125. $5-9.

AGFA (cont.)

Silette Rapid F - Parator 30-250. $5-9.
Silette Rapid L - Prontor 30-250 shutter. Uncoupled exposure meter. $7-12.

Solinette, Solinette II - c1952. Folding 35mm cameras. Solinar or Apotar f3.5/50. Prontor-SVS or Synchro-Compur. $20-30.

--Super Solinette - c1953-1957. Similar but with CRF. $30-45.

Speedex 6x9cm - c1936. Folding rollfilm camera. f4.5 in Compur. $15-20.

Speedex B2 - c1940. Horizontally styled 6x6cm rollfilm camera made in USA. f4.5 Anastigmat in ½-250 shutter. $12-18.

Speedex Jr. - c1940. Similar to the Speedex B2, but with fixed-focus lens in T&I shutter. $5-10.

Speedex 0 - c1938. Vertical style folding bed camera. Vest pocket (127 film) size. Leather covered with chrome and enamel side panels. Solinar f3.9 lens in Compur. $40-60.

Standard - c1927-31. A series of folding cameras in various models for rollfilm or plates.

Rollfilm models - Made in both 6x9cm and 6.5x11cm sizes. Various lenses and shutters. $10-20.

Plate models - For 6.5x9cm or 9x12cm plates. Various f4.5 or f6.3 lenses in Automat or Compur shutter. $20-40.

Deluxe plate models - Brown leather covering and brown bellows. Original price was only about 10% higher than standard plate model. Current collectors pay $125-175.

Superior - 1930-32. A deluxe folding camera for 8x14cm "postcard size" photos. Reddish-brown leather, brown bellows. Trilinear f6.3 or Solinear f4.5 in Compur. $175-200. *(Illustrated top of next page.)*

Synchro-Box - c1952. Metal box camera for 6x9cm on 120 film. Plastic covering and art-deco front. $1-5.

24

Agfa Superior

Synchro-Box (Made in India) - c1950. Unusual variant of Synchro Box; made by New India Industries Ltd, Baroda, India. Very rare. Only one recorded sale in 1985 for about $150.

Trolita - c1938-40. Self-erecting, folding bed camera for 6x9cm or 6x6cm on 120 rollfilm. Made of "Trolit" plastic (similar to bakelite). Leather bellows. Apotar f4.5/105mm. Prontor II shutter. $125-150.

Trolix - c1937. Trolit plastic box, 2¼x3¼". $20-30.

Ventura 66 - c1950. Among the first postwar products of Agfa Camerawerk. Horizontal folding camera for 6x6cm on 120. Agnar f4.5 in synchronized Vario to 200. $12-18.

Ventura Deluxe - c1950. Similar to the regular 66, but with Apotar f4.5, Prontor-S

or Compur and double exposure prevention. $12-18.

Ventura 69 - c1950. Vertically styled folding rollfilm camera for 6x9cm on 120 film. $12-18.

View cameras - Various models in 3¼x4¼ to 5x7 inch sizes. As collectible cameras, these do not create as much interest as they do for studio use. Collector value $40-75 with shutter and lens. If the camera has full movements, it is a usable item for commercial photographers and will fetch $100-250 without lens or shutter.

Viking - c1940. Folding cameras for 120 or 116 rollfilms. f6.3 or 7.7 lens. $8-12.

AGILUX LTD. (Croydon, England)
A subsidiary of Aeronautical & General Instruments, Ltd., from which the AGI names originate.

Agiflash 35 - Simple boxy grey plastic 35mm camera, identical to the Ilford Sprite 35. Fixed focus f8 lens; single speed shutter. Double exposure prevention. $8-12.

Agiflex - 6x6cm SLR originally made for the Royal Navy during WWII. Focal plane shutter 25-500. Styled similar to the Reflex Korelle. $50-75.

Agifold (rangefinder model) - c1955. 6x6cm folding camera. Built-in uncoupled rangefinder and extinction meter. Agilux anastigmat f4.5/75mm. $20-40.

Auto Flash Super 44 - c1961. Two-tone grey plastic camera for 4x4cm on 127 film. Automatic exposure; selenium meter adjusts aperture. Single speed shutter. Fixed focus. $10-15.

AHI - Japanese novelty subminiature of the Hit type. $10-15.

AIGLON - c1934. French subminiature. All metal, nickel-plated body with removable single-speed shutter attached to the lens cone. Special rollfilm records 8 exposures with meniscus lens. $125-150.

AIR KING PRODUCTS CO. INC.
(Brooklyn, NY)

Air King Camera Radio - The perfect marriage of a brown or red reptile-skin covered tube radio and concealed novelty camera for 828 film. $100-150.

AIRES CAMERA IND. CO. LTD. (Tokyo)

Aires 35-III - c1957-58. 35mm RF. f1.9/45mm in Seikosha MX. Single stroke lever advance. Bright frame finder. $20-30.

Aires 35-IIIC - c1958-1959. Improved version of III & IIIL, incorporating coupled LVS system, self-timer, and automatic parallax correction. Strongly resembles the Leica M3 from a distance. It was designed to accept Aires or Leica M3

cassettes. $30-45.

Aires 35-IIIL - c1957-1959. Similar to III, but with LVS shutter 1-500. Rewind knob has crank. $30-40.

Aires 35-V - c1959-1962. BIM, bayonet mount interchangeable lenses, fast f1.5 normal lens. Also available were f3.5/100mm and f3.2/35mm. With three lenses $75-100. With normal lens only $35-55.

Airesflex - c1953-55. 6x6cm TLR. Coral f3.5/75mm in Seikosha-Rapid shutter to 500. $35-50.

Penta 35 - c1960. Low-priced 35mm SLR. Non-interchangeable Q Coral f2.8/50mm lens accepts supplementary wide angle & telephoto lenses. Seikosha SLV 1-500. $40-60.

Penta 35 LM - c1961. Similar to Penta 35, but with f2 lens and BIM. $40-60.

Viscount - c1962. Low-price 35mm RF camera. Even with its fast f1.9 lens, it sold new for under $40. $20-30.

AIVAS (A. Aivas, Paris)
Beginner's Camera - c1910. ¼-plate tailboard camera. Mahogany body, blue cloth bellows. Brass barrel lens, gravity guillotine shutter. $125-150.

ALFAX MODEL I - Japanese camera for 4x4cm on 127 film. Recta Anastigmat f3.5/60mm in New Alfa shutter. $25-40.

ALIBERT (Charles Alibert, Paris)

Kauffer Photo-Sac a Main - c1895. Folding plate camera disguised as a handbag. Several models were made. One is styled like a square-cornered case which hinges from the middle and a strut-supported front extends. A similar model uses the strut-supported front but in a smartly styled handbag with a split front door hinged at the top and bottom. The other variation has the handbag shape but uses the bottom door as a bed to support the lens standard. Designed by Bernard Kauffer of Paris. Estimated: $2000-3000.

ALLIED CAMERA SUPPLY CO. (New York, NY)

Carlton Reflex - c1950. Black bakelite TLR-style box camera, identical to the Spartus Ful-Vue. Faceplate sports Allied name, but "Utility Mfg. Co." is molded inside the back. $5-10.

ALSAPHOT (France)
Dauphin, Dauphin II - Pseudo-TLR, 2¼x2¼". $15-25.

Maine - c1960's. Metal-bodied 35mm cameras with leatherette covering, all with Berthiot f2.8/45mm lens. Model I: basic knob-advance model. Model IIc: collimated viewfinder; lever advance. IIIa: built-in meter for automatic exposures. $15-20.

ALTHEIMER & BAER INC.
Photo-Craft - Black bakelite minicam, 3x4cm on 127 rollfilm. $4-8.

ALTISSA KAMERAWERK (B.Altmann, Dresden) *Also associated with E. Hofert of Dresden, eventually becoming Eho-Altissa. See Eho-Altissa.*

AMCO - Japanese paper "Yen" box camera for single exposures on sheetfilm in paper holders. Amco is larger than most cameras of this type, taking 4.5x6.5cm exposures. It is covered in brown & tan rather than the normal black. An unusual item for a collection of novelty cameras. $25-35.

AMEREX - Early Japanese 16mm Hit type subminiature. One of very few marked "Made in Occupied Japan". $25-30.

AMERICAN ADVERTISING & RESEARCH CORP. (Chicago)

Cub - c1940. Small plastic camera for

28x40mm exposures on 828 film. Simple lens and shutter. All plastic construction, similar to the Scenex. Toothpaste premium. (Original cost: 15 cents and a Pepsodent box.) Common but cute. $10-15.

AMERICAN CAMERA CO. (London)

Demon Detective Camera - Small metal camera for single round exposures on dry plates. Introduced in 1889 for 2¼" diameter photos on 2¼x2¼" plates (later called No. 1 size). A larger model (No. 2 size) for 3¾" plates was introduced in 1890. Funnel-shaped front with flat, rectangular back. The striking design of the back stamping (by W. Phillips of Birmingham) makes the back view more interesting than the front view of these cameras. $800-1200.

AMERICAN CAMERA MFG. CO.
(Northboro, Mass. USA) *This company was founded in 1895 by Thomas Blair, who had previously founded the Blair Tourograph & Dry Plate Co. in 1881 (later changed to Blair Camera Co.). He still held partial interest in the Blair Camera Co. until 1898, but internal difficulties had prompted him to leave the Blair organization about 1892. The American Camera Mfg. Co. was in business for only a short time, since Thomas Blair sold out to George Eastman about 1897. The company was moved to Rochester about 1899 and continued to operate under the American Camera Mfg. Co. name at least through 1904, even though owned by Kodak. By 1908, the catalogs showed it as the American Camera Division of Eastman Kodak Co. If all of this seems confusing, remember also not to confuse this with the American Optical Co., which is a completely different company.*

Buckeye Cameras:
No. 2 Buckeye - c1899-1908? Box

camera for 4x5" exposures. Similar to the Blair Hawk-eye box cameras. $40-60.

No. 3 Buckeye - c1895. Folding rollfilm camera. Maroon leather bellows. f8 lens. $40-60.

No. 8 Folding Buckeye - c1904. 4x5" rollfilm camera. Rollholder lifts up to focus on ground glass. $250-350.

Buckeye Special - c1897. Like the No. 2 Buckeye, but for rollfilm or glass plates. $75-100.

No. 1 Tourist Buckeye - c1895. Folding rollfilm cameras in sizes for 3½x3½" or 3¼x4½" exposures. Maroon bellows, wooden lens standard. $125-150.

Long Focus Poco - c1904. 4x5". Folding camera with maroon leather bellows. $75-100.

AMERICAN FAR EAST TRADING CO.

Santa Claus Camera - c1980. Novelty camera for 126 film. Santa Claus face forms the front of the camera. $15-20.

AMERICAN MINUTE PHOTO CO. (Chicago)
American Sleeve Machine - A street camera for tintypes, similar to the more common models by the Chicago Ferrotype Co. $75-125.

AMERICAN OPTICAL CO. (New York)
Acquired the John Stock Co. (including the C.C. Harrison Co.) in 1866 and was then bought out by Scovill Mfg. Co. in 1867.
Flammang's Patent Revolving Back Camera - c1886. Tailboard style view camera, with patent revolving and tilting back. Mahogany body with brass fittings. Tapered bellows, rising front. Usually found in 5x7" and 6½x8½" sizes. $150-175.

Henry Clay Camera - c1892. 5x7 inch folding plate camera. A well-made hand camera with many desirable features, such as double shift and swing front, fine

focusing, etc. Somewhat uncommon and quite distinctive. With original Wale shutter: $450-650.

John Stock Wet Plate Camera - c1866. Tailboard style studio camera for wet collodion plates. Examples we have seen ranged from 4x5" to 8x10" sizes. Square back allows vertical or horizontal format. Side-hinged ground glass viewing screen swings out of the way to insert plateholder. Drip trough protects bed from chemicals. Brass plateholder retaining springs stamped "John Stock Patented May 31, 1864" and "Assigned to Am. Optical Co." "Am. Optical Co. Manufacturer, NY" stamped at rear corners of bed. $400-800.

Plate camera - 5x8" horizontal format. Complete with lens, back, holder. $125-175.

Wet Plate Camera, 4-tube - c1866. Tailboard-style studio camera of heavy construction. Takes 4 exposures 2x2" each. $800-1200.

American Raylo Corp. Raylo Color Camera

AMERICAN RAND CORP.
Photo Binocular 110 - c1980. A 110 cartridge camera with 80mm telephoto lens built into 4x30mm binoculars. $35-45.

AMERICAN RAYLO CORP. (New York)
Raylo Color Camera - c1925. Magazine-loading color separation camera for 4.5x8cm plates. Automatic clockwork mechanism apportions the time through each color filter in the correct ratio to produce three negatives of even scale. Rare. $1500-2000. *(Illustrated bottom of previous page.)*

AMERICAN SAFETY RAZOR CORP. (New York)

ASR Fotodisc - c1950. A small cast metal camera with eye-level finder. A film disc in a special holder fastens by bayonet mount to the back of the camera. Takes 8 exp. 22x24mm on a film disc. $400-500.

AMICA INTERNATIONAL (Japan)

Eyelux - c1966. 35mm RF. f1.8/45mm lens in Citizen MVE shutter. $15-25.

ANNY - Plastic 120 rollfilm camera of the "Diana" type. $1-5.

ANSCO (Binghamton NY USA) *Formed by the merger of the E.& H.T. Anthony Co. and Scovill & Adams in 1902. The name was shortened to Ansco in 1907. A merger with the American interests in the German firm of Agfa in 1928 formed Agfa-Ansco. In 1939, Agfa-Ansco changed its name to General Aniline & Film Corporation, but still used the Agfa-Ansco name in advertising until 1943 when the Agfa name was dropped. The Ansco Division of General Aniline kept its name as the main banner of the company until the company name was officially shortened to GAF in 1967. More recently, GAF withdrew from the consumer photographic market but the Ansco name continues as part of Haking International. See also Agfa, Anthony, Scovill.*
Admiral - Black plastic twin lens box camera, 2¼x2¼". $1-5.

Anscoflex, Anscoflex II - c1954. All metal 6x6cm reflex-style camera. Gray & silver color. Front door slides up and opens finder hood. Model II has closeup lens and yellow filter built in and controlled by knobs on the front. $10-15. Slightly higher in Europe.

Anscomark M - c1960-1963. 35mm RF camera. Interchangeable bayonet mount Xyton f1.9/50mm or f2.8/50 Xytar lens. Viewfinder has frames for 100mm & 35mm lenses. Coupled meter. With 3 lenses: $60-85. With normal lens only: $25-35.

Anscoset - c1960. 35mm RF. BIM with match-needle operation, f2.8/45mm Rokkor. Made by Minolta for Ansco. $25-30.

Arrow - c1925. Cardboard box camera with leatherette exterior. Removable metal back; wooden interior section. "The Arrow" on strap, no other identification. Styled like an oversized Ansco Dollar Camera, but with two finders. Uncommon. $5-10.

Automatic No. 1A - c1925. Folding rollfilm camera for 6 exp. 2½x4¼" in six seconds.

Required a new film "No. 6A Automatic" since the regular 6A film only allowed 5 exposures. Spring-wound automatic film advance. Designed and patented in 1915 by Carl Bornmann, who had also designed the 1888 Antique Oak Detective Camera for Scovill & Adams and was still designing for the company. Anastigmat f6.3 lens. Orig. price about $75. $100-150.

Automatic Reflex - High quality TLR intro-duced in 1947 at the healthy list price of $262.50. This original model did not cock the shutter with the film advance, and was lacking flash sync. An improved model (sometimes called Model II, although not marked as such) has a sync post in the lower corner of the front plate, and features automatic shutter cocking. Shutter to 400. Ansco f3.5/83 Anastigmat lens. f3.2/83mm viewing lens. Ground glass focusing screen and optical eye-level finder. The list price had dropped to $165 by 1950. $75-125.

Autoset - c1961. 35mm RF camera. Similar to the Anscoset, but fully automatic shutter speed control rather than match-needle. $20-30.

Box cameras - Colors other than black: $8-12. Black models: $3-6.

ANSCO (cont.)

Buster Brown Box Cameras:
No. 0 Buster Brown - c1923. 4x6.5cm on 127 rollfilm. $5-10.
No. 2 Buster Brown - c1906-23. 2¼x3¼" on 120 (4A) film. $5-10.
No. 2A Buster Brown - c1910-24. 2½x4¼" on 118 film. $5-10.
No. 2C Buster Brown - c1917-23. 2⅞x4⅞" negatives. $5-10.
No. 3 Buster Brown - c1906. 3¼x4¼". $5-10.

Buster Brown Special, Nos. O, 2, 2A - c1923. Red covering and lacquered brass trim. $10-20.

Folding Buster Brown Cameras:
No. 1 Folding Buster Brown, Model B - c1910. $10-15.
No. 2A Folding Buster Brown - c1910's. $10-15.
No. 3 Folding Buster Brown - c1914. $10-15.
No. 3A Folding Buster Brown - c1910's. Postcard size. Deltax or Actus shutter. $12-18.

Buster Brown Junior - Folding camera for 116 roll. $8-12.

Cadet cameras:
Cadet B2 and D-6 box cameras - c1947. Basic rectangular box cameras. $1-5.
Cadet (I) - c1959. Black plastic camera with metal faceplate. $1-5.
Cadet Flash - c1960. Similar to the Cadet 4x4cm, but large built-in flash on top. $1-5.
Cadet II, Cadet III - c1965. Horizontally styled gray plastic cameras with aluminum faceplate for 127 film. Originally came in hard plastic carrying case. $1-5.
Cadet Reflex - c1960. Reflex brillant finder version of the Cadet. 4x4cm on 127. $4-8.

Century of Progress - Cardboard box camera with art-deco style World's Fair design on metal front. Made for the 1933 World's Fair at Chicago. $50-75.

Ansco Commander

Clipper, Color Clipper, Flash Clipper, Clipper Special - 1940's-1950's. A series of metal cameras with rectangular extensible front. $3-7.

Commander - Mid-1950's folding rollfilm camera. Agnar f6.3 zone focusing lens in Vario sync shutter. $15-20. *(Illustrated bottom of previous column.)*

Craftsman - c1950. A construction kit to build your own 6x9cm box camera. The camera kit was pre-tested by Ansco for several months before the decision was made to market it. Over 100 grammar school children participated in the tests. Current value of an original unused kit with assembly instructions $40-50. Assembled Craftsman $4-8.

Dollar Box Camera - c1910-28. A small 4x3½x2½" box camera for 127 film. Available in black or green. No strap. Some are identified "Ansco Dollar Camera" on the front. The same camera in red and with a strap was sold as the Kiddie Camera c1926-29. $10-15.

Flash Champion - Metal-bodied camera with rectangular extensible front. Similar to the Clipper cameras. $1-5.

Folding Ansco cameras: *(There is a certain amount of confusion over the correct name for some of these cameras, since Ansco catalogs called them by different names even within the same catalog. For example, the No. 4 Folding Pocket Ansco is the same as the No. 4 Ansco Model B, or the No. 4 Folding Ansco.)*
No. 1 Folding Ansco - c1924-28. Folding bed camera for 6x9cm. Anastigmat f7.5 in Ilex General shutter 1/5-100. $10-15.
No. 1 Special Folding Ansco - c1924-28. $10-15.
No. 1A Folding Ansco - c1915-26. For 116 film. Anastigmat f7.5 in Ilex. $10-15.
No. 3 Folding Ansco - c1914-28. For 118 film. $12-18.

No. 3A Folding Ansco - c1914-32. Common post-card size. Lenses: Wollensak, RR, Ansco Anast. Shutters: Ilex, Deltax, Bionic, Speedex. $10-20.
No. 4 Folding Ansco - c1905. Models C & D. 3¼x4¼ on 118 film. Horizontal format. Mahogany drop bed. Wollensak lens, Cyko Auto shutter. Nickel trim. $15-25.

No. 6 Folding Ansco

No. 5 Folding Ansco - c1907. Wollensak lens. Cyko Automatic shutter. Black bellows. $15-25.
No. 6 Folding Ansco - c1907. Models C & D. 3¼x4¼". Wollensak f4 lens. Red leather bellows. For roll or cut film. $20-30. *(Illustrated bottom of previous column.)*
No. 7 Folding Ansco - (Anthony & Scovill Co.) Postcard sized rollfilm camera. Last patent date 1894. Red bellows, brass barrel Wollensak lens. $20-30.
No. 9 Ansco, Model B - c1906. Horizontal style folding camera for 3¼x5½" on rollfilm. Cherry wood body, leather covered. Red bellows. Cyko shutter in brass housing. (Later models had black bellows & nickeled shutter.) $20-35.
No. 10 Ansco - pat. Jan. 1907. Folding camera for 3½x5" on 122 film. (Model A has removable ground glass back. Ansco Automatic shutter.) $20-30.

Goodwin cameras *Named in honor of the Rev. Hannibal Goodwin. Dr. Goodwin invented the flexible transparent rollfilm which has become the standard of the photographic industry. His 1887 patent application took over 11 years to process, by which time his idea was already in widespread use. The Goodwin Film & Camera Co., Inc. was the Premium and Special Sales Division of Ansco Photo Products Inc.*
No. 1 Goodwin Jr. - c1925. Strut-supported front pulls straight out. $15-25.
No. 1A Folding Goodwin - c1930. Folding bed rollfilm camera for 116 film. Says "Goodwin Film & Camera Co." on the shutter face. $10-20.
No. 2, 2A, 3 Goodwin - c1930. Box cameras. $5-10.

Junior *A series of folding rollfilm cameras, beginning with the Model A about 1910. At first horizontally styled, the later models switched to the vertical styling.*
Ansco Junior (Model A & Model B) - c1906-13. Horizontal style folding camera. 2½x4¼" exposures. RR lens. $15-25.
No. 1 Ansco Junior - c1924-32. 2¼x3¼" on 120 rollfilm. Vertical style. Originally available with Achromatic, Rectilinear, or Modico Anastigmat lens in Actus or Bionic shutter. Later versions had other options. $10-15.
No. 1A Ansco Junior - c1916-32. Like the No. 1, but 2½x4¼" on 116 film. $10-15.
No. 2C Ansco Junior - c1917-23. 2⅞x4⅞ on 130 film, otherwise like the No. 1 above. $15-25.
No. 3 Ansco Junior - c1923. 3¼x4¼ on 118 film. Introduced somewhat later than the other sizes. $10-18.
No. 3A Ansco Junior - c1916-31. 3¼x5½" on 122 film, otherwise like the No. 1 above. $15-25.

Juniorette No. 1 - c1923. Folding rollfilm camera for 6x9cm. Nearly identical to the

No. 1 Folding Ansco and No. 1 Ansco Junior, but with lower-priced f8 Single Achromatic lens in Deltax shutter. $8-12.

Karomat - c1951-56. 35mm strut-folding rangefinder camera, identical to the Agfa Karat 36. Early models have hinged knob on advance lever, and a depth of field calculator on top. Beginning about 1953, the advance lever has a fixed knob, and there is no longer a depth calculator. Schneider Xenon f2.8 or f2.0 in Synchro-Compur. $30-40.

Kiddie Camera - c1926-29. Listed in the catalogs along with the Dollar Camera, with shared description and photo. It is the same cardboard box camera, but with red covering and a strap. $10-15.

Lancer - c1959. Streamlined cast metal camera made for Ansco by Bilora. Identical in style to the Bilora Bella 44. Simple f8 lens in 2-speed shutter. Takes 12 exposures 4x4cm on 127 film. $10-15.

Lancer LG - c1962. Identical, but with uncoupled meter attached to the front. $15-25.

Memar - c1954-1958. Basic 35mm camera. Apotar f3.5/45 in Pronto. $12-18.

Super Memar - c1956-59. Similar to the Memar, but with CRF, f3.5 lens. $15-25.

Super Memar LVS - c1957-59. CRF, Synchro-Compur LVS shutter, and Solagon f2 lens. $25-35.

Memo cameras *The Memo cameras have presented a problem to some collectors who advertise one for sale and do not indicate which model they are selling. Ansco sold several different cameras which were simply called "Memo" with no further designation. In recent years, serious collectors and dealers have tried to identify them further by using the year of introduction along with the name.*

Memo (1927 type) - intro. 1927. 35mm half-frame. Wooden vertical box body with leather covering. Tubular optical finder on top. Makes 50 exposures 18x23mm on 35mm film in special cassettes which were originally made of wood. f6.3/40mm Ilex Cinemat or Wollensak Cine-Velostigmat lens. Sliding button on back for film advance, automatic exposure counter. Some models focus, others are fixed focus. A shutter release guard was added to later models. Although these sometimes sell for slightly more in Europe, they are fairly common in the U.S.A. $45-60.

Memo (Boy Scout model) - The "Official Boy Scout Memo Camera" has a wooden body painted olive-drab color and has a special nameplate with the official insignia, and comes in a matching olive-drab case. Much less common than the normal models. Camera only: $125-150. With case: $150-200.

Memo (wood finished) - The earliest variation of the 1927 type Memo, this had varnished wood and brass trim rather than leather covering. Less common than the others of the series. (Original ads in December 1926 and January 1927 illustrate this wood model.) $200-250.

Memo (1940 type) - see AGFA Memo.

Memo Automatic - c1963. Single frame, 18x24mm, camera for standard 35mm cartridges. Features spring-motor film advance. Made by Ricoh for Ansco, and identical to the Ricoh Auto Half. Also continued as the Memo II under the Ansco and GAF labels. $25-35.

Memo II - see Memo Automatic, above.

Memory Kit - c1923. A specially packaged outfit including a folding camera in a fitted polished wood box with 4 rolls of film. A metal plate on the box is suitable for engraving. Came with No. 1 Ansco Junior, No. 1 Folding Ansco, or No. 1 Readyset Royal. Complete with camera and original boxes of film: $50-75. Camera and presentation box only: $40-60.

Panda - c1939-50. Small black plastic camera with white trim for 6x6cm exposures. Ansco's answer to Kodak's Baby Brownie cameras. $2-6.

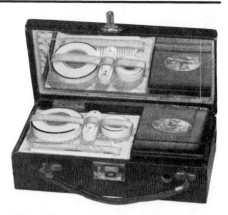

Photo Vanity - A small Ansco box camera concealed in one end of a case. May be operated from the exterior with the case closed. The case also contains art-deco designed lipstick, powder, rouge & comb, and a mirror in the lid. Apparently the vanity case was made by Q.L.G. Co. and fitted with an Ansco camera, so only the camera itself is actually on Ansco product. $650-1000.

Pioneer - c1947-1953. Plastic eye-level cameras in PB-20 & PD-16 sizes. Formerly called Agfa Pioneer. Common. $1-5.

Readyflash - A low-priced plastic eye-level camera for 6x9cm on 620 film. Sold new in 1953 for $14 with a flash, 6 bulbs, gadget bag & film. $2-6.

Readyset (No.1, 1A, Eagle, Special, etc.) - 1920's. Folding cameras. $10-15.

Readyset Royal, Nos. 1, 1A - c1925-32. Folding cameras with special leather coverings, usually brown, including pigskin &

Ansco No. 1A Readyset Traveler

ANSCO (cont.)

ostrich skin. These are not rare, and although they are seen advertised for sale at higher prices, they are generally available for $15-20. Somewhat higher in Europe.

Readyset Traveler - c1931. Folding cameras in No. 1 & 1A sizes (for 120 & 116 film). These are covered in canvas with colored stripes and have a matching canvas case. $15-20. *(Illustrated bottom of previous page.)*

Rediflex - c1950. Plastic twin lens box camera, 6x6cm on 620 film. $2-7.

Regent - c1953. Identical to the Agfa Solinette. Horizontally styled folding bed 35mm camera. Apotar f3.5 in Prontor-SV to 300. $15-25.

--Super Regent - intro. 1954. The Ansco equivalent of the Agfa Super Solinette. CRF. Solinar f3.5 lens in Synchro-Compur shutter. $35-50.

Semi-Automatic Ansco - c1924. Folding rollfilm camera. A lever on the rear of the drop bed actuates a spring-wound advance system. There are two distinct variations: One has the advance lever on the operator's right while the other has the advance lever on the left. It differs from the Automatic model which further couples the winding mechanism to the shutter release. Ansco Anastigmat f7.5/130mm in Ilex shutter. $75-125.

Shur-Flash - c1953. Basic box camera with flash attachment. $1-5.

Shur-Shot - c1948. A basic box camera with vertically striped aluminum front. Perhaps the most common of the Ansco box cameras. $1-5.

Speedex *See the listing of Speedex cameras under Agfa. Essentially the same cameras were* marketed under both the Agfa and Ansco names.

Speedex 1A - c1916. Folding camera for 116 film. Anastigmat f6.3 in Ilex Universal shutter. $12-20.

Vest Pocket Ansco: *(While we tend to think that all vest pocket cameras are for 4x6.5cm exposures on 127 film, Ansco called its No. 1 and No. 2 models "Vest Pocket" even though they were larger cameras.)*

Vest Pocket Model A - Designed with a folding bed, unlike the other vest pocket models above. B&L Zeiss Tessar lens. Ansco shutter. $20-30.

Vest Pocket No. O - c1916-23. For 4x6.5cm exposures on 127 film. Ansco Anastigmat f6.3 or Modico Anastigmat f7.5. Strut-supported front pulls straight out. $30-50.

Vest Pocket No. 1 - c1915-19. Folding camera for 6x9cm. Strut-supported front. Patents to 1912. Actus shutter. $15-25.

Vest Pocket No. 2 - c1915-24. Similar to the No. 1 and also for 6x9cm on 120 film. The unusual feature of this camera is the hinged lens cover. Ansco Anastigmat or f7.5 Modico Anast. Bionic or Gammax shutter. $20-30.

Vest Pocket Junior - c1919. Folding bed camera, 6x9cm on 4A (120) film. $12-20.

Vest Pocket Readyset - c1925-31. Folding bed camera for 4x6.5cm exposures on 127 film. Early models are covered with leather. Later models c1930 are enameled in a number of colors. $20-35.

Vest Pocket Speedex No. 3 - c1916-20. Folding bed rollfilm camera for 6x9cm on 4A (120) film. Tessar f4.5, Goerz-Celor f4.8, Ansco Anastigmat f5 or f6.3, or Modico Anastigmat f7.5 in Acme Speedex shutter. $8-12.

Ansco View - View cameras are difficult to price as collectibles because their main value lies in their usability. Any usable view camera with tilts and swings generally exceeds the price collectors would pay. Shutter & lens are even more important in estimating the value, since a good lens has more value than the camera itself. Collectible value, with older type lens & shutter $50-100. Usable value with full movements, not including lens $75-125.

Viking - c1946-56. Self-erecting folding bed camera for 6x9cm on 120 film. Agnar f6.3 or f4.5 lens in Pronto shutter to 200. $10-15.

ANTHONY *The oldest American manufacturer of cameras and photographic supplies. Begun by Edward Anthony in 1842 as E.Anthony. Edward's brother Henry joined him in 1852, and in 1862 the firm's name was changed to E. & H.T. Anthony & Co. In 1902, they merged with the Scovill & Adams Co. to form Anthony & Scovill, and five years later the name was shortened to Ansco, a contracted form of the two names. At the same time, they moved from their original location on Broadway to Binghamton, N.Y. (See also Agfa, Ansco, Scovill.)*

Ascot - c1899. Folding plate cameras. *Note: The plate & hand camera division of E.& H.T. Anthony Camera Co., which made the Ascot Cameras, merged with several other companies in 1899 to become the Rochester Optical & Camera Co. Ascot cameras are quite uncommon, since they were made for such a short time.*

Ascot Cycle No. 1 - 4x5" size. Orig. price $8 in 1899. $45-60.
Ascot Folding No. 25 - 4x5" size. $45-60.
Ascot Folding No. 29 - 4x5" size. Original price $15 in 1899. $45-60.

Ascot Folding No. 30 - The big brother of the above cameras, this one takes 5x7"

Ascot Folding No. 30

plates. Like the others, it has a side door for loading and storage of plate holders. $60-75.

Box cameras - c1903-06. Leather covered box for 3¼x4¼" on rollfilm: $20-30. Focusing model for 4x5" exposures on plates or with rollholder: $30-50.

Buckeye - c1896. Box cameras for 12 exposures on daylight-loading rollfilm. (Some models equipped for either plates or rollfilm.) Made in 3¼x4¼" & 4x5" sizes. These were probably by American Optical Co. with Anthony acting as a sales agent. These cameras were the competition for the Boston Bullseye and the Eastman Bullet cameras of the day. $30-50.

Anthony Clifton

Champion - c1890. A series of mahogany field cameras, in sizes from 4x5" to 8x10". Folding bed with hook-shaped "patent clamps" to hold it rigid. Rising front, swing back. Originally supplied with cone-shaped brass barrel single achromatic lens, case, holder, and tripod. $150-200.

Clifton - c1901. A series of view cameras with a great variety of movements including double-swing back and front, rising & shifting front, reversible back, front & rear rack focus. Made in 6 sizes from 5x7" to 14x17". $100-200. *(Illustrated bottom of previous column.)*

Climax Detective - A rather large wooden box "detective" camera from the late 1880's. It was called a detective camera because it didn't look like the large tripod-mounted bellows style view cameras which were the order of the day. It could be operated hand-held, and all the shutter controls could be operated without opening the box. A removable rear storage compartment holds five 4x5" double plateholders. Available in polished wood or leather covered models. At least one dealer asked $2500 for a complete example, but more realistically these fall into the range of $1200-1500.

Climax Portrait Camera - c1888. A large studio view camera, usually found in the 11x14" size, but made up to 25x30". Two sets of bellows allow long extension with telescoping bed. With brass barrel lens. $200-300.

Compact Camera - c1890's. A compact folding field camera based on English designs of the time. The lensboard folds flat against the bed using its center tilt axis. A rotating tripod top is built into the bed. The lens must be removed to fold the camera, and unfortunately many cameras of this style have become separated from their original lenses. Made in sizes from 5x7" to 8x10". $150-225. *(Illustrated top of next page.)*

Anthony Compact Camera

Daylight Enlarging Camera - c1888. View camera & enlarger for plates to 11½x11½". Masking back for enlarging. Rotating back & bellows. Without lens: $150-175.

Fairy Camera - c1888. Lightweight folding view camera. Similar in design to the more common Novelette camera, it featured a revolving back & bellows combination for horizontal or vertical orientation. It also offered rack & pinion focusing while the Novelette employed a sliding back with a fine-focus screw. The Fairy camera has a walnut body with nickel plated fittings. Made in 6 sizes from 4x5" to 8x10". $175-275.

Gem Box - c1877. A series of cameras for making multiple "gem" tintypes by using from 4 to 12 lenses on Anthony's Universal Portrait & Ferrotype Camera. Camera sizes from 3¼x4¼" to 6½x8½". Quite rare. We would recommend consultation with several reputable dealers or advanced collectors, since these would interest only a small group of collectors in the estimated price range of $1000-3000.

Klondike - c1898. Fixed focus box camera for 3¼x4¼" plates. Adjustable shutter speeds & diaphragm. $50-75.

Lilliput Detective - c1889. Detective camera in the shape of a miniature satchel. Takes 2½x2½" plates in double plateholders. A rare item. $2000-3000.

Normandie - According to the Anthony 1891 catalog, this was the "lightest, most compact, and easily adjustable, reversible back camera in the market." The spring-loaded ground glass back was a relatively

Anthony Novel

39

new feature at that time. Made in sizes from 4x5 to 14x17". Current value with original lens $125-175.

Novel - A family of view cameras from the 1880's with a rotating back & bellows combination. Although 4x5" & 5x7" sizes were made, by 1888 the Novel cameras were made only in sizes 8x10" and larger. The smaller sizes were replaced by the Novelette. With brass barrel lens $125-175. *(Illustrated bottom of previous page.)*

Novelette, Duplex Novelette - c1885. View cameras. Similar in design to the Novel, with the rotating back & bellows unit. The Duplex Novelette carried this idea one step further by allowing the bellows to be easily released from the lensboard. This permitted the user to convert from a 5x8" to an 8x10" back in seconds. Made in all standard sizes from 4x5" to 11x14" in basic, single swing, and double swing models ranging from $12 to $54. Current value with lens $175-250.

Novelette Stereo - Essentially the same camera, but fitted with twin lenses to make stereo views to enchant the pre-TV generation. $350-500.

PDQ - c1890. A detective box camera for 4x5" plates or films. Original price $20. Currently $600-850.

Satchel Detective Camera - Consists of a Climax Detective camera in a special covering designed to look like a satchel with a shoulder strap. The bottom of the satchel is completely open to allow access to the camera's controls. This outfit was called the "Climax Detective Satchel Camera" in the 1893 catalog, although earlier catalogs used the "Satchel Detective Camera" name. This is an extremely rare camera, and obviously the price would be negotiable. One sold at auction a few years ago in the range of $15,000-$20,000.

Schmid's Patent Detective Camera - The first hand-held instantaneous camera produced in America. Although two years earlier the Englishman, Thomas Bolas, produced and patented two hand-made prototype cameras which were hand-held with viewfinders, these were never commercially produced. Therefore the Schmid was the world's first "commercially produced" hand-held camera. Patented January 2, 1883 by Wm. Schmid, Brooklyn, NY. The earliest model for 3¼x4¼" plates featured a rigid one-piece carrying handle formed from a brass rod. The second model featured a folding handle. Later models had the focusing scale on the right side, and leather covering was optional. The 1891 catalog offers 6 sizes from 3¼x4¼" to 8x10", sizes above 4x5" on special order only. $3000-4000.

Stereo Solograph - c1901. Well-crafted lightweight folding-bed stereo camera for 4½x6½" plates. Mahogany body with morocco leather covering. Polished wood interior. Red Russian leather bellows. Rack & pinion focus. $300-350. *(Illustrated on back cover.)*

View cameras - Anthony made a variety of view cameras, most of which can be identified with a certain amount of research. However, it is relatively safe to say that most do not fall into the category of useful equipment today, and therefore can be classified strictly as collectible cameras. While some of the earlier models stir more interest, the later, more common types can generally be found in very good condition, with an original vintage lens, for $125-175.

APM (Amalgamated Photographic Manufacturers Ltd., London) *APM was formed in 1921 and brought together seven British photogrpahic companies: A. Kershaw and Son Ltd, Kershaw Optical Co., Marion and Co. Ltd, Marion and Foulgar Ltd, Paget Prize Plate Co. Ltd, Rajar Ltd, and Rotary Photographic Co. Ltd. APM aimed to bring together the resources of these companies which included both equipment manufacturers and producers of sensitised materials. The "APeM" tradename was adopted for many of its products.*
The amalgamation was never a commercial success despite the wide range of its products and on February 1, 1929 APM divided. The sensitised

materials manufacturers of Marion and Co., Paget, and Rajar formed Apem Ltd. and based themselves in the Watford factory of Paget. Apem was taken over and absorbed into Ilford Ltd c1932. The remaining companies all concerned with equipment production (except Rotary which undertook printing) remained as APM until c1930 when they regrouped as Soho Ltd. APM produced a wide range of cameras which tended towards the lower end of the market, although by 1928 studio cameras featured heavily alongside a vast number of accessories. Their cameras included the Apem press camera, Soho Reflex made by Kershaws and the Rajar No. 6 camera (1929). The Rajar is noteworthy because it was one of the first all plastic-bodied cameras and was distributed through premium schemes.

Box cameras - c1920's. Leather covered wooden box cameras, 2¼x3¼" and 2¼x4¼" sizes. Three stops; single speed. $5-10.

Focal Plane Camera, plate type - Strut-folding 9x12cm plate camera with focal plane shutter. Kershaw Anastigmat f4.5/5½" lens. $30-50.

Rajar No. 6 - Folding camera with four cross-swing struts. Body and front plate made of bakelite. Its 1929 introduction makes it one of the earliest bakelite rollfilm cameras. $10-17.

Reflex - Single lens reflex cameras in 2¼x3¼" and 3¼x4¼" sizes. Cooke Apem Anastigmat f4.5. $45-75.

APOLLO - c1951-54. Horizontally styled folding camera. 16 exposures 4.5x6cm on 120. Westar Anastigmat f3.5 lens. $20-30.

APPARATE & KAMERABAU (Friedrichshafen, Germany)
Akarelle - c1954. Unusually designed 35mm camera with two side-by-side finder windows. Lever wind. Prontor shutter. Various interchangeable lenses f2 to f3.5. $30-50.

Akarette - c1949. Similar to Akarelle. Model 0 is basic black enameled model with Radionar f3.5 lens. Model I has chrome faceplate, self-timer, and film reminder in advance knob. Model II has metal parts chromed, is leather covered, has strap lugs, and one of the following lenses: Radionar f3.5, Xenar f3.5, 2.8, or f2. $25-40.

Akarex (Models I & III) · c1953. 35mm. Rangefinder and lens are interchangeable as a unit. Isco Westar f3.5/45mm normal lens. Also available: Schneider Xenon f2/50mm, Tele-Xenar f3.5/90, and Xenagon f3.5/35mm. Camera, 3 lenses: $100-125. Camera with normal lens only: $50-75.

Arette · 35mm cameras of the late 1950's. Model A is basic. Model IA early models c1957 are basic. Later variation c1959 has bright frame. Model IB has meter. Model IC has CRF. Model ID has meter & rangefinder. $15-30.

Arette Automatic S · c1959. Built-in automatic meter. Color-Westanar f2.8/45mm in Prontormat. $25-35.

APPLETON & CO. (Bradford, England) Criterion · c1900. ½-plate mahogany field camera. Voigtlander lens with wheel stops. Thornton-Pickard shutter. $60-90.

ARCOFLEX · Japanese novelty camera of the "Hit" type. Not a reflex camera as the name would imply. A rather uncommon name. $15-25.

ARGUS, INC. (Ann Arbor, Michigan & Chicago, Illinois.) *Originally founded as International Research Corp., Ann Arbor, Michigan. The name was changed to "Argus, Inc." in 1944, the new name coming from their popular Argus cameras.*

A · 1936-41. 35mm cartridge camera with bakelite body. Argus Anastigmat f4.5/50mm in collapsible mount. Early models have fixed pressure plate, sprockets on one side of film. Later models have floating pressure plate and sprockets on both sides. Originally advertised in the following color combinations: black/chrome, gray/gunmetal, ivory/gold, and brown/gold. In actuality, the "gunmetal" may be chrome and the "gold" is definitely brass. Gold: $100-150. Gray: $25-35. Black: $10-20.

A (126 cartridge) · To avoid confusion with the original Argus A above: This is a recent 2-tone gray plastic camera for 126 "Instamatic" film. $1-5.

AF · 1937-1938. Same as A, but lens mount focuses to 15". $15-20.

A2 (A2B) · 1939-50. Similar to the A, but with extinction meter. Two position focus. Coated lens after July 1946. $12-18.

A2F · 1939-41. Like A2 (extinction meter) but also close focusing to 15". $15-25.

AA (Argoflash) · 1940-42. Synchronized for flash, otherwise similar to the "A". However, it has a simpler f6.3 lens and T&I shutter. $20-30.

FA · 1950-1951. The last of the "A" series with the original body style. Large flash socket added to the left end of the body. Argus Anastigmat f4.5/50mm. Two position focus. 25-150,B,T. $20-30.

A3 - 1940-1942. A streamlined version of the A series, with fully rounded body ends and a chrome top housing incorporating an extinction meter. Exposure counter on front. Body shutter release. $25-35.

A4 - 1953-1956. Body style completely different from the earlier "A" cameras. Boxy black plastic body with aluminum faceplate. Cintar f3.5/44mm. Sync. $10-17.

K - 1939-1940. One of the more desirable Argus cameras, the Model K is assumed to be a simplified version of the legendary Model D (a spring-motor autowind camera announced in 1939 but apparently never marketed). The Model K retained the same body style, but without the autowind feature. It did include a COUPLED extinction meter for its $19.50 original price. $175-200.

C - 1938-1939. The original brick-shaped camera with a non-coupled rangefinder. With speed range select switch: $60-80.

Without speed range select switch, as in C2: 30-45.

CC (Colorcamera) - 1941-42. Streamlined camera based on the A3 body, but with uncoupled selenium meter instead of extinction type. $35-50.

C2 - 1938-1942. Like the "C", but the rangefinder is coupled. Introduced just after the model C in 1938. An early "brick". $15-25.

C3 - 1939-66. The most common "brick". A solid, durable, and well-liked camera, like the C2, but with internal synch. Common. Somewhat higher in Europe. $10-15.

C3 Matchmatic - 1958-1966. Basically a face-lifted C3 in two-tone finish. Designed for use with a non-coupled clip-on selenium meter. Must be complete with meter to be valued as a collectible. Somewhat higher in Europe. $10-20.

C4 - 1951-1957. Similar to the Model 21 Markfinder of 1947, but with coupled rangefinder rather than bright frame viewfinder. Cintar f2.8/50mm. $25-35.

C4R - 1958. Like the C4, but with rapid film advance lever. $30-45.

C44 - 1956-57. Similar to the C4 series, but with interchangeable lens mount. Three-lens outfit: $50-85. With Cintagon f2.8/50mm normal lens: $35-50.

C44R - 1958-1962. Like the C44 but with rapid advance lever. Three-lens outfit: $60-90. With normal lens: $45-60.

C20 - 1956-58. Replaced the A4, using the same basic body style but incorporating a rangefinder. Brown plastic body. $15-20.

C33 - 1959-61. A new design incorporating features of the C3 and C4 series in a boxy body even less appealing than the famous brick. It did have a combined view/rangefinder and interchangeable lenses, and accepted an accessory coupled meter. Shutter cocking is coupled to the film advance lever. With normal lens: $15-25. Extra lenses $15-25.

21 (Markfinder) - 1947-52. A reincarnation of the A3 body style, with interchangeable lenses and a bright-frame finder. Cintar f3.5/50mm coated lens. $20-25.

Argoflex *There are a number of Argoflex twin-lens cameras, none of which cause any great excitement among collectors.*

Argoflex E - 1940-48. Focusing 3-element f4.5/75mm Varex Anastigmat. Shutter B-200. $15-20.
Argoflex EM - (Also called Argoflex II) 1948. Metal body. $15-20.
Argoflex EF - 1948-1951. Flash model. $15-20.
Argoflex 40 - 1950-1954. Beginning with this model, the lenses are no longer externally coupled, and the viewing lens does not focus. $10-15. *(Illustrated top of next page.)*
Argoflex Seventy-five - 1949-58. Black plastic body. Fixed focus. $5-10. Slightly higher in Europe.

Argoflex 40

Argus 75 - 1958-64. Brown plastic body. Continuation of the Argoflex Seventy-five with minor cosmetic changes. $5-10. Slightly higher in Europe.

Argus Super Seventy-five - 1954-1958. Like the Argoflex Seventy-five, but focusing Lumar f8/65mm coated lens. $10-15.

Autronic I, Autronic 35, Autronic C3 - 1960-1962. Although the camera bore several designations during its short life, it was really just one model. Similar in appearance to the C33, but incorporating a meter for automatic exposure with manual override. Cintar f3.5/50mm. Synch shutter 30-500, B. $15-25. (Often found with inoperative meter for about half as much.)

Camro 28 - Same camera as the Minca 28, but with a different name. $20-30.

Delco 828 - Same camera as the Minca 28, but with a differnt name. $20-30.

Lady Carefree - Cheap 126 cartridge camera made for Argus by Balda-Werke in Germany. Tan with brown covering or white

Argus Lady Carefree

with cream brocade covering. $1-5.

Model M - 1939-40. Streamlined bakelite camera for 828 film. Argus anastigmat f6.3 lens in a collapsible mount. For 8 exp. 24x36mm or 16 exp. 19x24mm. $40-60.

Minca 28 - (also called Model 19) 1947-1948. A post-war version of the streamlined bakelite Model M camera. Lunar f9.7 lens. (Also sold under the names "Camro 28" and "Delco 828".) $20-30.

V-100 - 1958-1959. Rangefinder camera made in Germany for Argus. Cintagon II f2/45mm or Cintar II f2.8/50mm in Synchro-Compur. BIM. $20-30.

ARNOLD, KARL (Marienberg, Germany)
*Producer of KARMA cameras, an abbreviation
of KArl ARnold, MArienberg.*

Karma - 6x6cm camera for 120 rollfilm.
Trapezoid-shaped body with black leather.
Eye-level telescopic finder and uncoupled
rangefinder. Meyer Trioplan f3.5/75mm
lens, helix focus. Focal plane shutter 25-
500, T. $200-250.

Karma-Flex 4x4 Model I - c1932-36.
Typical Karma body style, but twin-lens-
reflex, with two small closely spaced
lenses on front. Takes 4x4cm on 127 film.
Fixed focus f9 lens in M,Z shutter. Rare.
$500-750.

Karma-Flex 4x4 Model 2 - c1932-1937.
SLR for 4x4cm on 127 film. Ludwig Vidar
f4.5/60mm or Laack Ragolyt f4.5/60mm.
Guillotine shutter 25-100. Black leather
covered metal body. $275-325.

Karma-Flex 6x6cm - Rare model
resembling the Karma camera with a reflex
finder perched on top almost as if an
afterthought. Focal plane shutter to 500.
Victar f3.5/75mm in helical focusing
mount. This is much less common than
the 4x4cm models. $700-900.

Noviflex - c1935. SLR, 6x6cm on 120 film.
Schneider Radionar f2.9/75mm or Victor

f3.5/75mm lens. FP shutter 1/20-1/1000.
$150-200.

ARROW - Hit type novelty camera for
14x14mm on 16mm paper-backed rollfilm.
Japanese made: $8-12. Later Hong Kong
version: $4-8.

ARROW - Plastic 120 rollfilm camera of
the Diana type. $1-5.

ARS OPTICAL CO. LTD. (Japan)
Acon 35 - c1956-58. 35mm RF. Models I,
II, & IIL. Vita f3.5/45mm lens. $15-25.

ASAHI KOGAKU (Tokyo) *Founded in 1919, the Asahi Optical Co. began making projector lenses in the 1920's and camera lenses in 1931. During the war, Asahi production was strictly military. Their claim to fame is the introduction of the first Japanese 35mm SLR, the Asahiflex I of 1951, followed shortly in 1954 by the world's first instant-return mirror. The Asahiflex line became the Pentax line which remains among the major cameras of today.*

Asahiflex Cameras - *The early Asahiflex cameras made from 1951-1957 are considerably different from the later Pentax models. Aside from the fact that they are boldly marked "Asahiflex" on the front, there are several other features which distinguish them. The reflex viewing is waist-level only, and there is a separate eye-level finder. The lens mount is a screw-thread, but not the standard 42mm size.*

Asahiflex IIA - 1955. Like IIB, but with slow speed dial added to front. Also sold in USA by Sears as Tower 22. $60-100.

Asahiflex I - 1952. FP shutter 25-500. Single X-synch post on front for FP bulbs. No slow speed dial or patch. Takumar f3.5/50mm normal lens. The first Japanese 35mm SLR. Uncommon. $150-200. *(Illustrated on back cover.)*

Asahiflex Ia - 1953. Similar to model I, but with F and X synch posts on front. $75-120.

Asahiflex IIB - 1954. The world's first instant-return mirror. Takumar f2.4/58mm or f3.5/50mm. Early model without slow speed dial or patch: $125-175. Later version, c1955, with slow speed patch: $100-125.

Pentax (original) - 1957. In a completely new design from the earlier Asahiflex cameras, the Pentax incorporated an eye-level pentaprism, standard 42mm threaded lens mount, rapid advance lever, crank rewind, etc. $100-150.

Pentax K - 1958. Automatic diaphragm stop-down to pre-selected aperture. Shutter to 1000. Central microprism grid added to finder. Also sold as Tower 29 in U.S.A. $50-75.

Pentax S - 1957. Identical to the original Pentax, but with arithmetic progression of shutter speeds, 1,2,4,8,15,30,60,125,250, 500. Black rewind knob. $50-75.

Pentax Spotmatic - c1964. First Pentax with through-the-lens exposure metering. Named "Spotmatic" because prototype had spot meter, but production versions have averaging meter. Super Takumar f1.8/55mm. FP shutter B,1-1000. 450-75.

ASIA AMERICAN INDUSTRIES LTD. (Tokyo)
Orinox Binocular Camera Model AAI-720 - c1978. Camera for 110 film built into binoculars. $60-100. *(Illustrated top of next page.)*

47

Orinox Binocular Camera

ASIANA - Plastic 120 novelty camera of the Diana type. $1-5.

ASTRA - Japanese novelty subminiature of the Hit type. $10-15.

ASTROPIC - Japanese novelty subminiature of the Hit type. $10-15.

ATKINSON, J.J. (Liverpool, England)
Tailboard camera - ¼-plate size. Mahogany construction with brass landscape lens. $70-90.

Wet-plate Field Camera - c1870? For 12x16.5cm wet plates. Fine wood with brass trim. Square black bellows. Brass barrel lens with revolving stops. $250-350.

ATLAS-RAND
Mark IV - 126 cartridge camera with electronic flash. Made by Keystone. $4-8.

ATOM OPTICAL WORKS (Japan)
Atom-Six-I - c1951. Folding camera for 6x6cm on 120 rollfilm. Eye-level and waist-level finders. Seriter Anastigmat f3.5/75mm, Atom shutter B,1-200. $40-50.

Atom-Six-II - c1952. Similar, but dual-format for 6x6cm or 4.5x6cm on 120.

Separate finder for each size. Atom Anastigmat f3.5/75mm. N.K.S. shutter B,1-200. $50-60.

ATOMS (St. Etienne, France) *The ATOMS name is an acronym for "Association de Techniciens en Optique et Mecanique Scientifique", a company founded in 1946 to build twin-lens reflex cameras.*

Aiglon - A series of TLR style cameras in which the finder lenses are fixed focus, and the objective focuses by turning the front element. Various lenses in Atos I or II shutters. $30-40.

Aiglon Reflex - c1950. A better quality model with coupled Angenieux, Berthiot or Roussel f4.5 lenses. $35-45.

Atoflex - The best of ATOMS' TLR cameras with externally gear-coupled lenses. Angenieux f4.5 or f3.5 objective. Shutter 10-300. $40-50.

ATTACHE CASE CAMERA 007 - 1960's. Sophisticated toy from Japan. A James Bond style attache case with a spy camera, radio, telescope, and de-coder. $75-100.

AURORA PRODUCTS CORP.
Ready Ranger Tele-photo Camera Gun - c1974. A thoroughly modern collectible with some interesting features. The actual camera is a "Snapshooter" slip-on camera for 126 cartridges, which is little more than a lens and winding knob. The most interesting part is the outlandish telephoto attachment, shaped like a giant blue bazooka with a folding stock. It can usually be found today in new condition with the original box for $10-20.

AUTOMATIC RADIO MFG. CO. (Boston)
Tom Thumb Camera Radio - c1948. A great combination of a 4-tube portable radio and a plastic reflex novelty camera, all in a wooden body with gray and red exterior.

Identical in appearance to the "Cameradio" of Universal Radio Mfg. Co. $95-125.

B & R Manufacturing Co. (NY)

Photoette #115 - Small metal box camera with cardboard back. Covered with leather-pattern black fabric. 4.5x6cm on 127 film. Not common. $25-40.

B & W Manufacturing Co. (Toronto, Canada)
Press King - c1948-50. 4x5" press camera, similar to the Crown Graphic. Lightweight metal body, double extension bellows, drop-bed, revolving spring back. $100-150.

BABETTE - Hong Kong novelty camera

for 127 film. Also sold with the "Bazooka" name as a chewing gum premium. Various colors. $2-6.

BABY CAMERA - Small novelty "Yen" camera, available in both folding style and box type. Paper covered wood with ground glass back. Takes single sheets of film in paper holders for 3x4.5cm negatives. Folding style: $15-25. Box style:$10-20.

BABY FINAZZI - c1950. Made in Baden, Switzerland. Box camera for 6x9cm on 120 rollfilm. Red leatherette, red lacquered metal parts. $25-40.

BABY FLEX - c1950. Japanese TLR subminiature for 13x14mm exp. on 17.5mm paper-backed rollfilm. Sanko f3.5/20mm lens in Peace Model II shutter 1/25, 1/150. A rare subminiature. $400-600.

BACO ACCESSORIES CO. (Hollywood, CA)
Baco Press Club, Model B - c1950. Heavy, rigid-bodied cast metal press camera for 2¼x3¼" film holders. $40-60. *(Illustrated top of next page.)*

BAIRD, A.H.(Edinburgh, Scotland)
Single lens stereo camera - Tailboard style camera with sliding lensboard to allow either single or stereo exposures. Mahogany with brass fittings. Roller-blind shutter. $450-500.

Baco Press Club

Tropical Field Camera 5x7" - Brass bound field camera of light wood. Square-cornered bellows. $250-350.

BALDA-WERK (Max Baldeweg, Dresden)
Baldalette - c1950. Folding 35mm. Schneider Radionar f2.9/50. Compur Rapid or Pronto shutter. $30-40.

Baldalux - c1952. Folding camera for 6x9cm or 4.5x6cm on 120 film. Radionar f4.5 lens in Prontor SV shutter with body release and DEP. Eye level and reflex finders. $20-35.

Baldamatic I - c1959. 35mm rangefinder camera with non-changeable Xenar f2.8/45mm in Synchro-Compur. Bright frame finder with auto parallax correction. Match-needle metering. $15-25.

Baldamatic II - c1960. $20-30.

Baldamatic III - c1960. Similar, but interchangeable lenses. $45-65. (extra lenses additional).

Baldax 6x6 - c1935. Folding camera for 6x6cm on 120 film. Trioplan f2.9/75mm in Compur or Compur-Rapid. Newton finder with manual parallax adjustment. $25-35.

Baldax V.P. - c1930's. Compact folding camera for 16 exp. 4.5x6cm on 120 film. Available in a large variety of lens/shutter combinations, f2.8-f4.5. $25-35.

Baldaxette Model I - c1936. For 16 exp. 4.5x6 cm on 120 film. f2.9/75 Hugo Meyer Trioplan or f2.8/80 Zeiss Tessar. Rimset Compur or Compur Rapid shutter with self-timer. $50-75.
Model II - 12 exp. 6x6cm on 120. $50-75.

Baldessa - c1957. Basic 35mm with bright frame finder. No meter or rangefinder. Baldanar, Westanar, or Color Isconar f2.8/45mm, non-interchangeable. Vario or Prontor SVS. $10-20.

Baldessa Ib - c1958. 35mm, BIM, CRF, bright frame finder. Isco f2.8 lens. $15-25.

Baldi - c1930's. For 16 exp. 3x4cm on 127. f2.9 or 3.5/50mm Trioplan. $40-65.

Baldina - 1930's. Folding 35 (similar to the early folding Retina Cameras). Common combinations include: f3.5/50 Baldanar, f2/45 Xenon, f2.9/50 Xenar. Prontor-S or Compur Rapid shutter. $25-40.

Baldinette - c1951. Retina-style 35mm. Various shutter/lens combinations. $25-40. *(Illustrated top of next page.)*

Baldini - c1950. Retina-style folding 35mm camera, similar to the Baldinette. $15-30.

Baldix - c1952. Self-erecting folding camera for 6x6cm on 120 rollfilm. Baltar f2.9/75mm or Ennagon f3.5 in Prontor SV. $15-25.

Balda Baldinette

Baldixette - c1950's. 6x6cm rollfilm camera with telescoping front. Baldar f9/72mm in B,M shutter. $5-10.

Doppel-Box - c1933. Leather covered metal box camera. Dual format, 6x9cm or 4.5x6cm on 120. Two brilliant finders and folding frame finder. Universal Doppel f11 lens. Z,M shutter. Built-in portrait lens. $4-8.

Erkania - c1938. Box camera, 6x9cm on 120. Juwella Anastigmat f6.3/105mm. $4-8.

Fixfocus - c1938. Self-erecting dual-format folding bed camera for 6x9cm or 4.5x6cm on 120 film. Normally with Trioplan f4.5/105mm in Pronto. $10-15.

Gloria - c1934. Folding camera for 6x9cm or 4.5x6cm on 120 film. Folding eye-level finder and small reflex finder. Trioplan f3.8 in Compur. $15-25.

Hansa 35 - c1948-50. Folding 35mm

camera styled like Retina. Also sold under other names such as Central 35, etc. Westar f3.5/50mm in Prontor-S 1-300, B. $15-25.

Jubilette - c1938 (the 30th anniversary of Balda-Werk, thus the name). Folding 35mm similar to the Baldina. Baltar or Trioplan f2.9/50mm. Compur shutter. $15-30.

Juwella - c1939. 6x9cm folding rollfilm camera. Juwella f4.5 Anast. Prontor T,B, 25-125, self-timer. $10-15.

Mickey Rollbox - Small box cameras for 4x6.5cm exposures on 127 film. Original advertising featured the Disney characters, but the cameras are rather simple. Several variations: Model I: Meniscus lens. Model II: Double lens. Two-zone focusing. Built-in close-up lens. Cable release socket. Two tripod bushes. $15-25.

Piccochic - c1932. Vest-pocket camera for 16 exp. 3x4cm on 127 film. Normal lens: Ludwig Vidar f4.5/50mm. Also available: f3.5 Trioplan, f2.9 Vidonar, f2.9 Schneider

Xenar. Compur, Prontor, or Ibsor shutters. New prices ranged from $12.50 to $37.50. $35-60.

Pierrette - c1934. Unusual 4x6.5cm folding rollfilm camera with leather covered "clam-shell" front doors and strut-supported front. Trioplan f3.5/75 in Compur 1-300 or Pronto 25-100. Folding optical finder. Uncommon. $150-200.

Poka - c1929-38. Metal box camera for 6x9cm exp. on 120 rollfilm. Meniscus lens, simple shutter. $10-20.

Pontina - c1938. Self-erecting camera for 6x9cm on 120. Trioplan f3.8/105; Trioplan, Trinar, or Radionar f4.5; Tessar f4.5 or f3.8. Prontor or Compur shutter. $25-40.

Rigona - c1936-42. Folding camera for 16 exp. 3x4cm on 127 film. Similar to the Baldi. Normal lenses: f4.5 Vidanar, f2.9 Schneider Radionar, f2.9 Meyer Trioplan. Prontor shutter. $50-75.

Rollbox 120 - c1934. All metal 6x9cm box. Unusual variation with brown covering: $35-50. Normal models: $10-18.

Springbox - c1934. Uncommon strut-folding vest-pocket camera for two formats on 127 film. Takes 4x6.5cm or 3x4cm on 127 film. Doppel-Objectiv f11. $30-45.

Super Baldax - c1954-57. Folding rollfilm camera with CRF. 6x6cm on 120 film. Schneider Radionar f2.9/80 in Prontor SV 1-300, B; Balda Baltar f2.9 in Prontor SVS 1-300, B; or Enna Ennit f2.8/80 in Synchro Compur 1-500,B. $60-90.

Super Baldina (bellows style) - c1937-40. Folding "Retina-style" 35mm with CRF. Trioplan f2.9, Tessar f2.8, Xenon f2. Compur or Compur Rapid. $50-80. *(Illustrated top of next column.)*

Super Baldina, bellows style

Super Baldina (telescoping front) - c1955. 35mm cameras, with or without RF. $30-45.

Super Baldinette - c1951. CRF, f2 lens. Also sold as Hapo 35 by Porst. $35-50.

Super Pontura - c1938. Folding camera for 8 exp. 6x9cm on 120 film, adaptable for 16 exp. 4x6cm. CRF, automatic parallax compensation. f3.8 or 4.5 Meyer Trioplan. Compur Rapid to 400. $40-60.

BANIER - Plastic Diana-type novelty camera. $2-6.

BANNER - Novelty camera of Diana type. $2-6.

BAOCA BC-9 - c1985. Novelty 35mm camera from Taiwan. Small pseudo-prism. Retractable lens shade. $1-5.

BARCO - c1954. Japanese novelty subminiature of the Hit type. Simple fixed-focus lens, single-speed shutter. Unique construction- front half is cast aluminum. Shutter housing appears to be copper, not brass. In colors. $10-15.

BARON CAMERA WORKS
Baron Six - c1953. Horizontally styled self-erecting camera for 6x6cm and 4.5x6cm images on 120 film. Ciskol Anastigmat f3.5/80mm in N.K.S. shutter B,1-200. $45-65.

BARTHELEMY
Stereo Magazine Camera - c1905. Leather-covered wooden box camera for stereo exposures on 45x107mm plates. Changing mechanism for 12 plates. Guillotine shutter. $250-300.

BAUCHET (France)

Mosquito I - c1962. Plastic camera with rectangular telescoping front. Made by Fex for the Bauchet firm. Similar to the Ultra Fex. No sync or accessory shoe. $10-15.

Mosquito II - c1962. Like the Mosquito I, but with accessory shoe and flash sync. $10-15.

BAUDINET INTERNATIONAL
Pixie Slip-On - Lens & shutter assembly which snaps onto a 126 film cartridge to form a camera. $1-3.

BAUER - Folding camera for 8 exposures 6x9cm or 16 exposures 4x6cm on 620 rollfilm. Schneider Radionar f4.5/105. Vario sync. shutter. $15-25.

BAZIN & LEROY (Paris)
Le Stereocycle - c1898. Jumelle-styled stereo camera for 12 plates 6x13cm. Ross Rapid Rectilinear lenses. Guillotine shutter. $250-300.

BEAR PHOTO CO. (California)

Bear Photo Special - Simple metal box camera for 6x9cm. Made by Ansco for the Bear Photo Co. Decorative front plate with outline of bear. $15-20.

BEAURLINE INDUSTRIES INC.
(St. Paul, Minnesota)
Imp - A disposable mail-in camera, factory loaded. Camera is self-addressed to the processing lab. Plastic body covered with bright red or yellow paper. $10-15.
(Illustrated top of next page.)

Beaurline Imp

Pro - c1954. Disposable mail-in 35mm plastic camera, factory loaded with 12 exposure Ansco film. $10-15.

BECK (R & J Beck, Ltd., London)

Cornex Model A - c1903. Drop-plate magazine box camera for ¼-plates. Wood body with leatherette covering. Single Achromatic f11 lens. Shutter: T, 10, 20, 40, 80. Automatic exposure conter. $15-25.

Frena - c1897. Detective box magazine

cameras for special sheetfilms. 2⅝x3½, 3¼x4¼, and 4x5" sizes. More common and half as expensive in England. $100-150.

Frena Deluxe - c1897. For 40 exp. 6.5x9cm on special perforated sheet film. Covered with brown calves leather. Metal parts gold plated. $350-550.

Zambex - c1911. Folding camera for 3¼x4¼" plates. Mahogany body with leather covering. Nickel trim. Various shutters and lenses. $125-150.

BEDFORDFLEX - Twin lens novelty camera for 4x4cm on 127 film. $5-10.

BEICA - Japanese "Hit" type novelty camera. $10-15.

BEIER (Kamera-Fabrik Woldemar Beier, Freital, Germany) *Several major reference books have misspelled the name of this company. In an effort to keep the incorrect spellings from proliferating, we would like to affirm that the first name is spelled with an "o" and that the last name is NOT "Bayer".*

Beier-Flex - c1938. 2¼x2¼" SLR, similar to the Reflex Korelle. FP shutter to 500. Xenar f3.5/75mm lens. $175-225.

Beiermatic - c1961. Trioplan f3.5/45mm in Juniormatic Auto shutter. BIM. $12-18.

Beira (bed-type) - c1936? Horizontally-styled 35mm camera with self-erecting front. Top housing looks as though it were designed to include a rangefinder, but there is none. Trioplan f2.9/50mm lens in Compur (with Balda faceplate). Helical focusing. Only one recorded sale, at auction in 1986 for $95.

Beira (strut-type) - c1930. 35mm camera with pop-out front supported by scissor-

struts. Dialytar f2.7/50mm. Originally for non-standard film and without rangefinder. Later modified for standard 35mm film and unusual prismatic telescopic rangefinder added. This was called Model II in German advertising, but not in U.S.A. ads. Compur or Compur Rapid. Rangefinder model: $250-350. Without RF: $125-175.

Beirax - c1930's. Folding 6x9cm rollfilm camera. E. Ludwig Victar f4.5/105mm. Prontor or Vario shutter. $12-18.

Beirette (folding type) - ca. late 1930's. Compact, horizontal style folding 35mm camera. Cast metal body, leather bellows. Rodenstock Trinar lens:f2.9, 3.5, or 3.9 in Compur or Compur Rapid shutter. $150-200.

Beirette (rigid type) - c1966-on. Low cost East German 35mm cameras, various models, which were sold new as late as 1981 for $24. Used value $10-20.

Beirette K - c1960's. From VEB Beier, a version of the Beirette for Rapid cassettes. Meritar f2.9/45mm in Model II shutter. $10-15.

Beirette VSN - c1960's. Inexpensive 35mm camera. Meritar f2.8/45mm in Priomat 3-speed shutter with weather symbols. $10-15.

Edith II - c1925-33. Folding plate camera with leather covered aluminum body. Made in sizes for 6.5x9cm or 9x12cm plates. Various lens/shutter combinations, such as Fotar f6.3/105mm in Vario. $25-35.

Folding sheet film cameras - 3¼x4¼" or 9x12cm sizes. Rodenstock Trinar Anast. f4.5 or Betar f4.5 in Compur shutter. $25-35.

Lotte II - c1925-37. Leather covered aluminum folding plate camera. Made in 6.5x9cm and 9x12cm sizes. DEB. Rack and pinion focus. Various shutters and lenses. $25-35.

Precisa - c1937. Folding camera for 6x6cm on 120. 75mm lenses range from f2.9 to f4.5. AGC, Compur, or Compur Rapid shutter. $15-30.

Rifax - 6x9cm rollfilm. Rodenstock Trinar f3.8/105. Prontor II, 1-150. $20-30.

Rifax (Rangefinder model) - c1937. Vertical style folding-bed camera for 6x6cm or 4.5x6cm on 120 film. CRF. $50-75.

Voran - c1937-41. Self-erecting camera for 6x9cm and 4.5x6cm on 120 rollfilm. Various shutters and lenses. $20-40.

BEIL & FREUND (Berlin)
Plate Camera, 9x12cm. - c1890. f8 Anastoskop Meniscus lens. $75-125.

BELCA-WERKE (Dresden)

Belfoca - c1952. Folding camera for 8 exposures 6x9cm on 120. Some models are dual format, taking 6x9cm and with 6x6cm or 4.5x6cm. Folding frame finder. Prontor shutter, Ludwig Meritar f4.5 lens. $15-25.

Belfoca II - c1954. Similar to Belfoca, but with finder incorporated in top housing. Bonotar f4.5/105mm in Junior or Tempor shutter. $15-25.

Belplasca - c1955. Stereo 24x30mm on 35mm film. Tessar formula f3.5/37.5 Jena lenses. Shutter 1-200, sync. Very common, but popular among stereo enthusiasts. $300-375.

Beltica - c1951. Folding 35mm. Ludwig Meritar f2.9/50 or Zeiss Tessar f2.8/50. Ovus or Cludor shutter. $15-25.

BELCO - Small black-enameled cast metal camera for 36x36mm exposures on 127 film. Extinction meter. $35-50.

BELL-14 - c1960. Novelty 16mm subminiature styled like a 35mm. Simple fixed-focus lens, single-speed shutter. $15-25.

BELL & HOWELL (Chicago)
Dial 35 - Half-frame 35mm. Auto wind. Same as Canon Dial 35, but sold under B&H label. With unique molded plastic case: $50-70.

Electric Eye 127 - (originally announced in late 1958 under the name "Infallible".) A heavy all-metal box camera with automatic diaphragm and large eye-level optical finder. Normally with silver enamel and black leatherette, but also with black enamel and grey covering. 4x4cm on 127 film. $8-12.

Foton - c1948. 35mm spring-motor driven, 6 frames per sec. CRF. $700 original price (subsequently reduced to $500) made it a marketing failure. Discontinued in 1950. With Amotal f2.2/50 normal lens: $300-425.
Accessory lenses for Foton:
Cooke 4" - $150-200.
Cooke 12" - $300-400.
Accessory viewfinder - $60-90.

Stereo Colorist I

Stereo Colorist II

Stereo Colorist I - c1954-60. 35mm stereo. Rodenstock Trinar f3.5 lenses. Made in Germany for Bell & Howell. $100-175. *(Illustrated bottom of previous page.)*

Stereo Colorist II - c1957-61. Similar, but with rangefinder. $125-200. *(Illustrated bottom of previous page.)*

Stereo Vivid - c1954-60. Leather covered cast aluminum body. Steinheil Trinar f3.5/ 35mm Anastigmats, focus to 2½'. Shutter 1/10-1/100, MFX sync, with front squeeze release. Combined rangefinder-viewfinder with spirit level. Common. $75-100.

BELL CAMERA CO. (Grinnell, Iowa)
Bell's Straight-Working Panorama
Camera - c1908. Panoramic camera in which neither the film nor lens swings, pivots, or moves, which justified the cumbersome name. This camera is basically an extra-wide folding camera taking 5 exposures 3¼x11½" on rollfilm. On some models, knobs on top of camera allow user to change format in mid-roll to 3¼x5½" postcard size, 10 exposures per roll. $400-500.

BELL INTERNATIONAL CORP.

Bell Kamra Model KTC-62 - c1959. Combination 16mm cassette camera & shirt-pocket sized transistor radio. Identical to the Kowa Ramera, but not often found under this name. $100-125.

BELLCRAFT CREATIONS
Can-Tex - Plastic novelty camera, "Cardinal" type, for 16 exp on 127 film. $3-6.

BELLIENI (H. Bellieni & Fils, Nancy, France)
Jumelle - for 36 plates 9x12cm. Zeiss

Protar f8/136mm. Leather covered wood body. $150-200.

Stereo Jumelle - c1894. 6x13cm or 9x18cm stereo plate cameras with magazines backs. Some versions could also take panoramic exposures. Goerz or Zeiss lenses in aluminum barrel with brass diaphragm ring. 6 speed shutter. $100-150.

BENCINI (Milan, Italy) *Originally founded in 1937 as I.C.A.F., then C.M.F., and finally Bencini.*
Animatic 600 - c1955. Cassette camera for 126 film. $1-5.

Comet II

Comet, Comet II, Comet S - c1948. A series of cast aluminum cameras for 4x4cm & 3x4cm on 127 film. Model II has focusing lens and telescoping front. $10-20.

Comet 3, III - c1953. Unusual 3x4cm rollfilm camera styled vertically like a movie camera. Shutter B, 50. Model 3 is fixed focus, Model III has helical focus. $50-75.

Cometa - c1959. Cast aluminum camera for 4x4cm on 127 film. Integral accessory shoe cast into bottom. Aplanatic f8/55mm. Shutter B,50,100. $10-15.

Eno - Inexpensive 6x9cm rollfilm camera. $15-25.

Gabri - c1938. Metal box camera for 4x6cm on rollfilm. (Made by C.M.F. before it became Bencini.) f11/75mm lens in B, 30 shutter. $12-18.

Koroll - c1951. Cast aluminum camera for 6x6cm on 120 film. Telescoping front. Achromatic f11/150mm. Shutter B,50. $10-20.

Koroll 24 - c1953. For 16 exposures on 120 film. Achromatic lens, shutter B,50. $15-25.

Koroll S - c1953. Cast aluminum camera, extensible front. For 12 exposures on 120 film, or 16 exposures with insertable masks. Focusing f11 lens. Sector shutter, B, 50. $10-20.

BENETFINK (London)
Lightning Detective Camera - c1895. ¼-plate. Ilex string-cock shutter. $75-100.

Lightning Hand Camera - c1903. Falling-plate magazine camera for 12 plates 3¼x4¼". $35-50.

Speedy Detective Camera - Falling plate box camera with unusual 10-plate

Benson Victor

changing mechanism & counter. Guillotine shutter attached to inner side of hinged front. $75-100.

BENSON DRY PLATE & CAMERA CO.
Victor - Street Camera with cloth sleeve, tank, and tripod. Three-way internal film carrier holds tintypes or direct positive paper in 2½x3½", 1¾x2½" sizes or photo buttons. Below the film plane is a two-compartment storage drawer. Wollensak RR lens, two-speed shutter, helical focusing mount. $100-150. *(Illustrated bottom of previous column.)*

BENTLEY BX-3 - c1986. Novelty 35mm from Taiwan, styled to strongly resemble a 35mm SLR camera, and with metal weight added inside the plastic body to enhance the illusion of quality. $1-5.

BENTZIN (Curt Bentzin, Goerlitz, Germany) *(Succeeded by VEB Primar)*
Folding Focal Plane Camera - c1909-11. Strut-type folding camera with focal plane shutter to 1000. Made in various sizes from 6x9cm to ½-plate. A typical example in the 9x12cm size would have Tessar f6.3/150mm. $120-160.

Planovista - c1930. Twin-lens folding camera (NOT a reflex). A "taking" camera topped by a second "viewing" or "finder"

camera. Separate lens and bellows for each half. For 8 exposures 4x6.5cm on 127 film. Meyer Trioplan f3.5/75mm in Pronto shutter, 25-100, T, B. Top lens tilts down for automatic parallax correction. $500-750. *(The Planovista was made by Bentzin to be marketed by the Planovista Seeing Camera Co. Ltd. of London. The design is that of the Primarette, but with a new name.)*

Primar (Plan Primar) - c1938. 6.5x9cm folding plate/sheetfilm camera, double extension. Meyer Trioplan f3.8 or Zeiss Tessar f4.5. Rimset Compur. $65-95.

Primar Reflex - c1920's. 6.5x9cm or 9x12cm. Tessar f4.5 lens. $125-175.

Primar Klapp Reflex - c1920's. 9x12 cm folding reflex. Meyer Trioplan or Tessar f3.5/210mm. Focal plane shutter 1-300, T, B. $150-200.

Primarette - c1933-1937. Compact twin-lens folding camera as described above under "Planovista". Tessar f2.8 lens. $500-750.

Primarflex (Primar Reflex) - c1936. 6x6cm SLR. f3.5/105 Tessar. FP shutter. Uses rollfilm or single glass plates. Style similar to the Hasselblad, although pre-dating it by over 10 years. (Primar Reflex name appears to have been used after WWII for the same camera which was formerly called Primarflex.) $125-180.

Primarflex II - c1951. Similar to the Primarflex, but with interchangeable finder hood and optional pentaprism. Also sold under the name "Astraflex II". Both this and the earlier model tend to have shutter problems. $150-175.

Rechteck Primar (stereo) - c1912-1920's. Called "Primar Folding Hand Camera" in English language catalogues. Folding-bed camera with double extension bellows. Leather covered wooden body. 9x12cm and 10x15cm sizes. Tessar f4.5 lenses in Stereo Compur shutter. $300-500.

Stereo-Fokal Primar - c1923-29. Strut-type focal plane camera for stereo exposures on 6x13cm plates. Tessar f4.5/120mm lenses. $200-300.

Stereo Reflex - c1920's. 6x13cm stereo reflex. Gound glass back. Roja Detective Aplanat f6. FP shutter 20-1000. $400-450.

Stereo Reflex Primar - c1918-30. Reflex-style stereo camera for 6x13cm plates. Focal plane shutter to 1000. Tessar f4.5/120mm lenses. $250-450.

BERA - see Maschpriborintorg

BERMPOHL & CO. K.G. (Berlin, Germany) *Two distinctive designs in color-separation cameras were produced by Bermpohl. Miethe's Three-color camera took succesive exposures on a shifting plate. Bermpohl's Naturfarbenkamera (natural color camera) used beam-splitting mirrors to expose three plates at the same time.*
Bermpohl's Naturfarbenkamera - A beautifully constructed teakwood beam-splitting tri-color camera made in 9x12cm, 13x18cm (5x7"), and 18x24cm sizes. These rarely appear on the market, and are of interest to a limited number of collectors. Sales in the early 1980's were $1800-2200, but recent auction sales have been as low as $1100. Current estimate: $1000-1500.

Miethe/Bermpohl Camera - c1903. Folding bed camera of polished mahogany with brass trim, wine red bellows. Tall sliding back allows for three successive exposures through blue, green, and red filters. Goerz Dogmar f4.5/190mm or Goerz Doppel-Anastigmat f4.6/180mm lens. $1800-2500. Companion viewer, a 3-tiered wooden box with tilting base sells for about $1500.

BERNARD PRODUCTS CO.

Faultless Miniature - c1947. Boxy bakelite minicam for 3x4cm on 127 film. Metal art-deco faceplate. $1-5.

BERNER (W.Heinz Berner, Erfurt, Germany)
Field camera, 13x18cm - c1895-1900.

Wooden view camera with brass trim. Tapered green bellows with wine red corners. Double extension tailboard. Brass barrel lens with rollerblind shutter. $150-175.

BERNING (Otto Berning & Co., Duesseldorf, Germany) *Currently known as Robot Foto & Electronic GmbH & Co. K.G., the company was founded in 1933 and its first camera presented at the 1934 Leipzig Spring Fair.*

Robot I - c1934. For 1x1" exp. on 35mm film. Spring motor automatic film advance. Zeiss Tessar f2.8/32.5mm lens. Rotating shutter 2-500. Robot I cameras require special supply and take-up cassettes which open automatically inside the camera, and close when the camera is opened. Includes built-in lever-actuated green filter. Serial numbers below 30,000 with no letter prefix. $100-150.

Robot II - c1939-1950. Improved model of Robot I. Built-in flash synchronizer, but no filter. Enlarged finder housing includes right-angle finder. Various lenses f1.9, f2.8, f3.8, in 37.5 or 40mm focal lengths. Serial number has "B" prefix. $85-125.

Robot IIa - c1951-53. Similar to II, but takes standard 35mm or special Robot cartridges. Has accessory shoe. Double flash contacts on front. Available with tall double spring. "C" serial numbers. $95-125.

Robot Junior - c1955-58. Similar to IIa, but without right-angle viewing. Schneider Radionar f3.5/38mm. "J" serial prefix. $75-125.

Robot Luftwaffe Model - 1940-45. Most commonly found with 75mm lens. Pictured here with 40mm lens. Note the tall winding grip. "F" serial prefix. Not uncommon, but often overpriced by hopeful sellers. Some counterfeits have been made from civilian models. $125-175.

Robot Royal 24, III - c1954. Newer style but still for 24x24mm exposures. 24 has "G" serial prefix; III has "H" prefix. $200-350.

Robot Royal 36 - c1956. 24x36mm full-frame size, rather than the 24x24mm format of the other models. "Z" serial prefix. $225-300.

Robot Star - c1952-59. f1.9 Xenon. MX sync. "D" serial prefix. $100-140.

Robot Star II - c1960. New body style. "L" serial prefix. $100-150.

Bertram-Kamera - c1954-56. Press-type camera for 2¼x3¼" exposures. Unusual design for a press camera, with no bed. CRF. Parallax compensation. Tilt and swing back. Rack & pinion focus. Lenses are bayonet-mounted, rather than using interchangeable lensboards as did most contemporary press cameras. Lenses included Schneider Angulon f6.7/65mm wide angle, Xenar f3.5/105mm normal, and Tele-Xenar f5.5/180mm. Synchro-Compur 1-400 shutter. With normal, WA, and tele lenses: $500-800. With normal lens only: $300-350.

BERTSCH (Adolphe Bertsch, Paris) Chambre Automatique - c1860. A small brass box camera with fixed-focus brass barrel lens, and a permanently attached wooden plateholder designed for 2½x2½" wet plates. The camera case also housed the equipment and chemicals to prepare and develop plates in the field, while an outer case served as a darkroom. A museum-quality collectible. Estimated value $5000. Stereo version (c1864) would likely bring $6000-7000.

BESTA - Bakelite minicam for 3x4cm on 127 rollfilm. $3-7.

BIAL & FREUND (Breslau, Germany) Magazine Camera - c1900-05. Falling-plate type box camera for 12 plates, 9x12cm. Guillotine shutter. Two stops. $75-100.

BIANCHI (Alfred Bianchi, Florence Italy) Tropical Stereo Camera - Folding-bed style camera with polished walnut body, brass trim. $550-650.

BIFLEX 35 - An unusual Swiss subminiature for 11x11mm exposures in staggered vertical pairs on 35mm wide

rollfilm. Meyer Goerlitz Trioplan f2.8/20mm. Shutter 10-250. Quite rare. $600-900.

BILORA (Kuerbi & Niggeloh)
Bella (4x6.5 cm) - Cast aluminum eye-level camera for 8 exposures, 4x6.5cm on 127 film. All black enamel or blue-grey combination. $10-20.

Bella 35 - c1959. Simple cast aluminum camera for standard 35mm film. Trinar f2.8/45mm in Pronto. $10-20.

Bonita 66 - c1953. Twin-lens box camera covered with imitation reptile skin. Meniscus f9 lens. $10-15.

Box Cameras - c1950's. Simple lenses and shutters, some with sync. $4-9.

Bella 44 - c1958. Cast metal camera for 4x4cm exp. on 127 film. Styled like a 35mm camera. $8-12.

Bella 46 - c1959. Similar to the previous Bella cameras, but for 4x6cm on 127 film. Grey covering. $8-16.

Bella 66 - c1956. Aluminum body. 6x6cm exposures on 120 film. $8-12.

Bella D - c1957. For 4x6cm on 127 film. Achromat f8. Shutter 50,100. $10-15.

Bellina 127 - Compact camera for 4x4cm on 127. Rectangular collapsible front. Introduced ca. 1964, but still being sold as late as 1980 for $18 new. $10-15.

Blitz Box - c1948-58. Basic metal box camera with flash sync. Two speed shutter. Front lens focus. $8-12.

Boy - c1950. Small round-cornered bakelite box camera. Black: $10-18. Brown with gold trim: $30-50.

Bilora Radix

Cariphot - Name variation of Bilora box. Uncommon. $15-20.

Radix - c1947-51. Small 35mm camera for 24x24mm on rapid cassettes. Biloxar f5.6/38mm lens. Simple model has rotary B&I shutter. Better model has f3.5 lens, 5 shutter speeds, plus accessory shoe. $15-25. *(Illustrated bottom of previous page.)*

Stahl Box - c1950. Name variation of Bilora box. $5-10.

Standard Box - c1950's. Exactly as its name implies. It looks like all the rest of Bilora's many metal box cameras. With or without sync for those who object to too much standardization. $5-10.

BING (Germany)
Fita - c1931-36. Simple folding-bed rollfilm camera for 5x8cm. Meniscus f11/105mm. M,Z shutter. $15-30.

BINOCA PICTURE BINOCULAR - Japan. c1950. 16mm subminiature built into 2.5x opera glasses. Bicon f4.5/40mm fixed focus. Shutter B,25-100. Formerly sold higher, but is now settling in at $400-500 for white model. Red or blue somewhat higher.

Birmingham Criterion

BIOFLEX - c1965. Hong Kong. 6x6cm TLR-style plastic novelty camera. Two-speed shutter. Not to be confused with the all-metal Bioflex made by Tokiwa Seiki in Japan. $8-12.

BIRDSEYE CAMERA CORP. (New York City)
Birdseye Flash Camera - c1954. Plastic eye-level box camera similar to the Herbert-George Co. Savoy. $5-10.

BIRMINGHAM PHOTOGRAPHIC CO. LTD. (London)
Criterion - c1897. Simple box camera for ¼-plates. $75-100. *(Illustrated bottom of previous column.)*

BISCHOFF (V. Bischoff, Munich)

Detective camera - c1890. Box camera for 9x12cm plates. Polished wood body. Aplanat lens, iris diaphragm. Two-speed shutter. $600-800.

BLAIR CAMERA CO. *Thomas H. Blair applied for a patent in 1878 for a unique camera which included its own miniature dark-tent for in-camera processing of wet collodion plates. This camera, called the Tourograph, was built for him by the American Optical Division of Scovill Mfg. Co. In 1879, Blair incorporated as "Blair Tourograph Co." in Connecticut. In 1881, he moved to Boston and reincorporated as the Blair Tourograph & Dry Plate Co. (shortened to Blair Camera Co. in 1886). In 1890, Blair absorbed the Boston Camera Co., manufacturer of the Hawkeye cameras. In 1899, Eastman Kodak Co. bought Blair Camera Co., moving it to Rochester, N.Y. Beginning in 1908, it was no longer operated independently, but as the Blair Camera Division of Eastman Kodak Co.*

Baby Hawk-Eye - 1896-1898. A small 7 ounce box camera similar to Kodak's Pocket Kodak cameras. Much less common than the comparable Kodak cameras. Takes 12 exposures 2x2½" on daylight-loading rollfilm. $150-175.

Century Hawk-Eye - 1895-96. A leather covered wooden folding camera for

6½x8½" plates. Nearly identical to Folding Hawk-Eye cameras of the same vintage, but the opening for plate holders is at the side instead of at the top. $250-300.

Columbus - Box camera similar to the '95 Hawk-Eye Box, but with integrated rollfilm system and not for plates. $300-375.

Combination Camera - c1882. A 4x5" view camera with an accessory back in the shape of a truncated pyramid which allows it to use 5x7" plates. $250-350.

No. 3 Combination Hawk-Eye Model 1 - 1904-05. Replaced the No. 3 Focusing Weno Hawk-Eye. This camera is nearly identical to the better known Screen Focus Kodak Camera of the same year. The rollfilm back hinges up for focusing on the ground glass. $275-325.

English Compact Reversible Back Camera - c1888-98. Very compact view camera, made in 7 sizes from 3¼x4¼" to 10x12". Sunken tripod head in bed of camera. Mahogany body, brass trim. Double extension. $150-250.

Focusing Weno Hawk-Eye No. 4 - 1902-1903. (Advertised as the "Focussing Weno Film Camera" in England). Allowed use of No. 103 rollfilm or 4x5" plates, and groundglass could be used with either. Rollfilm holder pulls out from the top like a drawer. This design was probably the inspiration for the Screen Focus Kodak and Combination Hawk-Eye cameras which appeared in 1904. Double extension red bellows. Wood interior. B&L RR lens. Blair/ B&L pneumatic shutter. $325-375.

Folding '95 Hawk-Eye - c1895-1898. A 4x5 folding plate camera, basically a cube when closed. Similar to the No. 4 Folding Kodak Camera of the same period. Top back door for loading plate holders. Could also use roll holder. $225-275.

Folding Hawk-Eye 5x7 - c1892. Again, a cube-shaped camera when closed. Black lacquered wood with brass trim. Top back door accepts plate holders or Eastman Roll Holder. Model No.1 has built-in shutter. Model No.2 has exterior shutter and more movements. $275-350.

No. 3 Folding Hawk-Eye, Model 3 - 1905-07. Horizontal format folding rollfilm camera, 3¼x4¼". Wood interior. Maroon bellows. B&L RR lens. $35-50.

No. 4 Folding Hawk-Eye, Models 3 & 4 - 1905-13. Horizontal format folding rollfilm camera for 4x5" exp. Red double-extension bellows. Rapid Symmetrical lens. Hawk-Eye pneumatic shutter. Nickel trim. Wood focus rails. $30-50.

No. 4 Folding Weno Hawk-Eye - 1902. Horizontal style folding camera. Polished mahogany interior, leather exterior. Meniscus, R.R., or Plastigmat lens in B&L automatic shutter. $30-50.

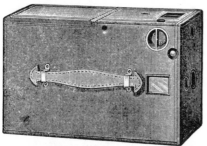

Hawk-Eye Camera (Also called **Hawk-Eye Detective Camera** or **Detective & Combination Camera**) - 1893-98. Originally made by Boston Camera Co., then continued by Blair. A large polished light wood box camera with brass fittings. Internal bellows focus. No leather covering. Takes 4x5" plates.
--First Blair version - Self-capping shutter cocked by a knob. Just below the knob on the side is a hole through which tension strengths of 1, 2, and 3 can be read. The distance scale window has become a small slit. Time release button on the front, instant release on top. $150-185.

--Improved model - Separate releases on top for time and instant. Distance scale is on the focusing knob on top. $100-175.

Hawk-Eye Camera (Leather Covered) - **1893-98.** Box camera for 4x5" plates in plate holders. Top back door hinges forward to change holders. Leather covered wood construction. Essentially the same as the Hawk-Eye camera above except for the leather covering. $100-150.

'95 Hawk-Eye Box - c1895. Box camera for plates, or will accept Blair rollholder. $300-350.

Hawk-Eye Junior - 1895-1900. For 3½x3½" on rollfilm or plates. $40-65.

Kamaret - intro. 1891. This 5½x6½x8¾" large box camera was advertised as being "one-third smaller than any other camera of equal capacity" because it was the first American box camera to move the film spools to the front of the camera. Made to take 100 exposures 4x5" on rollfilm. Other features include automatic film counter, double exposure prevention, and an attachment for using plates or cut film. $300-400.
- 5x7 size - Relatively rare, valued up to $650.

Lucidograph - c1885-86. A folding plate camera with all wood body. Front door hinges to side, bed drops, and standard pulls out on geared track. Tapered black bellows. Brass-barrel single achromatic lens with rotating disc stops. Made in several sizes: No. 1 for 3¼x4¼", No. 2 for 4¼x5½", No. 3 for 5x8". 5x8" model also has sliding front. These are not found often. $650-750. *(Illustrated top of next page.)*

Blair Lucidograph

Petite Kamarette - c1892. Small box camera, like the Kamaret but in a "petite" size for 3½" round exposures. $400-500.

**Stereo Weno (1902-03),
Stereo Hawk-Eye (1904-07) -** Leather covered, wood bodied stereo cameras. 3½x3½" exp. on rollfilm. Maroon bellows, simple B&L stereo shutter in brass housing. Blair Hawk-Eye models 1 & 2, 1904-06. EKC/Blair models 1907-16. $225-300.

Tourist Hawk-Eye - 1898-1904. Folding rollfilm camera. 3½x3½ or 4x5" size. Plain-looking wooden standard conceals lens and shutter. $120-140. (With optional accessory plate attachment add $50.)

Tourist Hawk-Eye Special - 1898-1901. Horizontally styled folding camera for 4x5" exposures on rollfilm (or plates with accessory back.) Unicum shutter. $100-140.

View cameras: with lens
4x5, 5x7 or 5x8 field type - $150-200.
6½x8½ - $175-225.
11x14 - $150-250.

No. 4 Weno Hawk-Eye

No. 2 Weno Hawk-Eye - 1904-1915. Box camera for 3½x3½" on 101 rollfilm. Similar to the "Bulls-Eye" series of the Boston Camera Co. $18-25.
No. 3 Weno Hawk-Eye - c1904. 3¼x4¼" box. $18-25.

No. 4 Weno Hawk-Eye - 1904-1915. Large 4x5" box camera. Single speed shutter. Two finders. $18-25. *(Illustrated bottom of previous column.)*

No. 6 Weno Hawk-Eye - 1906-07. Box for 3¼x5½" on 125 film. $18-25.
No. 7 Weno Hawk-Eye - 1908-1915. Box camera for 3¼x5½" on 122 rollfilm. $18-25. (Most commonly found model of the Weno Hawk-Eyes.)

BLAND & CO. (England) *Manufacturers of a variety of cameras for wet collodion plates. Bland & Co. cameras should be individually evaluated. We have seen examples sold at prices ranging from $395 to $3000. The large stereo, sliding-box, and collapsible types are obviously of much greater value than the more common view cameras.*

BLOCH (Edmund & Leon Bloch, Paris, France) *Leon was the manufacturer, while Edmund was the designer.*

Photo-Bouquin Stereoscopique - c1904. Stereo camera disguised as a book with the two objectives and the finder lens in the spine. For 45x107mm stereo plates. The camera is operated with the book cover open, and operating instructions in French are on the "first page". $3000-4000.

Photo Cravate - c1890. An unusual camera designed to be concealed in a necktie, with the lens masquerading as a tie-pin. The body of the camera is a flat metal box with rounded ends. Six 23x23mm glass plates are advanced on a roller-chain controlled by an exterior knob. The shutter is released by a concealed bulb release. Estimated current value: $3000-6000.

Physio-Pocket - c1904-1907. Camera disguised as a monocular, with deceptive right-angle viewer in eyepiece. Krauss Tessar f6.3 lens is concealed behind a small round hole in the side. This monocular camera was later sold with the Physiographe name. This basic design was later used in the Nettel Argus, Zeiss Ergo, etc. $900-1100.

Physiographe (monocular) - see description and price under Physio-Pocket above.

Physiographe (binocular) - A "binocular" version of the Physio-Pocket. The second side is actually a plate changing magazine for 12 plates, 4.5x6cm. $700-1000.

Physiographe Stereo - (Sold as "Watson's Stereo Binocular" in England.) Patented in 1896 and sold until the 1920's, the Physiographe Stereo camera resembles a pair of binoculars (slightly, larger than the regular Physiographe). Incorporating the deceptive angle viewfinder in one eyepiece, the other is used as a handle to slide out the plate magazine which is hidden in the second half. Takes 45x107mm plates. Current value: $800-1200. *Note: the first two models of the Stereo Physiographe used 5x12cm plates, with the earliest model using a leather bag for plate changing rather than the magazine. These early models would naturally be more valuable.*

vertically styled 35mm camera from Russia. Nomo f2.8/45mm lens. Shutter to 1/250. BIM. $75-125. *(Illustrated on back cover.)*

BOLLES & SMITH (L.M.Bolles & W.G. Smith, Cooperstown, NY)
Patent Camera Box - c1857. An unusual sliding-box style camera for in-camera processing of single 4¼x6½" wet collodion plates. With this camera, the photographer could sensitize, expose, and develop wet plates entirely within the camera. Patented in 1857, this pre-dates the famous (and less complicated) Dubroni camera. It is also more rare. $4000-6000.

**BOLSEY CORP. OF AMERICA
(New York)** *See also Pignons for Alpa cameras which were designed by Jacques Bolsey before his move to the United States. Cameras designed in the U.S.A. by Bolsey were manufactured by the Obex Corporation of America, Long Island, NY. and distributed by Bolsey. After June 1, 1956, all distribution was also taken over by Obex.*

BOBBY - Cast metal subminiature, similar to the Aiglon, but with black enamel finish. $75-125.

BOCHOD (VOSKHO) - c1970. Cyrillic letters look like Bochod, while Roman-lettered models read "Voskho". Unusual

Bolsey B - c1947-56. Compact 35mm with CRF. f3.2/44mm Anastigmat in helical mount. Shutter to 200, T,B. $20-25. Often found with inoperative shutter for $5-10.

Bolsey B2 - c1949-1956. Similar to the B, but with double exposure prevention and sync shutter. $15-25.

Air Force model - Identical to the B2, except for the top plate which, in typical government language says "Camera, Ground, 35mm" and "Property USAF". $75-100.

Army model, PH324A - An olive-drab and black version made for the U.S. Army Signal Corps. $75-100.

Bolsey B22 - c1953. Set-O-Matic. Wollensak Anastigmat f3.2 lens. If working $15-22.

Bolsey B3 - 1956. Similar to the 1955 Jubilee, but without the Set-O-Matic system. $20-30.

Bolsey C - c1950-1956. 35mm TLR. f3.2/ 44mm Wollensak Anast. Wollensak shutter, 10-200, B, T, synch. $25-45.

Bolsey C22 - c1953. Similar to C, but with Set-O-Matic. $30-50.

Bolseyflex - c1954. 6x6cm TLR, 120 film. f7.7/80mm lens. Made in Germany by Ising for Bolsey. The earlier model has a smaller finder hood and "Bolsey-Flex" is hyphenated. The later model has a larger finder hood which covers the shutter release, and "Bolseyflex" is not hyphenated. The same camera models were also sold by Sears under the Tower name. $15-20.

Explorer - c1955. f2.8 lens. Rapid wind. $20-30.

Explorer "Treasure Chest" outfit - In special display box with flash, case, instructions, guarantee, etc. $45-60.

Jubilee - c1955-56. 35mm camera with coupled rangefinder. Steinheil f2.8/45mm. Gauthier leaf shutter 10-200, B. $25-35.

La Belle Pal - c1952. A simplified and restyled 35mm camera. No rangefinder.

Manual front-element focusing. Wollensak f4.5/44mm anastigmat in Wollensak Synchro-Matic shutter. Originally was to be called Bolsey Model A, but apparently it was only marketed by La Belle as the Pal. Formerly sold in excess of $200. Currently: $75-125.

Bolsey 8 - 1956. Still or motion picture camera. Shutter speed variable from 1/50-1/600. Stainless steel body, size of cigarette pack. $100-150.

Bolsey Uniset 8 - 1961. Similar to Bolsey 8 but without variable shutter speeds. Rare. $175-275.

Bolsey Reflex - Original model, c1938. Mfd. by Pignons SA, Balaigues, Switzerland.

This camera is identical to the Alpa I, both cameras being developed by Jacques Bolsey shortly before he moved to the United States. 35mm SLR. 24x36mm format. Interchangeable lens. Focal plane shutter 25-1000. Focus with ground glass or split-image RF.
-Model A - c194?. Bolca Anastigmat f2.8/ 50mm. $800-1200.
-Model G - c1942. Angenieux f2.9/50mm. $150-250.
-Model H - c1942. Angenieux f1.8/50mm. $200-300.

BOLTA-WERK (later called Photavit-Werk GmbH. Nuernberg, Germany)

Boltavit - c1936. A small cast metal camera for 25x25mm exp. on rollfilm. Black enameled body or bright chrome plated. Both versions have black leather front panel. Doppel Objectiv f7.7 or Corygon Anastigmat f4.5/40mm lens. $75-125.

Photavit (Bolta-size) - c1937. Body design like the Boltavit, and uses Bolta-size rollfilm. All black body or chrome with black leather front panel. $60-90.

Photavit (35mm) - c1938. Models I, II, III, IV, V. Compact 35mm cameras for 24x24mm exposures on standard 35mm film, but in special cartridges. Film advances from one cartridge to the other. No rewinding needed, and the old supply cartridge becomes the new take-up cartridge. Wide variety of shutter & lens combinations. Standard model I of 1938 is black enameled with leather covering. Deluxe model I and all later models are chrome plated with leather covering. $50-75.

Photavit (828) - Post-war version, styled like the chrome and leather 35mm model, but for 828 rollfilm. $50-75.

BOOTS (London)
Boots Special - c1911. Lightweight compact folding field camera. Mahogany with brass fittings. Beck Rapid Symmetrical f8 lens. Thornton-Pickard rollerblind shutter. $60-85.

BOREUX (Armand Boreux, Basel, Switzerland)
Nanna 1 - intro. 1909. Folding stereo camera for 45x107mm plates. Streamlined body with rounded edges and corners. Clamshell-opening front with struts to support lensboard. Suter Anastigmat f6.8/62mm lenses. 3-speed guillotine shutter. Folding frame finder. Unusual design. $300-450.

BORSUM CAMERA CO. (Newark, N.J.)
see also Reflex Camera Co.– post 1909.
5x7 Reflex - patents 1896-1897. c1900. A very early American SLR. Measures 15x11x8½" when closed. Goerz Dagor Ser. III f7.7/16½" lens. Focal plane shutter. $300-350.

5x7 New Model Reflex - c1906. Large box camera with internal bellows focus. Small front door hinges down to uncover lens. Identical to the 5x7 Reflex of the Reflex Camera Co. $300-350.

BOSTON CAMERA CO. (Boston, Mass.)
Founded in 1884 by Samuel Turner, who later invented numbered paper-backed rollfilm. Boston Camera Co. began marketing the Hawk-Eye detective camera in 1888. In 1890, it was purchased by the Blair Camera Co., which continued to market improved versions of the Hawk-Eye cameras. About 1892, Turner left the Blair Co. and started a new company named "Boston Camera Manufacturing Co." which made "Bulls-Eye" cameras. Thus there are two separate "Boston" companies, both founded by Samuel Turner. The first made "Hawk-Eye" cameras and the second made "Bulls-Eye" cameras. It was this second company which held the rights to Turner's numbered rollfilm, and George Eastman purchased the company in 1895 to secure those rights.

Hawk-Eye "Detective" box cameras - c1888-1890 as a "Boston" camera, but continued by Blair after 1890. Large wooden box camera for 4x5" plates.

Rotating brass knob at rear focuses camera by means of internal bellows. Certain features distinguish it from the later Blair models: Wire tensioning device on the side; small shutter cocking lever in a curved front depression; top front shutter release; distance scale window on side near center. All wood box model: $200-275. Leather covered model: $150-200.

BOSTON CAMERA MFG. CO. *(see historical note above under Boston Camera Co.)*

Bull's-Eye box cameras - intro c1892. Simple, wooden, leather-covered box cameras for rollfilm. Very similar to the later Blair and Kodak Bull's-Eye cameras, but easily identified by the "D"-shaped red window. Historically important as the first cameras to use numbered paper-backed rollfilm and red windows. $75-125.

BOUMSELL (Paris)
Azur - c1950. A series of folding rollfilm cameras for 6x9cm on 120 film. $15-25. *(Illustrated top of next page.)*

Box Metal - c1950. Basic metal box camera for 6x9cm on 120 film. Imitation leather covered. $5-10.

35mm camera. Steinheil Cassar f2.8 or Meritar 45mm. Prontor-S or SV. $20-25.

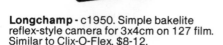

Boumsell Azur

Bower-X - c1951-1958. Folding camera for 620 rollfilm. Models I, II, and 63: $10-15. Colored models: $40-60. *(Bower-X Model II in burgundy illustrated above and on front cover.)*

BOX CAMERAS *The simplest, most common type of camera. Box cameras have been made by most camera manufacturers, and of most common materials from paper to plastic to metal. Many models are listed under the manufacturer in this guide, but to save you the trouble of looking, common boxes sell for Five Dollars or less, including sales tax, postage, and green stamps. They can make a fascinating collection without straining the average budget.*

BRACK & CO. (Munich)
Field camera - Square cloth bellows (black with red corners) extend backwards. A fine 18x24cm wood and brass camera with Rodenstock WA Bistigmat 24x30 lens with brass revolving stops. $175-225.

Longchamp - c1950. Simple bakelite reflex-style camera for 3x4cm on 127 film. Similar to Clix-O-Flex. $8-12.

BRADAC (Bratri Bradacove [Bradac Brothers], Hovorcovice, Czechoslovakia)
The Bradac Brothers began production in the 1930's with Kamarad I c1936 and Kamarad II about 1937. At the beginning of 1936, they closed their factory and part of their production was taken over by Optikotechna in Prague. The cameras were renamed Flexette (formerly Kamarad II) and Autoflex (would have been Kamarad IIa). The Autoflex does exist with Bradac Prague markings, however. See Optikotechna for the continuation of these cameras.
Kamarad (I) - c1936. TLR, 6x6cm on 120 film. Ludwig Dresden Bellar f3.9/75mm. Prontor II shutter. This was the first camera in the line which became Flexette, Autoflex, Optiflex, etc. from Optikotechna. $75-125.

Photo-Magic - c1950. Small bakelite eye-level camera similar to the MIOM. Black or wine-colored. Takes 4x6.5cm photos on 127 film. $15-25.

BOWER (Saul Bower Inc., NYC)
Bower 35 - c1952-58. Basic viewfinder

Kamarad MII - c1937. Same as (I), but Trioplan f2.9/75mm in Compur 1-250. $75-125.

BRAUN (Carl Braun, Nuernberg, Germany)

Gloria - c1953-60. Eye-level camera for 6x6cm on 120 film. Styled like an oversized 35mm RF camera. Uncoupled rangefinder. Telescoping front. Praxar f2.9/75mm in Pronto 25-200 or Prontor SVS 1-300. $15-25.

Gloriette - c1954. Non-RF 35mm camera 24x36mm. f2.8/45mm Steinheil Cassar. Prontor SVS shutter. $15-25.

Imperial 6x6 (eye-level) - c1953. Eye-level camera for 6x6cm on 120 film. Branar f8/75mm. Shutter B,25,75. Built-in meter. $15-25.

Imperial Box 6x6 (twin lens) - c1951. Twin-lens box cameras. Model S has single speed shutter, fixed focus lens. Model V has synchronized M,Z shutter, 2 stops. $5-10.

Imperial Box 6x9 - c1951. Standard rectangular box cameras. Model S has simple lens, Z,M shutter. Model V has two stops, synchronized Z,M shutter. $5-10.

Norca - c1953. 6x9cm folding rollfilm camera with cast aluminum body. Praxar f8 lens. Shutter 25,75. $12-18.

Pax - c1950. Compact metal camera with square extensible front. For 6x6cm on 120 film. Identical to the Paxina I. $10-20.

Paxette I - c1950's. Compact 35mm RF camera. Various models. $15-25.

Paxette IIM - c1953. 35mm camera with uncoupled rangefinder, interchangeable prime lenses. Normal lenses include f2.8/45mm Staeble-Kata, Cassarit, or Ultralit. Interchangeable front elements include Staeble-Telon f5.6/85 and Staeble-Choro f3.5/38mm. Body covering in various colors including brown, red, green, grey. $25-40.

Paxette Automatic Super III - c1958. Interchangeable f2.8/50 Color Ennit lens. BIM. $20-30.

Paxette Electromatic - c1960-62. 35mm with built-in meter. Model I with fixed focus f5.6, single speed shutter: $8-12. Model II with focusing f2.8, shutter 1/30-300: $10-20. Model Ia with interchangeable f2.8/40mm lens, mounted in front of the shutter: $25-35.

Paxiflash - c1961. Plastic eye-level box camera for 4x4cm on 127 film. Grey body: $20-30. Black body: $10-20.

Paxina I - c1952. Metal camera with square telescoping front. Paxanar f7.7/75mm lens. Shutter built into front has 30, 100, T. $5-10.

Paxina II - 6x6cm rollfilm camera. Round telescoping front. Staebler Kataplast f3.5/75 lens in Vario shutter. $5-10.

Super Colorette - c1957. 35mm RF cameras.
I - CRF, f2.8, rapid advance. $15-20.
Ib - Meter, 4-element lens. $20-25.
II - Interchangeable lenses. $25-30.
IIb - Like II, but with meter. $30-35.

Super Paxette - 35mm RF cameras, various models including I, IB, IIB, IIBL. Interchangeable lenses include: Xenar f2.8/50mm and Enna Color Ennit. Prontor shutter. $20-40.

Super Vier - c1965. Inexpensive black plastic camera with hot shoe for flash. As the name implies, it takes 4x4cm negatives on 127 film. Also sold as Paxiflash. Color 50mm lens. Unusual. $20-30.

BRIN'S PATENT CAMERA - London, c1891. A miniature detective camera hidden in an opera glass. Takes 25mm circular plates. f3.5/30 lens, simple front shutter. Very rare. $3000-4500. Replica recently made. $850.

BRIOIS (A. Briois, Paris)
Thompson's Revolver Camera - intro. 1862. Designed by Thompson. Brass pistol-shaped camera with scope, wooden pistol grip, but no barrel. Takes four 23mm dia. exposures in rapid succession on a 7.5cm circular wet-plate. Ground glass focusing through the scope which is above the cylindrical plate chamber. Petzval f2/40mm lens, single speed rotary behind-the-lens shutter. The lens is raised and sighted through to focus, then dropped into place in front of the plate, automatically releasing the shutter. The circular plate was then rotated a ¼ turn and was ready for the next exposure. Rare. Estimated value about $15,000.

BRITISH FERROTYPE CO. (Blackpool, England)
Telephot Button Camera - c1911. For 1" dia. ferrotype dry plates. Rapid Rectilinear lens, between-the-lens shutter. Like the Talbot Errtee Button Tintype Camera. $350-650.

BROOKLYN CAMERA CO. (Brooklyn, NY)
Brooklyn Camera - c1885. View camera for ¼-plates (3¼x4¼"), with collapsible bellows and non-folding bed. $200-250.

BROWNELL (Frank Brownell, Rochester, NY)
Stereo Camera - c1885. A square bellows dry-plate camera for stereo exposures. Historically significant, because Frank Brownell made very few cameras which sold under his own name. He made the first Kodak cameras for the Eastman Dry Plate & Film Co., and was later a Plant Manager for EKC. Rare. No recent sales.

BRUECKNER (Rabenau, Germany)
Field camera - c1900-10. Tailboard style cameras in various sizes including 9x12cm, 13x18cm, and 18x24cm. Fine wood body, brass trim, square black bellows. $125-175.

Schueler-Apparat (Student camera) - c1905-10. Tailboard camera for 9x12cm plates. Mahogany body with brass trim. String-set shutter built into wooden front. Voigtlander Collinear III f7.7 lens. $150-200.

BRUMBERGER 35 - c1960. 35mm RF camera designed to look like a Nikon S2. Non-changeable f2.8 or f3.5/45mm coated lens in leaf shutter to 300. Probably made by Nicca for Brumberger. $35-50.

BRUNS (Christian Bruns, Munich)

Detective camera - c1893. An unusual wooden box detective camera for 9x12cm plates. The unique design incorporates an auxiliary bellows with ground glass which mounts piggy-back on top of the camera. The camera lens slides up to double as a lens for this full-size ground glass viewer. $3000-3500.

BUESS (Lausanne)
Multiprint - A special camera for 24 small exp. on a 13x18cm plate which shifts from lower right to upper left by means of a crank on the back. Corygon f3.5/105mm lens, rotating shutter 1-100. Reflex finder.

Buess Multiprint

(Only 25 of these cameras were made. We know of only 2 examples. One sold at a German auction in 1976 for $820, the other in late 1984 for $450.)

BUICK MODEL 1 - Pre-war Japanese folding Ikonta-style camera for 6x6cm on 120 film. "Buick Model 1" on shutter face. This may only be the shutter name, but there is no other name on the camera. Kokko Anastigmat f4.5/7.5cm lens. Shutter speeds T, B, 25-150. $50-60.

BULL (D.M. Bull, Bullville, N.Y.)
Detective - c1892. 4x5" falling-plate magazine camera for 12 plates. Key locks back. Rare. $150-200.

BULLARD CAMERA CO. (Springfield, MA) *Founded about 1895 by Edgar R. Bullard, and absorbed into the Seneca Camera Co. about 1902.*
Folding Magazine Camera - c1898. For 18 plates in 4x5" format. First models (rare)

were made in Wheeling, West Virginia and were heavier and better made than the later ones made in Springfield, MA. Push-pull action of back advances plates. Front bed hinges down and bellows extend. Unusual, because the majority of the magazine cameras were box cameras, and did not employ folding bed or bellows. $250-275.

Folding plate camera, 4x5" - c1900. Polish mahogany interior. Red bellows. Reversible back. B&L or Rauber & Wollensak lens. Victor shutter. $60-80.

BURKE & JAMES, INC. (Chicago)
Cub - c1914. Box cameras. They stand out in a collection of box cameras because they load from the side. Made in 2A, 3, & 3A sizes. $5-10.

Grover - 1940's-1960's. Monorail view cameras in 4x5", 5x7", and 8x10" sizes. Valued as usable equipment rather than collectible, the most important consideration is the shutter and lens, which can vary greatly in value. Without lens or shutter $75-125.

Ingento: c1915.
1A Ingento Jr. - f6.3 lens. $15-20.
3A Ingento Jr. - Vertical format. Ilex lens. Ingento shutter. $15-25.

3A Folding Ingento, Model 3. - Horizontal format. Ilex lens. Ingento shutter. $15-25.

Korelle - *Marketed by Burke & James, but manufactured by Kochmann. See Kochmann.*

Panoram 120 - c1956-1971. Wide angle camera for 4 exposures 6x18cm (2¼x7") on 120 film. Originally sold with f4/5" Ross lens in focusing or fixed focus mount, single speed 1/100 sec shutter. With detachable ground glass back and magazines, we've seen them from $100-550.

PH-6-A - U.S. Signal Corps special wide angle camera for 5x7" filmholders. Wollensak f12.5 Extra Wide Angle lens in Betax No. 2 shutter. $75-100.

Rexo cameras:
Box camera - for 6x9cm rollfilm. $4-8.

1A Folding Rexo - c1916-31. For 2½x4¼ on 116 film. Anastigmat lens. $12-18.

1A Rexo Jr. - c1916-24. Folding camera for 2½x4¼ on 116 film. Single Achromatic or RR lens. Ilex shutter. $12-18.

2C Rexo Jr. - c1917-24. Folding camera. $12-18.

3 Folding Rexo - c1916-31. 3¼x4¼". RR or Anastigmat lens. Ilex shutter. $12-18.

3 Rexo Jr. - c1916-24. 3¼x4¼", single achromatic lens. Ilex shutter. $12-18.

3A Folding Rexo - c1916-24. Postcard-size camera. $15-20.

Vest Pocket Rexo - Wollensak Anastigmat lens in Ultex shutter. $15-20.

Rexoette - c1910. Box, 6x9cm. $8-10.

Press/View cameras:
2¼x3¼" & 3¼x4¼" - with lens: $40-60.
4x5 Watson Press - c1940. With Kodak Ektar f4.7/127mm lens: $90-110.

5x7 view - without lens: $60-100.
8x10 view - without lens: $100-150.

Watson-Holmes Fingerprint Camera - 1950's-1960's. A special purpose camera for making 1:1 reproductions of fingerprints or small objects. Front of camera rests on object being photographed and interior bulbs provide illumination. (Military version is called PH-503A/PF). $50-75.

BURLEIGH BROOKS INC. (Englewood, NJ)

Bee Bee - c1938-1941. German folding plate cameras sold in the USA under the "Bee Bee" name (for Burleigh Brooks). Model A for 6.5x9cm, Model B for 9x12cm. Bayonet mount for easy changing of lens and shutter. Identical to the Certo Certotrop cameras. $25-40.

Brooks Veriwide - 1970's. Wide angle camera using the Schneider Super Angulon 47mm lens (f8 or f5.6 versions) on a thin camera body compatible with the Graflex XL system. Price includes any one of the normal backs. f5.6: $550-650. f8: $450-550.

BURR, C.
Stereo camera - Mahogany tailboard camera with square leather bellows, twin brass-barreled Burr lenses and Thornton-Pickard roller blind shutter. $500-750.

Wet plate camera - c1860. Sliding-box style. Polished mahogany with brass barrel lens and brass fittings. Sliding back allows three exposures on a single 3¼x4¼" plate. $2500-3000.

BUSCH, Emil (Rathenow, Germany)
Foldin Plate Camera - 10x15cm. Double extension bellows. Rapid Aplanat Ser. D f7/170mm. $35-45.

Vier-Sechs - c1920. Strut-folding camera for 4.5x6cm plates. Leather covered wood body. Detectiv-Aplanat f6.8/75mm in Compound 25-100, B,T. Uncommon. $150-175.

BUSCH CAMERA CORP. (Chicago)
Pressman 2¼x3¼ - Miniature press camera. Although sometimes offered at higher prices, there is usually no shortage in the normal range of $50-90.

Pressman 4x5 - f4.7 Ektar, Optar, or Raptar lens. Press camera styled like Graphic. $125-170.

Verascope F-40 - c1950's. Stereo camera for 24x30mm pairs of singles. f3.5/40mm Berthiot lens. Guillotine shutter to 250. RF. Made by Richard in France but sold under the Busch name in the U.S.A. Generally considered to be one of the best stereo cameras, and not often found for sale. $350-475.

BUTCHER (W.Butcher & Sons, London)
William Butcher set up in business as a chemist in Blackheath, South London in 1860. However, it was not until c1894 that Butchers began manufacturing photographic goods under the "Primus" trademark. The photographic business was run by Mr. W.F. Butcher and Mr. F.E. Butcher, sons of the founder William Butcher. The business grew very rapidly so that by February 1902 it moved to Camera House,

Farringdon Avenue, London EC. Some cameras and accessories continued to be made at Blackheath and much was bought from contract manufacturers, notably German firms. The Butchers Watch Pocket Carbine and Popular Pressman reflex cameras were made for Butchers by Ica.
The outbreak of war in 1914 caused the cessation of its German supplies and resulted in Butchers pooling manufacturing resources with Houghtons to form the Houghton-Butcher Manufacturing Co. Ltd in 1915. This company made products for both firms which remained separate until their selling operations were finally merged in January 1, 1926 to form Houghton-Butcher (Great Britain) Ltd. Although the Butcher firm had joined forces with George Houghton, and eventually became a part of Ensign Ltd., it still remained a family tradition, and two of Butcher's grandsons were still associated with the Ensign firm in the 1930's. Check Houghton-Butcher for cameras not listed here.

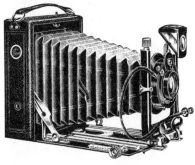

Cameo - A series of folding cameras for plates, introduced around the turn of the century and continuing for many years in all sorts of variations. In the common sizes with normal lens and shutter: $20-35.

Cameo Stereo - c1906-15. Folding bed style stereo camera for plates. Aldis, Beck, or Cooke lens. The No. 0 and No. 1 models are simpler, with T,B,I shutter. The No. 2 features rack focusing, DEB, rising front, and shutter speeds to 1/100. $125-160.

Carbine cameras - A series of folding cameras primarily for rollfilm, but most models have a removable panel in the back

Butcher Carbine No. 5

which allows the use of plates as well. Quite a variety of models with various lenses and shutters. The models with better lenses and shutters obviously bring the better prices. $20-40.

Clincher - c1913-19. Falling-plate wooden box cameras in several sizes. Morocco leatherette covering. T&I shutter. No. 1 takes 6 plates, 2¼x3¼". No. 2 takes 6 plates, 3¼x4¼". No. 3 takes 12 plates, 3¼x4¼". No. 4 takes 6 plates 9x12cm. $15-25.

Dandycam Automatic Camera - c1913-15. Box camera for ferrotype buttons. Daylight-loading magazine holds 12 plates of 1" (25mm) diameter. Wooden body with Morocco leatherette covering. $350-400.

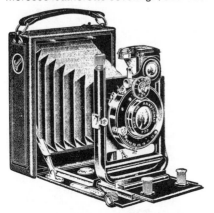

Klimax - 1910's. Aluminum folding plate camera. Morocco leather covering. In various sizes from ¼ to ½ plate. Model I is single extension, while Model II is double extension. A great variety of shutter and lens combinations were available. $20-30.

Little Nipper - c1900. Simple box cameras for glass plates. One model for 4.5x6cm, and the larger model for 6.5x9cm plates. Add-on finder is similar to that of the original Brownie camera of the same era. $40-60.

Maxim No. 1 - c1903. A leather covered wooden box camera for 6x6cm exposures on rollfilm. A rather scarce box camera from the days of the first "Brownie" cameras. $35-50.

Maxim No. 2 - Similar, but 6x9cm. $20-30.

Midg - c1902-20. A series of drop-plate magazine box cameras in 3¼x4¼" or postcard (3¼x5½") sizes. The No. 0 is the simplest, with built-in shutter and lens. Shutter speed dial is low on the front. The models 1, 2, 3, & 4 have a hinged front which conceals the better lens and shutter. We have seen these advertised and even sold occasionally at higher prices, but they generally sell with difficulty in the range of $25-30.

Popular Pressman - c1913-26. Butcher's entry into the field of reflex cameras, in 3¼x4¼" & 3¼x5½" sizes. Focal plane shutter. Generally found with f4.5 lens by Beck, Aldis, Cooke, Dallmeyer, or Ross. $75-115.

Royal Mail 15-lens Postage Stamp Camera

Reflex Carbine - c1925. 6x9cm 120 film SLR. Aldis Uno Anastigmat f7.7/4¼". Two separate releases for T & I. Body of wood covered with black leather. $90-120.

Royal Mail Postage Stamp Camera - c1907-1915. Wooden box camera for multiple exposures on a single 3¼x4¼" plate. Two major variations exist:
The 3-lens model will take 3 or 6 exposures on a plate by shifting the lensboard. Current value: $750-1000.
The 15-lens model simultaneously exposes 15 stamp-sized images on the plate. The 15-lens models previously sold as high as $1500-2000. Recent auction prices have been in the $750-1000 range.
(Illustrated top of next column.)

Stereolette - c1910-1915. Miniature folding-bed stereo camera for 45x107mm plates. Zeiss Tessar f6.3 or f4.5 in Compound Shutter. $250-400.

Watch Pocket Carbine - c1920. Compact folding rollfilm cameras, horizontal or vertical styles, in 6x6cm, 6x9cm, and 6.5x11cm exposure sizes. Leather covered metal body. Normally with f7.7 Aldis Uno Anast. in Lukos II shutter. $40-50.

Tropical Watch Pocket Carbine - c1923. Like the regular models, but with black unleathered body and Russian leather bellows. $100-150.

BUTLER (E.T. Butler, England)
Patent Three-Colour Separation Camera - A mahogany camera for three exposures on separate plates through the use of semi-silvered mirrors. The front and focusing mechanism are very similar to the Butcher Popular Pressman reflex, but with an additional cube on the back. Made in sizes for 2¼x3¼", 3¼x4¼", and 4¼x6½" plates. $2000-3500.

BUTLER BROS. (Chicago)
Pennant Camera No. 20 - Box camera for 4x5" plates in standard plateholders which load through a door at the top rear. $25-35. *(Illustrated top of next page.)*

Butler Pennant Camera

CADOT (A. Cadot, Paris)
Scenographe Panoramique - Jumelle style 9x18cm plate camera. One lens rotates to center position to change from stereo to panoramic mode. $250-350.

CAILLON (Paris)

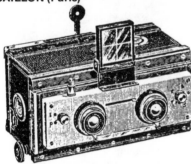

Bioscope - c1915-25. Rigid-bodied jumelle style stereo cameras in 6x13 and 8x16cm sizes. Convertible for use as a panoramic camera. $200-300.

Kaloscope - c1916. Folding bed stereo camera. Leather covered teak body. Lacour-Berthiot or Hermagis f6.8, or Zeiss Tessar f6.3/112mm lenses. Lensboard can be shifted to use left lens for panoramic pictures. $275-325.

Megascope - c1915. Jumelle style stereo with changing magazine for 12 plates, 6x13cm. Rising/falling front. Folding frame viewfinder. Leather covered metal body. Hermagis f6.3/85mm lenses, guillotine shutter ½-200. $100-150.

Scopea - c1920-25. Jumelle-style stereo

camera. Made in 45x107mm and 6x13cm sizes. Various lenses include: Berthiot Olor f6.8/85, or Roussel Stylor f6.3. Three speed shutter, 20-100. $75-100.

CAM-O CORP. (Kansas City, MO)
Ident - 35mm TLR "school camera" for bulk rolls of 46mm film. Wood body. f9.5/114mm. $50-75.

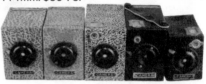

CAMERA - c1930's. Yes, that's the full name of this small Japanese paper "Yen" box camera for single 3x5cm exposures on sheetfilm in paper holders. Ground glass back. Black: $10-15. Colored: $25-35.

CAMERA CORP. OF AMERICA
(Chicago) *Original name "Candid Camera Corp. of America" 1938-1945 was shortened to "Camera Corp. of America" in 1945. Ceased operations about 1949 and sold its tools and dies to Ciro Cameras Inc. This is not the same company as the Camera Corp of America (Detroit) which sold the Camcor camera c1956-59, and also not the same as the Camera Corp. of America (Hicksville, NY) also known as Chrislin Photo Industry, which sold the Chrislin Insta Camera c1966-71 (see listing under Chrislin).*

Cee-Ay 35 - 1949-1950. Wollensak f4.5 Anastigmat in Synchro Alphax 25-150,T,B or Wollensak Anastigmat f3.5 in Synchro Alphax 10-200,T,B. $40-55.

Perfex Cameras (listed chronologically): *Note: Perfex cameras are often found with inoperative or sticky shutters, usually at about half the normal prices listed below.*

Perfex Speed Candid - 1938-39. Bakelite-bodied 35mm, non-coupled RF. f3.5/50mm or f2.8 interchangeable Graf Perfex Anast. Cloth FP shutter 25-500, B. $40-55.

Perfex Forty-Four - 1939-40. Aluminum-bodied 35mm CRF. Interchangeable f3.5

or 2.8/50mm Graf Perfex Anastigmat.
Cloth FP shutter 1-1250, B, sync.
Extinction meter. $30-40.

Perfex One-O-One

Perfex Thirty-Three - 1940-41. Scienar
Anastigmat f3.5 or f2.8/50mm. FP shutter
25-500, B, sync. CRF. Extinction meter.
$35-45.

Perfex Fifty-Five - 1940-1947. f3.5 or 2.8
Scienar or Wollensak Velostigmat lens.
FP shutter, 1-1250, B, sync. CRF.
Extinction meter-exposure calculator to
1945. $25-35.

Perfex Twenty-Two - 1942-45. Scienar
Anastigmat f3.5. FP shutter 1-1250, B,
sync. CRF. Extinction meter. Black or
aluminum body. $35-45.

Perfex DeLuxe - 1947-1950. The first of
the post-war Perfex models, it introduced
the stamped metal body to replace the
original die-cast design. Wollensak f2.8 or
f2.0 lens. $30-40.

Perfex One-O-One - 1947-1950. With
Ektar f3.5 or f2.8 lens in Compur Rapid
shutter: $40-50. With Wollensak Anast.
f4.5/50mm lens in Alphax leaf shutter 25-
150, T, B: $30-40. *(Illustrated top of next
column.)*

Perfex One-O-Two - 1948-50. With Ektar
f3.5 or f2.8 lens in Compur Rapid shutter:
$40-50. With Wollensak f3.5/50mm lens
in Alphax shutter: $30-40.

CAMERA MAN INC. (Chicago)
Champion - Black plastic "minicam" for
16 exp. on 127 film. $8-12.

President - A lofty name for a nicely
styled but rather simple black plastic
minicam for 3x4cm on 127 film. $5-10.

Silver King - An art-deco styled plastic
minicam with a metal back. $10-15.

CAMERA OBSCURA - Pre-photographic
viewing devices used to view or to trace
reflected images. While technically these

are not cameras, they did indeed lead to the development of photography in an attempt to fix their image. Original examples which pre-date photography are highly prized, but to a small group of collectors, and they vary widely in price depending on age, style, and condition. $750-3000.

CAMERETTE - Japanese novelty "yen" box camera for single exposures on sheet film in paper holders. $10-15.

CAMOJECT LTD. (England)

Camoject - Unusual bakelite subminiature for 14x14mm exposures. $75-100.

CANADIAN CAMERA CO. (Toronto, Canada)
Glenco No. 4 - 4x5" folding plate camera. Leather covered, red bellows, reversible back. Brass-barrel lens and brass trim. Wollensak shutter. $60-90.

CANDID CAMERA SUPPLY CO.
Minifoto Junior - Black plastic minicam for 127 film. Identical to the Falcon Miniature, and actually made by Utility Mfg. Co. for Candid Camera Supply Co. $5-10.

CANON INC. (Tokyo) *Originally established in 1933 as Seiki-Kogaku (Precision Optical Research Laboratory), this firm concentrated on 35mm cameras. (There is a rare Seiki subminiature for 16mm film which was made by a different company also named Seiki-Kogaku.) The Seiki-Kogaku name was used through the end of WWII. In 1947, the company name was changed to Canon Camera Co., and the Seiki-Kogaku name was dropped. The Canon name was derived from the first 35mm cameras designed by the company in 1933, which were called Kwanon.*

Most of the historical and technical information, photographs, and structuring of this section are the work of Dr. Peter Dechert, who is widely regarded as one of the world's leading collectors and historians in the field of Canon rangefinder cameras. His special interest is now the Seiki-Kogaku cameras and accessories. The price estimates for the early Canon cameras are from Dr. Dechert, since information on the sales of these rare cameras is quite limited. We appreciate his help in this area. Dr. Dechert has graciously volunteered to help other collectors with questions if they will enclose a self-addressed stamped envelope with their queries, or call 5:00-9:00 PM Mountain Time or on weekends. You may contact him at: P.O. Box 636; Santa Fe, NM 87504 USA. Telephone: 505-983-2148. Dr. Dechert is the author of Canon Rangefinder Cameras: 1933-1968, published by Hove Foto Books. It is available in the U.S.A. at $22.95 list.

PRODUCTION QUANTITIES of CANON RANGEFINDER CAMERAS: *Altogether approximately 600,000 Canon Leica-derived RF cameras were made between 1935 and 1968. About half this total was composed of the four most common models: IID, IVSB, P, and 7. The following table groups RF Canons according to the number produced.*
1-99 - Kwanon, JS, S-I, 1950, IIA, IIAF, IIIA Signal Corps.
100-999 - Hansas, Original, J, NS, J-II, Seiki S-II, IIC.
1000-2999 - S, IV, IID1, IIS, IIF2.
3000-9999 - S-II, IIIA, IVF/IVS, VT-Deluxe, VT-Deluxe-Z, VT-Deluxe-M, VL, VL-2, VI-T.
10000-19999 - IIB, III, IIF, IVSB2, IID2, IIS2, L-1, L-2, L-3, VI-L, 7s.
20000-35000 - IID, IVSB.
90000-95000 - P.
135000-140000 - 7

SERIAL NUMBER RANGES of CANON RANGEFINDER CAMERAS: *Rangefinder Canons after the Hansa/Original and J series were numbered more or less consecutively as they were produced (with many large gaps) and, until #700,001, without regard for model identification. The next table shows the models produced within the several serial number ranges.*
Kwanon, Hansa, Original - No top serial number; use the number on the lens mount.

CANON (cont.)

1000-3000 - J, JS (1938-42)
8000-9000 - J-II (1945-46)
10001-15000 - S, NS, S-I (1938-46)
15001-25000 - Seiki S-II, Canon S-II
(1946-49)
25001-50000 - IIB, IV trials (1949-51)
50001-60000 - IIC, III, 1950, IV (1950-51)
60001-100000 - IIA, IIAF, IID, IID1, IIF, III,
IIIA, IIIA Signal Corps, IV, IVF, IVS, IVSB
(1951-53)
100001-169000 - IID, IID1, IIF, IIS, IVSB,
IVSB2 (1953-55). REUSED for 7s and 7sZ
(1964-68)
170001-235000 - IID2, IIF2, IIS2, IVSB2
(1955-56)
500001-600000 - VT, VT-Deluxe,
VT-Deluxe-Z, VT-Deluxe-M, L-1, L-2, L-3,
VL, VL-2 (1956-58)
600001-700000 - VI-L, VI-T (1958-60)
700001-800000 - P (1958-61)
800001-999000 - 7 (1961-64)
*Various prototypes and trial models were
numbered outside the above ranges.*

SEIKI-KOGAKU CANONS - *Canon
cameras made between 1933 and 1947 were
manufactured by Seiki-Kogaku. Their early
lenses, lens mounts, and finder optics were
designed and in most cases manufactured by
Nippon Kogaku. Serenar lenses made by
Seiki-Kogaku were phased in slowly during
WWII on Model J and X-Ray Canons, and on
other Canons from 1946. Prices on all Canons
marked "Seiki-Kogaku" are quite variable,
depending on demand, supply, and location
world-wide, and are best considered
negotiable.*

KWANON SERIES (1934-1935) - These
were largely mock-ups and a few working
prototypes. The only working Kwanon
known today is a very roughly-made Leica II
copy repurchased by Canon Japan from a
private owner in the 1960's. Canon has
made one or more inexact copies of this
Kwanon for promotional purposes.

ORIGINAL SERIES (1935-1940) - *The
only Canons with the exposure counter on the
front face of the body. Speeds 25-500. Nikkor
f3.5 lens (early ones have black face without
serial number). Pop-up finder. Serial numbers
on lens mount and inside of baseplate. Wide
variation in details, especially in early production.*

Original Canon - *Most Canon Hansas were
sold through Omiya Trading Co. and marked
with Omiya's "Hansa" trademark. A smaller
number were sold directly and not so marked;
for some years collectors used to call the latter
the "Original Canon." Both Canon/NK Hansas
and Canon Hansas are found without "Hansa"
logos, and since they are less common than the
"Hansa" marked versions they may bring
somewhat increased prices. Hansas and non-
Hansas of equal vintage are, however, essentially
identical cameras and all varieties were known
at the time simply as "the Canon Camera." The
type designation "Original Canon" is now
outmoded and should not be used except to
describe the non-Hansa variation.*

Canon / NK Hansa - 1935-1937. Original
series features, but occasionally with
random parts originally made for use on
Kwanon cameras. The earliest Hansas
were assembled at Seiki Kogaku Kenkyujo
under the supervision of Nippon Kogaku
managers between 10/1935 and 8/1937,
and these were marked "Nippon Kogaku
Tokyo" next to the camera serial number
on the focusing mount. Design elements
came from both companies, and these
cameras can be considered forerunners
of both "Nikon" and "Canon" descendents.
Recent prices start at about $3000 and
can go much higher for examples with
identifiable Kwanon-associated parts.

Canon Hansa - 1937-40. In August 1937
Seiki Kogaku Kenkyujo was reorganized
and refinanced as Seiki Kogaku K.K.K.
Shortly thereafter the "Nippon Kogaku
Tokyo" name was dropped from the
camera body. Although the camera
remained essentially the same, it was

hereafter primarily a "Canon" product and not directly a "Nikon" predecessor; nor did these later cameras incorporate Kwanon parts. Recent prices from $2250 depending on cosmetic values.

J SERIES (1939-1946) - *No rangefinder. Viewfinder is built into top housing. "Canon", "Seiki-Kogaku", and serial number on top.*

J - 1939-1944. Speeds 20-500. No cover patch on slow dial area. Finder housing cut straight from front to back beside a large rewind knob. Nikkor f4.5 or f3.5 in screw mount similar to but not interchangeable with Leica mount. Price negotiable. $4000 and up.

JS - 1941-45. Identical to J except for slow dial on front face, speeds 1-500. Some were modified after manufacture from model J cameras, either by the factory or elsewhere. Limited production, most for armed forces. Price negotiable. $5000 and up.

J-II - 1945-1946. Like the J, but finder housing nests around smaller rewind knob similar to Leica. No slow speeds. Slow dial area usually covered by metal patch, sometimes by body covering material. Nikkor or Seiki-Kogaku Serenar f3.5 in same mount as J and JS. Price negotiable. $2500+.

S SERIES: *Retained the Hansa pop-up finder until 1946, but moved the frame counter to the top beneath the advance knob, like Leica. Retained the Original Series' bayonet lens mount until 1946.*

S - 1938-1946. Slow dial on front, lever-operated to avoid fouling focusing mount. Considerable detail variation in cameras and lenses, particularly during wartime. Canon records use the designation "S-I" for a small number made after the war, but these were assembled from left-over parts and are hard to distinguish from wartime production. A Japanese Navy version, marked entirely in Japanese, was made c1942. Nikkor f4.5, f3.5, f2.8, and f2 lenses. $1750+.

NS - 1940-1942. Like the S, but without slow speeds. Considerable variation in construction, but none with patch over slow dial area. Nikkor f4.5 and f3.5 lenses. $2500 and up.

Seiki S-II - 1946-1947. "Seiki-Kogaku" on the top plate. Combined single-stage rangefinder-viewfinder. Speeds 1-500. Formed metal body (a few late ones were die-cast). Earliest production retained the J-type lensmount. Slightly later production had a lensmount with sufficient "slop" to accomodate J-lenses or Leica-derived lenses. Final version has Leica thread mount. Nikkor f3.5, Seiki-Kogaku f3.5 and f2 lenses in versions to fit all three mounts. With "Seiki-Kogaku" markings: $300-500. (If not marked "Seiki", see Canon S-II below.)

X-RAY CANONS: *Dr. Mitarai, one of the early Canon founders, was especially interested in making cameras to record the images on X-ray screens, and these formed a considerable part of Canon's early production. Three versions of the earliest model were produced, marked as "Seiki" with bird logo, "X-Ray Canon 35", and "Canon CX-35", from about 1939 until 1956, when more elaborate units in 35mm, 60mm, and 70mm were substituted. The three early versions are interesting because they used Nikkor and Seiki-Kogaku Serenar (later Canon Serenar) f2 and f1.5 lenses. Most X-ray cameras were scrapped when replaced, and are hard to find. On the other hand, most collectors are not particularly interested in finding them. Prices negotiable. VG, complete with lens and mount: $500+.*

CANON CAMERA CO. CANONS: *In September of 1947, the company name was changed from Seiki-Kogaku to Canon Camera Co. At the same time, the lens names were changed from Seiki-Kogaku Serenar to Canon Serenar. In 1952, the Serenar lens name was dropped and they were called simply "Canon" lenses.*

CANON II SERIES (1947-1956): *All Canon II cameras have a top speed of 500 and film loading through the baseplate. Nikkor lenses were discontinued in 1948.*

Canon S-II - 1947-1949. Like the Seiki S-II, but almost all have die-cast bodies, later production with thicker wall than early production. No finder magnification adjustment. Nikkor f3.5, Canon Serenar f3.5 and f2 lenses. $200-250.

IIB - 1949-52. First 3-way magnification control of combined rangefinder-viewfinder operated by 2-piece lever under rewind knob. Speed dials split at 20. No flash synch rail or original factory synch. Serenar f3.5 & f1.9 collapsible lenses. $125-200.

IIC - 1950-1951. Like IIB, but speed dials split at 25. Same lenses. $250-350.

IIA - 1952-1953. No slow speeds. Slow dial area covered by metal patch with body covering insert. No synch. Price negotiable, very rare. $1000+

IIAF - 1953. Like IIA, but with flashbulb synch by side rail. Canon f3.5 or f2.8 lenses. Price negotiable, extremely rare.

IID - 1952-1955. Like IIC, but one-piece VF selector lever. No flash synch or film reminder dial. Speed dials split at 25. Canon f3.5, f2.8, f1.8 lenses. $90-140.

IID1 - 1952-1954. Like IID, but film speed reminder built into wind knob. $90-140.

IID2 - 1955-1956. Like IID1, but speed dials split at 30. Canon f2.8 or f1.8 lenses. $90-140.

IIF - 1953-55. Fast and slow speed dials split at 25. Top speed 500. Side synch rail. No X-synch position on speed dials. Canon f3.5, f2.8, f1.8 lenses. Some are model-identified on loading diagram. $80-125

IIF2 - 1955-1956. Like IIF, but speed dials split at 30. $100-150.

IIS - 1954-1955. Like IIF, but includes X-synch setting on slow dial at 1/15 area. Lock on slow speed dial. Some are model-identified on loading diagram. $125-175.

IIS2 - 1955-1956. Like IIS, but speed dials split at 30 and X-synch also marked on top dial at 1/45 area. $100-150.

CANON III SERIES: *All Canon III cameras have speeds 1-1000 on two dials, film loading through baseplate, and NO flash synch.*

III - 1951-1952. Two-piece finder selector

lever. No film speed reminder. Canon Serenar f1.9 lens. $125-175.

IIIA - 1951-1953. Like III but one-piece finder selector lever, and film speed reminder in wind knob. There are many varieties of III/IIIA hybrids. These are not uncommon and not a lot more valuable than true examples of either type. $100-150.

IIIA Signal Corps - 1953. A small run of very late IIIA cameras marked on the baseplate "U.S. ARMY. SIGNAL CORPS". 50mm, 28mm, 135mm, and 800mm Canon Serenar lenses for these cameras were also so marked. Cameras and lenses were otherwise identical to the standard model, and their current prices depend on demand and supply. $500 and up.

CANON IV SERIES: *All Canon IV cameras have two-dial speeds 1-1000, film loading through baseplate, and side-mounted flash synch rails. (Note: Hybrid variations of models IV through IVSB exist, partly because of running changes during manufacture and partly because of authorized updating. These are not uncommon and are not greatly more valuable than true examples of each type.)*

Canon 1950 - 1950. An early version of the Canon IV, marked "Canon Camera Co. Ltd." and with other mechanical and cosmetic differences. Serenar f1.9 lens, serial numbers between 50000 and 50199. Only 50 were made; most were sold by C. R. Skinner, San Francisco, as model "IIC" (Canon's original short-lived designation) or "IVM" (Skinner's own later designation). Few remain; when found they command $1200 or more.

IV - 1951-1952. Two-piece finder magnification lever. No film speed reminder. No X-synch. Serenar f1.9 lens. "Canon Camera Co. Inc." maker's logo. $200-300.

IVF - 1951-52. One-piece finder selector lever. Film speed reminder in wind knob. No X-synch. No lock on slow dial. Built-up interior wall next to film supply chamber. Serenar f1.8 lens. $125-175.

IVS - 1952-1953. Like IIF but flat die-cast wall next to film supply chamber. $90-140.

Canon VT-Deluxe

IVSB (IVS2) - 1952-55. X-synch marked on slow dial at 1/15 area. Slow dial locks at 25, at which speed dials are split. Canon f1.8 lens. Model IVSB was known as IVS2 in many countries including USA, but IVSB is proper factory manufacturing designation. $100-160.

VT-Deluxe-Z - 1957-58. Like VT-Deluxe but with baseplate opening key. Prices as VT-Deluxe.

VT-Deluxe-M - 1957-58. Marked simply "VT-Deluxe", but with factory-installed metal shutter curtains and silver-coated finder optics. Prices as VT-Deluxe.

CANON L SERIES: *All Canon L cameras have back loading, thumb lever wind on top, two speed dials split at 30. Lenses as on V cameras.*

IVSB2 - 1954-1956. Like IVSB but speed dials split at 30 and X-synch also marked on top dial at 1/45 area. $100-150.

CANON V SERIES: *All Canon V cameras load through a hinged back, have two speed dials split at 30, and wind with a trigger that folds into the baseplate. Normal lenses were 35mm and 50mm in speeds between f2.8 & f1.2.*

L-1 - 1956-1957. Identified on bottom. Cloth shutter curtains. No self-timer. Some VL prototypes with metal curtains may also be marked "L-1". Black $400-500. Chrome $125-175.

L-2 (1956-1957), L-3 (1957-1958) - Identified on bottom. Common in Japan but scarcer in USA. $150-225.

VT - 1956-1957. Identified on front of baseplate (a few prototypes marked simply "Model V"). Numerous small manufacturing variations during production. $125-175.

VT-Deluxe - 1957. Identified on front of baseplate. Cloth shutter curtains. No baseplate opening key. Chrome or black enameled bodies. Black $300-500. Chrome $125-175. *(Illustrated top of next column.)*

VL - 1958. No model identification. Like L-1 but metal shutter curtains and self-timer. Speeds to 1000. X & FP synch. $225-250.

VL-2 - 1958. No model identification on body. Like VL but has speeds to 500 only. Common in Japan, rare in USA. $175-250.

LATE CANON RF SERIES: *These cameras all have back loading, single speed dial on top with 1-1000 range. Lenses varied, the 50mm f1.4 and f0.95 (on 7 & 7s only) are most desirable.*

VI-L - 1958-1960. No model identification on body. Top lever wind. Single speed dial. Black $425-550. Chrome $175-225.

VI-T - 1958-1960. Identified on front of baseplate. Last baseplate trigger wind model. Black $400-500. Chrome $175-225.

P - 1958-61. Identified on top, this model also exists with special 25th anniversary and Japanese army markings. Numerous running changes during manufacture. Black $400. Chrome $100-125. Add $100 for rare 50mm f2.2 lens.

7 - 1961-1964. Identified on top. The most common of all RF Canons, and usually overpriced. Reasonable prices: Black $300-450. Chrome $110-175. Black or chrome with f0.95 add $150-300.

7s - 1964-1967. Identified on top, with RF adjustment port in front of shutter speed dial: $250-325. Add $150-300 for f0.95 lens.

7sZ - 1967-68. Also marked "7s" but with RF adjustment port above second "n" in "Canon" logo on top of camera. $250-350.

BLACK RF CANONS: *The following models are known to exist with black enameled bodies: IVSB (never commercially available), L-1, VT-Deluxe, VT-Deluxe-M, VI-L, VI-T, P, and 7. Produced in relatively small quantities, these black Canons usually command higher prices than the equivalent chrome versions, on the order of two-times with considerable paint wear to 3-times in excellent condition. A black 7s has been reported but not confirmed.*

EARLY CANON SLR CAMERAS: *This list includes all Canon SLR's produced during the period that Leica-mount RF's were still being made. Each model is identified on its body. Some were issued in black as well as chrome.*
Canonflex - 1959-1960. Canon's first SLR. $75-125.
Canonflex RP - 1960-1962. $75-100.
Canonflex R2000 - 1960-62. First 35mm SLR with shutter to 2000. $100-150.
Canonflex RM - 1961-1964. Built-in selenium meter. $60-125.

Canonex - 1963-1964. The first auto-exposure Canon SLR. $65-85.
FX - 1964-1966. $75-90.
FP - 1964-1966. $75-90.
Pellix - 1965-1966. $150-250 in Excellent or better.
Pellix QL - 1966-1970. $100-140.
FT - 1966-1972. $85-125.
TL - 1968-1972. $85-110.
EX-EE - 1969-1973. Interchangeable front elements. $75-90.

CANONET CAMERAS - A long-lived and very popular series of rangefinder cameras with non-changeable lenses. The first Canonet was introduced in 1960 and the series continues through the current G-III models. Sometimes with f2.8 lens, but more commonly found with f1.7 or f1.9 lenses. $30-50.

DEMI CAMERAS - A series of half-frame cameras with built-in meters. Initiated in 1963-64 with Demi and continued as Demi II (1964-65), Demi S (1964-66), Demi C and Demi Rapid (1965-66), Demi EE17 (1966-71), Demi EE28 (1967-70). $30-50.

Dial 35 - 1963-67 (Model 2: 1968-71). Half-frame 35mm camera with spring actuated motor drive. Unusual styling with meter grid surrounding the lens and round spring housing extending below the body to serve as a handle. $50-75.

CAPITAL MX-II - c1986. Novelty Taiwan 35mm, styled with small pseudo-prism. $1-5.

CAPITOL 120 - 2¼x3¼" metal box camera. Body identical to Metropolitan Industries Chix 120, but no B.I. U.S. Capitol dome pictured on front plate. $15-25.

CAPTA, CAPTA II, SUPER CAPTA - c1940's. Black bakelite cameras for 4.5x6cm on rollfilm. Top styling similar to Kaftax. Super Capta lens. Two speed shutter. $12-18.

CARDINAL CORP. (U.S.A.)

Cardinal, Buckeye, Photo Champ, & Cinex - All are nearly identical small plastic novelty cameras for 16 exp. on 127 film. Similar cameras by other manufacturers include "Halina-Baby", "Can-Tex" etc. $4-6.

CARMEN (France) - c1930's. Small black enameled stamped metal camera for 24x24 exp. on 35mm wide paper backed rollfilm on special spools. Meniscus lens, simple shutter. Also sold under the name "Pygmee". $75-125.

CARPENTIER, Jules (Paris)

Photo Jumelle - c1890's. Rigid-bodied, binocular styled camera. One lens is for viewing, the other for taking single exposures. This is not a stereo camera, as many jumelle-styled cameras are. Magazine holds 12 plates. To change plates, a rod extending through the side of the camera is pulled out and pushed back in. Various models in 6x9cm and 4.5x6cm sizes. $50-100. (There is also a very rare Stereo version. Price would be negotiable.)

CENTURY CAMERA CO. *Century began operations in 1900, which probably explains the company name well enough. In 1903, George Eastman bought controlling interest in the* *company. In 1905, Century took control of the Rochester Panoramic Camera Company, which had recently introduced the Cirkut camera. In 1907 it became "Century Camera Div., EKC". Following that, it was in the Folmer-Century Division of EKC which became Folmer Graflex Corp. in 1926.*

Copying/Enlarging/Reducing Camera - c1900-1910. Professional studio camera for copying photographs. Front & rear bellows. $75-125.

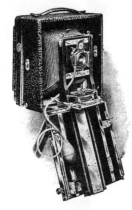

Field cameras - c1900's. Since many of the Century cameras are not fully identified, this listing is provided as a general reference. (Classified by size, with normal older lens & shutter. A good usable lens in a synchronized shutter will add to the values given here):
4x5 - (including models such as #40, 41, 42, 43, 46.) $75-125.
5x7 - (including model 15, etc.) $60-110.
6½x8½ - $85-125.
8x10 - $110-170.
11x14 - $150-250.

Grand - c1901-08. Folding cameras for plates. Leather covered wood body. Red bellows. 4x5", 5x7" or 6½x8½" size with normal lens and shutter: $75-100. With triple convertible lens: $125-150.
Grand Sr. - c1903-08. Deluxe model plate camera in 5x7" or 6½x8½" size. $100-150.

Long Focus Grand - c1902-05. Similar, but with additional rear track for extra bellows extension. $150-200.

Stereo plate camera - c1900's. 5x7" folding style. $325-375.

CERTO KAMERAWERK (Dresden, Germany)
Certix - c1930's. 6x9cm folding rollfilm camera. Various shutter/lens combinations cause prices to vary widely. $15-50.

Certonet - c1926. 6x9cm folding 120 film camera. f4.5/120mm Schneider Radionar. Vario or Pronto shutter, T,B, 25-100. $20-30.

Certo-phot - Rigid bodied simple 120 rollfilm camera for 6x6cm exp. $10-15.

Certo Six - c1950's. 6x6cm folding 120 rollfilm camera. CRF. Tessar f2.8/80mm, Synchro Compur or Prontor SVS. $75-125.

Certoplat - c1929-31. Folding bed plate camera, 9x12cm. Rack and pinion focus. Rising front. Meyer Plasmat f4 or Schneider Xenar f3.5/150mm. Compur 1-200. $40-60.

Certoruf - c1929. Folding bed camera for 9x12cm plates. Double extension bellows. Ennator or Unofokal f4.5 in Compur. $30-40.

Certosport - c1930's. Folding plate cameras, 6.5x9cm & 9x12cm sizes. Double extension bellows. Normally with f4.5 Meyer or Schneider in Compur or Ibsor. $30-45.

Certotix - c1931. Folding camera for 6x9cm on 120 rollfilm. $15-20.

Certotrop - c1929-41. Folding plate cameras, 6.5x9 & 9x12cm sizes. $50-70.

Damen-Kamera - c1900. Lyre-shaped body covered in alligator skin. Looks like a stylish woman's handbag when closed. ¼-plate size. Same camera was sold by Lancaster as the Ladies Gem Camera and by Dr. Adolf Hesekiel & Co. as the Pompadour. (See Lancaster for illus.) Rare, price negotiable. Estimate: $7500+.

Dollina - *Folding 35mm cameras made from the 1930's to the 1950's. Since the various models are not well identified on the camera body, there has been a certain amount of confusion among buyers and sellers. Hopefully the distinguishing features and illustrations here will help sellers to correctly identify their cameras.*

Dollina "0" - c1937. No rangefinder. Certar f4.5 in Vario or f2.9 in Compur. $40-50.

Dollina I - 1936-39. No rangefinder. All black or with chrome metal parts. Compur 1-300 or Compur Rapid 1-500 shutter. Radionar f2.9, Xenar f2.9 or f3.5, or Tessar f2.8 lens. $35-60.

Dollina II - c1936. Rangefinder above body, focus knob above rangefinder. Compur or Compur Rapid. Various lenses including f2 Xenon, f2.8 Tessar and f2.9 Radionar. $30-50. (Somewhat lower in Europe.)

Dollina III - c1938. Separate eyepiece rangefinder incorporated in body. Focus knob on same plane as advance and rewind knobs. $60-90.

Dolly Vest Pocket cameras - c1934-40. *There were two major styles produced concurrently. The "miniature" or 3x4cm model has a straight pop-out front with scissor-struts. The V.P. or 4.5x6cm model is a self-erecting bed type capable of taking either 4x6.5cm or 3x4cm size on 127 film.*

Dolly 3x4 (miniature) - c1932-37. Compact strut camera for 16 exp. 3x4cm on 127 film. f2.9, 3.5, or 4.5 lens. Vario, Pronto, or Compur shutter. Deluxe models have radial focusing lever and optical finder. Original prices ranged from $11 to $70. Currently: $40-50.

Dolly Vest Pocket - c1936. Also called Dolly Model A. Self-erecting bed style. 8 or 16 exp. on 127 film. A variation of this camera, marketed as the "Dolly Model B" had interchangeable backs for plates or rollfilm. The same camera, in both rollfilm & combination models was sold under the name "Sonny". $40-50. *(Illustrated top of next page.)*

Certo Dolly Vest Pocket

Doppel Box - c1935. Box camera for 8 exp. 6x9cm or 16 exp. 4.5x6cm on 120 film. Format changeable by turning a dial. Single speed shutter, Certomat lens. $25-35.

KN35 - c1973. Inexpensive 35mm VF. Non-changeable Kosmar f2.8 lens. $10-15.

Plate camera - 9x12cm. DEB. $35-50.

Super 35 - c1956. Like the Super Dollina II above, but with Light Value Scale (LVS) and MXV shutter. $40-70.

Super Dollina - c1939. Rangefinder incorporated in body. Focus knob on right side. Separate eyepiece for rangefinder. Tall knobs sit above flat top plate. Not synchronized. Compur Rapid shutter with f2 Xenon or f2.8 Xenar or Tessar. $50-70.

Super Dollina II - c1951. (Also called Super Certo II, Certo Super 35, Certo 35.) Like pre-war Super Dollina, but with single eyepiece for viewfinder & rangefinder. Flat

knobs recessed into chrome top housing. Compur Rapid MX sync shutter with f2.8 or f3.5 coated Tessar or f2 Heligon. $35-65.

Supersport Dolly, models without and with RF

Supersport Dolly - c1935-41. Folding 120 film camera for 12 exp. 6x6cm or 16 exp. 4.5x6cm. Available with or without CRF. After November 1938, an extinction meter was built into the rangefinder housing. Various lenses f2, f2.8, f2.9. Rimset Compur. With rangefinder: $60-80. No RF: $40-60.

CHADWICK (W.I. Chadwick, Manchester, England)
Hand Camera - c1891. Black-painted mahogany box camera for single plates. Externals controls. Rack & pinion focusing. Kershaw shutter. Rotating waterhouse stops. $150-225.

Stereo Camera - c1890. ½-plate tailboard stereo. Mahogany body, brass trim, rectangular black bellows. Accepts single or stereo lensboard. Brass barrel Chadwick 5" lenses with rotating waterhouse stops.

Thornton-Pickard roller-blind shutter. Other lens variations exist. $550-800.

CHADWICK-MILLER
Fun-Face Camera - c1979. Novelty cameras for 126 cassettes. Little boy's or girl's face on front of camera with lens in nose. $10-15.

CHAPMAN (J.T. Chapman, Manchester, England)
The British - c1900. ¼-plate magazine camera. Wray Rapid Rectilinear f8 lens, rollerblind shutter. $100-150.

The British - c1903. Folding camera in ¼ and ½-plate sizes. Brass lens, waterhouse stops. Red double extension bellows, brass trim. $150-200.

The British - c1903. Full-plate size. Mahogany body, brass trim. Black tapered double extension bellows. Wray brass f8 lens with iris diaphragm. $175-250.

Millers Patent Detective Camera "The British" - c1900. Black ebonized wood detective box camera for ¼-plates. Falling-plate mechanism. String-cocked rollerblind shutter behind hinged front. Rack focusing. Also available with brown reptile skin covering. $50-75.

Stereoscopic Field Camera - ½-plate folding stereo view. Dovetailed mahogany construction with brass trim. Twin Wray 5x4 lenses with iris diaphragm. $275-325.

CHARMY - Novelty camera of "Hit" type. $15-25.

CHASE - Novelty camera of "Cardinal" type for 16 exp. on 127 film. Identical to the Wales-Baby and Halina-Baby. Made in Hong Kong. $5-8.

CHASE MAGAZINE CAMERA CO., (Newburyport, Mass. USA)
Chase Magaazine Camera - c1899. For 12 plates 4x5". Plates advanced (dropped) by turning large key at side. Variable apertures. Shutter speeds I & T. $75-125.

CHICAGO CAMERA CO. (Chicago, Ill.)
Photake - c1896. A seamless cylindrical camera made to take 5 exposures on 2x2" glass plates. f14/120mm achromat lens, Guillotine shutter. A very unusual camera which originally sold for a mere $2.50. $600-900.

CHICAGO FERROTYPE CO. (Chicago, Ill.)
Founded by Louis & Mandel Mandel, the Chicago Ferrotype Co. was the United States' leading producer of direct positive "street" cameras for tintypes, button tintypes, paper prints, and post cards. See also "PDQ Camera Co."

Mandel No. 2 Post Card Machine - c1913-1930. A direct positive street camera for five styles of photos from postcards to buttons. $75-125.

Mandelette

Wonder Automatic Cannon Photo Button Machine

Mandelette - Direct positive street camera, 2½x3½". Camera measures 4x4½x6". Sleeve at rear, tank below. Simple shutter and lens. A widely publicized camera which sold for about $10.00 in 1929. $50-75. *(Illustrated on previous page.)*

PDQ Street Camera - including models G & H. For direct positive 6x9cm paper prints. $60-90.

Wonder Automatic Cannon Photo Button Machine - c1910. An unusual all-metal street camera for taking and developing 1" dia. button photographs. $300-600. *(Illustrated on previous page.)*

CHILD GUIDANCE PRODUCTS INC.

Mick-A-Matic - c1971. Camera shaped like Mickey Mouse's head. Lens in nose. Original model uses the right ear for a shutter release. Later models have a shutter release lever between the eye and ear. Although these cameras took a speculative jump a few years ago, they have settled back to a more normal price range. Actually, they are not hard to find at these prices. Original (ear shutter) model: $40-60. Later models: $20-30.

CHIYODA KOGAKU SEIKO CO. LTD.

Konan-16 Automat - c1950. 16mm subminiature. The precursor of the Minolta-16. Very similar in style, but much heavier. "Made in Occupied Japan." Rokkor f3.5/25mm fixed focus, shutter T,B, 25-200, sync. $60-90.

Minolta - *Although the Minolta cameras were made by Chiyoda, we have listed them under the more widely recognized name- Minolta.*

CHIYODA SHOKAI (Japan)
CHIYOTAX CAMERA CO. LTD.

Chiyoka 35 - c1951. Rare Japanese copy of the Leica Standard camera. Hexar f3.5/50mm lens in collapsible mount. FP 1/20-500,B. $500-700.

Chiyoko - 6x6cm TLR. Seikosha MX shutter. f3.5 Rokkor lens. $35-50.

CHRISLIN PHOTO INDUSTRY
(Hicksville, NY) *Also DBA Camera Corporation of America, but not related to the other companies which also used that name.*

Chrislin Insta Camera - c1965-69. Blue plastic box camera for 8 self-developing 60 sec. prints per roll. Eye level viewfinder in handle. This was in direct competition with the Polaroid Swinger camera, and never got off the ground. $60-100.

CHURCHIE'S OFFICIAL SPY CAMERA - Hong Kong novelty 127 rollfilm camera with tiny adhesive label advertising Churchie's. $1-5.

CHURCHILL - Black bakelite minicam, 3x4cm on 127 film. $5-10.

CIA STEREO - c1910. Manufacturer unknown. Stereo box camera for two 6x9cm exposures on 9x12cm plates. Meniscus lens with 3 stops. Individual lenses may be closed off for single exposures. Folding frame finder. Rare. $125-150.

CIMA KG. (Fuerth, Germany)
Luxette, Luxette S - c1954. Eye-level camera for 4x4cm on 127 film. Metal body with black crinkle finish. Roeschlein Cymat f7.7 in Cylux 25-100 shutter. (Luxette S has Synchro-Cylux shutter.) $15-20.

CINESCOPIE - c1929. Made in Brussels, Belgium. Early 35mm camera for 24x24mm exposures on 35mm film in special spools. Manual film advance without automatic stop or exposure counter. A wire feeler inside is perhaps used to audibly count sprocket holes when advancing film. O.I.P. Labor f3.5/ 50mm lens in Ibsor T,B, 1-150. Removable front section allows shutter and lens to be used with an enlarger. $400-600.

CINEX DELUXE - Unusually styled grey and black plastic "minicam" for 16 exp. on 127 film. Streamlined design. Available with either chrome or black faceplate, for those who may want one of each. $3-7.

CIRO CAMERAS, INC. (Delaware, Ohio)
Ciro 35 - c1949-54. 35mm RF. Basically the same camera as the Cee-Ay 35 from Camera Corp. of America. Ciro bought the design and dies and made only minor cosmetic changes. It still did not fare well, and soon was in the hands of Graflex.

Graflex sold the Ciro 35, then modified it to make the Graphic 35. Three models: R- f4.5, S- 3.5, T- f2.8. Black body less common: $25-40. Chrome: $15-25.

Ciroflex - c1940's. Common 6x6cm TLR, models A through F, all similar, with each new model offering a slight improvement. Models A-D: $15-25. Models E,F (better, less common): $25-35.

CITY SALE & EXCHANGE (London)
Used the trade name "Salex" from an abbreviated form of their name.
Field cameras - Lightweight folding cameras, similar to the Thornton-Pickard models. With normal lens and shutter such as Unicum or Thornton-Pickard. $100-150.

CIVICA PG-1 - c1985. Cute 110 camera

with sliding lens cover. Two bird-like cartoon characters dancing on round lens cover. Black back with blue or white front. Made in Taiwan. $15-20.

CLARUS CAMERA MFG. CO. (Minneapolis, Minn.) *The Clarus company never did well, because they could not escape their reputation, although they finally managed to make their camera work.*

MS-35 - 1946-1952. Rangefinder 35mm camera. Interchangeable Wollensak f2.8/50mm Velostigmat lens. Focal plane shutter to 1000. At least two versions made. (Shutters tend to be erratic and sluggish, which would decrease the value from the listed price.) $25-45.

CLASSIC 35 - *This name has been applied to several entirely different cameras, the earliest of which is a tiny die-cast aluminum camera with black horizontal stripes, made by Craftsmen's Guild. The others were imported to the USA and sold by Peerless Camera Co. of New York. To avoid further confusion, we are listing these full-frame models here.*

Classic 35 - c1956. Made by Altissa-Werk in USSR occupied Germany. Same as Altix camera. Trioplan f2.9 coated lens. $15-20.

Classic II - c1957-58. Made in Japan. Original price $18. $15-20.

Classic III - c1959. Made in Japan. Original price $18. $15-20.

Classic IV - c1960. Fujita Opt. Ind., Japan. Orig. price of $20 reduced to $14. $15-20.

CLOPIC "REPORTER" - Paris, c1903. Strut-folding camera for 9x12cm plates or magazine back. Flor Berthiot f4.5 or Tessar f3.5/135mm lens. FP ½-200 shutter. $150-200.

CLOSE & CONE (Chicago, Boston, NY)

Quad - c1896. Box-plate camera. The only camera using the new "Quadruple plateholder", an unusual mechanism which turned the four plates into the focal plane. The camera which measured 4⅝x4⅝x6" for 3½x3½ plates was advertised in 1896 as "the largest picture and smallest camera combined ever made", and it cost $5.00 new. $100-125.

CLOSTER (Italy)

IIa - c1950. Bottom loading 35mm VF camera. Mizar f4.5/50mm lens. Closter shutter to 300. $30-40.

C60 - c1960. Simple plastic and aluminum 35mm. Lambron f7/50mm lens, single-speed shutter. $15-25.

Olympic - c1959. Inexpensive plastic and metal 127 rollfilm camera, 3x4cm. f8/56mm lens. $5-10.

Princess - c1951. RF 35mm. Aires f3.5/ 50mm lens, Rimset 1-300 shutter. $25-40.

Sport - c1956. Viewfinder 35mm. Closter Anastigmat f8/50, two-speed shutter. $9-15.

Sprint - Inexpensive 35mm. f7/50mm lens in Sincro-Closter shutter to 150. $10-20.

C.M.C. - Japanese novelty camera of "Hit" type. With gold colored metal parts: $35-50. With colored leatherette: $30-40. Chrome with black leatherette: $8-12.

COLIBRI - Subminiature plastic camera for 13x13mm on special rollfilm. Post-war

Germany, U.S. Zone. $75-100.

COLLEGIATE CAMERA NO. 3 - Small Japanese novelty box camera for single paper film holders. $15-20.

COLLINS (C.G.Collins, London)
"The Society" - c1886. Full plate compact mahogany field camera produced under license as an improved version of McKellin's Treble Patent Camera of 1884. $175-225.

COLORFLASH DELUXE CAMERA - Identical to the Diana DeLuxe. Accessory flash uses AG-1 bulbs. $1-5.

COLUMBIA OPTICAL & CAMERA CO. (London)
Pecto No. 1A - c1902. Polished mahogany 4x5" plate camera. Red bellows. Shutter built into lensboard. $60-100.

Pecto No. 5 - c1897. Folding bed camera for 9x12cm plates. B&L RR lens. Unicum shutter Double extension bellows. Rising front. Leather covered wood body. $50-75.

Pecto No. 7 - c1900. 5x7" leather covered hand & stand camera. Double extension red bellows. RR lens, shutter 1-100. $75-125.

C.O.M.I.

Luxia, Luxia II - c1949. Small 35mm half-frame cameras. Delmak f2.9/27mm lens, between-the-lens shutter. Chrome trim. Colored: $400-600. Black: $350-400.

COMPAGNIE FRANCAISE DE PHOTOGRAPHIE

Photosphere - c1888. One of the first all-metal cameras. For plates, or could take special roll back for Eastman film. Shutter in the form of a hemisphere. Unusual 13x18cm (5x7") size: $1000-1600. Smaller

8x9cm size: $800-1200. Stereo model (world's sexiest camera, according to an expert on the subject): $4000-6000. Medium 9x12cm size: $900-1200.

COMPASS CAMERAS LTD. (London)
Mfd. by Jaeger LeCoultre & Cie., Sentier, Switzerland for Compass Cameras Ltd.

Compass Camera - c1938. The ultimate compact 35mm rangefinder camera system. A finely machined aluminum-bodied camera of unusual design and incorporating many built-in features which include:f3.5/50mm lens, RF, right-angle finder, panoramic & stereo heads, level, extinction meter, filters, ground glass focusing, etc. For 24x36mm exposures on glass plates, or on film with optional roll back. The high prices in the current market are due primarily to collector enthusiasm, not rarity, since they are regularly offered for sale. Complete outfit: $800-1100. Camera only: $500-700.
Compass Tripod - Rare accessory for the Compass camera. $200-250.

COMPCO Miraflex & Reflex cameras - c1950. Low-cost twin lens box cameras of the 1950's. $5-8.

CONCAVA S.A. (Lugano, Switzerland)

Tessina - c1960. For 14x21mm exp. on

35mm film in special cartridges. The camera, about the size of a package of regular-sized cigarettes, is a side-by-side twin-lens reflex. One lens reflects upward to the ground glass for viewing. The other lens, a Tessinon f2.8/25mm, reflects the image down to the film which travels across the bottom of the camera. Shutter speeds 2-500. Spring-motor advance for 5-8 frames per winding. Available in chrome, gold, red, black. Gold camera: $300-450. Red: 250-300. Black: $200-250. Chrome camera: $150-200. Various accessories, including wrist strap, prism finder, meter, watch, etc. will add to the value.

Tessina Accessory Watch - Rectangular watch with Tessina logo on face. Made to fit on top of Tessina camera. Rare. $125-150

CONLEY CAMERA CO. (Rochester, Minn.) *In addition to the cameras marketed under their own label, Conley also made many cameras for Sears, Roebuck & Co. which were sold under the Seroco label, or with no identifying names on the camera.*

Conley Junior - c1917-22. Folding rollfilm cameras, similar in style to the better known Kodak folding rollfilm cameras. $15-25.

3¼x5½" Folding Plate Camera - c1900-

1910. Vertical, postcard size. Fine polished wood interior, nickel trim. Double extension red bellows. f8/6½" lens in Wollensak Conley Safety Shutter. $35-50.

4x5" Folding Plate Camera - c1900-10. Most commonly found size of the Conley folding models. Black leather covered wood body. Polished cherry interior. Red bellows. Usually with Conley Safety Shutter and one of the following Wollensak lenses: Rapid Symmetrical, Rapid Orthographic, Rapid Rectilinear, or occasionally with the Wollensak 6"-10"-14" Triple Convertible (worth more). Normally found in case side by side with holders "cycle" style. $50-75.

5x7" Folding Plate Camera - c1908-17. Except for size, similar to the two previous listings. $60-100.

6½x8½" View - c1908-17. Least common size among Conley cameras. $125-175.

8x10" View - c1908-17. Prices vary depending on accessories, particularly lens and shutter, since large format shutters and lenses still have some value as useful equipment. $125-175.

Folding rollfilm camera - c1917. 3¼x5½ "postcard" size, on 122 film. Vitar f6.3 Anastigmat in B&L Compound shutter. Similar to the Kodak folding rollfilm cameras which are much more common. $15-25.

Kewpie box cameras: c1917-22.
No. 2 - For 120 film. Loads from side. Rotating disc stops on front of camera. $12-18.
No. 2A - for 2¼x4½ exp. $12-18.

No. 2C - for 2⅞x4⅞" exposures. $12-18.
No. 3 - 3¼x4¼ exp. $12-18.
No. 3A - 3¼x5½ "postcard" size. $15-20.

Long Focus Revolving Back Conley Model XV - c1909-18. Introduced in 1909, the "Model XV" designation was added in 1910. Self-casing folding view camera with double-extension bellows and rack & pinion focus. Mahogany body covered with bear grain leather. Made in 5 sizes to 6½x8½". Rapid Orthographic lens in Conley Safety shutter. $50-100.

Magazine Camera - c1908-12. Leather covered wooden box camera for 4x5" 12 plates. Plates advanced by crank on right side of camera. $45-60.

Panoramic Camera - c1911-1917. Pivoting-lens panoramic camera for 140 degree views, 3½x12". Design based on patents acquired in 1908 from the Multiscope & Film Co. of Burlington, Wisconsin. Four speeds were possible. Without a fan, the equivalent shutter speed was 1/50th of a second. Attaching the smallest of the three fans gave 1/25th; the medium and large fans giving 1/12 and 1/6. Rapid Rectilinear f8 lens, iris diaphragm. Original price of $17.50 in 1911. Current value $250-350.

Snap No. 2 - Strut-type folding camera for 6x9cm on 120 film. Design with cross-swing struts is more typical of Ansco than Conley cameras. $15-25.

Stereo box camera - c1908. For 4¼x6½" plates in plateholders. Simple shutter, I & T. Meniscus lenses. $200-225.

Stereo Magazine camera - c1903. Drop-plate magazine box camera for stereo images on glass plates. $250-300.

Stereoscopic Professional - c1908. Folding camera for stereo images on 5x7" plates. Wollensak Regular double valve stereo shutter. Rise and shift front. (Note: similar models without full movements are of nearly equal value.) $300-350.

Truphoto No. 2 - Folding camera for 120 rollfilm. One of the most interesting features is the pivoting brilliant viewfinder. Both lenses of the finder are rectangular, each oriented a different direction. Pivoting the finder automatically presents the properly oriented rectangle for composition while the other serves as the finder's objective. Fixed focus Meniscus lens. T & I shutter. Very uncommon. Not listed in any Conley or Sears catalogs. $15-20.

CONTESSA, CONTESSA-NETTEL

(Stuttgart) *Contessa merged with Nettel in 1919. In 1926, a large merger joined Contessa-Nettel with Ernemann, Goerz, Ica, and the Carl Zeiss Optical Co. to form Zeiss-Ikon. See also Nettel, Zeiss.*

Adoro - c1921. 6.5x9cm and 9x12cm folding plate cameras. Double extension bellows. f4.5 Tessar in Compur. $25-40.

Tropical Adoro - c1921. Like the regular model, but teak wood, brown leather bellows, nickeled trim. $300-400.

Altura - c1921. 3¼x5½". Citonar 165mm lens in dialset Compur shutter. $40-60.

Citoskop Stereo - c1924. 45x107mm. Tessar f4.5/65mm lenses. Stereo Compur. $200-225. *(Illustrated top of next column.)*

Clarissa (Tropical) - 4.5x6cm plate camera. Light colored wood body with red bellows. Brass struts, standard, and lens barrel. FP shutter 1/20-1000. Meyer Goerlitz Trioplan f3/75mm. $800-1200.

Citoskop Stereo

Cocarette - c1920's. Folding bed rollfilm cameras made in 2 sizes,6x9cm on 120 film & 2½x4¼" on 116 film. Many combinations of shutters & lenses. $20-30.

Cocarette Luxus - with brown leather and bellows. $75-125.

Deckrullo-Nettel - c1919-26. Folding plate camera with focal plane shutter. 6.5x9cm with Tessar f4.5/120mm, 9x12cm size with Zeiss Tessar f4.5/150mm, or 10x15cm size with Tessar f4.5/180mm. Black leather covered body. Ground glass back. $75-130.

Deckrullo (Tropical model) - c1919-26. Folding 9x12cm plate camera. Teakwood body partly covered with brown leather. Light brown bellows. f4.5/120mm Tessar. FP shutter to 1/2800 sec. $400-500.

Deckrullo-Nettel Stereo - Focal plane shutter. 6x13cm size with Tessar f4.5/90mm lenses or more commonly in 10x15cm size with f4.5 or f6.3/12cm Tessar. $225-275. *(Illustrated top of next page.)*

Deckrullo-Nettel Stereo

Deckrullo Stereo (Tropical) - c1921-25. Folding teakwood-bodied stereo plate cameras. GG back, brown bellows, nickel trim. FP shutter to 2800. 9x12cm size with f2.7/65mm Tessars. 10x15cm size with Double Amatars f6.8 or Tessars f6.3 or f4.5. 10x15cm size takes panoramic exposures with a small eccentric lensboard for one lens (9x12cm could be special ordered with this feature). $850-1200.

Donata - c1920's. Folding plate or pack camera, 6.5x9cm and 9x12cm sizes. f6.3 Tessar or f6.8 Dagor. Compur shutter. Ground glass back. $25-45.

Duchessa - c1913-25. 4.5x6cm folding plate camera. Citomar Anastigmat f6.3/75mm, Compur 1-100. $200-250.

Duchessa Stereo (Focal Plane Type) - c1913-14. Compact strut-folding stereo for 45x107mm plates. FP shutter. Dagor f6.8, Tessar f6.3, f4.5 lenses. $225-325.

Duchessa Stereo (Front Shutter Type) - c1913-22. Compact 45x107mm folding stereo with lazy-tong struts. Crackle-finish on lensboard. Compound, Compur, or Derval shutter. Lenses include Citoplast, Teronar, Tessar, Tessaplast, Hellaplast, Dagor. Most common with Tessar f4.5 and Compur 1-250. $200-300.

Ergo

Duroll - c1913-25. Folding cameras with interchangeable plate or roll backs. 6x9, 9x12, & 9x14cm sizes. $25-35.

Ergo - c1913-26. Monocular-shaped camera for 4.5x6cm plates. Tessar f4.5, Compur 25-100,B. Right angle finder. $700-800. *Illustrated bottom of previous column. (Earlier model was the Nettel Argus, later model was the Zeiss-Ikon Ergo.)*

Miroflex - c1924. Single lens reflex for 9x12cm plates. Tessar 4.5/150mm lens. FP shutter to 2000. $200-250. *The later Zeiss-Ikon Miroflex is more often found than the Contessa models.*

Onito - c1919-26. 9x12cm. Lenses include: Double Anastigmat Citonar f6.3, Nostar f6.8, or Nettar Anastigmat f4.5/135mm. Derval 25-100; Gauthier or Ibsor 1-100. Also in 6.5x9cm and 10x15cm sizes. $20-35.

Piccolette - c1919-26. Folding vest-pocket camera, 4x6.5cm exp. on 127 film. Tessar f4.5/75mm, Triotar f6.3, or meniscus f11 lens. Dial Compur or Achro shutter. $35-55.

Piccolette Luxus

Piccolette Luxus - c1924. Brown leather covering and tan bellows. $250-325. *(Illustrated bottom of previous page.)*

Pixie - c1913. Compact strut camera for 4x6cm on rollfilm. Lazy-tong struts support front with built-in 3-speed shutter. Rare. $200-275.

Recto - c1921. Small lazy-tong strut camera for 4.5x6cm plates. (A low-priced version of the Duchessa.) Acro shutter 25, 50, 75. $125-175.

Sonnar - 9x12cm folding plate camera. Double extension bellows. f4.5/135mm Contessa-Nettel Sonnar. Compur 1-200. $25-40.

Sonnet - c1920's. Tropical folding plate cameras, 4.5x6cm and 6.5x9cm sizes with teakwood bodies. f4.5 Zeiss lens. Dial Compur 1-300. Light brown bellows. 4.5x6cm size: $350-450. 6.5x9cm size: $200-300.

Stereax, 45x107mm - c1912-19. Stereo camera with folding bed and struts. Choroplaste 60mm lens. Focal plane shutter 1/5-1/1200. $150-250.

Stereax, 6x13cm - c1919-27. Strut-folding stereo in leather covered and tropical versions. Tessar f4.5/90mm lens. Focal plane shutter 1-1200. Wire sports finder with side pieces that expand the view for panoramic exposures. Tropical: $450-650. Leathered: $150-250.

Steroco - c1921. A cheaply made stereo camera for 45x107mm. f6.3 Tessars, Compur. $100-175.

Taxo - c1921. 9x12cm folding plate camera. f8/135 Extra Rapid Aplanat. Duvall shutter to 100. $25-35.

Tessco - c1913-26. Folding plate cameras in 6.5x9, 9x12, & 10x15cm sizes. Double extension bellows. GG back. Contessa-Nettel Sonnar f4.5 or Citonar f6.3. Dial Compur 1-200. $35-50.

Tropical plate cameras - c1920's. 6x9cm size. Zeiss Tessar f4.5/120mm. Compur shutter 1-250. Finely finished wood, reddish-brown bellows, brass trim or combination of brass and nickel trim. General guidelines: Single lens reflex: $1500-2500. Strut-type with focal plane shutter: $400-700. Bed-type with front shutter: $300-400.

CORD
Cord Box 6x9 - c1946. Simple, poorly constructed cardboard box camera. Boyer Meniscus lens. $5-10.

CORFIELD (K.G. Corfield, England)
Formed in 1948, this company is important because it represents a British post-war quality camera manufacturer. The company was taken over by Guinness and ceased camera production in late 1961, and finally closed in 1971.
Corfield 66 - 1961. SLR for 6x6cm on 120 film or cut film backs. Lumax f3.5/95mm interchangeable lens. FP shutter 1-500. $75-125.

Periflex - 35mm Leica copies for 36 exp. 24x36mm. Interchangeable Lumax f2.8/50mm or f1.9 or f2.8/45mm. Focal plane shutter to 1000. Unusual through-the-lens periscope reflex rangefinder which, despite its cumbersome appearance, worked quite well. Most often found in England at indicated prices. Occasionally found at slightly higher prices outside of England.

Periflex - 1953. $50-100.
Periflex 2 - 1958. $50-100.
Periflex 3 - 1957. $50-100.

Periflex 3a - 1959. Better and more collectible than the Gold Star model, according to one of our English consultants, but prices do not seem to follow. $60-115.

Periflex 3b - 1961. $50-100.

Periflex Interplan - 1961. $40-80.

Periflex Gold Star - c1961. (There is a gold star on the front.) Periscope viewfinder. Interchangeable Lumax f1.9 or f2.8/50mm lens. Focal plane shutter 1-300. $75-150.

CORNU CO. (Paris)
Fama - Small cast-metal 35mm camera. Interchangeable shutter and lens mount. Normally found with Flor f2.8/50mm. $30-45.

Ontobloc - c1946. 35mm compact camera. Dark grey hammertone painted cast metal body. Based on the Reyna, but with rigid, non-collapsible front. Som Berthiot Flor f3.5/50mm lens in Coronto Paris ½-300 3-blade shutter. $40-60.

Ontoflex - c1938. TLR for 6x9cm on 120 film. Rotating back for horizontal or vertical format. Model A is for rollfilm only. Model B has interchangeable rollfilm and plate backs. Berthiot f3.5, Tessar f3.5 or f3.8 in Compur. $250-300.

Ontoscope - c1934. Rigid-body stereo cameras, made in the popular 45x107mm and 6x13cm sizes in a number of variations: Focusing/non-focusing, Magazine back/plate back, Panoramic/non-panoramic. $100-175. Inclusion of beautifully constructed Cornu rollfilm back for 127 or 120 film will add to the value.

Ontoscope 3D - Stereo camera for 24x30mm frames on 35mm film. Cast metal

body, Flor Berthiot f3.5/40mm lenses. Shutter speeds 1-100 set by knob between the lenses. Additional speeds of 200 and 400 by employing a supplementary spring controlled by another knob. Very rustic in comparison with the contemporary Richard Verascope F40, and much more rare. Probably only a few hundred made. $375-500.

Reyna II - c1942. Telescoping front 35mm camera. Black hammertone painted cast metal body. Berthiot Flor f3.5/50mm. Front lens focus. Compur Rapid to 500. $20-30.

Reyna Cross III - c1944. (Made now by P. Royet at St. Etienne in the "free zone" during the German Occupation.) Black painted cast aluminum bodied 35mm. f3.5 Berthiot or f2.9/45mm Cross. Two blade shutter 25-200, B. $20-30.

CORONET CAMERA CO. (Birmingham, England)
Coronet Camera Co. 1926-1946
Coronet Ltd. 1946-1967
Standard Cameras Ltd. c1931-1955

This company was formed c1926 by F.W. Pettifer and manufactured a large number of cheap box and folding cameras until c1967. Many of its cameras were distributed via premium schemes or mail order catalogues. Most of its pre-war box cameras and post-1945 plastic molded cameras appear with different nameplates and lens panel stylings. The company linked up with Tiranty of Paris after WWII to produce cameras and avoid French import restrictions. These cameras usually have "Made in France" and French instructions on controls and include the Rapide, Le Polo, Weekend, and Fildia.

Throughout its life the firm produced various Coronet accessories, flash units, close-up filters and viewers and its own Coronet film in 120 and 127 sizes. Close links between Coronet, Standard Cameras Ltd. and Conway cameras exist with camera molds and body parts being interchanged. Over 50 different Coronets exist.
Ajax - c1935. Box camera for 6x9cm. Blue leather covering. Anastigmat f7.7. Shutter 25-100. $30-40.

Ambassador - c1955. Metal & bakelite box camera for 6x9cm. Quite attractive with chromed hinged covers over brilliant finders. Two small levers above shutter release engage time exposure and green filter. Fixed focus lens. $15-20. *(Illustrated top of next page.)*

Box cameras - c1935. Coronet made a great variety of box cameras, most of which are common and not in great demand by collectors. Some were made in France after WWII because of French import restrictions. $5-15.

Coronet Ambassador

Cameo - Bakelite subminiature for 13x18mm on rollfilm. Meniscus lens, simple shutter. $40-60.

Consul - Bakelite and metal box camera for 6x9cm on 120 film. Red & green enameled metal faceplate. $15-20.

Coronet 66 - Black bakelite eye-level camera with metal back. Takes 12 exp. on 120 film. Two synch sockets. $15-20.

Cub - Plastic bodied camera for 28x40mm on 828 film. Spring-loaded telescoping front. Folding optical finder. Fixed focus; single shutter speed; no flash sync. $12-18.

Cub Flash - Similar to the Cub, but with flash sync. Also has T & I shutter, f11 or f16, non-folding optical finder, and hinged front leg. $12-18.

Eclair Lux - c1950's. Metal box camera for 6x9cm on 120 film. Made in France by Tiranty under license from Coronet. Several faceplate variations. $10-15.

F-20 Coro-Flash - Reflex style box camera

for 6x6cm on either 620 or 120 film. Fixed focus; Time or Instant shutter. Built-in green filter. $10-15.

Fildia - c1950. Cardboard 6x9cm box camera with hexagonal metal faceplate. Made in France by Tiranty under license from Coronet. $8-12.

Flashmaster - Black bakelite eye-level finder, metal back. Takes 12 exposures on 120 rollfilm. Two synch sockets. $10-15.

Midget - c1935. A small colored bakelite 16mm novelty camera. Taylor Hobson Meniscus lens f10. Single speed 1/30. Six exposures on special rollfilm. Original price $2.50. Current values (in order by rarity): Blue: $75-100. Green: $70-85. Brown, black, or red: $50-75.

Polo - Leatherette-covered metal box camera for 6x9cm on 120 film. Made in France. Boyer Menisque lens, single speed shutter. $5-10.

Rapide - Folding 6x9cm rollfilm camera. Body release. Eye-level optical finder. Made in France by Tiranty under license from Coronet. $10-15. *(Illustrated top of next column.)*

Coronet Rapide

Rex - c1950. Cardboard 6x9cm box camera with round metal faceplate. Made in France by Tiranty. Menisque Boyer lens. $8-12.

"3-D" Stereo Camera - c1953. Inexpensive plastic stereo camera for 4 stereo pairs or 8 single exp. 4.5x5cm on 127 film. Single speed shutter, 1/50. Twin f11 meniscus fixed focus lenses. At least four variations exist. $25-35.

Victor - Black bakelite eye level camera

Craftsmen's Classic 35

for 4x4cm on 127 film. Focusing f11 lens in synch shutter. $8-12.

Vogue - c1937. A brown bakelite-bodied folding camera which uses "Vogue 35" film, a spool film similar to Eastman Kodak 828. Fixed focus lens. Simple B&I shutter. $60-80 in USA. (Only about $20-25 in England.)

COSMIC - Mid-1960's Russian 35mm. f4/40mm lens. Shutter 1/5-1/250. $10-20.

CRAFTEX PRODUCTS
Hollywood Reflex - c1947. (Including models A-E, Sportsman, Sightseer, etc.) Cast metal twin-lens reflex style cameras. Generally simple construction, although at least one model had externally coupled lenses for true reflex focusing. $10-15.

CRAFTSMAN SALES CO.

Cinex Candid Camera - Black plastic "minicam" for 16 exp. on 127. $3-7.

CRAFTSMEN'S GUILD
Classic 35 - c1948. Small, streamlined half-frame 35mm. Die-cast aluminum body. Satin finished with black horizontal stripes or leather covered. Some examples have recessed knobs and buttons. Fixed focus Craftar f4.5/32mm. Single speed shutter. $75-100. *(Illustrated top of previous column.)*

CROMA COLOR 16 - Japanese subminiature nearly identical to Mykro Fine Color 16, but green, red, brown, or black bakelite. (Styled like the Whittaker Pixie.) Often chipped where the front section attaches to the back, and sometimes at the latch cogs. Mint: $100-125. Chipped: $40-60.

CROWN CAMERA - Japanese novelty subminiature of the Hit type. $15-20.

CROWN CAMERA CO. (NY)
Dandy Photo Camera - intro. 1910. Simple paper-covered box camera for 1½" circular plates in paper holders. Meniscus lens, simple shutter. Originally sold in an outfit with developing tank, chemicals, lifting spoon, and illustrated instructions, all in a cardboard carton. Full outfit: $250-300. Camera only: $75-100.

CRUISER CAMERA CO.
Cruiser - Folding camera for 6x9cm

exposures on 120 rollfilm. Probably made by Wirgin. Cast metal body with leatherette covering. Wirgin Edinar f6.3/105mm lens. Vario shutter B, 25,50,100. PC sync. $10-15.

CRUVER-PETERS CO. INC. *Later called Palko, Inc.*

Palko camera - c1918-1930's. The only folding rollfilm camera with provision for ground glass focusing without film removal. Based on a 1912 patent of W.A. Peters. Production was apparently started during WWI with the U.S. Government as the primary customer. Adjustable image size of ⅓, ⅔, or full postcard size. B&L Tessar f4.5 lens in Acme to 300. Original price from $70 in 1918 to $122 in the early 1930's, but closed out at $65 with case. $600-750.

CRYSTAR - "Hit" type novelty camera for 14x14mm exposures on 17.5mm paper-backed rollfilm. $8-12. (These bring about twice that amount at German auctions.) With colored leatherette: $25-35.

CRYSTARFLEX - c1953. Japanese TLR. Magni Anast. f3.5/80mm in Magni synch shutter. $20-28.

CURTIS (Thomas S. Curtis Laboratories, Huntington Park, CA)
Curtis Color Master - c1948. 4x5" tri-color camera. Ilex Patagon f4.5/5½" lens, Acme shutter. CRF. $325-375.

Curtis Color Scout - c1941. Tri-color camera, 2½x3". Ektar f4.5/80mm, Compur 1-200 shutter. CRF. $325-375.

CYCLONE - *Western Camera Co. manufactured Cyclone cameras until about 1899, when it was taken over by the Rochester Optical Co., which continued to produce Cyclone models. We have listed Cyclone models under each of these makers.*

DACO DANGELMAIER - see Dacora.

DACORA KAMERAWERK (Reutlingen & Munich)
Dangelmaier (1952)
Daco Dangelmaier (1954)
Dacora Kamerawerk (1970)
Dacora Kamerawerk at Munich (1972-1976)
Originally located in Reutlingen, the company name went through several changes. For the sake of unity, we are listing all cameras here regardless of the company name at the time of manufacture.

Daci, Daci Royal - Metal box camera for 12 exp. 6x6cm on 120 film. Red: $30-40. Grey, or green: $10-20. Black: $8-10.

Daco, Daco II - c1950. Black bakelite box cameras with slightly curved sides and rounded corners. Similar in style to the common metal Daci camera. Daco has f11 lens; Daco II has f8. Uncommon. $40-50.

Dacora I - folding camera for 12 exp. 6x6cm on 120. Eunar f3.5/75mm. Prontor 1-100. $15-20.

Dacora-Matic 4D - c1961-66. 35mm with coupled meter. Four shutter release buttons for focus zones. Lens rotates to proper

Dacora-Matic 4D

focus as release button is pushed. $20-25.

Digna - c1958. Simple camera with tubular telescoping front for 6x6cm on 120. Very common. $5-10.

Dignette - c1957-1959. Basic 35mm VF camera with f2.8 lens, 1/300 shutter. (Orig. price $18.) $7-14.

Instacora E - c1966. A high-quality camera for 126 cartridges. Electric eye, 1/30-1/125 speeds, zone focusing Color Dignar f3.5/45mm lens. $15-20.

Royal - c1955. Folding camera for 6x6cm on 120. Uncoupled RF. Ennagon f3.5 or 4.5 lens in Pronto. (Orig. $31-34.) $30-40.

Subita - c1953. Horizontally styled self-erecting folding camera for 6x6cm on 120 film. Subita f6.3/75mm Anastigmat in Singlo 25,75,B shutter. Advertised originally as a low-priced camera at 45 marks. Uncommon. $12-18.

Super Dignette - c1960's. Non-RF 35mm with built-in meter. Cassar, Dignar, or Isconar f2.8/45mm. Pronto LK, Prontor LK, or Vario LK shutter. $10-20.

DAGUERREOTYPE CAMERAS - *The earliest type of camera in existence, many of which were one-up or limited production cameras. Since so few of even the commercially made models have survived time, most Daguerreotype cameras are unique pieces, and price averaging is senseless. However, to keep the novice collector or casual antique dealer from making any big mistakes before consulting with a recognized authority, we will give one example: A half-plate American sliding-box-in-box style is likely to be in the $5000 & up range.*

DAIDO SEIKI CO. (Japan)
Daido Six Model I - c1953. Horizontally styled folding camera for 6x6cm or 4.5x6cm on 120 film. Side-by-side viewfinder for the two image sizes almost gave the appearance of a rangefinder camera. C.Daido Anastigmat f3.5/75mm in N.K.S. B,1-200. $75-100.

DAIICHI KOGAKU (Japan)
Waltax - c1950. Folding Ikonta-style camera for 16 exp. on 120 rollfilm. Kolex f3.5/75mm lens in Dabit shutter 1-500. $25-40.

Waltax Jr. - c1951. Copy of Ikonta A. For 16 exposures 4.5x6cm on 120 or 620 film. Bio-Kolex f4.5/75mm lens. Okako shutter 25-150. $25-40.

Zenobia - c1949. Folding camera for 16 exp. 4.5x6 cm on 120 film. Styled like the early Zeiss Ikonta cameras. Hesper f3.5/75mm Anastigmat. DOC Rapid shutter 1-500, B. (Similar to Compur Rapid.) $25-35.

Zenobiaflex - c1953. Rollei-style TLR with Neo-Hesper f3.5/75mm in Daiichi Rapid shutter. $35-50.

DAISHIN SEIKI K.K.

Hobby Junior - c1965. 24x36mm on paper-backed "Bolta" size film. Daishin f8/35mm lens, single speed shutter. $15-25.

DALE - Japanese novelty subminiature of "Hit" type. $10-15.

DALLMEYER (J. H. Dallmeyer, London)
Founded c1860 by J.H. Dallmeyer.
Naturalist - c1900. SLR. Long extension bellows attached to front of cubical body. Tube with eye-piece extends from top of body for critical focusing. ¼-plate. Long focus lens such as Dallmeyer No. 1 Grandax Telephoto f4/10". FP shutter to 800. $300-550.

Press Reflex - c1930's. Graflex-style SLR 3¼x4¼". Dallmeyer Popular Telephoto f1.6/12" lens. FP shutter 15-1000. $200-250.

Snapshot Camera - c1929. Folding camera for 6x9cm filmpacks. Cross-swinging strut design. Two-speed shutter built into front. $60-85.

Speed Camera - mid-1920's. Press-type

camera equipped with the Dallmeyer "Pentac" f2.9 lens, the fastest anastigmat lens of its time. This lens, as well as the ⅛ to 1/1000 sec. FP shutter, account for the camera's name. Small 4.5x6cm size: $100-175. 6.5x9cm or 3¼x4¼": $100-150.

Stereo Wet Plate camera - c1860. Sliding box style. Brass bound corners on finely crafted wood body. Brass barrel Dallmeyer lenses (consecutively numbered) with wooden flap shutter. $2000-2600.

Tailboard-style view cameras - c1930's. ½-plate, full-plate sizes. Mahogany, brass trim, maroon bellows. Rack focus. Dallmeyer R.R. or Triple Achromatic. $135-200.

Wet Plate Sliding Box Camera - Mid-1860's. $800-1200.

DAME, STODDARD & KENDALL (Boston)
Hub (Box camera) - Top loading box camera for 4x5" plates. $20-30.

Hub (Folding) - Late 1890's leather covered folding camera for 4x5" plates. Side door at rear for inserting and storage of plateholders. Rotary shutter built into wooden lensboard. Simple lens. $50-60.

DAMOIZEAU (J. Damoizeau, Paris)
Cyclographe a foyer fixe - c1894. An early panoramic camera which revolves on its tripod while the film is transported in the opposite direction past the focal plane slit. Capable of exposures up to 360 degrees (9x80cm). $7500-8500.

DAN CAMERA WORKS (Tokyo) *Later became Yamato Camera Industry (Yamato Koki Kogyo Co. Ltd.) which made the Pax cameras.*
Dan 35 Model I - c1946-48. Japanese compact camera for 15 exp. 24x24mm on paper backed 35mm wide Bolta-sized film. Removable top. Dan Anastigmat f4.5/40mm. Silver-B shutter B, 25-100. $50-75.

Dan 35 Model II - c1948-50. Similar, but

with body serial number, automatic frame counter, removable bottom. $50-75.

Dan 35 Model III - c1949. 24x32mm exposures on Bolta-size rollfilm. Dan Anastigmat f3.5/40mm, Silver-B shutter B,25-100. $50-75.

DANCER (J. B. Dancer, Manchester, England)
Stereo Camera - c1856. For stereo pairs on 12 plates 3½x7". A nicely finished wooden stereo camera which set a new record for the highest price paid for an antique camera, $37,500.00 in 1977.

Tailboard view camera - Mahogany ½-plate camera. Ross Rapid Symmetrical lens with wheel stops. Gravity shutter. $100-150.

DANGELMAIER - see Dacora

DARIER (Albert Darier, Geneva, Switzerland)
Escopette - c1888. Invented by Darier, manufactured by E.V. Boissonas (Geneva). Wooden box camera with wooden pistol grip, giving it the general appearance of a pistol. The grip and two small brass front legs serve as a tripod. Brass metal parts. This was one of the first cameras to use the same rollfilm as the No. 1 Kodak Camera, taking 110 exposures 68x72mm. Steinheil Periscopic f6/90mm lens. Spherical shutter with trigger release. Speeds variable by adjusting spring tension. Rare. Estimated: $5000+

DAVE - Simple box camera for 6x9cm on 120 film. Meniscus f11/105mm lens. $5-10.

DAVY CROCKETT - Not the box camera by Herbert-George but a black plastic minicam style for half-frame 127. $30-40.

DAYDARK SPECIALTY CO. (St. Louis, MO)
Photo Postcard Cameras - "Street" cameras for photo postcards or tintypes, complete with developing tank, dark sleeve, RR lens, Blitzen Daydark shutter. $100-150.

Tintype Camera - small amateur model. Measures 4½x5x7¼. $50-100.

DBGM, DBP, DBPa: *The "DB" stands for "Deutsches Bundesrepublik". The endings of the abbreviations are: "Gebrauchs Musterschuetz", "Patent", and "Patent Auslegeschrift", trademark and patent notices which would indicate West German post-war construction.*

DEARDORFF (L.F.) & SONS (Chicago, IL) *Established as camera builders in 1923, the company name goes back to 1893 when Laben F. Deardorff started a camera repair company. In 1923 Laben was commissioned by a group of Chicago architects to build 10 cameras to photograph that new Chicago wonder, the skyscraper. Amazingly enough, five of the first 10 cameras built still exist, four of them in daily studio use! To this day, a member of the Deardorff family is involved in the daily production of cameras. These cameras are primarily "user" cameras though there are a few who collect them avidly. There were no serial numbers until 1951.*

The condition of these cameras can vary greatly because those sold to studios generally have seen very hard use, while those sold to individual users may have been "babied" and may remain in mint condition even though they are 20-40 years old. L.F. Deardorff is a manufacturing concern that has made MANY one-of-a-kind cameras and accessories through the years. All were well made, but in checking used equipment make sure that all parts are present or it may be useless. On cameras, make sure all racks, rears, wood panels, and especially bellows are in good working order. The bellows are one of the most expensive parts to replace. Be wary of a camera with taped bellows. Tape causes great stress on the camera when closed and this in turn can cause damage to the wood parts.

The "refinished" price reflects a camera that has been PROFESSIONALLY restored by Ken Hough Photographic Repair Service, the only authorized Deardorff service center in the USA. Fully restored cameras include new bellows, wood work and parts where needed, and a duplicate of the factory finish. These cameras may be rated as LN-. All prices were compiled by Ken Hough. He may be reached for any questions regarding the Deardorff camera at 219-464-7526. We are also indebted to Jack Deardorff for the history of the early cameras, and to Merle Deardorff for the history of the Baby Deardorff.

8x10" Cameras
The early (pre-1926) cameras are of a light colored, finished mahogany. This wood was taken from the bar tops of Chicago taverns that were closed down during prohibition. Beginning in 1926, the wood was a deep red color.

First series - 1923. Ten cameras. Parquet style bed. Lensboard opening measures

5½x6". Only the first series had this size lensboard. No recent reported sales.

Second series - 1924. 25 cameras. Parquet style bed. Standardized 6x6" wooden lensboard. Aluminum front standard. Current value: Refinished- $1600. Good condition- $400.

Third series - 1924. 25 cameras. Same as the Second series, but all aluminum front standard. Refinished: $1550. Good: $400.

Fourth series - 1925. 75 cameras. Same as the Third Series, above.

Standard V8 -- 8x10"

1936 8x10 with front swing conversion.

- 1926-1937. Wood is deep red in color. Standardized construction with familiar four piece bed, narrow knobs with fine knurling, all brass parts painted with a special gold lacquer. Lensboards have a thinner rabbet on the front. Refinished with front swings: $1650. Refinished: $1200. EX: $900. Good: $500.

- 1938-1948. Same as above but brass parts are nickel plated and knobs are wider. Refinished with front swings: $1650. Refinished: $1200. EX: $950. Good: $500.

- 1949. Front swings are standard as is the round bed plate. Nickel plated parts. Refinished: $1650. EX+: $1200. VG: $800. Good: $400. Serial numbers began in 1951 with #100; it was then called the 8x10 View.

AN Series - A large group of 8x10" cameras made for the Army and Navy. There is no difference in these cameras from the standard models except for a small rectangular plate on the bottom of the bed that gives a government Number and model number.

5x7" Old Style (OS) V5

1937 5x7, original 4½x4½ lensboard

- 1929-1937. Same basic construction as the 8x10" cameras of this time. Red finish on wood. Original square cornered 4½x4½" lensboard, or factory modified 4x4" board. Refinished: $600. VG: $350. Fair: $200.

- 1938-1948. Same construction as the 8x10" cameras of this time. Original round or square cornered 4½x4½" lensboard, or factory modified 4x4" lensboard. Refinished: $650-800. EX: $350-400. VG: $250-350. Good: $150-250. Fair: $100. *Note: This camera may also be seen in a "yellow" colored wood. These were made of Spanish cedar wood because of the wartime shortage of mahogany that was being used in PT boats. Prices may be slightly lower.*

- 1949-present. Redesigned camera body. Front swings, round bed plate, and nickel plated parts are standard. Square cornered 4x4" lensboard. Serial numbers began in 1951 with #100; it was then called the 5x7 View. Refinished: $800-1200. EX: $600. VG: $450. Good: $350.

4x5" Old Style (OS) V5
- 1929-1937. Same as the 5x7" camera, but with a 4x5" reducing back.

- 1938-1948. Same as the 5x7" camera, but with a 4x5" reducing back.

- 1949-present. Redesigned camera body. Front swings, round bed plate, and nickel plated parts are standard. Square cornered 4x4" lensboard only. Serial numbers began in 1951 with #100. Since that time it has been known as the 4x5 Special. Refinished: $900-1200. EX: $650. Good: $400-500.

1936 Baby Deardorff Prototype

Baby Deardorff V4 - Designed by Merle Deardorff, this camera looks like a miniature 4x5" or 5x7" camera. It takes up to a 4x5" back. 3½x3½" lensboard only.

First style - 1936 only. Wood separator strips on bed between front and rear extension. Twelve prototype cameras were made to test the market. These were recalled for evaluation by Merle Deardorff after about one year. Only eight were returned and these were destroyed when their beds were found inferior. The remaining four examples are all known to exist, one in everyday use.

Second style - 1940-1945. Extruded extension guides, L-shaped guides on front sliding panel. Refinished: $1200-1400. EX: $1000. VG: $450. Good: $400.

Third style - 1945-49. Same as the Second style, but with U-shaped guides on front sliding panel. Refinished: $1200-1450. EX: $1100. VG: $500. Good: $450.

Backs available for Baby Deardorff:
- Standard 4x5" still manufactured.
- 3¼x4¼" Graflex style: $60-80
- 2¼x3¼" standard CFH type: $80-100.
- 35mm back. This was a Kodak 35 body that was mounted on a sliding panel with a ground glass focusing screen, similar to a Leica Focoslide, but vertical in normal operation. Only reported sale: $120.

Triamapro - An ultra precise 4x5" Press Style camera, featuring a rotating back, front and rear swings, front rise, and lateral sliding front. May be seen with Hugo Meyer or Kalart rangefinder. Backs seen are standard cutfilm back, either Graflex or Grafloc style. The word Triamapro means TRIple extension, AMAteur, & PROfessional.

1938 Triamapro

Usually seen in good to VG condition. EX: $1000. G-VG: $350-500. Note: there were also two 5x7" Triamapro cameras built. No reported sales.

11x14" Cameras:
Early style - Looks like a giant 8x10" view camera. Has no front swings. Many were built for the US Marines for "on the beach" photo reconnaissance. Came with tripods whose legs could be used as bayonets! EX: $1200. VG+: $800.

Second style - Similar to the Early style, but with front swings. Made in small numbers since 1951. In 1987, it sells new for $5500. Refinished: $3500. EX+: $2550. EX: $2000.

Commercial Cameras - 8x10" or 11x14" cameras that must be used on 700 lb. Bi-post stands, 8', 10', or 12'. Also known as the "Dog house type". It is almost always found in large studios.
8x10" - Seldom found for sale. Refinished: $2100. VG: 1500. Good: $900.
11x14" - Refinished: $2600. EX: $2000. VG: $1600. Good: $1000. Fair: $400.
Bi-post stands - $900-1600.

16x20" View - Only two were made. No reported sales.
12x20" View - Special order only. One sold in 1983, EX+, for $3200.

5x7" Home Portrait - 1940-present. Still in stock, new. EX: $75. Good: $50.

DEBONAIR - Hong Kong 120 rollfilm novelty camera of the Diana type. $1-5.

DEBRIE (Ets. Andre Debrie, Paris)

Sept - c1923-27. Spring motor drive camera for still, rapid sequence, or cine. 18x24mm on 5m cartridge of 35mm film. Roussel Stylor f3.5/50mm. First model has square motor housing with single spring. Later, the double-spring model with round motor housing was added. (Burke & James Inc., Chicago, was selling both models as late as 1940!) Not hard to find. $100-150.

DEFIANCE MFG. CO.
Auto Fixt Focus - c1916-20. Well-made

folding camera with bed and lazy-tong strut construction. Camera can be focused in the open or closed position. Self-erecting front assumes correct focus when opened. Goerz f4.8 or f6.8 in Acme shutter. $25-30.

DEJUR-AMSCO CORP. (New York)

DeJur D-1 - c1955-57. VF 35mm, imported from Germany. Lever film advance cocks shutter. DEP. Interchangeable lenses: Staeble-Kata f2.8/45mm normal, f5.6 tele, or f3.5 W.A. Original price for the 3-lens outfit was under $100. With normal lens: $15-20. Tele & W.A. lenses each: $15-20.

Dejur Reflex - c1952. TLR. DeJur f3.5 Chromtar lens. Wollensak Synchromatic 10-200 shutter. $30-45.

DELOYE (Paris)
le Prismac - c1905. Built by A. Devaux. Early rollfilm stereo camera. Two 90 degree prisms reflect the image at right angles from the lenses onto the film, allowing for a more compact body than usual. Used Pocket Kodak Camera size #102 rollfilm. Kenngott Anastigmat f8/54mm lenses, 5-speed guillotine shutter. Rare. Estimate: $1500-2500.

DELTAH CORPORATION
Deltah Unifocus - Unusual folding vest-pocket camera for 127 film. $15-25.

DELUXE PRODUCTS CO. (Chicago)
Delco 828 - Streamlined bakelite camera for 828 film. Identical to the Argus Minca 28, this camera merely sports the name of its distributor. $20-25.

Remington - Plastic "minicam" for 3x4cm on 127. $5-10.

DELUXE READING CORP. (Topper Toy Div.)

Secret Sam Attache Case - c1960's. Plastic attache case containing a take-apart pistol and a 127 film camera which can be used with the case closed. $50-90.

Secret Sam's Spy Dictionary - c1966. Novelty which incorporates a camera in a plastic "book" which also shoots plastic bullets (ouch!). The camera takes 16 exp. on 127 film. $75-95.

DEMARIA (Demaria Freres, Demaria-LaPierre, Paris)
Dehel - Folding 120 rollfilm cameras. f4.5 or f3.5/75mm lens. AGC shutter. $15-25.

Jumelle Capsa - (Demaria Freres) - 6x13mm stereo camera. $175-225.

Plate Camera - Strut-type folding camera for 6x9cm plates in single metal holders. Black enamel finish. Demaria Anast. Sigmar f6.3 in Vario 25,50,100,T,B. Unusual and complicated focusing system with radial lever operated cam sliding a large plate whose two diagonal slots engage pins at either side of the shutter housing. $25-35.

DEROGY (Paris)
Single lens stereo camera - Light walnut view camera with sliding front panel and slotted back for single or stereo exposures. Entire bellows rotates to change from horizontal to vertical exposures. Brass trim and brass barrel Derogy lens. $375-425.

Wooden plate camera - c1880. 9x12cm. Derogy Aplanat No. 2 brass barrel lens. Black tapered bellows, polished wood body, brass trim. $175-200.

DETECTIVE CAMERAS - *The earliest "Detective" cameras were simply designed as a box or case. Before long, they were disguised in all shapes and sizes. The original box, satchel, and case cameras are commonly referred to by the name "detective", while the later disguised/concealed varieties normally are not. Disguised cameras seem to have a special appeal and therefore the prices have remained strong despite the ups and downs of our economy. The magic of the mere name "detective" for an otherwise ordinary-looking box camera has worn thin in the current market and those prices have softened. In any case, they are listed by manufacturer's name.*

DETROLA CORP. (Detroit, Mich. c1939-1940) *All letter models listed below are similar "minicam" type cameras for 3x4cm on 127 film. Except for Model A, all have rectangular aluminum plate in center of front. The "W" in models GW, HW, and KW indicates the Wollensak lens.*
Model A - Basic minicam. Meniscus fixed focus. $10-20.

Model B - Duomicroflex f7.9 lens. Extinction meter. $12-18.
Model D - similar, f4.5 lens. $10-20.
Model E - similar, f3.5 lens. $15-20.

Model G - Ilex Anastigmat f4.5. No meter. $15-20.
Model GW - Basic model with Wollensak Velostigmat f4.5. $12-18.

Model H - extinction meter. $15-20.
Model HW - similar to GW, but with meter. $15-20.

Model K - Detrola Anastigmat f3.5, extinction meter. $15-20.
Model KW - Wollensak anastigmat f3.5 lens. $15-20.

Model 400 - A Leica-inspired CRF 35mm camera with interchangeable Wollensak Velostigmat f3.5 or f2.8 lens. Focal plane shutter to 5000. Sync. (Original cost about $70.) $175-275.

DEVIN COLORGRAPH CO. (New York)
(After 1940, Devin-McGraw Colorgraph Co., Burbank California. All rights sold c1950 to Bob Frazer of Altadena, CA.)
Tri-Color Camera - c1939. For making color separation negatives. Original professional size for 5x7". Apo-Tessar f9/12" lens. Dial Compur shutter. $400-475.
6.5x9cm size - intro. c1938. Goerz Dogmar f4.5/5½" lens. Compound shutter. $450-550.

DEVRY - see QRS DeVry Corp.

DEVUS - c1950. USSR. 6x6cm TLR. Copy of Voigtlander Brillant, similar to Lubitel. Momo f4.5/75mm, 1/15-250. $30-40.

Scenographe (Original model) - c1876. A very early collapsible bellows camera. Wooden body with green silk bellows. Gate-type wooden struts support wooden front with sliding lensboard. Takes single or stereo exposures on 10x15cm plates. Very unusual. Several sales from 1984-86 with original wooden case, holder, and ground glass for $4000-5000. Later models with cloth bellows have been offered for half that amount. *(Illustrated on front cover.)*

DIAMOND JR. - c1898. Top loading box camera for 3¼x4¼" plates. $50-75.

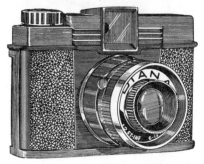

DIANA - Novelty camera for 4x4cm on 120 film. The same camera exists under many other names with only minor variations in style. (Diana-F is synchronized for flash.) $1-5.

DIANA DELUXE CAMERA - Novelty 120 rollfilm camera. Body release, helical zone focus, hot shoe, imitation meter cell. $1-5.

DIONNE F'2 - Hong Kong "Diana" type novelty camera. $1-5.

DIPLOMAT - "Hit" type novelty camera. $8-12.

DORIES - "Diana" type novelty camera. $1-5.

DORYU CAMERA CO.

Doryu 2-16 - c1955. Unusually designed subminiature camera disguised as a pistol. Flash cartridges are shaped like bullets. 10x10mm on 16mm film. $2500-3000.

DOSSERT DETECTIVE CAMERA CO. (NYC)

Detective Camera - c1890. 4x5" box-plate detective camera. Leather covered to look like a satchel. Sliding panels hide lens and ground glass openings. Entire top hinges forward to reveal the plate holders for loading or storage. $750-950.

DOVER FILM CORP.
Dover 620 A - c1950. A plastic & chrome camera for 16 exp. 4.5x6cm on 620 film. Somco meniscus f9, 5 rotary disc stops. Single speed shutter. Built-on flash. $10-15.

DRGM, DRP: *"Deutsches Reichs Gebrauchs Musterschuetz", "Deutsches Reichs Patent",* trademark and patent notices which would indicate German construction before WWII.

DRUCKER (Albert Drucker & Co., Chicago)
Ranger - c1940. A stark-looking focal plane camera, 16 exposures on 127 film. Six speeds, 25-200 plus B. Polaris f2.0 or f2.8/50mm Anastigmat lens in collapsible mount with Leica thread. Sold originally by Burke & James for $30 with f2 lens, on a

par with the lower-priced 35mm, rollfilm, and plate cameras of the day. During 1986, some dealers were asking $200, but we have no confirmed sales. With original lens, and with shutter working (that would be rare!) it might approach that figure. However, for the body only, with typically messed-up shutter, it shouldn't bring more than $50-60.

DRUOPTA (Prague, Czechoslovakia)
Druoflex I - c1950's. 6x6cm bakelite TLR. Druoptar f6.3/75mm, Chrontax 1/10-200. Copy of Voigtlander Brillant. $35-45.

Vega II - c1949-51. Basic 35mm camera without rangefinder. Non-interchangeable Druoptar f4.5/50mm in Etaxa 10-200,B,T. Collapsible front. $35-50.

Vega III - c1957. Like Vega II, but Druoptar f3.5 lens in synchronized Chrontax shutter. Accessory shoe on top. $35-50.

Stereo camera for 45x107mm - c1910. RR lenses. $200-250.

DUBRONI (Maison Dubroni, Paris) *The name Dubroni is an anagram formed with the letters of the name of the inventor, Jules Bourdin. Although anagrams and acronyms have always had a certain appeal to writers, and inventors, the story in this case is quite interesting. It seems* *that young Jules, who was about twenty-two years old when he invented his camera, was strongly influenced by his father. The father, protective of the good reputation of his name, didn't want it mixed up with this new-fangled invention.*

Dubroni camera - c1860's. Wooden box camera with porcelain interior for in-camera processing. (Earliest models had amber glass bottle interiors and no wooden sides on the body.) Five models were made, the smallest taking photos 5x5cm. Previously sold easily at $3000-3500. One very complete outfit with case, pipettes, bottles, tripod, and instructions, brought just over $6000 in 1986. Recent auction sales for the camera alone: $1500-2200 range.

Wet-plate tailboard camera - c1870. Wood body with brass trim. Rectangular brown bellows. 9x12cm. Dubroni brass lens, rack focusing, waterhouse stops. $600-800.

DUCATI (Societa Scientifica Radio Brevetti Ducati - Milan, Italy)
Ducati - c1938-50. 15 exp. 18x24mm on 35mm film in special cassettes. Two major variations are rangefinder and non-RF models. FP shutter to 500. Normally with f3.5 or 2.8 Vitor, or f3.5/35mm Ducati Etar lens. Better models have interchangeable lenses. Used to sell in the $200-300 range. Recent auction sales range from $125-160. *(Illustrated on next page.)*

DUCHESS - c1887. British ½-plate field camera. Mahogany body, brass trim, maroon bellows. RR brass barrel lens. $150-200.

DUFA (Czechoslovakia)
Pionyr - Red-brown bakelite eye-level camera for 6x6cm or 4.5x6cm on 120 film. Helical telescoping front. Similar in styling

to the Photax cameras. Meniscus lens, T&M shutter. $15-20.

DURST S.A. *Most photographers know Durst for their enlargers. However, at one time they made some solid, well-constructed, innovative cameras.*

Durst 66 - 1950-54. Compact light grey hammertone painted aluminum body with partial red or black leather covering. 12 exp. 6x6cm on 120 film. Durst f2.2/80mm Color Duplor lens. Shutter ½-200, B, sync. $25-35.

Automatica - 1956-63. 36 exp. 24x36mm on standard 35mm cartridge film. Schneider Durst Radionar f2.8/45mm. Prontor 1-300, B, and Auto. (Meter coupled to shutter by pneumatic cylinder.) $100-125.

Duca - 1946-50. Vertically styled 35mm

Durst Gil

EASTERN SPECIALTY MFG. CO.
(Boston, MA)

Ducati without and with RF
camera for 12 exp. 24x36mm on Agfa Karat Rapid cassettes. Ducan f11/50mm. T & I shutter. Zone focus. Rapid wind. Aluminum body. Made in black, brown, blue, red, & white with matching colored pouch. $65-85.

Gil - c1938-42. Box camera for 6x9cm on rollfilm. Black metal body with imitation leather covering. Functions labeled in language of destination country, either German, Italian, Swedish or English. Approximately 50,000 made. This was the first camera made by Durst. Uncommon. $35-50. *(Illustrated top of next column.)*

Springfield Union Camera - c1899. Premium box camera for 3½" square plates. Four plates could be mounted on the sides of a cube, and each exposed, in turn, by rotating the cube inside the camera. An unusual design from a technical standpoint, and visually appealing with the boldly lettered exterior. $350-450.

EARL PRODUCTS CO.

EASTMAN DRY PLATE & FILM CO.
EASTMAN KODAK CO.

Scenex - c1940. Small 3x4cm plastic novelty camera. Similar to the Cub. $8-12.

EARTH K.K. (Japan)
Guzzi - c1938. Cast metal subminiature. Eye-level frame finder. Fixed-focus lens; B,I shutter. $100-150.

After designing the Eastman-Cossitt detective camera which was not marketed, the first camera produced by the Eastman Dry Plate & Film Co. was called "The Kodak", and successive models were numbered in sequence. These numbers each introduced a specific new image size and continued to represent that size on many cameras made by

Kodak and other manufacturers. The first seven cameras listed here are the earliest Kodak cameras, and the remainder of the listings under Eastman Kodak Co. are in alphabetical order by series name and number. Some of the Eastman models listed are continuations of lines of cameras from other companies which were taken over by Eastman. Earlier models of many of these cameras may be found under the name of the original manufacturer.

For more detailed information on Kodak cameras including production dates, original prices, identification features, and photographs of each model, see "Collectors Guide to Kodak Cameras" by Jim and Joan McKeown. $12.95 at bookstores, camera stores, or by mail from Centennial Photo, Rt. 3, Grantsburg, WI. 54840, USA.

No. 2 Kodak Camera - Oct. 1889-1897. Also similar and still quite rare, but more common than the previous models. Factory loaded for 60 exp. 3½" dia. $275-325.

The Kodak Camera (original model) - ca. June 1888 through 1889. Made by Frank Brownell for the Eastman Dry Plate & Film Co. Factory loaded with 100 exposures 2½" diameter. Cylindrical shutter, string set. Rapid Rectilinear lens f9/57mm. This was the first camera to use rollfilm, and is a highly prized collectors' item. $1700-2300.

No. 3 Kodak Camera - Jan. 1890-1897. A string-set box camera, factory loaded for either 60 or 100 exp. 3¼x4¼". Bausch & Lomb Universal lens, sector shutter. $325-400.

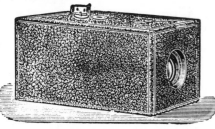

No. 1 Kodak Camera - 1889-1895. Similar to the original model, but with sector shutter rather than cylindrical. Factory loaded for 100 exp. 2½" dia. RR lens f9/57mm. $575-700.

No. 3 Kodak Jr. Camera - Jan. 1890-97. A relatively scarce member of the early Kodak family. Factory loaded with 60 exp. 3¼x4¼" on rollfilm. Could also be used with accessory plate back. B&L Universal lens, sector shutter. Overall size: 4¼x5½x9". $275-325.

No. 4 Kodak Camera - Jan. 1890-1897. String-set box camera, factory loaded for 48 exp. 4x5", but with capacity for 100 exp. for prolific photographers. B&L Universal lens. sector shutter. $250-300.

No. 4 Kodak Jr. Camera - Jan 1890-97. Similar to the No. 3 Kodak Jr. Camera, but for 4x5". Factory loaded for 48 exp. on rollfilm. B&L Universal lens, sector shutter. Can also be fitted for glass plates. $350-400.

ANNIVERSARY KODAK CAMERA - A special edition of the No. 2 Hawk-Eye

Camera Model C, issued to commemorate the 50th anniversary of Eastman Kodak Co. Approximately 550,000 were given away to children 12 years old in 1930. Covered with a tan colored reptile-grained paper covering with a gold-colored foil seal on the upper rear corner of the right side. (On a worn example, the gold coloring of the foil seal may have worn off and left it looking silver.) Like New w/Box: $25-35. Mint, but without box: $20-25. VG to Excellent: $15-20.

AUTOGRAPHIC KODAK CAMERAS *The Autographic feature was introduced by Kodak in late 1914, and was available on several lines of cameras. Listed here are those cameras without any key word in their name except Autographic or Kodak.*

No. 1A - 1914-1924. For 2½x4¼" exp. on No. A116 film. Black leather and bellows. $10-15.
No. 3 - 1914-1926. 3¼x4¼" on A118 film. $15-20.
No. 3A - 1914-1934. 3¼x5½" (postcard size) on A122 film. This is the most common size of the Autographic Kodak Cameras. $15-25.

No. 4 - This is actually a No. 4 Folding Pocket Kodak Camera with a retrofit back, available in 1915. A No. 4 Autographic Kodak Camera was never made. *See No. 4 Folding Pocket Kodak Camera.*

No. 4A - This too is not an Autographic Kodak Camera, but simply a 1915 retrofit back on a No. 4A Folding Kodak Camera. *See No. 4A Folding Kodak Camera.*

AUTOGRAPHIC KODAK JUNIOR CAMERAS

No. 1 - 1914-1927. 2¼x3¼" on 120 film. $14-20.
No. 1A - 1914-1927. 2½x4¼" exp. on A116 film. Very common. $12-18.
No. 2C - 1916-1927. 2⅞x4⅞". A very common size in this line. $15-20.
No. 3A - 1918-1927. 3¼x5½" on A122. $12-18.

AUTOGRAPHIC KODAK SPECIAL CAMERA

No. 1 - 1915-1926. No CRF. $35-50.
No. 1A - 2½X4¼". 1914-1916 without CRF: $30-40. 1917-1926 with CRF: $25-50.

No. 2C - 1923-1928. CRF. $30-50.
No. 3 - 1914-1924. No CRF. 3¼x4¼" on A118. Uncommon size, fairly rare. $35-55.
No. 3A - 3¼x5½" on 122. 1914-1916 without CRF: $30-40. 1917-1933 with CRF (including the common Model B): $40-60.

No. 3A Signal Corps Model K-3 -
A specially finished version of the No. 3A Autographic Kodak Special Camera with coupled rangefinder. Body covered with smooth brown leather with tan bellows. Gunmetal grey fittings. B&L Tessar f6.3 in Optimo shutter. Name plate on bed says "Signal Corps, U.S. Army K-3" and serial number. One hundred of these cameras were made in 1916. Rare. $500-850

AUTOMATIC 35 CAMERAS

Automatic 35 Camera - 1959-1964. An improved version of the Signet 35 Camera design. Built-in meter automatically sets

the diaphragm when shutter release is pressed. Flash sync. posts on side. $15-25.

Automatic 35B Camera - 1961-1962. Kodak Automatic Flash shutter. $15-25.

Automatic 35F Camera - Built-in flash on top for AG-1 bulbs. $15-25.

Automatic 35R4 Camera - Built-in flashcube socket on top. $15-25.

BANTAM CAMERAS - *For 28x40mm exp. on 828 rollfilm.*

Six-20 Boy Scout Brownie Camera

(Original) - 1935-38. Rigid finder. $30-40.

Bantam RF Camera - 1953-57. Coupled rangefinder 3' to infinity. Shutter 25-300. Non-interchangeable f3.9/50mm Kodak Ektanon Anastigmat. $25-40.

f8 - 1938-42. Rectangular telescoping front rather than bellows. Kodalinear f8/40mm. $15-20.

f6.3 - 1938-47. Kodak Anastigmat f6.3/53mm. Collapsible bellows. Like original model, but has folding optical finder. $15-25.

f5.6 - 1938-41. Kodak Anastigmat f5.6/50mm. Collapsible bellows. $20-35.

f4.5 - 1938-48. Kodak Anastigmat Special f4.5/47. Bantam shutter 20-200. Bellows. The most commonly found Bantam. $20-30.

--Military model - Signal Corps, U.S. Army PH502/PF, Ord. No. 19851. $150-200.

Bantam Colorsnap - Made by Kodak Ltd, London. Kodak Anaston, single speed. $5-9.

Bantam Special Camera - Compur Rapid

shutter (1936-40) is more common than the Supermatic shutter (1941-48). CRF 3' to infinity. With Supermatic: $140-160. With Compur Rapid: $100-150.

Flash Bantam Camera - 1947-53. Early model (1947-48) has Kodak Anastigmat Special f4.5/48mm. Shutter 25-200. $25-35. Later model 1948-53 with Kodak Anastar f4.5/48mm is more common. $25-30.

BOY SCOUT BROWNIE CAMERA, SIX-20 BOY SCOUT BROWNIE CAMERA -Simple box cameras. Special metal faceplate with Boy Scout emblem. Made in 1932 for 120 film; in 1933-1934 for 620 film. Rare 120 model: $100-150. More common in 620 size: $50-75. *(Illustrated on previous page.)*

The Brownie Camera, (original)

BOY SCOUT KODAK CAMERA - 1929-33. For 4.5x6cm on 127 rollfilm. This is a vest-pocket camera in olive drab color with official Boy Scout emblem engraved on the bed. With original green bellows and matching case. $80-120. With replacement black bellows: $50-60.

BROWNIE CAMERAS
(Original) - Introduced in February, 1900, this box camera was made to take a new size film, No. 117 for 2¼x2¼ exposures. The back of the camera fit like the cover of a shoe-box. Constructed of cardboard, and measuring 3x3x5" overall, this camera lasted only four months in production before the back was re-designed. A rare box camera. With accessory waist-level finder. $475-550. *(Illustrated top on next column.)*

No. 0 - A small (4x3¼x6cm) box camera of the mid-teens for 127 film. Slightly larger than the earlier "Pocket Kodak" of 1895. Cute, but not scarce. $15-20.

No. 1 - In May or June of 1900, this improved version of the original Brownie Camera was introduced, and became the first commercially successful Brownie camera. Although not rare, it is historically interesting. $35-45. With accessory finder, winding key and orig. box. $75-100. *The earliest examples of this camera were marked "The Brownie Camera". When additional sizes were introduced, the designation was changed to "No. 1". The early examples would bring an extra $25-35.*

No. 2 - 1901-33. Cardboard box camera for 6 exposures 2¼x3¼" on 120 film, which was introduced for this camera. Meniscus lens, rotary shutter. (An early variation had smooth finish and the same rear clamp as the No. 1. This variation has an estimated value of $20-25. Most have grained pattern cloth covering. Later models some of which were also made in London came in colors. Black: $3-8. Colored: $20-25. *(Colored models bring more in Europe.)*

Baby Brownie Camera - 1934-41. Bakelite box camera for 4x6.5cm exp. on 127 film. Folding frame finder. $3-6.

No. 2A - 1907-33. Cardboard box camera for 2½x4¼" on 116 film. Black: $3-8. Later Colored models: $20-25.
No. 2C - 1917-34. Box camera for 2⅞x4⅞" on 130 film. $3-8.
No. 3 - 1908-34. Box camera for 3¼x4¼" on 124 film. $3-8.

Baby Brownie (Kodak Ltd.) - The British-made version of the Baby Brownie. Like the USA model, but with a 'brief time plunger' above the lens. Uncommon in the U.S. $20-35.

Brownie 44A - 1959-66. Made by Kodak Ltd. Plastic eye-level box camera, 4x4cm on 127 film. Dakon lens, single speed. $5-9.

Brownie 127 Camera - 1953-59. Made in England. Bakelite body with rounded ends, as if slightly inflated. Several variations of faceplate style: plain, horizontally striped, diagonally checkered. $5-8.

Baby Brownie, New York World's Fair Model - 1939. A special version of the Baby Brownie was made in 1939-1940 for the World's Fair, with a special New York World's Fair faceplate. $150-200.

Baby Brownie Special - 1939-54. Bakelite box camera for 4x6.5cm exp. on 127 film. Rigid optical finder. $3-8.

Beau Brownie Camera - 1930-33. A simple No. 2 or No. 2A Brownie (box) camera, but in classy two-tone color combinations of blue, green, black, tan, or rose. Either size in rose: $60-100.
No.2 - Color other than rose: $25-40.
(Illustrated on next page.)
No. 2A - Color other than rose: $30-45.

Brownie Auto 27 Camera - 1963-64. Electric-eye version of Brownie Super 27. $6-9.

No. 2 Beau Brownie Camera

Brownie Bull's-Eye Camera - 1954-60. Vertically styled bakelite camera with metal faceplate and focusing Twindar lens. For 6x9cm on 620 film. Black: $3-8. Gold: $5-12. *See also "Six-20 Bull's-Eye Brownie Camera" below.*

Brownie Bullet Camera - 1957-64. A premium version of the Brownie Holiday Camera. 4.5x6cm on 127 film. $1-5.

Brownie Bullet II Camera - 1961-68. Similar to the Brownie Starlet camera (USA type). Not like the Brownie Bullet Camera! 4.5x6cm exp. on 127 film. $1-5.

Brownie Chiquita Camera - Same as the Brownie Bullet Camera, except for the faceplate and original box which are in Spanish. With original box: $10-20. Camera only: $5-10.

Brownie Fiesta Camera - 1962-66; Fiesta R4- 1966-69. $1-5.

Brownie Flash Camera - Black bakelite box camera identical to Brownie Hawkeye Flash Model. Made in France for the French market. "Brownie Flash Camera Made in France" on front plate. $10-20.

Brownie Flash IV - London-made brown metal box camera with tan covering. Built in close-up lens and yellow filter. With matching canvas case: $15-25. Camera only: $10-20.

Brownie Flash 20 Camera - 1959-62.

Styled like the Brownie Starflash Camera, but larger size for 620 film. $4-8.

Brownie Flash Six-20 Camera -
Post-war name for Six-20 Flash Brownie Camera. Trapezoidal metal body. With flash: $4-8.

Brownie Flash B - Kodak Ltd. in London. Metal box camera, brown and beige color. Shutter B, 40,80. $10-20. Add $5-10 for original canvas case.

Brownie Flashmite 20 Camera - 1960-65. $1-4.

FOLDING BROWNIE CAMERAS
Identifiable by their square-cornered bodies and horizontal format. The No. 3 and No. 3A are at least ten times more commonly found for sale than the No. 2, although prices are much the same. These cameras sell in Europe for about double the USA price.

No. 2 - 1904-07. Maroon bellows, wooden lens standard. For 2¼x3¼" on 120 film. $20-30. Slightly higher in Europe.
No. 3 - 1905-15. 3¼x4¼" on 124 film. $20-30.
No. 3A - 1909-15. 3¼x5½" "postcard" size. Maroon bellows. The most common size. $20-25.

FOLDING AUTOGRAPHIC BROWNIE
CAMERAS *These are a continuation of the Folding Brownie Camera series, but with the addition of the "Autographic" feature. Some of the earlier examples still have the square corners of the earlier style.*

No. 2 - 1915-26. 2¼x3¼" on 120 film. Very common. $8-16.

No. 2A - 1915-26. 2½x4¼". By far the most common size of this line. $8-16.
No. 2C - 1916-26. 2⅞x4⅞" exp. $15-22.
No. 3A - 1916-26. 3¼x5½". $10-20.

FOLDING POCKET BROWNIE
CAMERAS *Horizontal folding rollfilm cameras. Square-cornered bodies. Early models with red bellows are bringing higher prices in Europe.*

No. 2 - 1907-15. 2¼x3¼". A continuation of the No. 2 Folding Brownie, but with metal not wooden lensboard. $12-20.
No. 2A - 1910-15. 2½x4¼" on 116 film. With red or black bellows. $15-22.

Brownie Hawkeye Camera - 1949-51; Flash Model, 1950-61. Molded plastic box camera for 2¼x2¼" exp. on 620 film. $1-3.

Brownie Holiday Camera - 1953-57;

Flash model, 1954-62. 4x6.5cm exp. on 127 film. $1-5.

Brownie Junior 620 Camera - 1934-36. Metal box camera. Made by Kodak A.G. Dr. Nagel-Werk and not imported to the U.S.A. $15-25.

Brownie Model I - Kodak Ltd., London. 6x9cm. $12-18.

Popular Brownie Camera - 1937-40. Made by Kodak Ltd., London. Box camera for 6x9cm on 620 film. $8-12.

Portrait Brownie Camera, No. 2 - 1929-35. Kodak Ltd. 6x9cm on 120 film. $15-25.

Brownie Reflex Camera - 1940-41; Synchro model, 1941-52. 1⅝x1⅝" exp. on 127 film. $1-5.

Brownie Reflex 20 Camera - 1959-66. Reflex style like the Brownie Starflex Camera, but larger for 620 film. $1-5.

Six-16 or Six-20 Brownie Cameras - 1933-41. Cardboard box cameras with metal art-deco front. $1-5. *(Illustrated top of next page.)*

Six-20 Brownie Camera

strap on side. For 2¼x3¼" exp. on 620 film. $10-20.

Six-20 Flash Brownie Camera, Brownie Flash Six-20 Camera - 1940-54. Metal trapezoidal box camera, sold under both names. 2¼x3¼" exp. on 620 film. $1-5.

Six-16 or Six-20 Brownie Junior Cameras - 1934-42 box cameras. $1-5.

Brownie Six-20 Camera Model C,D,E,F - 1950-59. 2¼x3¼" exp. on 620 film. Made by Kodak Ltd., London. $10-15.

Six-16 or Six-20 Brownie Special Cameras - 1938-42. Trapezoid-shaped box. $1-5.

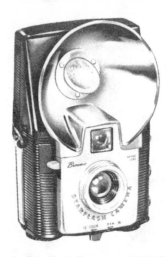

Brownie Starflash Camera - 1957-65. Black, blue, red, or white. $1-5.

Six-20 Bull's-Eye Brownie Camera - 1938-41. Black bakelite trapezoidal body with eye-level finder above top. Braided

Brownie Starflex Camera - 1957-64. 4x4cm on 127 film. $1-5.

Brownie Starmite Camera - 1960-63; Starmite II, 1962-67. $1-4.

Brownie Starlet Camera (USA) - 1957-62. 4x4cm on 127. $1-5.

No. 2 Stereo Brownie Camera - 1905-10. Similar to the Blair Stereo Weno Camera. For 3¼x2½" exposure pairs on rollfilm. Red bellows. Stereo Brownie Cameras are much less common than comparable Stereo Hawk-Eye Cameras. $250-350.

Brownie Starlet Camera (Kodak Ltd.) - 1956. 4x6.5cm on 127. $5-10.

Brownie Starluxe II - French-made version of the Brownie Starflash II. $8-12.

Brownie Super 27 - 1961-65. $3-8.

Brownie Starmatic Camera - 1959-61; Starmatic II, 1961-63. 4x4cm on 127 film. Built-in automatic meter. $5-10.

Brownie Starmeter Camera - 1960-65. Uncoupled selenium meter. $5-10.

Target Brownie Six-16 and Six-20, Brownie Target Six-16 and Six-20 Cameras - Metal and leatherette box cameras. Introduced in 1941. Name changed from Target Brownie to Brownie Target in 1946. Six-16 discontinued in 1951; Six-20 in 1952. $1-5.

Brownie Twin 20 Camera - 1959-64. Waist level and eye-level finders. $1-5.

Brownie Vecta - Grey plastic 127 camera made in England. $10-15.

BUCKEYE CAMERA - c1899. Eastman Kodak Co. purchased the American Camera Mfg. Co., which originated this model. The Eastman camera is nearly identical to the earlier version. A folding bed camera of all wooden construction, covered with leather. Lens standard of polished wood conceals the shutter behind a plain front. Style is very similar to the No. 2 Folding Bull's-Eye Camera. An uncommon rollfilm model. $75-125.

BULL'S-EYE CAMERAS *After Kodak took over the Boston Camera Manufacturing Co., it continued Boston's line of cameras under the Kodak name. (See also Boston Bull's-Eye.) Bull's-Eye cameras are often stamped with their year model as were other early Kodak cameras. Leather exterior conceals a beautifully polished wooden interior.*

No. 2 - 1896-1913. Leather covered

wood box which loads from the top. 3½x3½" exposures on 101 rollfilm or double plateholders. Rotary disc shutter. Rotating disc stops. $30-45.

No. 3 - 1908-1913. This model loads from the side. 3¼x4¼" on No. 124 film. Less common than the No. 2 and No. 4. $30-40.

No. 4 - 1896-1904. Nine models. Side-loading 4x5" box for 103 rollfilm. Internal bellows focus by means of an outside lever. $40-55.

No. 2 Folding Bull's-Eye Camera - 1899-1901. For 3½x3½" exposures. Scarce. $100-125.

BULL'S-EYE SPECIAL CAMERAS
1898-1904 *Similar to the Bull's-Eye box cameras above, but with higher quality RR lens in Eastman Triple Action Shutter.*
No. 2 - 3½x3½" exposures on 101 rollfilm. $50-75.

No. 4 - 4x5" exp. on 103 rollfilm. $60-80.

BULLET CAMERAS

Bullet Camera (plastic) - 1936-42. A cheap & simple torpedo-shaped camera with fixed focus lens mounted in a spiral-threaded telescoping mount. Common, inexpensive, yet novel. $6-12.

Bullet Camera, New York World's Fair Model - 1939-40. A special World's Fair version of the Bullet camera, marked "New York World's Fair" on a metal faceplate. In colorful original box: $150-175. Camera only: $80-100.

No. 2 Bullet Camera - 1895-96, improved model 1896-1900, double plateholder option 1900-1902. Box camera for 3½x3½" exposures on glass plates or on rollfilm which was first introduced in 1895 for this camera and later numbered 101. Measures 4½x4½x6". Some models named by year and marked on the camera. $25-35.

No. 4 Bullet Camera - 1896-1900. A large leather covered box. 4x5" exposures on No. 103 rollfilm (introduced for this camera) or could be used with a single plateholder which stores in the rear of the camera. $50-75. *(Illustrated bottom of previous column.)*

BULLET SPECIAL CAMERAS
1898-1904. *Similar to the No. 2 and No. 4 Bullet Cameras above, but with a higher quality RR lens in Eastman Triple Action Shutter.*

No. 2 - $50-80.   **No. 4** - $100-150.

No. 4 Bullet Camera

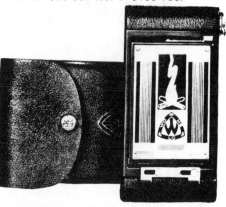

CAMP FIRE GIRLS KODAK - 1931-34.

131

Century of Progress

Folding vest-pocket camera with Camp Fire Girls emblem on the front door and "Camp Fire Girl's Kodak" on the shutter face. This is a very rare camera, unlike the less rare Girl Scout or the common Boy Scout models. With matching case: $250-350. *(Illustrated bottom of previous page.)*

CARTRIDGE KODAK CAMERAS *Made to take "cartridge" film, as rollfilm was called in the early years.*
No. 3 - 1900-1907. For 4¼x3¼" exp. on No. 119 rollfilm, which was introduced for this camera. This is the smallest of the series. Various shutters and lenses. $60-75.

No. 4 - 1897-1907. For 5x4" exp. on 104 rollfilm (introduced for this camera). This is the first of the series. Leather covered wood body, polished wood interior. Red bellows. Various shutters/lens combinations. (Orig. price was $25.) $60-75.

No. 5 - 1898-1900 with wooden lensboard and bed; 1900-1907 with metal lensboard. For 7x5" exp. on No. 115 rollfilm or on plates. (No. 115 rollfilm, introduced for this camera, was 7" wide to provide the 7x5" vertical format.) Red bellows. Various shutters/lens combinations. $70-90.

CENTURY OF PROGRESS, WORLD'S FAIR SOUVENIR - Made for the 1933 World's Fair. Box camera for 2¼x3¼" exposures on 120 film. $100-150. *(Illustrated top of previous column.)*

CHEVRON CAMERA - 1953-56. For 2¼x2¼" on 620 film. Kodak Ektar f3.5/78mm lens. Synchro-Rapid 800 shutter. $140-175.

CIRKUT CAMERAS, CIRKUT OUTFITS
Manufactured by:
Rochester Panoramic Camera Co. 1904-05;
Century Camera Co. 1905-07,
Century Camera Division of Eastman Kodak Co. 1907-1915;
Folmer & Schwing Div. of EKC 1915-17;
F&S Dept. of EKC 1917-26;
Folmer Graflex 1925-45;
Graflex, Inc. (sales only) 1945-49.
For obvious reasons of continuity, we are listing all Cirkut equipment under the Eastman Kodak heading rather than split it among all these various companies.

Basically, a Cirkut OUTFIT is a revolving-back cycle view camera with an accessory Cirkut back, tripod, and gears. A Cirkut CAMERA is designed exclusively for Cirkut photos and cannot be used as a view camera. Both types take panoramic pictures by revolving the entire camera on a geared tripod head while the film moves past a narrow slit at the focal plane and is taken up on a drum. These cameras are numbered according to film width, the common sizes being 5, 6, 8, and 10 inches.
NOTE - All prices listed here are for complete outfits with tripod and gears.

No. 5 Cirkut Camera - 1915-1923. With Turner Reich 6¼, 11, 14" Triple Convertible lens. $500-650.

No. 6 Cirkut Camera - 1932-49. With 7, 10, 15½" Triple Convertible. $800-1000.

No. 6 Cirkut Outfit - 1907-1925. (5x7 RB Cycle Graphic). With Series II Centar lens: $450-700. With Graphic Rapid Rectilinear convertible 5x7 lens: $500-750.

No. 8 Cirkut Outfit - 1907-1926. Based on 6½x8½ RB Cycle Graphic. Uses 6" or 8" film. With 10½, 18, 24" Triple Convertible lens: $700-900.

No. 10 Cirkut Camera - 1904-1941. Uses 10", 8", or 6" film. This is the most desirable as a usable camera. Before 1932, used 10½, 18, 24" Triple Convertible. From 1932-41, used 10, 15½, 20" lens. With either Triple Convertible lens: $1500-2000.

No. 16 Cirkut Camera - 1905-1924. Takes 16", 12", 10", or 8" film. Quite rare. Limited production. $2500-3000.

NO. 1 CONE POCKET KODAK - c1898. A very unusual early Kodak camera which is essentially a non-folding box version of the Folding Pocket Kodak camera. Early records indicate that 1000 were shipped to London, from where they were apparently shipped to France. Since 1981 at least two examples have surfaced. Price negotiable. Rare. *(Illustrated top of next column.)*

Colorsnap 35 - 1959-63. **Model II** - 1964-67. Basic 35mm camera based on the earlier Bantam Colorsnap body. Plastic and metal construction. Kodak Anaston f3.9 lens. Single speed shutter. $8-12.

No. 1 Cone Pocket Kodak

COQUETTE CAMERA - 1930-31. A boxed Kodak Petite Camera in blue with matching lipstick holder and compact. Art-deco "lightning" design. $500-750.

DAYLIGHT KODAK CAMERAS 1891-95
The Daylight Kodak Cameras are the first of the Kodak string-set cameras not requiring darkroom loading. All are rollfilm box cameras with Achromatic lens and sector shutter, taking 24 exposures on daylight-loading rollfilm.
"A" - 2¾x3¼". (Orig. cost- $8.50). $800-1300.

"B" - 3½x4". (Orig. cost $15.00) $450-600.
"C" - 4x5". (Orig. cost- $25.00) $400-500.
(Also available in a plate version called "C" Special Glass Plate Kodak Camera.)

DUAFLEX CAMERA - Models I-IV. 1947-60. Cheap TLR's for 2¼x2¼" on 620 film. $4-7. (Add $2-4 for focusing models.)

DUEX CAMERA - 1940-42. 4.5x6cm on 620 film. Helical telescoping front. Doublet lens. $10-15.

DUO SIX-20 CAMERA - 1934-37. Folding

camera for 16 exposures 4.5x6cm on 620 film. Made in Germany. f3.5/70mm Kodak Anast. or Zeiss Tessar lens. Compur or Compur Rapid shutter. $35-50.

DUO SIX-20 SERIES II CAMERA (without RF) - 1937-39. Folding optical finder on top. No rangefinder. $35-45.

DUO SIX-20 SERIES II CAMERA w/RANGEFINDER - 1939-40. Rangefinder incorporated in top housing. Kodak Anastigmat f3.5/75mm lens. Compur Rapid shutter. Uncommon. $225-300.

EASTMAN PLATE CAMERA, No. 3, No. 4, and No. 5 - c1903. No. 3 in 3¼x4¼", No. 4 in 4x5", and No. 5 in 5x7". Folding bed cycle style plate cameras with swing back more typical of some of the Rochester Optical Co. earlier models. Double extension bellows. RR lens. Kodak shutter. $65-100.

1978-. Simple 110 pocket cameras for 13x17mm exposures. $1-5.

KODAK EKTRA - 1941-48. 35mm RF. Interchangeable lenses & magazine backs. Focal plane shutter to 1000. A precision camera which originally sold for $300 with the f1.9/50mm lens. Current value with f1.9/50mm: $375-450.

Ektra accessories:
- 35mm f3.3: $90-125.
- 50mm f1.9: $60-75.
- 50mm f3.5 (scarce): $100-150.
- 90mm f3.5: $90-120.
- 135mm f3.8: $100-125.
- 153mm f4.5: $750-1000.
- Magazine back: $100-125.
- Ground glass back: $175-225.

KODAK EKTRA II - Yes, there is an Ektra II, c1944. Apparently made as an experimental model. We know of only one extant example (ser. #7021), which also had a spring-motor auto advance back. Price information not available.

KODAK EKTRA 1, 2, 200 CAMERAS -

EMPIRE STATE CAMERAS - c1893-1914. View cameras, usually found in 5x7", 6½x8½", and 8x10" sizes. With original lens and shutter: $100-150.

KODAK ENSEMBLE - 1929-33. A Kodak Petite Camera with lipstick, compact, and mirror in a suede case. Available in beige, green, and old rose. $350-450.

EUREKA CAMERAS 1898-99
Box cameras for glass plates in standard holders which insert through side door. Storage space for additional holders.

No. 2 - 3½x3½" exp. on plates or on No. 106 Cartridge film in rollholder. $45-70.

No. 2, Jr. - same size, but cheaper model for plates only. $50-75.

No. 4 - Made in 1899 only. For 4x5" exposures on No. 109 Cartridge film in rollholder. $50-75.

THE FALCON CAMERA - 1897-98. Style similar to the Pocket Kodak Camera, but larger. 2x2½" exposures on special rollfilm. $50-75.

NO. 2 FALCON CAMERA - 1897-99. Box camera for 3½x3½" exposures on No. 101 rollfilm. Knob on front of camera to cock shutter. Leather covered wood. $40-60.

FIFTIETH ANNIVERSARY CAMERA - (see Anniversary Kodak Camera)

FISHER-PRICE CAMERA - c1984. Pocket 110 cartridge camera with cushioned ends. Made by Kodak for Fisher-Price. New, in box: $20-30.

FLAT FOLDING KODAK CAMERA - 1894-95. Kodak's first folding camera with integral rollfilm back. Marketed only in England. RARE. Very few exist. $800-1200.

FLEXO KODAK CAMERA, No. 2 - 1899-1913. Box camera for 12 exp. 3½x3½" on No. 101 rollfilm. The most unusual feature is that the sides and back come completely off for loading, and are held together only by the leather covering. It is very similar in outward appearance to the Bull's-Eye series, but was slighty cheaper when new. The same camera was marketed in Europe under the name "Plico". Achromatic lens, rotary shutter. (Orig. cost-$5.00). $25-35.

FLUSH BACK KODAK CAMERA, No. 3 - 1908-15. A special version of the No. 3 Folding Pocket Kodak Camera for 3¼x4¼" exposures on 118 film, or for glass plates. B&L RR lens in B&L Auto shutter. Made for the European market and not sold in the U.S.A. $40-60.

FOLDING KODAK CAMERAS

There are two distinct styles of "Folding Kodak" cameras which share little more than a common name. The earlier models, numbered 4, 5, and 6 by size, resemble a carrying case when closed, and are easily identifiable by the hinged top door which hangs over the sides like a box cover. The later model can be distinguished by its vertical format and rounded body ends in the more common style. We are listing the early models first followed by the later one.

FOLDING KODAK CAMERAS
(early "satchel style") *There are three variations of the No. 4 and No. 5: Sector shutter in 1890-1891; Barker shutter, 1892; and the Improved version with B&L Iris Diaphragm shutter and hinged drop bed, 1893-1897.*

*No. 4 Folding Kodak Camera
with early sector shutter*

*No. 4 Folding Kodak Improved Camera
with B&L Iris Diaphragm shutter*

No. 4, No. 4 Improved - 1890-1897. For 48 exposures 4x5" on glass plates or rollfilm in rollholder. $350-450.

*No. 5 Folding Kodak Camera
with Barker shutter*

No. 5, No. 5 Improved - 1890-1897. Similar specifications, but for 5x7" rollfilm or plates. $450-550.

No. 5 Improved with stereo lensboard - The same camera as the No. 5 Folding Kodak Improved Camera, but with a stereo lensboard and a partition for stereo work. Rare. No recent sales.

No. 6 Improved - 1893-1895. Similar, but for 6½x8½". Since the No. 6 was not introduced until 1893, it was only made in the "Improved" version with B&L Iris Diaphragm shutter. This size is even less common than the others. $700-1000.

NO. 4A FOLDING KODAK CAMERA -

1906-1915. Vertical folding-bed camera similar to the "Folding Pocket" series. For 6 exp., 4¼x6½" on No. 126 rollfilm. (126 rollfilm, made from 1906-1949, is not to be confused with the more recent 126 cassettes.) Red bellows. $75-125.

FOLDING POCKET KODAK CAMERAS

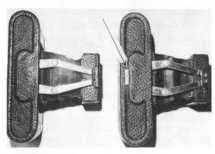

Folding Pocket Kodak Cameras:
Original model (left) has 4 round openings on front, lens cone, and no backlatch slide. Second model (right) has only two finder openings, no lens cone and has metal backlatch slide.

The Folding Pocket Kodak Camera -
Renamed No. 1 after 1899. For 2¼x3¼" exp. on No. 105 rollfilm. Leather covered front pulls straight out. Double finders concealed behind leather covered front. Red bellows. The earliest production models (c1897-1898) included a sequence of changes which led to the more standard "No. 1". The true "Original" had ALL of these features, and later models had some.
1. Recessed lens opening, a wooden "cone" shape (the shutter is quite different from later versions because of this odd opening.)
2. All brass metal parts are unplated.
3. There are four small openings on the face, two of which are used for finders.
4. No locking clasp for the back.
5. Patent pending.
6. Flat bar provided for horizontal standing, but no vertical stand.

--Original model - all features above: $150-200.
--Transitional models - Brass struts, but not all of the above features: $125-150.
--Nickeled struts - c1898-99: $60-80.

No. 0 - 1902-1906. Similar in style to the original. For 4.5x6cm exposures on No. 121 film which was introduced for this camera. It is the smallest of the series, but by no means the first as some collectors have been misled to believe. $70-90

No. 1, (pull-out front) - 1899-1905. Nickeled struts. Similar to the original model. $45-70.

Twin-finders variation

No. 1, (bed-type) - 1905-1915. For 2¼x3¼" exposures. Recognizable by the domed front door, red bellows, and twin sprung struts for the lensboard. Self-erecting bed. Various models. With twin-finders (made briefly): $40-60. With single, reversible finder: $20-35.

No. 1A, (pull-out front) - 1899-1905. Similar to the original FPK, but for 2½x4¼" exposures. $35-50.

No. 1A, (bed-type) - 1905-1915. For 2½x4¼" exposures on 116 rollfilm. Domed front door, twin sprung struts, red bellows. Self-erecting bed. Various models. With twin-finders (made briefly): $40-55. With single, reversible finder: $20-35.

No. 1A Folding Pocket Kodak Camera R.R. Type - 1912-1915 and **No. 1A Folding Pocket Kodak Special Camera** - 1908-1912. Similar to the regular "1A" but with better lenses and shutters. $25-40.

No. 2 - Horizontal style camera for square exposures 3½x3½" on No. 101 rollfilm.

Front is not self-erecting. Bed folds down, and front standard pulls out on track. Flat rectangular front door. First model (1899-1905) has leather covered lensboard with recessed lens and shutter: $50-70. Later models (1905-1915) have wooden standard with exposed shutter and lens: $35-45.

No. 3 - Vertical style folding-bed camera for 3¼x4¼" exposures on 118 rollfilm. Flat rectangular front door. Early models (1900-1903) with leather covered lensboard concealing the rotary shutter: $35-65. Later models (1904-1915) with exposed lens and shutter: $15-25.

No. 3 Deluxe - 1901-03. A No. 3 Folding Pocket Kodak with brown silk bellows and Persian Morocco covering. Rare. $200-400.

No. 3A - 1903-1915. Vertical folding-bed camera for 3¼x5½" exposures on 122 rollfilm (introduced for this camera). Flat, rectangular front door. Red bellows. Polished wood insets on bed. By far the most common model of the FPK series. $18-28.

No. 4 - 1907-15. Vertical folding-bed camera for 4x5" on 123 film. Red bellows, polished wood insets on bed. $45-60.

GENESEE OUTFIT - c1886. An early and relatively unknown 5x7" view camera made by Frank Brownell for the Eastman Dry Plate & Film Co. Complete with plateholders, brass-barrel R.R. lens with waterhouse stops, etc. $200-250.

GEORGE WASHINGTON
BICENTENNIAL CAMERA - c1932. One of the rarest of Kodak box cameras. This one, like the 50th Anniversary of Kodak camera is based on the No. 2 Rainbow Hawk-Eye Model C, but with special colored covering and a seal on the side. This camera is a very attractive blue, with an art-deco front plate with an enameled red, white, and blue star. Unfortunately, due to the depressed economy in 1932, Kodak decided not to market the camera, and only a few examples are known to exist. You will probably never find one, but if you do, the authors and many of their friends would like very much to get into a bidding war over it, and it would probably bring $500-1000.

GIFT KODAK CAMERA, No. 1A - 1930-1931. A special rendition of the No. 1A Pocket Kodak Junior Camera. The camera is covered with brown genuine leather, and decorated with an enameled metal inlay on the front door, as well as a matching metal faceplate on the shutter. The case is a cedar box, the top plate of which repeats the art-deco design of the camera. To go one step further, the gift box is packed in a cardboard box with a matching design.

Original price in the 1930 Christmas season was just $15.00. A few years ago these brought a bit more, but enough appeared to fill the demand and reduce the price. Camera with original brown bellows, cedar gift box, instructions and original cardboard box: $350-400. Camera with gift box: $150-225. Camera only: $50-75. *(Illustrated above and on the back cover.)*

GIRL GUIDE KODAK CAMERA - British version of the Girl Scout Kodak Camera. Blue enameled body with Girl Guide emblem. Blue case. $75-100 in England. Slightly higher in the U.S.A.

GIRL SCOUT KODAK CAMERA - 1929-1934. For 4.5x6cm exposures on 127 film. Bright green color with official GSA emblem engraved on the bed. $75-100.

HAPPY TIMES INSTANT CAMERA - 1978. A special two-tone brown premium version of "The Handle" camera with

Coca-Cola trademarks. Originally sold for $17.95 with purchase of Coca-Cola products. Current value: $30-35.

for 4x6.5cm on 127 film. Made by Kodak Ltd., London. Fixed focus lens, flip-flop shutter. $20-35.

CARTRIDGE HAWK-EYE CAMERAS (Box cameras)
No. 2 - 1924-1934. 2¼x3¼". $4-8.
No. 2A - 1924-1934. 2½x4¼". $4-8.

FILM PACK HAWK-EYE CAMERAS
No. 2 - 1922-1925. Box camera for 2¼x3¼" film packs. All metal construction. $8-15.
No. 2A - 1923-1925. Box camera for 2½x4¼" film packs. $8-15.

HAWKETTE CAMERA, No. 2 - c1930's. British made folding Kodak camera for 2¼x3¼" exposures on 120 rollfilm. Folding style like the Houghton Ensignette with cross-swinging struts. Body of brown marbled bakelite plastic. These cameras were used as premiums for such diverse products as Cadbury Chocolates and Australian cigarettes. A very attractive camera. Common in England. $35-55.

HAWK-EYE CAMERAS *The Hawk-Eye line originated with the Blair Camera Co. and was continued by Kodak after they absorbed the Blair Co. See also Blair Hawk-Eye.*

Hawkeye Ace - c1938. Small box camera for 4x6.5cm on 127 film. Made in London. Similar to Baby Hawkeye, but with leatherette covering on front. Fixed focus lens, T & I shutter. $20-30.

Baby Hawkeye - c1936. Small box camera

HAWKEYE FLASHFUN, FLASHFUN II CAMERAS - $3-6.

FOLDING HAWK-EYE CAMERAS
No. 1A - 1908-1915. 2½x4¼". Red bellows. Various lens/shutter combinations. With Meniscus or RR lens in Kodak Ball Bearing or pneumatic shutter: $15-25. With Zeiss-Kodak Anastigmat or Tessar IIB lens in Compound shutter: $15-25.

No. 3 - 1904-15. Models 1-9. 3¼x4¼" exp. on 118 film. Horizontal format. $15-25.

No. 3A - 1908-1915. Models 1-4. 3¼x5½" exp. on 122 film. Horizontal format. $15-25.

No. 4 - 1904-1913. Models 1-4. 4x5" exposures on 103 rollfilm. $25-30.

Six-16 or Six-20 - 1933-1934. $15-25.

FOLDING HAWK-EYE SPECIAL CAMERAS - In three sizes, with Kodak Anastigmat f6.3 lens.
No. 2 - 1928-1933. $10-20.
No. 2A - 1928-1930. $10-20.
No. 3 - 1929-1934. $10-20.
No. 3A - c1929. $15-20.

FOLDING CARTRIDGE HAWK-EYE CAMERAS
No. 2 - 1926-1933. 2¼x3¼" on 120 film. Kodex shutter. Colored models: $15-25. Black: $6-12.
No. 2A - 1926-1934. 2½x4¼" on 116 film. Single Achromatic or RR lens. $9-18.

No. 3A - 1926-1935. 3¼x5½" on 122 flm. Kodak shutter. RR or Achromatic lens. $10-15.

FOLDING FILM PACK HAWK-EYE CAMERA, No. 2 - 1923. Hawk-Eye shutter. Meniscus Achromatic lens. 2¼x3¼" exposures on film packs. $12-18.

RAINBOW HAWK-EYE CAMERAS *Box cameras, similar to the Cartridge Hawk-Eye, but in colors: blue, green, maroon, vermillion.*

No. 2 - 1929-1933. 2¼x3¼" exposures. Colors: $10-18. Black: $4-8.
No. 2A - 1931-1932. Same, but in 2½x4¼" size. Colors: $10-18. Black: $4-8.

FOLDING RAINBOW HAWK-EYE CAMERAS *Similar to the Folding Hawk-Eye Cameras, but available in black and colors: blue, brown, green, old rose. (Subtract 35% for black replacement bellows.)*
No. 2 - 1930-1934. 2¼x3¼". $25-45.
No. 2A - 1930-1933. 2½x4¼". $25-45.

FOLDING RAINBOW HAWK-EYE SPECIAL CAMERAS 1930-1933. *In black and colors: blue, brown, green, maroon.*
Nos. 2, 2A - $50-80.

HAWK-EYE SPECIAL CAMERAS - *Deluxe model box cameras with embossed morocco-*

grain imitation leather.
No. 2 - 1928-1933. $12-18.
No. 2A - 1928-1930. $12-18.

STEREO HAWK-EYE CAMERA - A continuation of the Blair Stereo Hawk-Eye series produced through 1916, and labeled "Blair Division of Eastman Kodak Co." A folding stereo camera taking twin 3½x3½" exposures. Various models, numbered in sequence, offered various lens/shutter combinations. Mahogany interior, brass trim, red bellows. $150-250.

TARGET HAWK-EYE CAMERAS, No. 2, No. 2 Junior, No. 2A, Six-16, and Six-20 - Simple box cameras. No. 2 available in black only, others available in black, blue, and brown. 1932 and 1933. Black: $1-5. Colors: $12-18.

VEST POCKET HAWK-EYE CAMERA - 1927-1934. 4.5x6cm exposures. Single or Periscopic lens. $15-25.

VEST POCKET RAINBOW HAWK-EYE CAMERA - 1930-1933. Same as the V.P. Hawkeye, but in black or colors: blue, green, orchid, and rose. Black: $20-30. Colors, with original colored bellows: $50-70. Higher in Europe.

WENO HAWK-EYE CAMERAS *Box cameras originally made by Blair Camera Co. and continued by Eastman Kodak Co. until 1915. See also Blair Weno Hawk-Eye Camera.*
No. 2 - 3½x3½". $20-25.

No. 4 - 4x5". $20-25.
No. 5 - 3¼x4¼". $20-25.
No. 7 - 3¼x5½". Introduced in 1908 after Blair became a part of EKC. $25-35.

INSTAMATIC CAMERAS *Introduced in 1963, using the new 126 cartridge. A variety of models made, most of which are still too new and common to be collectible. To give a fairly complete list in a small space, we have grouped them together by features.*

Basic models - 100, 104, 124, 44, X-15, X-15F: $1-3.

With meter - 300, 304, 134, 314, X-30, X-35, X-35F: $5-10.

Spring motor models - 150, 154, 174, X-25: $10-20.
Spring Motor & meter - 400, 404, 414, X-45: $15-25.

f2.8 metered models - 324, 500, 700, 704, 714: $25-50.

f2.8, meter, motor, RF - 800, 804, 814, X-90: $25-50.

Instamatic Reflex - 1968-74. SLR for 126 cartridges. Interchangeable lenses. CdS meter. With Xenar f2.8/45mm or Xenon f1.9/50mm lens: $100-150.

Instamatic S-10 & S-20 - 1967-72. Compact models with rectangular pop-out front. Advance knob on end. S-20 has meter. $5-10.

INSTANT CAMERAS - In October 1985, after nine years of patent litigation with Polaroid, Kodak was banned from making and selling instant cameras and film. The ban took effect January 1986, at which time Kodak announced a trade-in program. The owners of 16.5 million cameras were given a chance to trade in their cameras for a new camera, a share of Kodak common stock, or $50 worth of Kodak merchandise. The obvious immediate effect on the value of used Kodak instant cameras was that Kodak would pay more for them than most collectors would. Some speculators started hoarding the cameras, even though the trade-in limit was three cameras per person. Fortunately, greed did not engulf the collector market. During the time that the rebate program was in effect, I saw several Kodak instant cameras offered for sale at camera collector trade fairs for just a few dollars, and at the end of a two-day show, they remained unsold. By June of 1986, several class action lawsuits had been filed against Kodak by owners of the instant cameras, and the courts brought Kodak's rebate plan to a halt pending the outcome of these suits, which asked, among other things, for a cash rebate option. At the time of this writing, it is expected that any rebate offers by Kodak will be postponed by court action for at least a year and probably longer. As for the value of the cameras as collectibles, we can only give our opinion as to how collectors will react. Of the 16.5 million Kodak instant cameras in circulation, certainly there will be more than enough to go around for all of the world's collectors, and we do not expect their value to be significant. I have passed up my share of them at flea markets and camera shows for less than $5 each, though I would pay that much for a nice clean example of a model I didn't already have. A few of the top-of-line models, special-purpose types, or commemorative models will attract more collector interest, as they would have done without the legal hoopla. As for the common models, once the rebate programs have run their course, we expect that they will be readily available on the collector market in the same price range as common box cameras, Instamatic cameras, and Polaroid cameras.

JIFFY KODAK CAMERAS *Common rollfilm cameras with pop-out front, twin spring struts. The vest pocket model has a Doublet lens, other models have Twindar lens, zone focus. Note: Back latch is often broken which reduces the value by 40-50%.*
Six-16 - 1933-37. Art-deco enameled front. 2½x4¼" on 616 film. $10-15.

Six-16, Series II - 1937-42. Similar to the Six-16, but imitation leather front instead of the art-deco. Not as common. $12-18.

Six-20 - 1933-37. Art-deco front. 2¼x3¼" on 620 rollfilm. $10-15.

Six-20, Series II - 1937-48. Similar, but with imitation leather front. $12-18.

Vest Pocket - 1935-42. 4.5x6cm on 127 rollfilm. Black plastic construction. $10-15.

KODAK BOX 620 CAMERA - 1936-37. All black metal box camera with leatherette covering. Made by Kodak A.G., Stuttgart. $12-18.

KODAK JUNIOR CAMERAS *Two of Eastman's first cameras bore the name Junior along with their number: No. 3 Kodak Jr., and the No. 4 Kodak Jr. Both are box cameras with string-set shutters, and are listed at the beginning of the Eastman Kodak section.*
The models listed here are folding-bed cameras. Nos. 1 and 1A were introduced in 1914 shortly before the Autographic feature became available. These cameras had a short life-span, with the Autographic Kodak Junior Cameras taking their place. (See Autographic Kodak Junior Cameras.)
No. 1 - 2¼x3¼" on 120 rollfilm. $12-18.
No. 1A - 2½x4¼" on 116 film. $12-18.

Six-16 - 1935-37. 2½x4¼" on 616 film.

Octagonal shutter face. Self-erecting bed. $15-25.
Six-20 - 1935-37. Similar, but 2¼x3¼" on 120 film. $15-20.

Six-16, Series II - 1937-40. Similar. $12-18.
Six-20, Series II - 1937-40. Similar. $12-18.

Six-16, Series III - 1938-39. Self-erecting. Streamlined bed supports. $12-18.
Six-20, Series III - 1938-39. Self-erecting. Streamlined bed supports. $12-18.

KODAK REFLEX CAMERAS - *Twin lens reflex cameras with Kodak f3.5 lens in Flash Kodamatic shutter.*
Kodak Reflex - 1946-49. $25-30.

Kodak Reflex IA - Introduced December 1950. Kodak Reflex IA cameras are Kodak Reflex cameras with the original

ground glass replaced by an Ektalite field lens. The conversion kit included the lens and bezel, nameplate, and screws. The original cost of the conversion kit was $10.00. Conversions were made by Kodak and other repair organiztions. The number of converted cameras is unknown. Much less common than the Kodak Reflex and Reflex II models. $50-75.

Kodak Reflex II - 1948-54. $25-30.

KODAK SERIES II, SERIES III CAMERAS - *Folding rollfilm cameras from the same era as and similar in appearance to the Pocket Kodak folding cameras.*
No. 1 Kodak Series III Camera - 1926-1931. 2¼x3¼" exp. on 120 film. $15-20.
No. 1A Kodak Series III Camera - 1924-1931. 2½x4¼" exp. on 116 film. $12-18.
No. 2C Kodak Series III Camera - 1924-1932. 2-7/8x4⅞" exp. on 130 film. $12-18.

No. 3 Kodak Series III Camera - 1926-1933. 3¼x4¼" exp. on 118 film. $20-30.

No. 3A Kodak Series II Camera - 1936-1941. 3¼x5½" exp. on 122 film. $30-45.
No. 3A Kodak Series III Camera - 1941-1943. 3¼x5½" exp. on 122 film. $30-45.

KODAK 35 CAMERA - 1938-48. For 24x36mm exposures on 35mm cartridge film. Various lens/shutter combinations. No rangefinder. Very common. $10-20.

KODAK 35 CAMERA (Military Model PH-324) - Olive drab body with black trim. PH-324 printed on back. $75-125.

KODAK 35 CAMERA, with Rangefinder - 1940-51. f3.5 Kodak Anast. Special or Kodak Anastar lens. Kodamatic or Flash Kodamatic shutter. Very common. $20-25.

KODET CAMERAS
No. 3 Folding Kodet Camera - Vertically styled folding bed camera, similar to the No. 4 but slightly smaller. Probably sold only in England. Rare. Estimated value: $400-450.

No. 4 Kodet Camera - 1894-97. For 4x5" plates or rollfilm holder. Leather covered wooden box. Front face hinges down to reveal brass-barrel lens and shutter. Focusing lever at side of camera. $250-300. *(Illustrated top of next column.)*

146

No. 4 Kodet Camera

No. 4 Folding Kodet Camera - 1894-97. Folding-bed camera, 4x5" plates or special rollholder. Basically cube-shaped when closed. Early model has variable speed shutter built into wooden lens standard. Brass barrel lens with rotating disc stops: $300-400. Later models with Gundlach or B&L external shutters: $250-350.
No. 4 Folding Kodet Junior Camera - 1894-97. Rare. Estimate: $300-450.
No. 4 Folding Kodet Special Camera - 1895-97. $250-350.

No. 5 Folding Kodet Camera
No. 5 Folding Kodet Special Camera - 1895-97. $250-350.

MATCHBOX CAMERA - 1944-45. Simple metal and plastic camera shaped like a matchbox. Made for the Office of Secret Services. ½x½" exposures on 16mm film. Rare. $1500-1800.

MEDALIST CAMERAS - *For 2¼x3¼" on 620 film. Kodak Ektar f3.5/100mm.*
Medalist I - 1941-48. Supermatic shutter to 400, B. No sync. Split image RF. $75-100.

Medalist II - 1946-53. Flash Supermatic shutter. $85-125.

MONITOR CAMERAS - *1939-48. Folding rollfilm cameras, available in two sizes:*
Six-16 - 2½x4¼" on 616 film. f4.5/127mm lens. Kodamatic or Supermatic, 10-400. Less common of the two sizes. $15-25.

Six-20 - 2¼x3¼" on 620 film. f4.5 lens. $18-25.

A, B, and C Ordinary Kodak Cameras

MOTORMATIC 35 CAMERAS - *Similar to the Automatic 35 series, but with motorized film advance. Made in 3 variations:*

Motormatic 35 Camera - 1960-62. Flash sync. posts on end of body. $25-40.

Motormatic 35F Camera - 1962-67. Built-in flash on top for AG-1 bulbs. $20-40.

Motormatic 35R4 Camera - 1965-69. Built-in flashcube socket on top. $20-35.

NAGEL *Some cameras made by Kodak A.G., Stuttgart (formerly Dr. August Nagel Werk) are continuations of cameras formerly sold under the Nagel brand. These cameras may be found under their model name in both the Eastman and Nagel sections. (e.g. Pupille, Ranca, Regent, Vollenda.)*

ORDINARY KODAK CAMERAS 1891-95
A series of low-priced wooden Kodak box cameras without leather covering called "Ordinary" to distinguish them from the Daylight, Folding, Junior and Regular Kodaks, as they were called at that time. All are made for 24 exposures on rollfilm. All have Achromatic lens, sector shutter. They differ only in size and price.

"A" - 2¾x3¼". (Original cost $6.00.) $1000-1400.

"B" - 3½x4". (Original cost $10.00.) $700-800.

"C" - 4x5". (Original cost $15.00.) $700-800. (Also available in a plate version called "C" Ordinary Glass Plate Kodak Camera.)

PANORAM KODAK CAMERAS *A series of rollfilm panoramic cameras in which the lens pivots and projects the image to the curved focal plane. Although designed basically for wide views, it could also be used vertically.*

No. 1 - April 1900-26. For 2¼x7" exposures on No. 105 rollfilm for an angle of 112 degrees. (Original cost $10.) Model A: $250-300. Models B, C, D: $200-250.

No. 3A - 1926-28. Takes 3¼x10⅜" exposures on 122 rollfilm for an angle of 120 degrees. This is the least common of the series, having been made for only two years. $160-220.

No. 4, (Original Model) - 1899-1900. Has no door to cover the swinging lens. For 3½x12" on No. 103 rollfilm. 142 degree angle. Rapid Rectilinear lens. (Original cost $20.) $175-225.

No. 4, Models B, C, D - 1900-1924. Same as the original model, but with a door over the lens. $120-160.

PEER 100 - c1974. An Instamatic 92 camera whose exterior is designed to look

like a package of Peer cigarettes. Used as a sales promotion premium. $275-325.

PETITE CAMERA - 1929-33. Vest Pocket Kodak Model B in colors: blue, green, grey, lavender, and old rose. For 4.5x6cm on 127 film. Meniscus lens, rotary shutter. With original bellows, matching case: $100-125. With black replacement bellows: $50-70. *See also Kodak Ensemble, Coquette.*

- **"Step Pattern"** - Rather than the normal fabric covering on the front door, some of the Petite cameras had an enameled metal front in an art-deco "step" pattern. These currently bring from $125 for a nice example with replacement black bellows to $200 for an excellent example with original colored bellows, original box and instructions.

PIN-HOLE CAMERA - ca. late 1920's and early 1930's. This is a small kit which consists of 5 cardboard pieces, gummed tape, a pin to make the hole, and instuction booklet. These were given to school children for use as science projects. We have seen a number of unused kits offered for sale at prices from $195 to $350. Obviously these are no longer for kids to play with. Assembled: $75-100.

PLICO - European name variation of the Flexo. $35-50.

POCKET INSTAMATIC CAMERAS - Introduced 1972 for the new 110 cartridge. 13x17mm exposures. Most models are too new to be collectible. $1-5. *Better models (40, 50, 60) have more value as usable cameras.*

POCKET KODAK CAMERAS *Except for the first camera listed here, the Pocket Kodak cameras are of the common folding rollfilm variety.*

The Pocket Kodak (box types) - 1895-1900. A tiny box camera for 1½x2" exposures on No. 102 rollfilm which was introduced for this camera. An auxiliary plateholder could also be used. Single lens; pebble-grained leather. Earliest 1895 model has a separate shutter board with sector shutter and round viewfinder. Later models have the shutter mounted on the inside of the camera, and it is removed when loading film. Shutter type changed from sector to rotary in 1896. Indentified by model year inside bottom. $75-100.

Pocket Kodak Cameras (folding types) - *All of these incorporate the Autographic feature, but the word Autographic does not form part of the name.*
No. 1 - 1926-31, black; 1929-32, colors. 2¼x3¼" on 120 film. Colors (blue, brown, green or grey): $20-30. Black: $7-12.

No. 1A - 1926-31, black; 1929-32, colors.

2½x4¼" on 116 film. Colors (blue, brown, green, grey): $20-30. Black: $8-13.

No. 2C - 1925-32. 2⅞ x 4⅞" on 130 film. Black only. $10-15.

No. 3A - 1927-34. 3¼x5½" on 122 film. Black only. $12-20.

POCKET KODAK JUNIOR CAMERAS - 1929-32. *Folding bed camera available in black, blue, brown, green. Meniscus lens in Kodo shutter.*

No. 1 - 2¼x3¼" on 120 film. Black: $7-12. Colors: $12-20.
No. 1A - 2½x4¼" on 116 film. Black: $8-13. Colors: $12-20.

POCKET KODAK SERIES II CAMERAS

No. 1 - 1922-31. Focusing and fixed focus models. Black only. $10-15.

No. 1A, (black) - 1923-31. Focusing and fixed-focus models. $10-15.

No. 1A, (colors) - 1928-32. Available in beige, blue, brown, green, and grey. Meniscus Achromatic lens in Kodex shutter. Originally came with matching carrying case. $15-25.

POCKET KODAK SPECIAL CAMERAS -
Kodak Anastigmat f6.3, f5.6, f4.5 lenses in Kodamatic shutter. (No. 2C not available with f6.3.) Black only. Models with f4.5 lens are hard to find and would be worth about 30-40% more.

No. 1 - 1926-34. 2¼x3¼" on 120 film. $15-25.
No. 1A - 1926-34. 2½x4¼" on 116. $15-25.
No. 2C - 1928-33. 2⅞x 4⅞" on 130. $15-25.
No. 3 - 1926-33. 3¼x4¼" on 118. $15-25.

PONY CAMERAS *All models except the 828 are for 24x36mm exposures on 35mm film.*
II - 1957-62. Non-interchangeable Kodak Anastar f3.9/44mm. Bakelite body. $10-15.

IV - 1957-61. Non-interchangeable Kodak Anastar f3.5/44mm lens. $10-15.

135 - 1950-54; Model B, 1953-55; Model C, 1955-1958. The first Pony Camera for 35mm film. Non-interchangeable Kodak Anaston f4.5 or f3.5 lens in focusing mount. $8-12.

135 (Made in France) - 1956. Angenieux f3.5/45mm. Shutter 1/25-1/150, B. $12-18.

828 - 1949-59. The first in this series, it took No. 828 film. Easily distinguished from the later 35mm models by the lack of a rewind knob on the top right side of the camera next to the shutter release. $10-15.

PREMO CAMERAS *Kodak took over the very popular Premo line of cameras from Rochester Opt. Co. See Rochester for earlier models.*

PREMO BOX FILM CAMERA - 1903-08. For filmpacks. 3¼x4¼" or 4x5" sizes. Achromatic lens, Automatic shutter. $8-15.

CARTRIDGE PREMO CAMERAS - Simple rollfilm box cameras.

No. 00 - 1916-22. 1¼x1¾". Meniscus lens. The smallest Kodak box camera. $50-75.

No. 2 - 1916-23. 2¼x3¼". $10-16.
No. 2A - 1916-23. 2½x4¼". $10-16.
No. 2C - 1917-23. 2⅞ x 4⅞. $10-16.

FILM PREMO CAMERAS - Wooden-bodied folding bed cameras for filmpacks. Four sizes, 3¼x4¼ through 5x7", usually found in the 3¼x4¼" & 3¼x5½" sizes.

No. 1 - 1906-16. Simple lens and shutter. $20-30.
No. 3 - 1906-10. Various lens/shutter combinations. $25-40.

FILMPLATE PREMO CAMERA - 1906-16

Folding camera for plates or filmpacks. 3¼x4¼", 3¼x5½", 4x5" sizes: $30-45. 5x7" size: $40-60.

FILMPLATE PREMO SPECIAL - 1912-1916. The Filmplate Premo Camera with better lens/shutter combinations was called the Filmplate Premo Special after 1912. (Only the version with Planatograph lens was still called Filmplate Premo.) $40-60.

PREMO FOLDING CAMERAS - Folding cameras for plates or filmpacks.

Premo No. 8 - 1913-22. Planatograph lens (or Anastigmat on the 3¼x5½") in Kodak Ball Bearing shutter. Made in 3 sizes: 3¼x5½", $25-35. 4x5", $25-35. 5x7", $30-50.
Premo No. 9 - 1913-23. Various lens/shutter combinations. 3 sizes: 3¼x5½", $25-35. 4x5", $25-35. 5x7", $30-50.

Premo No. 12 - 1916-26. 2¼x3¼" on plates, packs or rollfilm. Various lens/shutter combinations. $25-35.

FOLDING CARTRIDGE PREMO CAMERAS - Folding-bed rollfilm cameras. Meniscus Achromatic or Rapid Rectilinear lens.

No. 2 - 1916-26. 2¼x3¼" on 120 film. $7-10.

No. 2A - 1916-26. 2½x4¼" on 116 film. $8-12.
No. 2C - 1917-23. 2⅞ x 4⅞" on 130 film. Uncommon size. $12-18.
No. 3A - 1917-23. 3¼x5½" on 122 film. $8-12.

PREMO JUNIOR CAMERAS - Filmpack box cameras. Simple lens and shutter.

No. 0 - 1911-16. 1¾x2¼". $15-20.
No. 1 - 1908-22. 2¼x3¼". The first model to be introduced, in 1908 it was called simply Premo Jr. $12-18.
No. 1A - 1909-21. 2½x4¼". $15-20.
No. 3 - 1909-19. 3¼x4¼". $15-20.
No. 4 - 1909-14. 4x5". $15-20.

POCKET PREMO CAMERAS
Pocket Premo C - 1904-16. 3¼x4¼" and 3¼x5½" sizes. Uses plates or filmpacks. Black or red bellows. $20-30.

Pocket Premo, 2¼x3¼" - 1918-23. Self-erecting, folding bed camera for filmpacks only. Mensicus Achromatic lens, Kodak Ball Bearing shutter. $20-30.

PONY PREMO CAMERAS - Folding plate cameras. The 4x5" and 5x7" sizes could also use filmpacks or rollfilm.
Pony Premo No. 1 - 1904-12. 4x5". Inexpensive lens and shutter. $30-50.

Pony Premo No. 2 - 1898-1912. Inexpensive lens/shutters. Made in 3 sizes: 3¼x4¼", $30-50. 4x5", $35-55. 5x7", $60-90.

Pony Premo No. 3 - 1898-1912. With inexpensive lens/shutter combinations. 3¼x4¼", $35-45. 4x5", $35-60. 5x7", $60-90.

Pony Premo No. 4 - 1898-1912. Various lens/shutter combinations. 4x5", $35-50. 5x7", $60-100.

Pony Premo No. 6 - 1899-1912. Various lens/shutter combinations. For plates. 4x5", $40-60. 5x7", $60-90. 6½x8½", much less common, $75-125. 8x10", $75-125.

Pony Premo No. 7 - 1902-1912. Various lens/shutter combinations. For plates. 4x5", $40-60. 5x7", $60-90. 6½x8½", much less common, $75-125.

STAR PREMO - 1903-08. Folding bed camera for 3¼x4¼" exposures on plates or filmpacks. Various lens/shutter combinations. $35-50.

PREMOETTE CAMERAS - *Leather-covered wood-bodied "cycle" style cameras in vertical format. For filmpacks. Models with better lens/shutter combinations were referred to as Premoette Special for a few years.*

(no number) - 1906-08. 2¼x3¼". Became the No. 1 in 1909 when the No. 1A was introduced. $25-35.

No. 1 - 1906-12. 2¼x3¼". $20-30.

No. 1A - 1909-12. 2½x4¼". $20-35.

PREMOETTE JUNIOR CAMERAS - *Leather-covered aluminum-bodied folding bed cameras for filmpacks. The bed folds down, but not a full 90 degrees. There is no track on the bed, but the front standard fits into one of several slots at the front of the bed for different focusing positions. These cameras, although not terribly uncommon in the USA, are currently worth about double the US price in Europe.*
(no number) - 1911-12. 2¼x3¼". Became the No. 1 in 1913 when the No. 1A was introduced. $15-25.

No. 1 - 1913-23. 2¼x3¼". $25-35.
No. 1 Special - 1913-18. Kodak
Anastigmat f6.3 lens. $30-35.

No. 1A - 1913-18. 2½x4¼". $30-35.
No. 1A Special - 1913-18. Kodak
Anastigmat f6.3 lens. $40-50.

PREMOETTE SENIOR CAMERAS -
1915-23. Folding bed camera for
filmpacks. 2½x4¼", 3¼x4¼", and 3¼x5½"
sizes. (The only Premoette made in the
3¼x5½" size.) Similar in design to the
Premoette Jr. models. Kodak Anastigmat
f7.7 or Rapid Rectilinear lens. Kodak Ball
Bearing shutter. $15-25.

PREMOETTE SPECIAL CAMERAS
1909-1911. *Versions of the Premoette No. 1*

and No. 1A with better lenses and shutters. In
1912, the name "Special" was dropped and
these lens/shutter combinations were listed as
options on the Premoette No. 1 & No. 1A.
No. 1 - 2¼x3¼". $20-25.
No. 1A - 2½x4¼". $20-30.

PREMOGRAPH CAMERAS *Simple boxy
single lens reflex cameras for 3¼x4¼"
filmpacks. Not to be confused with the earlier
Premo Reflecting Camera, found under the
Rochester heading in this book.*

Premograph (original) - 1907-08. Single
Achromatic lens. Premograph Reflecting
shutter. $175-225.

Premograph No. 2 - 1908-09. Better
lens. Premograph Reflecting or
Compound shutter. $125-175.

PUPILLE - 1932-35. Made in Stuttgart,
Germany by the Nagel Works. For 3x4cm
exp. on 127 film. Schneider Xenon
f2/45mm. Compur shutter 1-300. $200-
250. *(Illustrated top of next page.)*

QUICK FOCUS KODAK CAMERA, No. 3B
- 1906-11. An unusual focusing box
camera for 3¼x5½" exposures on No. 125
film. Achromatic lens, rotary shutter. Focus
knob (lever on early models) on side of
camera is set to proper focal distance.
Upon pressing a button, the front pops
straight out to proper distance, focused
and ready. Original cost: $12.00. $100-150.

RANCA CAMERA - 1932-34. Made by
Kodak A.G. 3x4cm exposures on 127 film.
Similar to the Pupille Camera, but with
dial-set Pronto shutter. Nagel Anast. f4.5
lens. $175-250.

RECOMAR CAMERAS - 1932-40.
*Kodak's entry into the crowd of popular compact
folding long-extension precision view cameras.
Made in Germany by the Nagel Works.*

Pupille

REGENT CAMERA - 1935-39. Made by
Nagel Works in Stuttgart, Germany. Dual
format, 6x9cm or 4.5x6cm on 620 film.
Coupled rangefinder incorporated into
streamlined leather covered body. Zeiss
Tessar f4.5 or Schneider Xenar f3.8 or f4.5
lens. Compur-S or Compur Rapid shutter.
$150-200.

REGENT II CAMERA - 1939. Made by
Kodak A.G. in Germany. For 8 exposures
on 120 film. Schneider Xenar f3.5 lens.
Compur Rapid shutter. Coupled rangefinder
in chrome housing on side of camera.
Quite rare. $800-1200.

REGULAR KODAK CAMERAS *"Regular"*
*is the term used in early Kodak advertising to
distinguish the No. 2, 3, and 4 "string-set" Kodak
cameras from the Junior, Folding, Daylight, and
Ordinary models. The "Regular Kodak" cameras
are listed at the beginning of the Eastman section,
where we have called them by their simple original
names: No. 2, 3, and 4 Kodak cameras.*

Model 18 - 2¼x3¼". Kodak Anastigmat
f4.5/105mm in Compur shutter. $45-65.
Model 33 - 3¼x4¼". Similar, but 135mm
lens. More common than the smaller
model. $50-75.

RETINA CAMERAS - *A series of 35mm cameras made in Germany by Kodak A.G.* **Model "I"s have no rangefinder.**

(original model- Type 117) - 1934-35. Film advance release wheel next to winding knob. Top film sprocket with short shaft. Rewind release on advance knob. Large diameter advance and rewind knobs. Black finish with nickel trim. Schneider Xenar f3.5/50mm in Compur to 1/300. $60-90.

(original model, second version- Type 118) - 1935-1937. Film advance release lever at rear of top housing. Full length film sprocket shaft with top sprocket only. Rewind release on advance knob. Schneider Xenar f3.5/80mm in Compur Rapid to 1/500. $40-80.

(I) (Type 119) - 1936-38. Not called "I" until 1937. Recessed exposure counter between advance knob and viewfinder. Rewind release lever to right of film advance release button. Black lacquered metal parts. Lacks accessory shoe.

Reduced diameter advance and rewind knobs. Five milled rows on rewind knob. Kodak Ektar or Schneider Xenar f3.5 lens in Compur or Compur Rapid shutter. Not marketed in the USA. $40-75.

(I) (Type 126) - 1936-38. Not called "I" until 1937. Made with black or chrome trim. Accessory shoe (or 2 mounting screws) between finder and rewind knob. Five milled rows on rewind knob. Lenses available were: Kodak Ektar f3.5 (USA market), Schneider Xenar f3.5, Zeiss Tessar f3.5, Rodenstock Ysar and Angenieux Alcor (European market). Compur Rapid shutter. $40-60.

I (Type 141) - 1937-39. Body shutter release inside edge of exposure counter disc. Seven milled rows on rewind knob. Chrome trim. Kodak Anastigmat or Schneider Xenar f3.5. Compur or Compur Rapid shutter. Only the version with the Ektar lens in Compur Rapid shutter was sold in the USA. $30-50.

I (Type 143) - 1939. Like the Type 141, but with black trim. No accessory shoe. Schneider Xenar f3.5 in Compur shutter. Not imported into the USA. $50-65.

I (Type 148) - 1939. Taller top housing. Body release next to exposure counter. Cable release socket next to shutter release. Double exposure prevention. Kodak Anastigmat Ektar or Schneider Xenar f3.5 lens. Compur or Compur Rapid shutter. Only the Ektar/Compur Rapid version was sold in the USA. $45-70.

I (Type 149) - 1939. Like Type 148, but black lacquered edges of body. Schneider Xenar f3.5 lens in Compur shutter. No accessory shoe. Not imported into the USA. $40-60.

I (Type 010) - 1946-49. Similar to Type 148. Made from pre-war and wartime parts. USA imports have EK prefix on the serial number in the inside back. f3.5 coated and uncoated Retina Xenar, Kodak Anastigmat Ektar, or Rodenstock Ysar. Compur Rapid shutter. Made by Kodak A.G., except for the Kodak Ektar coated lens which was made in the USA. Only the Retina Xenar coated lens was sold in the USA. $25-50.

I (Type 013) - 1949-54. Full top housing with integral finder. Knob film advance. Retina Xenar f2.8 or f3.5 in Compur Rapid shutter. Not imported into the USA. $30-50.

Ia (Type 015) - 1951-54. Full top housing with integral finder. Rapid film advance lever on top. Shutter cocking mechanism coupled to film transport. Retina Xenar f3.5 in Compur Rapid shutter, or Retina Xenar f2.8, Rodenstock Heligon f3.5, or Kodak Ektar f3.5 in Synchro-Compur shutter. Not imported into the USA, but is still a very common model. $30-55.

Ib (Type 018) - 1954-58. Rapid film advance lever at bottom. Body corners rounded. Rectangular strap lugs at body ends. Metal shroud covers bellows. Retina Xenar f2.8 lens in Synchro-Compur. Not imported into the USA. $30-50.

IB (Type 019) - 1957-60. Uncoupled selenium meter. Extra front window for bright frame illumination. Retina Xenar f2.8 in Synchro-Compur. Not imported into the USA. $65-90.

IBS (Type 040) - 1962-63. Retina Xenar f2.8 in Compur. Not imported into the USA. $50-75.

IF (Type 046) - 1963-64. Rigid body. Built-in AG-1 flash on top. Recessed rewind knob. Coupled selenium meter. Prontor LK shutter distinguishes this from the IIF. Retina Xenar f2.8 in Prontor 500LK. Not imported into the USA. $60-90.

Model "II"s all have coupled rangefinders.

II (Type 122) - 1936-37. Lever film advance. Coupled rangefinder with separate eyepiece. Two round rangefinder windows. Kodak Anastigmat Ektar f3.5, Schneider Xenon f2.8 or f2.0 lens. Compur Rapid shutter. Not imported into the USA. Scarce. $85-135.

II (Type 142) - 1937-39. Knob film advance. Coupled rangefinder with separate eyepiece. Two round rangefinder windows. Kodak Anastigmat Ektar f3.5, Schneider Xenon f2.8 or f2.0 lens in Compur Rapid. The version with the Ektar lens was not sold in the USA. $55-75.

II (Type 011) - 1946-49. Like IIa, Type 150. No strap lugs. Single eyepiece range/viewfinder. Viewfinder image moves when focusing. No film type indicator on top. Kodak Ektar or Retina f2.0 coated lens, or uncoated Xenon or Heligon lens. Compur Rapid shutter. Only the Xenon version was imported into the USA. $65-85.

II (Type 014) - 1949-50. Single eyepiece range/viewfinder. Film type indicator under rewind knob. Retina Xenon or Heligon lens in Compur Rapid shutter. Not imported into the USA. $60-80.

IIa (Type 150) - 1939. Coupled rangefinder with single eyepiece. Small extensible rewind knob. Strap lugs at body ends. Kodak Ektar f3.5, Schneider Xenon f2.8 or f2.0 lens. Compur Rapid shutter. Not imported into the USA. $60-85.

IIa (Type 016) - 1951-54. Rapid rewind lever with built-in exposure counter. Strap lugs on front viewfinder. Retina Xenon or Heligon f2.0 lens in Synchro-Compur shutter. Compur Rapid shutter also used with the Xenon. Made by Kodak A.G. Only the Xenon/Synchro-Compur version was sold in the USA. $45-60.

IIc (Type 020) - 1954-57. Viewfinder windows not equal in size. Bright frame for normal lens only. Film advance lever on bottom of body. No built-in exposure meter.

MX sync. Retina Xenon-C or Heligon-C f2.8 in Synchro-Compur. Interchangeable front elements change the 50mm normal lens to a 35mm wide angle or 80mm telephoto lens. Made by Kodak A.G. Only the Xenon-C version was sold in the USA. $60-100.

IIC (Type 029) - 1958. Large finder windows of equal size. Bright frames for 3 lenses. Retina Xenon-C or Heligon-C f2.8 len with interchangeable front elements available. Synchro-Compur shutter. Not imported into the USA. $60-75.

IIF (Type 047) - 1963-64. Rigid body. Built-in AG-1 flash holder. Accessory shoe recessed in top housing. Similar to the IF, but with Synchro-Compur Special shutter. Match-needle visible only in finder. Retina Xenar f2.8 lens. Not common. $50-80.

IIS (Type 024) - 1959-60. Like the IIIS, but without interchangeable lenses. Retina Xenar f2.8 lens in Synchro-Compur. Not imported into the USA. Uncommon. $60-75.

IIIc (Type 021) - 1954-57. Like the IIc, but

Retina IIIS

120 were made c1977 for the 50th anniversary of Kodak A.G. Another source gives the date c1982. These have a meter setting for up to ASA 3200 rather than 1300 as earlier. Film reminder dial is like later models such as Retina Automatic III (3 sections for Color outdoors, Color indoors, B&W) rather than various film names as earlier IIIC. One failed to sell at auction in 1986 for its reserve price of about $875. No confirmed sales.

IIIS (Type 027) - 1958-60. The first Retina with a non-folding body. Interchangeable lenses: Retina Xenon or Heligon f1.9, Retina Xenar or Ysarex f2.8. Synchro-Compur shutter. Only the Xenar and Xenon versions were sold in the USA. $50-80. *(Illustrated top of previous column.)*

with coupled selenium meter. Bright frame for normal lens only. Retina Xenon-C or Heligon-C f2.8 lens with interchangeable front elements. Synchro-Compur shutter. Only the Xenon-C version was sold in the USA. Very common. $65-85. *(Although occasionally sold for around $150 these are very common and nearly always available in the lower price range.)*

S1 (Type 060) - 1966-69. Rigid plastic body. Built-in flashcube socket. No meter. Manual exposure with weather symbols. Schneider Reomar f2.8 lens in Kodak 4-speed shutter with B. In Europe: $25-45.

S2 (Type 061) - 1966-69. Like the S1, but with coupled selenium meter. Schneider Reomar f2.8 lens in Kodak 4-speed shutter with B. Not imported into the USA. In Europe: $25-45.

IIIC (Type 028) - 1958-60. Coupled selenium meter. Equal sized finder windows. Bright frames for 3 lenses. Retina Xenon-C or Heligon-C f2.0 lens with interchangeable front elements. Synchro-Compur shutter. Only the version with the Xenon-C lens was sold in the USA. Very common. $100-150. *(These, too, are often advertised for sale at much higher prices but are nearly always available in this price range because they are so common.)*

IIIC (New Type) - A small quantity of IIIC cameras was assembled using mainly original parts. One source indicates that

Retina Automatic III

RETINA AUTOMATIC CAMERAS
I (Type 038) - 1960-62. Rigid body. Coupled selenium meter. Shutter release on front. Retina Reomar f2.8. Prontormat-S shutter. Not imported into the USA. At European auctions, these bring $20-30.

II (Type 032) - 1960-63. Coupled automatic meter. Shutter release on front. No rangefinder. Retina Xenar f2.8. Compur shutter. Not imported into the USA. In Europe: $25-45.

III (Type 039) - 1960-64. Like the Automatic II, but with coupled rangefinder. Retina Xenar f2.8. Compur shutter. $35-45. *(Illustrated bottom of previous page.)*

RETINA REFLEX CAMERAS

(original model- Type 025) - 1956-58. Single lens reflex. Interchangeable front lens elements. Retina Xenon-C or Heligon-C f2.0 lens. Synchro-Compur MXV shutter. Only the Xenon-C version was sold in the USA. $40-60.

III (Type 041) - 1960-64. Meter needle visible in finder. Shutter release on front. Retina f1.9 Xenon or Heligon, or Retina f2.8

Xenar or Ysarex lens. Synchro-Compur MXV shutter. Made by Kodak A.G. Only the Xenar and Xenon versions were sold in the USA. $50-70. (Add $10-15 for f1.9 lens.)

IV (Type 051) - 1964-67. Small window on front of SLR prism to show settings in finder. Folding crank on rewind knob. Hot shoe. Retina f1.9 Xenon or f2.8 Xenar lens. Synchro-Compur X shutter. $85-105. (Add $10-15 for f1.9 lens.)

S (Type 034) - 1959-60. Coupled meter. Interchangeable Retina lenses: f1.9 Xenon or Heligon, or f2.8 Xenar or Ysarex. Synchro-Compur MXV shutter. Only the versions with the Xenar and Xenon lenses were sold in the USA. $50-75.

RETINETTE CAMERAS
(original model- Type 147) - 1939. Folding 35mm camera with self-erecting front. Horizontal style, not like the other folding Retina cameras. Body curved out to a flat bed. Bed hinged at bottom of camera. Kodak Anastigmat f6.3/50mm. Kodak 3-speed shutter. Not imported into the USA. $200-275.

(Type 012) - 1949-51. Horizontal body style. Bed swings to side. Half top-housing is chromed. Housing ends at viewfinder window. No accessory shoe. Separate cable release socket. Enna Ennatar or Schneider Reomar f4.5 lens in Prontor-S shutter. Not imported into the USA. $75-125.

(Type 017) - Horizontal body style. Bed swings to side. Full length top housing. Bed is deeper than Type 022. Accessory shoe. Release button threaded for cable release. Schneider Reomar or Xenar f4.5 lens. Prontor SV shutter. Only the Reomar version was sold in the USA. $25-45.

(Type 022) - 1954-58. Non-folding style. Rectangular front plate without the "V" design. Single finder window. Schneider Reomar f3.5 lens. Compur Rapid shutter. Not imported into the USA. $25-35.

F (Type 022/7) - 1958. Non-folding style. Same body as Type 022. Made by Kodak A.G. for export to France without lens or shutter. $50-75.

Retinette IA, Type 042

I (Type 030) - 1958-60. Non-folding style. A continuation of the Type 022 style. Rectangular front plate with "V" design. Two windows. Schneider Reomar f3.5. Compur Rapid shutter. Not imported into the USA. $25-45. (This camera was exported to Kodak-Pathe, France as Type 030/7 and to Kodak Ltd., England as Type 030/9.)

IA (Type 035) - 1959-60. Non-folding style. "V"-shaped front plate. No zone dots on lens rim. Schneider Reomar f3.5 lens. Pronto or Vero shutter. Not imported into the USA. $25-40. (Type 035/7 was the export version for Kodak-Pathe, France.)

IA (Type 042) - 1960-63. Non-folding style. "V"-shaped front plate. Click stops for zone focus, zones marked by dots on focus ring. Accessory shoe is not a "hot" shoe as on later Type 044. Schneider Reomar f2.8 lens. Pronto shutter. $25-35. *(Illustrated bottom of previous column.)*

IA (Type 044) - 1963-67. Non-folding style. "V"-shaped front plate. Hot shoe distinguishes this model from the Type 042. Schneider Reomar f2.8 Prontor 250S or 300S shutter. $30-40.

IB (Type 037) - 1959-63. Non-folding style. "V"-shaped front plate. No hot shoe. Built-in meter. Schneider Reomar f2.8 lens. Pronto-LK shutter. Not imported into the USA. $30-45.

IB (Type 045) - 1963-66. Non-folding style. "V"-shaped front plate. Built-in meter. Hot shoe. Schneider Reomar f2.8. Pronto 500-LK shutter. Not imported into the USA. $30-45.

II (Type 160) - 1939. Folding style. Bed swings to the side. Table stand on bed. Deeper bed than on Type 147. Body not curved. Black enameled half-top housing. Ribbed front standard. Kodak Anast. f3.5 or f4.5 lens. Kodak 4-speed or Compur shutter. Not imported into the USA. $45-70.

II (Type 026) - 1958. Non-folding style. A continuation of the Type 022 style. Rectangular front plate with "V" design. Two finder windows. Shutter cross-coupled with diaphragm. Schneider Reomar f2.8. Compur Rapid shutter. Not imported into the USA. Not commonly found in the USA. $35-50.

IIA (Type 036) - 1959-60. Non-folding style. "V"-shaped front plate. Built-in meter. No hot shoe. Schneider Reomar f2.8. Prontormat shutter. Not imported into the USA. $35-50.

IIB (Type 031) - 1958-59. Non-folding style. Rectangular faceplate with "V" design. No hot shoe. Built-in meter. Schneider Reomar f2.8. Compur Rapid shutter. Not imported into the USA. $35-55.

SCREEN FOCUS KODAK CAMERA
One of the first cameras to provide for the use of ground glass focus on a rollfilm camera. The rollfilm holder hinges up to allow focusing. Similar to Blair's No. 3 Combination Hawk-Eye and the earlier Focusing Weno Hawk-Eye No. 4.

No. 4 - 1904-10. For 4x5" exposures on No. 123 film, which was introduced for this camera. Various lens/shutter combinations. $250-325.

KODAK SENIOR CAMERAS - 1937-39. Folding bed rollfilm cameras.

Six-16 - 2½x4¼". $15-30.
Six-20 - 2¼x3¼". $15-30.

Signet 30

Signet 80

SIGNET CAMERAS - *A series of cameras with coupled rangefinders for 24x36mm exposures on 35mm film.*
30 - 1957-59. Kodak Ektanar f2.8/44mm lens. Kodak Synchro 250 shutter 4-250. $18-28. *(Illustrated on previous page.)*

35 - 1951-58. Kodak Ektar f3.5/44mm lens. Kodak Synchro 300 shutter. $18-28.

40 - 1956-59. Kodak Ektanon f3.5/46mm lens. Kodak Synchro 400 shutter. $18-28.

50 - 1957-60. Styled like the Signet 30, but with built-in exposure meter. Kodak Ektanar f2.8. Kodak Synchro 250 shutter. Built-in meter. $20-35.

80 - 1958-62. Interchangeable lenses. Behind-the-lens shutter. Built-in meter. $40-55. *(Illustrated on previous page.)*

Signal Corps Model KE-7(1) - A version of the Signet 35, made for the U.S. Army Signal Corps. Olive drab color or U.S.A.F. black anodized model. No serial number on the body. $100-125.

SIX-THREE KODAK CAMERAS 1913-15
A variation of the Folding Pocket Kodak Cameras with f6.3 Cooke Kodak Anastigmat lens in B&L Compound shutter. (The camera itself is identified

as a Folding Pocket Kodak Camera, but the official name is the Six-Three Kodak Camera.)
No. 1A - 2½x4¼" exp. on 116 film. $20-35.
No. 3 - 3¼x4¼" exp. on 118 film. $15-25.

No. 3A - 3¼x5½" exp. on 122 film. $18-25.

KODAK SIX-16 and SIX-20 CAMERAS
1932-34. *Folding bed cameras in black or brown. Enameled art-deco body sides. 616 and 620 films were introduced for these cameras.*

Six-16 - 2½x4¼". $15-25.
Six-20 - 2¼x3¼". $15-25.

KODAK SIX-16 and SIX-20 CAMERAS, IMPROVED MODELS *Folding bed cameras. Similar to the earlier models, but improved design on the bed-support struts, recognizable by black enameling.*

164

Six-16, Improved - 1934-36. 2½x4¼".
$20-30.
Six-20, Improved - 1934-37. 2¼x3¼".
$20-30.
Either size with Compur shutter: $30-50.

SPECIAL KODAK CAMERAS *Earlier than the Kodak Special Six-16 and Six-20 Cameras listed below. These cameras are similar to the Folding Pocket Kodak cameras but with better lenses in B&L Compound shutters. They were discontinued in 1914 when the Autographic feature was introduced, and became Autographic Kodak Special Cameras.*
No. 1A - 1912-14. 2½x4¼". $20-40.
No. 3 - 1911-14. 3¼x4¼". $20-40.

KODAK SPECIAL SIX-16 and SIX-20 CAMERAS - 1937-39. *Folding bed cameras, similar to the Kodak Junior Series III Cameras, but with better lens and shutter.*
Six-16 - 2½x4¼". $15-30.

Six-20 - 2¼x3¼". $15-30.

SPEED KODAK CAMERAS
No. 1A - April 1909-1913. For 2½x4¼" on 116 rollfilmFocal plane shutter to 1000. Kodak Anast. f6.3, Tessar f6.3 or f4.5, and Cooke f5.6 lens available. $175-225. *(Illustrated top of next page.)*

No. 3A - 1910-14. 3¼x5½" (postcard size). $30-50.

No. 4A - 1908-13. For 4¼x6½" exp. on No. 126 rollfilm. (No. 126 rollfilm was made from 1906-1949.) Focal plane shutter to

No. 1A Speed Kodak Camera

1000. f6.3 Dagor, Tessar, or Kodak Anastigmat or f6.5 Cooke lens. $300-325.

KODAK STARTECH CAMERA - c1959. Special purpose camera for close-up medical and dental photography. Body style similar to the Brownie Starflash. 1⅝x1⅝" exp. on 127 film. Full kit with flash shield, 2 close-up lenses, original box: $40-50. Camera only: $10-20.

STEREO KODAK CAMERAS *See also Brownie Stereo and Hawk-Eye Stereo in the Eastman section.*

Kodak Stereo Camera (35mm) - 1954-

1959. For pairs of 24x24mm exposures on standard 35mm cartridge film. Kodak Anaston f3.5/35mm lenses. Kodak Flash 200 shutter 25-200. Common. Sometimes seen at higher asking prices, but easy to find for: $70-100.

Stereo Kodak Model 1 Camera - 1917-1925. Folding camera for 3⅛x3-3/16" pairs on No. 101 rollfilm. Kodak Anast. f7.7/5¼" lens. Earliest version has Stereo Automatic shutter, later with Stereo Ball Bearing shutter. $250-300.

No. 2 Stereo Kodak Camera - 1901-05. Kodak's only stereo box camera. 3½x6" stereo exposures on No. 101 rollfilm. Rapid Rectilinear f14/125mm lens. $300-350.

Kodak Stereo Viewers:
Model I - Single lenses. $30-40.
Model II - Doublet lenses. AC/DC model: $75-85. DC only: $60-70.

STERLING II - c1955-60. Made by Kodak Ltd. in London. Folding camera with Anaston f4.5/105mm lens in Pronto 25-200 shutter. $10-20.

KODAK STYLELITE POCKET CAMERA - c1979. 13x17mm exposures on 110 cartridge film. Similar to the Pocket Instamatic Cameras, but longer body holds built-in electronic flash. Made for premium use. $4-8

SUPER KODAK SIX-20 - 1938-44. The first camera with coupled electric-eye for automatic exposure setting. Takes 2¼x3¼" exposures on 620 film. Kodak Anastigmat Special f3.5 lens. Built-in 8 speed shutter. $700-1000.

KODAK SUPREMA CAMERA - 1938-39. 2¼X2¼" exp. on 620 rollfilm. Schneider Xenar f3.5/80mm lens in Compur Rapid 1-400 shutter. Once considered rare, but quite a few have surfaced since the price jumped to $300-400.

KODAK TELE-EKTRA 1 & 2 CAMERAS TELE-INSTAMATIC CAMERAS TRIMLITE INSTAMATIC CAMERAS - Late 1970's cameras for 13x17mm

exposures on 110 cartridge film. Similar to the Pocket Instamatic Cameras. Too new to establish a "collectible" value. Very common. $1-5.

TOURIST CAMERAS

Kodak Tourist Camera - 1948-1951. Folding camera for 2¼x3¼" on 620 film. With Kodak Anastar f4.5 in Synchro-Rapid 800: $40-60. With Kodak Anaston f4.5, f6.3, f8.8 or Kodet f12.5 lenses: $8-15.

Kodak Tourist II Camera - 1951-58. With Kodak Anastar f4.5 in Synchro-Rapid 800: $30-50. Low priced models: $8-15.

VANITY KODAK CAMERA - 1928-33. A Vest Pocket Kodak Series III Camera in color: blue, brown, green, grey, and red, with matching colored bellows. 4.5x6cm exposures on 127 rollfilm. Camera only: $50-80. With matching satin-lined case: $100-175. *The original colored bellows were fragile and many were replaced with more durable black bellows, which reduce the collector value of the camera by 30-50%.*

Vanity Kodak Model B Camera from the Vanity Kodak Ensemble

VANITY KODAK ENSEMBLE - 1928-29. "Vanity Kodak Model B" on shutter face. A Vest Pocket Kodak Model B Camera in grey, green, or beige. With lipstick, mirror, compact, and change pocket. $350-400.

Vest Pocket Kodak Camera

VEST POCKET KODAK CAMERAS
For 4.5x6cm exposures on 127 rollfilm.
Vest Pocket Kodak Camera - 1912-14. Trellis struts. No bed. Meniscus Achromatic lens is most common. f6.9 is uncommon, but the least common is the Kodak Anastigmat f8 lens introduced in the Fall of 1913 with the Gift Case. Kodak Ball Bearing shutter. $15-25. *(Illustrated bottom of previous column.)*

Vest Pocket Autographic Kodak Camera - 1915-26. Trellis struts. No bed. Similar to the Vest Pocket Kodak Camera, but with the Autographic feature. Meniscus Achromatic, Rapid Rectilinear or Kodak Anastigmat f7.7 fixed focus lens. Kodak Ball Bearing shutter. Common. $15-25.

Vest Pocket Autographic Kodak Special Camera - 1915-26. Like the regular model, but with Persian morocco covering and various focusing and fixed focus lenses. $25-35.

Vest Pocket Kodak Model B Camera - 1925-34. Folding bed camera (with autographic feature until about 1930). Rotary V.P. shutter. $20-40.

Vest Pocket Kodak Series III Camera - 1926-33. Folding bed camera with autographic feature. Diomatic or Kodex shutter. f6.3 or f5.6 Kodak Anastigmat lens, or f7.9 Kodar. $20-30. *Colored models: see Vanity Kodak Camera, above. (Illustrated on next page.)*

Vest Pocket Kodak Special Camera (early type) - 1912-14. Trellis struts. No bed. Like the Vest Pocket Kodak Camera, but with Zeiss Kodak Anastigmat f6.9 lens. $40-60.

Vest Pocket Kodak Special Camera (later type) - 1926-35. Folding bed camera with autographic feature. Same as the Series III, but better lens: f5.6 or f4.5 Kodak Anastigmat. $40-60.

Vest Pocket Kodak Series III Camera

VIGILANT CAMERAS *Folding rollfilm cameras with folding optical finders and body release. Lenses available were Kodak Anastigmat f8.8, f6.3, f4.5, and Kodak Anastigmat Special f4.5 lens. The Vigilant Cameras were a less expensive alternative to the Monitor Cameras.*

Six-16 - 1939-48. 2½x4¼" on 616 film. $15-25.

VIEW CAMERAS - *Because of the many uses of view cameras, there are really no standard lens/shutter combinations, and because they are as much a part of the general used camera market as they are "collectible", they are listed here as good second-hand cameras, the main value being their lenses. Prices given here are for cameras in Very Good condition, no lens.*
5x7" - $80-150.
6½x8½" - $50-100.
8x10" - Have increased in value in recent years. The very common model 2D is inexpensive when compared with current model 8x10 cameras, and for many purposes will perform as well. $200-275.

Six-20 - 1939-49. 2¼x3¼" on 620 film. $12-20.

VIGILANT JUNIOR CAMERAS
Folding bed rollfilm cameras similar in style to the Vigilant Cameras. Non-optical folding frame finder. No body release. Kodet or Bimat lens.

Six-16 - 1940-48. 2½x4¼" on 616 film. $12-18.

169

KODAK WINNER POCKET CAMERA - 1979-. Premium version of the Trimlite Instamatic 18 Camera. Brown and tan in color. 13x17mm exp. on 110 cartridge film. $5-10.

Six-20 - 1940-49. 2¼x3¼" on 620 film. $10-15.

VOLLENDA CAMERAS
Mfd. by Kodak A.G., formerly Nagel-Werk, in Stuttgart, Germany. See also NAGEL-WERK for earlier models.

KODAK WORLD'S FAIR FLASH CAMERA 1964-1965 - Sold only at the 1964 New York World's Fair. 1⅝x1⅝" exposures in 127 film. Body design very similar to the Hawkeye Flashfun, but has a rigid awning over the lens. (The original box, shaped like the pentagonal Kodak pavillion, doubles the value of this camera.) Camera only: $5-10.

ZENITH KODAK CAMERAS - 1898-99. Rare box cameras made in two sizes: No. 3 for 3¼x4¼" and No. 4 for 4x5" plates. Except for the name, they are identical to the Eureka cameras of the same period. They accept standard plateholders through a side-opening door, and allow room for storage of extra holders. Made in England. Not often found. $100-150.

3x4cm size - 1932-37. Folding bed camera with self-erecting strut-supported lensboard. Radionar f3.5 or f4.5 lens. $35-60.

620 - Two different cameras: vertical style for 6x9cm, 1934-39; and horizontal style for 6x6cm, 1940-41. $18-33.

Junior 616 - 1934-37. Vertical style. 6.5x11cm. $20-35.

Junior 620 - 1933-37. Vertical style. 6x9cm. $20-35.

EBNER, Albert & Co. (Stuttgart)

Ebner, 4.5x6cm - c1934-35. Horizontally styled version of the streamlined brown bakelite camera. Meyer Goerlitz Trioplan f4.5/7.5cm, Compur T,B, 1-300. Front-element focus. Unusual parallelogram folding frame finder. $100-150.

black, but also available in green, red, and walnut. $1-5.

EDER PATENT CAMERA - c1933. Unusual German horizontal twin-lens (non-reflex) camera for plates or rollfilm in sizes 4.5x6cm, 6x6cm, and 6x9cm. Resembles a folding-bed stereo camera, but one lens makes the exposure while the other is simply a viewing lens. Tessar or Xenar f4.5 taking lens, Edar Anastigmat f4.5 viewing lens. Compur shutter to 300. Rare. Estimate: $750-1000.

Ebner, 6x9cm - c1934-35. Folding camera for 8 exp. on 120 film. Streamlined bakelite body. Tessar f4.5/105mm, Radionar f4.5, or Xenar f4.5 lens. Rim-set Compur shutter 1-250. Very similar to the Pontiac, Gallus, and Nagel Regent cameras of the same vintage. $100-150.

ECLAIR - c1900. 13x18cm wooden field camera with brass trim. Tapered green bellows with black corners. Euryscop Extra Rapide Series III brass barrel lens. $125-175.

EDBAR INTERNATIONAL CORP. (Peekskill, NY)
V.P. Twin - c1939. Small plastic novelty camera for 3x4cm on 127 film. Made in England for Edbar. Most common in

EHIRA K.S.K. (Ehira Camera Works, Japan)
Astoria Super-6 IIIB - c1950. 6x6cm on 120 rollfilm. Super Ikonta B copy. Lausar f3.5/85; shutter 1-400,B. CRF. $150-175.

Ehira-Six - c1948-55. Copy of the Zeiss Super Ikonta B, complete with rotating wedge rangefinder. Tomioka f3.5/85mm lens in Ehira Rapid shutter B,1-400. $75-100.

Weha Chrome Six (also Ehira Chrome Six) - c1937. A modified version of the Ehira Six design, using a telescoping tube front rather than the bed and bellows design. It retains the Ikonta-type rangefinder. $100-125.

EHO-ALTISSA (Dresden) *Founded by Emil Hofert as Eho Kamerafabrik (c1933?). The first Altiflex cameras were introduced c1937, named for Berthold Altmann. The company name changed to Amca-Camera-Werk in 1940, and after the war became VEB Altissa-Camera-Werk.*

Altiflex - c1937-49. 6x6cm TLR for 120 films. f4.5/75mm Ludwig Victar, f4.5 or 3.5 Rodenstock Trinar, or f2.8 Laack Pololyt lenses. Prontor or Compur shutter. $25-35.

Altissa II

Altiscop - c1937-42. Stereo camera for six pairs of 6x6cm exposures on 120 rollfilm. Ludwig Victar f4.5/75mm lenses. Vario-type shutter 25,50,100,B,T. Original price in 1942: $60. Current value: $75-85.

Altissa - c1938. Pseudo-TLR box camera for 12 exposures on 120 film. The finder on this model is like many of the cheap TLR cameras - just an oversized brilliant finder (not coupled to focusing mechanism). Hinged viewing hood. Rodenstock Periscop f6 lens. Simple shutter. Black hammertone finish. $15-30.

Altissa II - c1938. Similar to the Altissa described above, but with unusual viewfinder which can be changed from eye-level to waist-level viewing. Trinar Anastigmat f3.5/75mm in Compur 1-30. Originally sold for $25 but closed out in 1939 by Central Camera Co. for $14.75. Uncommon. $35-50. *(Illustrated bottom of previous column.)*

Altix, I,II,IV - c1955. Low-priced 35mm camera. Body release, viewfinder, advance & rewind knobs all above the top plate. Synchronized. Meritar or Trioplan f2.9 lens. (Original price $20). $15-25.

Altix-N - c1959. Improved version of the Altix, with top housing incorporating the viewfinder. Interchangeable Trioplan f2.9/50mm lens. Lever film advance. Accessory shoe. $15-30.

Altix NB - c1960. Similar to N, but with built-in meter. $15-30.

Eho box, 3x4cm - c1932. For 16 exposures on 127 film. (Nicknamed "Baby Box" in this small size, although we have no evidence that it was ever called by that name except by collectors.) f11/50mm Duplar lens. Simple shutter, B & I. Metal body. Rarest of the Eho boxes. $50-75.

Eho box, 4.5x6cm - For 16 exposures on 120 film. $25-40.

Eho box, 6x9cm - c1930's. Rodenstock Periscop or Duplar f11 lens. Simple box shutter. With green leather covering: $25-35. Black: $15-25.

Eho Stereo Box camera - c1930's. For 5 stereo pairs 6x13cm or 10 single 6x6cm exp. on 120. B,I shutter. Duplar f11/80mm lens. $70-95.

Juwel - Box camera for 6x6cm on 120. Eye-level finder in roof-shaped housing on top of body. Appears to be simply a name variation of the eye-level Altissa "Brillant" camera. $15-20.

Mantel-Box 2 - c1930's. Small metal box camera with leatherette covering. Takes 4.5x6cm exposures. Duplar f11 lens. "Mantel-Box 2" on front under lens. Rare. $75-100.

EIKO CO. LTD (Taiwan)

Can Cameras - c1977-83. Modeled after the original 250ml Coke Can Camera from Japan, these cameras are all shaped like a 250ml beverage can, but with different product labels: Budweiser, 7-up, Coca-Cola, Mickey Mouse, Pepsi-Cola, Snoopy. $15-35.

Elgin

E.L.C. (Paris)
l'As - c1912. Folding 4.5x6cm plate camera with cross-swinging struts. Rotary disk stops in front of simple shutter. The name means "Ace". $150-200.

ELECTRONIC - Japanese subminiature of the Hit type. $10-15.

ELGIN LABORATORIES
Elgin - Unusual eye-level camera for 828 film. Stainless steel body with leatherette covering. $30-40. *(Illustrated bottom of previous column.)*

Elgin Miniature - Plastic minicam for 3x4cm on 127 film. $3-7.

ELITE - Japanese novelty subminiature of Hit type. $8-12.

ELLISON KAMRA COMPANY
(Los Angeles, CA) *Michael Ellison and Edward S. McAuliffe filed for a patent in 1926 for a novel two-blade shutter, which was used in the Ellison Kamra and later in the similar, but smaller and more common QRS Kamra.*

Ellison Kamra - c1928. A long brick-shaped black bakelite camera for bulk loads of 35mm film in special cassettes. Similar in styling to the later QRS Kamra, but with a hinged bakelite door which covers the simple fixed-focus lens. The film crank, which also serves as a shutter release, is usually not broken on the Ellison model although rarely found intact on the later QRS model. $100-125.

ELMO CO. LTD. *(Originally founded by Mr. H. Sakaki in 1921 as Sakaki Shokai Co.) Although more widely recognized for their movie equipment, there were several still cameras as well.*
Elmoflex - Twin lens reflex cameras, made in several variations from the first model of 1938 through the last one introduced in 1955. f3.5/75mm lens. 6x6cm on 120 rollfilm. $35-50.

ELOP KAMERAWERK (Flensburg, Germany) *Also associated with the Uca Werkstatten of Flensburg. Makers of ELCA cameras. ELCA = ELop CAmera.*

Elca, Elca II - c1948-51. 35mm camera with Elocar f4.5/35mm lens. Elca has single speed shutter, while Elca II has Prontor S or Vario. Takes 50 exp. 24x24mm on standard 35mm cassette. Black painted and nickeled metal body. Model I: $55-80. Model II, less common: $75-100.

EMMERLING & RICHTER (Berlin)
Field Camera - for 13x18cm plates. Wooden body. Nickel trim. Without lens: $75-125.

EMPIRE 120 - All metal box camera for 6x9cm. $4-8.

EMPIRE-BABY - Black plastic novelty camera for 16 exp. on 127. Made in Macao. $5-10.

EMPIRE SCOUT - Inexpensive eye-level camera from Hong Kong for 6x6cm on 120 film. Simple focusing lens; three stops. B & I shutter. $1-5.

EMSON - Japanese novelty camera of Hit type. 14x14mm exposures on 16mm paper backed rollfilm. $10-15.

ENCORE CAMERA CO. (Hollywood, CA)

Encore De Luxe Camera - c1940's-50's. An inexpensive cardboard novelty camera. Factory loaded. User returns complete camera & film to factory with $1.00 for processing. (Vaguely reminiscent of the "You push the button...." idea which made Eastman rich and famous, but the audience didn't want an Encore.) $15-20.

Hollywood Camera - Another novelty mail-in camera, sometimes used as an advertising premium. $15-20.

ENJALBERT (E. Enjalbert, Paris) Colis Postal - c1886. An unusual detective camera consisting of the Alpinist folding camera tied with a cord. The package even included a mailing label to complete the disguise. Extremely rare. No known sales. Estimated value: $5000+.

Photo Revolver de Poche - c1883. Highly unusual camera which very closely resembles a pistol. The cylinder contained a magazine mechanism for 10 plates, each 16x16mm. This camera is extremely rare and highly desirable. It is certainly a "world class" collectible, and price would be negotiable. Estimate: $10,000-20,000.

ENSIGN LTD. *The successor company to Houghton-Butcher. For sake of continuity, we have listed all Ensign cameras under the Houghton heading.*

ENTERPRISE CAMERA & OPTICAL CO. Little Wonder - c1900. Not related to the 1930's metal Little Wonder camera. Miniature box camera for 2x2" plates. Made of two cardboard boxes sliding into one another. Almost identical to the Yale and Zar cameras. $60-90.

Little Wonder (compliments the Boston) - ca. late 1890's. A rare variation of the Little Wonder camera, this special promotional edition was gold-stamped on the back: "Compliments The Boston, St. Paul Minn." Takes 5x5cm plates, and came originally with chemistry and paper for making prints. $75-125.

ENTERPRISE REPEATING CAMERA - c1900. A very unusual box camera which employs a rotating drum to hold and position five glass plates, 6.5cm square. There were several other cameras which used the same system, but apparently none ever gained much support, since any camera using this method for changing plates is quite rare. Similar in function, though not in appearance are the Mephisto, the Photo-Quint and a rare Ernemann Bob, all from about 1899-1900. $150-200. *(Illustrated top of next page.)*

Enterprise Repeating Camera

E.R.A.C. SELLING CO. LTD. (London)

Erac Pistol Camera - c1938. An unusual disguised subminiature. The outer bakelite shell is shaped like a pistol, complete with trigger. Inside is a small cast metal "Merlin" camera that is coupled to the trigger, which takes the picture and winds the film. Meniscus f16 lens in single speed shutter. A few years ago, a few sold for $300-475, but that price brought them out of the woodwork, and now they are settling in at $100-200.

ERKO FOTOWERKE (Freital, Germany)
Erko - 9x12cm folding plate camera. Wood body covered with black leather. Erko Spezial Anastigmat f8 or Erko Fixar f6.8/135mm lens. Ibso shutter, T, B, 1-150. $35-45.

ERNEMANN (Heinrich Ernemann Werke Aktien Gesellschaft, Dresden, Germany) *Founded 1889 by Heinrich Ernemann. Became Heinrich Ernemann AG in 1898. Purchased the Herbst & Firl Co. of Goerlitz in 1900. Merged with Contessa-Nettel, Goerz, Ica, and Carl Zeiss Optical Co. to form Zeiss-Ikon in 1926. Some Ernemann cameras continued under the Zeiss-Ikon name.*

Bob Cameras (c1910-1920's) *Early English-language advertisments called these cameras "Ernemann's Roll Film Cameras" before the name "Bob" was used. All are folding bed style rollfilm cameras with rounded body ends. Frequently the model name is on the bed or near the handle.*

Bob 00 - c1924-25. For 6x9cm on 120 film, or single metal plateholders. Aplanat or Anastigmat f6.8 lens. $20-35.

Bob O - c1913. Folding camera for ¼-plates or rollfilm. Ernemann Rapid Detective or Detective Aplanat lens in Auto shutter. $25-35.

Bob I - c1913. Folding rollfilm or plate camera. 8x10.5cm (¼-plate) or postcard sizes. Single extension, rack & pinion focus. Aplanat f6.8 or Double Anastigmat f6. Bob, Automatic, or Auto Sector shutters. $25-35.

Bob II - c1913. 8x10.5cm or postcard size. Very similar to the Bob I, but with double extension bellows, focus scales for complete lens or rear element only. $25-35.

Bob III (horizontal style) - c1906. Early, horizontal folding bed camera for 10x15cm on rollfilm, or 9x12cm plates. Leather covered wood body. Double extension wine red bellows. Detective Aplanat f6.8 or Roja Busch Aplanat f8 in Bob shutter. Two variations of this camera sold at Cornwall's Auction in 1985-86 for $185-200.

Bob III (vertical style) - c1926. 6x9cm folding bed rollfilm camera. Aluminum body, rigid U-shaped front. Chronos shutter. $20-30.

Bob IV - c1926. Similar to Bob III, but with radial focusing and rising front. $25-35.

Bob V - c1924-26. 4x6.5 cm, 6x6cm,

6x9cm, 6.5x11cm, 7.25x12.5cm, and 8x10.5cm sizes. Radial lever focusing. 4x6.5cm: $75-125. Larger sizes: $30-45.

Bob V (stereo) - c1911. Folding bed stereo camera for 45x107mm on No. 0 rollfilm. $175-250.

Bob X - 45x107mm stereo version. $175-250.

Bob XV - c1912-14. Folding rollfilm cameras in 4x6.5cm, 6x9cm, and 8x10.5cm sizes. The larger model also takes 9x12cm plates. $30-45.

Bob XV Stereo - c1913-14. Stereo model for 45x107mm on rollfilm. Folding bed style with self-erecting front. $175-250.

Bobette I - c1925. Folding camera for 22x33mm format on 35mm paper-backed rollfilm. This is a strut folding type without bed. Ernoplast f4.5 lens. $150-250.

Bobette II - Similar to Bobette I, but with folding bed construction and radial lever focusing. Ernoplast f4.5, Ernon f3.5, or Ernostar f2 lens in Chronos shutter. With Ernostar (The first miniature camera with f2 lens): $300-500. With Ernoplast or Ernon: $100-150.

Combined ¼-plate, Postcard, Stereo, Plate & Rollfilm Camera - c1907. That is actually the name it was called in the

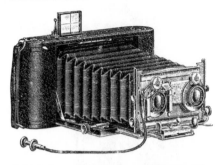

British Journal Almanac advertisment for 1907. Horizontally styled folding bed camera for 3¼x4¼" rollfilm or 3½x5½" plates. Probably a predecessor of the Stereo Bob. Shifting front allows use of both lenses for stereo or one lens for single photos. Triple extension with rack focusing. $225-300.

Combined Postcard and Stereo, Model VI - see Heag VI Zwei-Verschluss-Camera

Combined Stereo and Half-Plate Focal-Plane Camera - see Heag IX.

Double Shutter Camera - see Heag VI Zwei-Verschluss-Camera.

-6.5x9cm size. - Ernostar f1.8 lens. $600-1000.

-9x12cm size. - Ernostar f1.8/165mm lens. FP shutter 1/15-1/1500. Rare. Only one confirmed sale in October 1984 at about $3000.

Ermanox Reflex - c1926. SLR for 4.5x6cm plates. Ernostar f1.8/105mm lens in helical focusing mount. $600-1000. (One passed at auction in late 1985 with high bid of $550 against a $1000 reserve.)

Erni - c1924. Simple box camera for plates. Folding frame finder. T&I shutter. Achromatic lens. Rare in any size. 4.5x6cm: $175-225. 6.5x9cm or 9x12cm: $160-185. Stereo 45x107mm: $175-225.

Ernoflex Folding Reflex: *Originally called "Folding Reflex" and later "Ernoflex Folding Reflex" in English-language catalogs and ads. Called Klapp-Reflex in German. Five basic types: Original type, Model I (single extension), Model II (triple extension), Miniature Ernoflex, and Stereo Ernoflex. (The latter two are listed under "Miniature" and "Stereo".)*

Ermanox - 4.5x6cm rigid-bodied model, c1924. Originally introduced as the "Ernox". Metal body covered with black leather. Focal plane shutter, 20-1000. Many were apparently supplied after the Zeiss merger with an Albada finder bearing Zeiss-Ikon identification. Ernostar f2/100mm (rarer and earlier) or f1.8/85mm lens. $800-1200.

Ermanox (collapsible bellows model) - c1926-1929. Strut-folding "klapp" type camera.

177

Ernoflex Folding Reflex Model II

(Ernoflex) Folding Reflex, original type - c1914. Folding SLR with drop bed and rack focus. Made in ¼-plate size only. Single or double extension models. Ernemann f6.8 or Zeiss Tessar f4.5 lens. $175-250.

Film K - c1917-24. *Leather covered wood box camera. Meniscus f12.5 lens in T&I shutter.*
6x6cm size - The rarest Ernemann box camera. $75-100.
6x9cm size - The most common size. $20-40.

Ernoflex Folding Reflex Model I - c1924-1926. Unlike the original version, this model has no bed, but scissor-struts to support the front, and helical focus mount for the lens. Single extension only. 6.5x9cm, 3¼x4¼", or 9x12cm sizes. Ernotar f4.5, Ernon f3.5, or Zeiss Tessar f4.5. $200-300.

Ernoflex Folding Reflex Model II - c1924-26. Triple extension. An intermediate front is supported by trellis struts and moves to infinity position upon opening the camera. For additional extension, a front bed with a double extension rack extends beyond the intermediate front. This allows for extreme close-ups with the normal lens, or long focal length lenses may be used for telephoto work. Quarter plate or 9x12cm size. $300-400. *(Illustrated top of next column.)*

6.5x11cm, 7.25x12.5cm sizes - $30-45.

Film U - c1925. Box camera for 6x9cm on rollfilm. More compact than the 6x9cm Film K, because it has a collapsing front. Folding frame finder. Doublet lens in automatic shutter. $40-60.

Folding Reflex: see Ernoflex Folding Reflex.

Globus - c1900. 13x18cm folding camera. Double extension bellows. Focal plane shutter. Goerz Double Anastigmat f4.6 brass-barreled lens. Polished wood body with brass trim. $350-550. *(Illustrated top next page.)*

Ernemann Globus

Heag I

Heag *An acronym for Heinrich Ernemann Aktien Gesellschaft. Used mainly to identify a series of folding bed plate cameras. English-language advertising did not always use the name "Heag", but usually the model number was used.*
Heag 0 - c1918. 6.5x9cm and 9x12cm plate cameras. Single extension. $25-35.

Heag 00 - c1914. A cheap single

extension model in 6.5x9cm and ¼-plate sizes. T,B,I shutter. $30-40.

Heag I - c1914. Folding-bed camera in 6.5x9cm, ¼-plate, postcard, or ½-plate sizes. Single extension. Black imitation leathered body. Detective Aplanat f6.8. Ernemann Automat shutter. $25-40. *(Illustrated in previous column.)*

Heag I Stereo - c1904. Folding bed stereo camera for 9x12cm plates. Leather covered wood body. Red tapered double-extension bellows. Detective Aplanat f6.8 lenses. Ernemann Automat shutter ½-100. $225-275.

Heag II - c1911-1926. Similar to Heag I, but with rack focusing, genuine rather than imitation leather. 6.5x9cm, ¼-plate, postcard, and ½-plate sizes.
Model I (single extension) and Model II (double extension). Aplanat f6.8 lens. $30-50.

Heag III - c1926. All metal body. U-shaped front standard. Single extension. 6.5x9cm or 9x12cm sizes. $25-40.

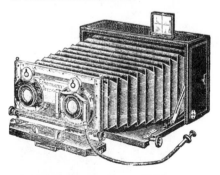

Heag IV (stereo) - c1907. Folding bed camera for stereo photos on plates. Double extension, rack focusing. Ernemann Aplanat or Anastigmat f6.8. $175-225.

Heag V - intro. 1924. A single extension camera like the Heag III, but with radial lever focus, micrometer rising front. $25-35.

Heag VI (Zwei-Verschluss-Camera) - c1907. Leather covered folding bed plate camera in 3¼x4¼" or 3½x5½" size. Focal plane shutter to 1/2000. Inter-lens shutter T,B,1-100. Double extension, rack focusing. English ads often call it "Double Shutter Camera" and German ads call it "Zwei-Verschluss-Camera" with neither mentioning the "Heag" name, but Ernemann catalogs use the Heag VI name and "Zwei-Verschluss-Camera" as a sub-heading. $150-250. (See "Tropical" for teak version of this camera).

Heag VI (Zwei-Verschluss-Camera)

(stereo) - c1907. This is a stereo version of the "Double Shutter Camera Model VI", available in postcard or ½-plate sizes. Focal plane and front shutters. English-language advertising called it the "Combined Postcard and Stereo, Model VI". $300-400.

Heag VII - intro. 1924. Similar to the Heag V, but also includes double extension with rack focusing. 6.5x9cm, or 9x12cm sizes. Vilar f6.8, Ernotar f4.5, or Tessar f4.5. Chronos shutter. $30-40.

Heag IX Universal Camera - c1904-07. An interesting design for a dual-purpose strut camera. The basic design is for a stereo lensboard. To use for single photos, a separate lensboard with its own bellows & struts allows the extra extension needed for the longer focus of the single lens. In English-language ads, this was called "Combined Stereo and Half-Plate Focal-Plane Camera". With stereo or extensible lensboard: $225-275.
With both lensboards: $400-450. *(Single lens version illustrated on next page.)*

Heag IX Universal Camera, with single lens

Heag XI - c1913-26. Leathered wood body and aluminum bed. DEB. R&P focus. Rise, fall, cross front. Swing back. Focusing scales for complete lens or rear element. Anastigmat f6.8 or f6, Aplanat f6.8. ½-plate or postcard sizes. $30-50. (See "Tropical Heag XI" for teakwood model).

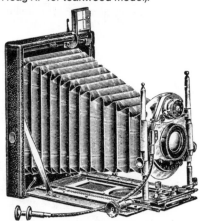

Heag XII - c1906-1913. ¼-plate or ½-plate sizes. $35-50.

Heag XII Model III (stereo) - c1925. Folding bed stereo/panorama camera for 9x18cm plates. Double extension with rack focusing. Micrometer rise, fall, cross front. $150-200.

Heag XIV - c1910. *Folding two-shutter cameras. Pneumatic front shutter plus FP 50-2500.*
-- 4.5x6 cm. - Ernemann Doppel Anastigmat f6/80mm. Front shutter 1-100. $100-150.
--9x12cm - Ernon f6.8/120mm. $75-125.

Heag XV (4.5x6cm plate) - c1911-14. Vertical format self-erecting folding plate camera, 4.5x6cm "vest pocket" size. Early variations have two rigid reflex finders on the front of the bed. Later models have a single folding finder. Both of these types exist in focusing and fixed focus versions. Ernemann Double Anastigmat f6.8/80mm in Automat shutter 1-100. $75-125.

Heag XV (6.5x9cm plate) - c1912. Rarer in this size. Like the 4.5x6cm model with reversible folding finder. Radial lever focusing. Ernemann Detective Aplanat #00 f6.8 lens. Automat shutter 1-100. $60-70.

Heag XV (rollfilm type) - c1914. Self-erecting rollfilm camera, similar to the Heag XV plate model above, but taller body with rounded ends for rollfilms. Aplanat f6 in Auto 3-speed, T,B shutter. $30-50.

Heag XVI - c1913. Folding camera with detachable rollfilm back for use with 9x12cm plates. Ernemann Detectiv Aplanat f6.8. $150-175.

Heag (tropical model) - listed with "Tropical" cameras, later in this heading.

"Klapp" cameras - *The word "klapp" indicates a folding camera, and came to be used primarily for folding cameras of the strut type. In the case of Ernemann, it was used for their strut-folding plate cameras with focal plane shutters. In English language advertising, these were usually called "Focal Plane Cameras". These cameras were also available in tropical models.*

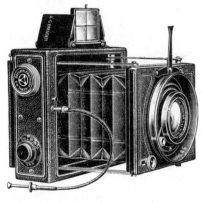

Klapp - c1905-1926. Strut-folding focal plane cameras in 6.5x9cm, 3¼x4¼" or 9x12cm, 3½x5½" or 10x15cm, 4x5", and 12x16.5cm sizes. Early models had single-pleat bellows, unprotected Newton finder, and more complex shutter controls on two metal plates on side. Later models had normal pleated bellows, Newton finder with protective clamshell cover, and two round shutter knobs on side. Ernostar f2.7, Ernotar f4.5, Tessar f4.5, or Ernon f3.5 lenses. $100-200.

Liliput - c1914-26. Economy model 4.5x6cm or 6.5x9cm folding bellows vest pocket camera. Fixed-focus achromatic lens and T, I shutter. Folding frame finder. 4.5x6cm: $90-140. 6.5x9cm: $45-65.

Liliput Stereo - c1919-25. Stereo version of the compact folding Liliput camera for 45x107mm. Meniscus lens. Guillotine shutter. $125-200.

Magazine Box - Drop-plate box camera for twelve 3¼x4¼" plates. $150-175.

Mignon-Kamera - c1912-19. 4.5x6cm compact folding camera with cross-swing struts. Usually with Detectiv Aplanat f6.8. Z,M shutter. $100-135.

Miniature Ernoflex 4.5x6cm (formerly "Folding Reflex") or Miniature Klapp-Reflex - c1925. Strut-type folding reflex for 4.5x6cm plates. Ernon f3.5/75 or Tessar f4.5/80mm lens. Focal plane shutter to 1000. One of the smallest folding SLR cameras ever made. $600-1000.

Miniature Klapp (4.5x6cm) - c1925. Body style like the later "Klapp" style above, but also with front bed/door. Ernostar f2.7/75mm, Tessar f3.5, Ernotar f4.5, or Ernon f3.5. Focal plane shutter to 1000. $200-300. *(Illustrated top of next page.)*

Miniature Klapp

Reflex - c1914. Non-folding (Graflex-style) SLR with tall focus hood and flap over lens. Reversing back. FP shutter to 1/2500, T. Removable lensboard with rise and fall.

Rolf I

Double extension, rack & pinion focus. 6.5x9cm, 3¼x4¼", 4¼x6½" sizes. Ernemann f6.8 Double Anastigmat or Zeiss Tessar f4.5. $150-200.

Rolf I - c1924-25. Folding vest pocket camera for 127 film. Leatherette covered body. Rapid Rectilinear f12/75mm lens. T,B,I shutter. $30-40. *(Illustrated bottom of previous column.)*

Rolf II - c1926. Similar to Rolf I, but with genuine leather covering, Chronos precision shutter, Ernemann Double Anastigmat f6.8 or Ernoplast f4.5. $30-40.

Simplex Ernoflex - c1926. Simple box-form SLR. No bellows. Helical focusing lens mount. FP shutter with 16 speeds 1/20-1/1000 sec. Cover for folding hood has front hinge on some models and rear hinge on others. 4.5x6cm size: $300-400. 6.5x9cm or 9x12cm size: $125-175.

Stereo Bob - see Bob above.

Stereo Ernoflex - c1926. A stereo version of the Miniature Ernoflex camera for

45x107mm. Scissor-struts support lensboard. Full width top door, but focus hood on one side only. FP shutter 1/10-1000. Ernotar f4.5, Ernon f3.5, or Tessar f4.5 lenses. $800-1000.

Stereo Reflex - c1913. Rigid body jumelle form stereo camera with reflex viewing. Full width viewing hood. FP to 2500, T. Ernemann Anastigmat f6 or f6.8, Zeiss Tessar f6.3 or f4.5,or Goerz Dagor f6.8 lenses. $300-500.

Stereoscop-Camera

Prices increased rapidly a few years ago, and are now holding steady. There is quite a difference in price between the focal plane shutter models and inter-lens shutter types.

Stereo Simplex - c1920. Non-collapsing, "jumelle" style stereo camera for 45x107mm plates. This is not a reflex model, but has only a wire frame finder. Ernemann Doppel lens f11/60. Guillotine shutter, T, B, I. $75-125.

Tropical Heag VI (Zwei-Verschluss-Camera) - c1914. Horizontally styled ¼-plate folding bed camera of teak with brass fittings. Triple extension, removable lensboard. FP shutter to 1/2500. Front shutter T,B,½-100. Ernemann Anastigmat f6 or Zeiss Tessar. $800-1000.

Stereo Simplex Ernoflex - c1926. Simple reflex stereo box camera. No bellows. Ground glass focus on both sides, but reflex focus on one side only. Ernon f3.5/75mm lenses in externally coupled helical mounts. FP shutter 25-1000. $400-600.

Stereoscop-Camera - c1901. Stereo box camera for 9x18cm stereo pairs. Fixed focus meniscus lenses. B&I shutter. $200-300. *(Illustrated top of next column.)*

Tropical cameras - *All tropical cameras, including Ernemann, are relatively uncommon.*

Tropical Heag XI - c1920-30. (Zeiss-Ikon after 1926.) Vertically styled 9x12cm folding bed camera. (NOT focal plane type.) Teak body, brown double extension bellows, brass fittings. Ernemann Vilar f6.8/135mm, Ernar f6.8, Ernoplast f4.5, or Ernotar f4.5 lens in Chronos B shutter to 100 or Chronos C shutter 1-300. $550-800.

Tropical Klapp - Strut-folding focal plane camera. Same features as normal "Klapp" camera, but polished teak body with lacquered brass trim. $700-950.

Unette - c1924-29. Miniature box camera for 22x33mm exposures on rollfilm. Overall size: 3x3½x2¼". Two speed (T&I) shutter. f12.5 meniscus lens. Revolving stops. $125-175.

Union - c1907. Folding-bed plate camera. Leather covered wood body. Wine red single extension bellows. Large Newton viewfinder. Meyer Anastigmat f7.2/135mm. Ernemann ½-100 shutter. $75-90.

Union Zwei-Verschluss - c1911. Folding bed plate camera, 9x12cm. Leather covered wood body. Double extension wine red bellows. Focal plane shutter 1/50-2500. Meyer Aristostigmat f6.8/120mm in Ernemann ½-100 front shutter. $150-175.

Universal - c1900. 13x18cm double extension folding plate camera. Polished wood body, brass trim. Goerz Double

Velo Klapp

Anastigmat f4.6 brass-barreled lens. Focal plane shutter. $350-550.

Velo Klapp - c1907-14. A low-priced focal plane camera with speeds to 1/2000 (later models 1/2500), but without time exposure capability. Aplanat f6.8 lens. $100-150. *(Illustrated bottom of previous column.)*

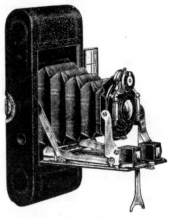

Vest Pocket Focal Plane Camera - c1911. This is a double shutter folding bed rollfilm camera with rounded body ends. The body of the camera is identical in appearance to the early Heag XV (rollfilm type) but with dual reflex finders on the bed. The important difference is that it includes a focal plane shutter to 1/2500. The front shutter is a Bob or Simple Auto. Rare. Negotiable. Estimate: $250-450.

Zwei-Verschluss-Camera - see Heag VI and Union.

ESPIONAGE CAMERA (French) - WWII vintage subminiature for 45 exp. 8x11mm. Metal FP shutter to 250. An uncommon camera, usually found without the lens: $350-400. With lens (rare): $600-700.

ESSEM - 5x7" folding camera. RR lens in B&L shutter. Mahogany interior, red bellows. $60-90.

ESSEX - Plastic minicam, styled like Falcon Minicam Jr., Metro-Cam, Regal Miniature, etc. $1-5.

ESTES INDUSTRIES (Penrose, Colorado)

Astrocam 110 - c1979. Small 110 camera designed to be launched via rocket to take

aerial photos. Shoots one photo per flight. The 1/500 second shutter is activated at ejection just prior to parachute deployment. With companion Delta II rocket in original box: $25-40.

ETA (Prague, Czechoslovakia)

Etareta - c1950-1955. Non-rangefinder 35mm camera. Etar II f3.5/50mm in Etaxa 10-200,B,T. Collapsible front. $25-35.

ETTELSON CORP. (Chicago)

Mickey Mouse Camera - A black bakelite box camera with red trim. Has Mickey Mouse nameplates on the front, rear, and on the advance knob. This is an uncommon camera, especially if found in its original box. Camera only: $50-75. Complete with original box: $100-125.

ETUI - *A style of thin-folding plate camera c1930's. The most common model using the word Etui in its name is the KW Patent Etui.*

EULITZ (Dr. Eulitz, Harzburg)
Grisette - c1955. Bakelite 35mm. 45mm achromat lens, simple shutter. $35-50.

EUMIG (Austria)
Eumigetta - 6x6cm rollfilm camera. Eumar f5.6/80mm lens. $20-30.

EVES(Edward Eves Ltd., Leamington Spa, England)
Blockmaster One-Shot - c1954. Color separation camera utilising beam-splitting mirrors to make 3 filtered exposures on 4x5" plates. Schneider Xenar f4.5/210mm lens in Compound shutter. $700-900.

EXCO - Simple box-type stereo camera, also useable for single exposures. Double anastigmat lenses. $100-125.

EXPO CAMERA CO. (New York)

Easy-Load - c1926. Small box camera for 1⅝x2½" exposures on rollfilm in special cartridges, called Expo "Easy-Load" film. Meniscus lens, rotary sector shutter. Red, brown, or green: $50-80. Black: $35-55.

Police Camera - c1911-24. A tiny all-metal box camera for 12 exposures on special cassettes. Fixed focus achromatic lens, 2 apertures. Cloth focal plane shutter, T & I. $165-245.

Watch Camera - Introduced c1905, produced for about 30 years. Disguised as a railroad pocket watch. Takes picture through the "winding stem", while the "winding knob" serves as a lens cap. Special cartridges. This is an interesting camera, but actually quite common since it was marketed for so long. Several variations exist. Black or blue enameled

Expo Watch Camera

versions, rare: $550-700. Chrome camera only, complete with lens cap: $75-100. With reflex finder and original box: $100-125. Add $35 for cartridge.

FABRIK FOTOGRAFISCHE APPARATE (Luebeck, Germany)

Fotal - c1950. Round subminiature for 8x12mm exp. on Special-Rollfilm. Prontor II 1/250 shutter. Optar Anastigmat f2.8/20mm lens. Blue leather covering. $800-1200.

FAISSAT (J. Faissat, Limoges)
Field camera, 9x12cm - c1895-1900. Tailboard-style camera with single-extension by rack and pinion. Fine wood body with brass trim. Brass barrel lens for waterhouse stops. $160-180.

FALCON CAMERA CO. (Chicago) *The history of the Falcon Camera Company is somewhat unclear. The Falcon line was begun by the Utility Manufacturing Co. of New York about 1934. One source indicates that Utility, which also made Spartus cameras, was sold to Spartus Corp. in 1940, the new firm taking its name from the Spartus cameras. (The Utility name continued to be used at least as late as 1942, however, on price lists for Falcon cameras.) While ownership may have belonged to Spartus, the Falcon Camera Co. name was used in advertising in 1946, as was the Spencer Co. name. In fact, we have a camera with the Falcon Camera Co. name, but its instruction book bears the Spencer Co. name. Both of these companies operated out of a building at 711-715 W. Lake St. in Chicago, which is also the address of the Spartus Camera Co., Herold Mfg. Co., and Galter Products. If this is not confusing enough, we should add that the founder of the original Utility Manufacturing Co., Mr. Charles Fischberg, was later prominent in Herbert-George, Birdseye, and Imperial companies. See also Utility Mfg. Co. for Falcon cameras.*

Falcon Miniature - c1947. Bakelite minicam for 3x4cm on 127 rollfilm. $4-8.

Falcon Miniature Deluxe - c1947. Brown marbelized bakelite minicam for 3x4cm on 127 film. Folding eye-level finder. $4-8.

Falcon Minicam Senior - Another 35mm style camera for 3x4cm on 127 film. Cast aluminum: $8-12. Bakelite: $3-7.

Falcon Rocket - Minicam for 3x4cm on 127 rollfilm. $4-8.

FALLOWFIELD (Jonathan Fallowfield Ltd., London)

Facile - c1890. Mahogany box detective magazine camera. A grooved box carries the fresh plates over a slot where they drop into a second grooved box behind the lens. A milled knob simultaneously moves the top box forward and the lower box backward so that each successive plate drops into the plane of focus in front of the previous one. An uncommon camera, which was designed to be concealed as a package wrapped in paper. Early mahogany model: $750-1000. Later black painted model: $350-450.

Miall Hand Camera - c1893. A very unusual and rare detective camera disguised as a gladstone bag. In addition to its unusual shape, it boasted the ability to be reloaded, 12 plates at a time, in broad daylight. Original advertising states that this camera was made only to order, which helps account for its rarity. Price negotiable. Estimate: $8000-10,000.

Peritus No. 1 - Mahogany field camera for 10x12" plates. Ross-Goerz Patent Double Anastigmat f7.7/14" lens. $100-150.

Prismotype - c1923. Direct positive street camera for 2½x3½" cards. Unusual design with reflecting turret eliminates the lateral reversal common to most direct positive cameras. $700-1000.

Tailboard cameras - Various sizes, ½-plate to 10x12". Dovetailed mahogany construction with square bellows. Rising and sliding front. Rack focus. With brass barrel lens: $100-175.

FAMA - German single extension folding plate camera, 9x12 size. Verax f8/135 or Sytar f6.3/135 in Vario shutter. $25-35.

FED *(Dzerzhinsky Commune, Kharkov, Ukraine) Russian Leica copies. Space does not permit a complete history here, and we certainly could not compete with the excellent history of the Dzerzhinsky Commune presented by Oscar Fricke in the quarterly "History of Photography" April 1979.*
Fed - c1934-55. Copies of Leica II(D) and III cameras. Usually with FED f3.5/50mm lens. $45-60.
Fed 2 - c1955. Removable back, combined VF/RF, self-timer, sync. $35-60.
Fed 3 - c1968. Lever film advance. $30-40.
Fed 4 - c1968. Built-in meter. $30-45.
Note: The Fed 2, 3, and 4 are common in Europe, but not in the U.S.A., so they sell for up to 50% above these figures in the U.S.

FEDERAL MFG. & ENGINEERING CO. (Brooklyn, NY)

Fed-Flash - c1948. Low priced camera for 8 exp. 4x6.5cm on 127 film. Original prices: Camera $9.95, Case $3.95, Flash $4.51. Finally closed out in 1956 at $4.95 for the complete outfit. Current value: $5-10.

FEINAK-WERKE (Munich)
Folding plate camera - 10x15cm. Horizontal format. Double extension bellows. Schneider Xenar f4.5/165mm. Dial Compur to 150. Leather covered metal body. $75-100.

**FEINMECHANISCHE WERKSTAETTEN
(Karl Foitzik, Trier, Germany)**

Foinix - c1951-55. 6x6cm folding camera, horizontal style like Ikonta B. Steinar f3.5/75mm coated lens. Singlo, Vario, Pronto, Prontor, or Synchro-Compur. Rangefinder model: $30-50. Regular models: $15-20.

Foinix 35mm - c1955. 35mm viewfinder camera. Foinar f2.8 or f3.5/45mm. Vario or Pronto shutter. Rapid wind lever. $25-35.

Unca - c1953. Similar to the Foinix, also for 6x6cm. f3.5 lens. Prontor-S shutter. $20-30.

FEINOPTISCHE WERKE (Goerlitz, Germany) *Successors to the Curt Bentzin Co.*
Astraflex-II - c1952. 6x6cm SLR. Astraflex was the U.S.A. name given to the camera by Sterling-Howard Corp., while the Primar Reflex II camera was distributed exclusively in the U.S.A. by Ercona Camera Corp. The two cameras are nearly identical, and prone to shutter problems. Tessar f3.5/105mm coated lens. Focal plane shutter, T, B, to 1000. Excellent working condition: $150-200. With shutter problems: $75-100.

FEINWERK TECHNIK GmbH (Lahr, Germany)

Mec-16 - ca. late 1950's. Gold-colored subminiature for 10x14mm exposures on 16mm film in cassettes. f2.8 lens. Shutter to 1000. In original presentation case: $50-65. Camera only: $30-50.

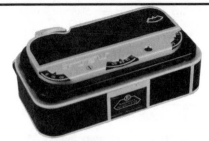

Mec 16 (new style) - An unusual variation of the Mec 16 camera, this model has body styling similar to the Mec 16SB, with aluminum-colored metal and black leatherette. With case & chain: $65-75. Camera only: $50-60.

Mec-16 SB - c1960. Similar but with built-in coupled Gossen meter and f2 Rodenstock Heligon lens. The first camera with through-the-lens metering. With presentation case: $60-75. Camera only: $45-60.

FERRANIA (Milan, Italy) *Manufacturer of cameras and film. Currently owned by the 3M company.*

Condor I, Ic - c1950. 35mm rangefinder cameras with front leaf shutter. Some models have "Ferrania" on the top, while others do not. The shutter face bears the name of "Officine Galileo" in either case, and the camera is variously attributed to both companies. This camera is often described as a Leica copy by vendors with imagination. $50-90.

Condor Junior - c1950. Similar to normal Condor, but without rangefinder. Galileo Eliog focusing f3.5/50mm lens. Iscus Rapid shutter 1-500. $50-70.

Elioflex - c1950-53. Inexpensive TLR. Focusing Galileo Monog f8 in B,25-200 shutter. Non-focusing reflex finder. $25-35.

Eura - c1959. Plastic and aluminum eye-level box camera for 6x6cm. Focusing lens; T,I shutter. $5-10.

Euralux 44 - c1961. Smaller version of the Eura, made for 4x4cm on 127 film. Built-in flash with fan reflector. $12-18.

Ibis - c1950. Small cast aluminum camera for 4x6cm on rollfilm. $15-20.
Ibis 6/6 - c1955. Cast aluminum body. Gray or black imitation leather. $15-20.

Lince 2 - c1962. Inexpensive metal 35mm. Cassar f2.8/45mm. Vero shutter. $12-18.

Lince Rapid - c1965. Inexpensive 35mm camera for rapid cassettes. Dignar Anastigmat in 3-speed shutter. $12-18.

Rondine - c1948. Small all metal box camera for 4x6.5cm exposures on 127 film. Measures 3½x3½x2½". Meniscus f8.8/75 Linear (focusing) lens. Simple shutter with flash sync. Available in black, brown, tan, green, blue, & red. Fairly common. $20-30.

Tanit - c1955. Small eye-level camera for 3x4cm on 127 film. $20-30.

Zeta Duplex - c1940-45.
Zeta Duplex 2 - c1946. Metal box camera for 6x9cm or 4.5x6cm on 120 film. Achromat f11 lens. P,I shutter. Olive or grey: $15-25. Black: $10-15.

FERRO (Buttrio-Udine, Italy)

G.F. 81 Ring Camera - 1981. Subminature camera built into a large gold finger ring. Takes special discs of film, 25mm diameter. Variable speed guillotine shutter. Removable reflex finder doubles as screwdriver to set the controls. Originally packed in a handsome wooden case. Very limited production. $800-1000.

G.F. 82 - c1982-83. Similar to the G.F. 81, but with fixed viewfinder. $575-800.

FETTER (France)
Photo-Eclair - c1886. A French version of the concealed vest camera, designed by J.F. Fetter and manufactured by Dubroni in Paris. Similar to the Gray and Stirn Vest camera in outward appearance. Several variations exist, the major difference being that early models had the lens toward the top. While later models c1892 were inverted so that a waist-level finder could be used above the lens. Takes five photos 38x38mm, changed by rotating the back. $1200-1800.

FEX (France)
Elite - c1965. Dual format plastic eye-level camera for 6x9 or 6x6cm on 120 film. Rectangular extensible front. Extinction meter. $10-15.

Impera - Simple black plastic eye-level camera for 4x4cm on 127 film. $1-5.

Rubi-Fex 4x4 - c1965. Inexpensive plastic camera for 127 film. $5-10.

Superfex - c1945. Bakelite camera, 4x6.5cm exposures on 127 rollfilm. Spec Fexar lens, single speed shutter. $5-15.

Superior - c1940's. Black bakelite camera for 4.5x6cm, similar to the Superfex. Fexar Super lens. T,M shutter. $5-15.

Ultra-Fex - Post-war camera for 6x9cm on 120 rollfilm. Plastic body, extensible front. Fexar lens. Simple shutter 25-100. $10-15.

Ultra-Reflex - c1952. Twin-lens plastic box camera for 6x6cm. Fexar lens. $8-12.

Uni-Fex - c1949. Black plastic eye-level box camera for 6x9cm on 120 film. Rectangular telescoping front. T,I shutter. $5-10.

FIAMMA (Florence, Italy)
Fiamma Box - c1925. Small metal box camera for 3x4cm on 127 film. Black crackle-finish paint. Mensicus lens, T&I shutter. $15-20.

FILMA (Milano, Italy)
Box cameras - c1936. 4.5x6cm and 6x9cm sizes. Front corners are rounded. Achromat lens, guillotine shutter. $20-28.

FINETTA WERK (P. Saraber, Goslar)
Ditto 99 - Same as the Finetta 99 below.

Finetta - c1950. Basic 35mm camera without rangefinder or motor drive. Finetar f2.8/45mm interchangeable lens. Originally $30. Currently: $23-35.

Finetta 99 - c1950. Spring motor camera. 36 exposures 24x36mm on 35mm film. Interchangeable Finetar f2.8/45mm lens. Focal-plane shutter 25-1000. Light grey. Excellent working condition: $100-150. (Deduct at least 50% for non-working example.)

Finetta Super - Finetar f2.8/45mm. Central shutter 25-100. $25-35.

Finette - Aluminum body. Achromat Finar f5.6/43mm. Simple shutter, T,B,I. $15-25.

FIPS MICROPHOT - Tiny black plastic subminiature for 13x13mm on special rollfilm. Made in Western Germany. $75-100.

FIRST CAMERA WORKS (Japan) *First Camera Works was a tradename used by Kuribayashi. Most cameras produced under this name were marketed by Minagawa Shoten.*

First Six - c1936. Copy of Zeiss Ikonta for 6x6cm on 120 film. Toko Anastigmat f3.575mm. Seikosha T,B,1-250 shutter. Vertical body. (See Tokiwa Seiki for a later First Six, c1950's.) $45-65.

FISCHER (C.F.G. Fischer, Berlin)
Nikette - c1932. Black bakelite-bodied folding camera with pop-out strut-supported front. Luxar f3.5 lens. $75-125.

Nikette II - c1932. Similar, but Maxar f3.5/50mm lens; black or colored body. $75-125.

FIVE STAR CAMERA CO.
Five Star Candid Camera - Plastic novelty minicam for 3x4cm on 127 film. $4-8. *(Illustrated top of next column.)*

FLASH CAMERA CO.
Candid Flash Camera - 3x4cm. $4-8.

Five Star Candid Camera

FLASHLINE - Plastic & metal eye-level box camera from Japan, 6x6cm on 120 film. Fixed focus. Two speeds marked with weather symbols, plus B. PC sync post on front. $1-5.

FLEKTAR - c1955. 6x6cm TLR made in USSR occupied East Germany. Row Pololyt f3.5/75mm lens. $25-35.

FOLMER & SCHWING
Folmer & Schwing (NYC), 1887.
Folmer & Schwing Mfg. Co. (NYC), 1890.
Folmer & Schwing Mfg. Co. of N. Y., 1903.
Folmer & Schwing Co., Rochester (EKC), 1905.
Folmer & Schwing Div. of EKC, 1907.
Folmer & Schwing Dept. of EKC, 1917.
Folmer-Graflex Corp., 1926.
Graflex, Inc., 1945.
Because of the many organizational changes in this company which are outlined above, and in order to keep the continuous lines of cameras together, we have chosen to list their cameras as follows regardless of age of camera or official company name at time of manufacture:
Cirkut Cameras- see Eastman Kodak Co.
Graflex, Graphic Cameras- see Graflex

Banquet cameras - c1915-29. Banquet cameras are essentially view cameras with wide proportions for panoramic photographs. They were originally used to photograph entire rooms of people at banquets, and required a wide angle lens with extreme coverage. Surprisingly, these cameras are still used for the same purposes today, and maintain their value as usable equipment based on the prices of current cameras. In any case, the lens with the camera is an important consideration in determining the value. At least one filmholder should be included in the prices listed here. The film holders would be expensive if purchased separately. Common sizes are 7x17" and 12x20". With an appropriate wide angle lens: $350-650. Without a lens, they bring $250-450.

Finger Print Camera - c1917-29. Portable fingerprint camera. Contains four battery operated lights. Leather covered. Kodak f6.3 lens. $50-75.

Sky Scraper Camera - c1904-15. Special purpose view camera incorporating an extra high rising lensboard and a back with extreme tilt to correct for architectural distortion. It was the perfect solution to the problem of taking photographs of the skyscrapers of the early 1900's. With lens & shutter: $350-500. Without lens: $200-300.

FOSTER INSTRUMENTS PTY. LTD. (Australia)
Swiftshot "Made in Australia" - c1950. This is the same basic camera as the Model A below, but without a model number. Instead, the faceplate is marked "Made in Australia" below the Swiftshot name. $10-15. *(Illustrated on back cover.)*

Swiftshot Model A - c1950. Metal box camera for 6x9cm exposures on either 620 or 120 rollfilm. Color and texture variations of the covering include: snakeskin pattern in green & brown or tan & brown; lightly pebbled surface in olive green, etc. Vertically striped faceplate in green or brown. $8-12.

FOTAX MINI, FOTAX MINI IIa - c1948. Sweden. Bakelite camera for 25x25mm on special 35mm rollfilm. f8/35mm lens. $40-60.

FOTET CAMERA CO. (London)
Fotet - c1932. Vest-pocket camera with strut-supported front. Takes 16 exposures 3x4cm on 127 film. Meyer Trioplan f3.5 or f4.5 lens. Vario, Pronto, Ibsor, or Compur

shutter. Identical to the Korelle 3x4cm strut-folding type. $35-50.

FOTH (C. F. Foth & Co., Berlin)

Derby (original) - 1930-31. The only Derby for 24x36mm on 127 rollfilm. Identified by its small image size. Originally with folding Newton finder, later with an optical telescopic viewfinder. Foth Anastigmat f3.5/50mm, FP 1/25-1/500. Very rare. $75-125.

Derby (I) - c1931-36. 3x4cm on 127 rollfilm. Optical telescopic viewfinder. Foth Anastigmat f3.5 or f2.5/50mm, FP shutter 1/25-1/500. No self-timer. Black or brown leather covering. This model was referred to as Derby until the improved version with a self-timer was introduced. It then was called the Derby I and the self-timer version was called the Derby II. Not often seen. $30-40. (With Elmar lens add $150.)

Derby II - c1934-42. 3x4cm on 127 rollfilm. Optical telescopic viewfinder. FP 1/25-500, ST. Foth Anastigmat f3.5 or f2.5/50mm. Black or brown leather covering. There were also two rangefinder additions to this camera that were not made by Foth. The first, made in France c1937-40, had a black and chrome rangefinder that was added to the top of the camera body. The range-finder remains stationary on the body when the struts extend the front. A focusing knob coupled to the RF was added to the front plate. The second, c1940-42 US-made chrome RF was mounted above the front plate, not to the top of the body. When the struts are extended, the RF also moves forward. A vertical bar connects the helical lens mount to the RF. This CRF could be added to any Derby II, by returning it to the US distriburor. Advertisements in the U.S. referred to the Derby II without the added CRF as the "Standard" model or "Model I", and called the Derby II with the US added CRF simply Derby II or Derby Model II. With French CRF: $150-175. With US CRF: $125-165. Without CRF: $25-40.

Folding rollfilm cameras - c1933. For 116 or 120 rollfilm. Foth Anastigmat lens. Waist level & eye level finders. $20-25.
-- Deluxe version - Alligator skin covering and black or colored bellows. $75-100.

Foth-Flex - c1934. TLR for 6x6cm on 120. Foth Anastigmat f3.5/75mm. Cloth focal plane shutter 25-500, B. $65-90.

Foth-Flex II - c1935. Similar, but shutter has slow speeds to 2 second. Focusing lever replaces knob focusing c1938. $75-100.

FOTO-FLEX CORP. (Chicago)
Foto-Flex - Twin-lens box camera of unusual design. The small viewing and taking lenses are both within the round front disc which resembles a normal lens. (Design is similar to the 35mm Agfa Flexilette.) Takes 4x4cm on 127 film. One model has a cast metal body. Another has a plastic body with a cast metal faceplate. Interior of body is marked "Hadds Mfg. Co." Apparently Hadds manufactured the body or the entire camera for the Foto-Flex Corp. $10-15.

FOTO-QUELLE (Nuernberg, Germany)
Founded in 1957, Foto Quelle steadily grew to become the world's largest photographic retailer. Their "Revue" brand is known worldwide, made up of cameras produced by major manufacturers for sale under the "Revue" name.

Revue 3 - c1970. Same as Fed 3, but made for Foto-Quelle, a large German photographic distributor. "Revue 3" printed on front of top housing. $25-40.

Revue 16 KB - c1960's. Name variation of the Minolta 16 MG subminature. Rokkor f2.8/20mm lens. Programmed shutter 30-250. With case, chain, flash, & filters: $20-40.

Revue Mini-Star - c1965-70. Name variant of the Yashica Atoron, a subminiature for 8x11mm on Minox film. $30-40.

FOTOCHROME, INC. (U.S.A.)

Fotochrome Camera - c1965. "Unusual" is a kind description for this machine, designed by the film company to use a special direct-positive film loaded in special cartridges. The camel-humped body houses a mirror which reflects the 5.5x8cm image down to the bottom where the "color picture roll" passed by on its way from one cartridge to another. Single speed shutter coupled to the selenium meter. Made by Petri Camera in Japan. $20-30.

FOTOFEX-KAMERAS (Fritz Kaftanski, Berlin)

Minifex - c1932. Unusual looking subminiature for 36 exposures 13x18mm on 16mm film. Large Compur, Pronto, or Vario shutter dwarfs the tiny body. $325-500.

Visor-Fex - c1933. Unusual folding rollfilm camera for 6x9cm or 4.5x6cm on rollfilm. Also accepts single plateholders while the rollfilm is still loaded in the camera. The rollfilm back has a darkslide, and the back hinges down to allow use of ground glass or plateholder. Catalog advertising claimed that this was the first and only camera in the world to allow ground glass focusing between rollfilm exposures while film was loaded. (Actually, the Palko camera predates it for the rollfilm and ground glass

Visor-Fex

claims, but does not accept plates.) Uncommon. Most recent auction sales at about $75.

FOTOKOR - c1930. Russian folding plate camera. Gomz f4.5/135mm lens in 25-100,K,D shutter. $25-40.

FOTOTECNICA (Turin, Italy)
Bakina Rakina - c1946. Inexpensive camera for 3x4cm on 127 film. Clippertar f9 lens; B&I shutter. $15-20.

Bandi - c1946. Box camera covered in brown leather, with blue front. 6x6cm on 120 rollfilm. Aplanat 75mm lens, shutter 25-100. $25-30.

Filmor - c1950. Metal box cameras for 6x6cm or 6x9cm exposures. Achromat lenses, guillotine shutter. $15-25.

Rayflex - c1946. Simple 6x9cm box camera. Duotar Optik f9 lens, guillotine shutter. $12-18.

Francais Kinegraphe

FRANCAIS (E. Francais, Paris)
Cosmopolite - c1892. Early twin-lens reflex camera, box-shaped when closed. Side hinged front door conceals brass barrel lenses. $700-900.

Kinegraphe - c1886. Very early twin-lens reflex. Polished wood body, exterior brass barrel lens with waterhouse stops. Sold in England by London Stereoscopic Co. as "Artist's Hand Camera". $850-1200. *(Illustrated bottom of previous page.)*

Photo-Magazin - c1895. French magazine camera for 6.5x9cm plates. Leather changing bag. String-set shutter. $400-475.

FRANCYA - 14x14mm Japanese subminature of the "Hit" type. $10-15.

FRANKA-WERK (Beyreuth, Germany)

Rolfix - ca. WWII, pre- and post. A dual-format folding camera for 120 film. Some take 8 or 12 exposures per roll, others take 8 or 16 exposures. Post-war models made in U.S. occupied zone from pre- and post-war parts. $10-20.

Rolfix Jr. - c1951-55. Folding camera for 8 exposures 6x9cm or 12 exposures 6x6cm on 120 rollfilm. Frankar f4.5/105 in Vario 25,50,200,B. Standard model has folding direct eye-level finder. Deluxe model has non-folding optical finder in small add-on top housing. $10-20.

Solida - *Pre- and post-war folding cameras for 12 exposures, 6x6cm on 120 film.*
Solida I - f6.3/75mm. $12-22.
Solida II - Anastigmat f3.5 in Vario shutter. $25-40.
Solida III - Radionar f2.9/80mm in Prontor SVS. $30-50.

Solida Jr. - c1954. Horizontal folding 120 rollfilm camera, 6x6cm. f6.3/75mm lens. Shutter B,25,75. $10-15.

FRANKE & HEIDECKE (Braunschweig)
Heidoscop - Three-lens stereo camera for stereo pairs on plates or cut film, in two sizes: 45x107mm and 6x13cm. Named for the designer, Reinhold Heidecke, these were the first cameras made by Franke & Heidecke. Both models have Stereo Compound shutters.

45x107mm size - 1921-41. Carl Zeiss Jena Tessar f4.5/55mm lenses. $250-300.

6x13cm size - 1925-41. Carl Zeiss Jena Tessar f4.5/75mm lenses. $350-450. (Add $100-150 for 120 rollback.)

Rollei-16 - 1963-67. (#2,700,000-2,727,999). Subminiature for 12x17mm exposures on 16mm film. Tessar f2.8/25mm. Outfit with case, flash, filter: $50-75. Camera only: $35-55.

Rollei-16S - 1966-72. (#2,728,000-2,747,882). Subminiature. Cream snake: $150-200. Black snake: $60-90. Green: $100-150. Red: $100-150. Black: $40-60.

Rollei 35 - 1967-75. (#3,000,000-on). Tessar f3.5/50mm. Model from Germany: $80-110. From Singapore: $70-90. In gold: $400-500.

Rollei 35B - 1969-78. (#3,600,000-on). Zeiss Triotar f3.5/40mm. $60-90.

Rollei 35C - intro. 1969. ($3,600,000-on). $75-100.

Rollei 35LED - 1978-80. $45-60.

Rollei 35S - intro. 1974. In gold, as new in box: $700-1000. In silver, as new in box: $150-180. Black, as new: $125-175. Chrome, like new: $85-100.

Rollei 35T - 1976-80. Black or chrome. $75-100.

Rollei A26 - c1973-78. Self-casing pocket-sized 126 cartridge camera. Sonnar f3.5/40mm. Programmed shutter 30-250. With case, flash: $50-60. Camera only: $25-30.

Rolleicord - *A series of 6x6cm TLR cameras.*

I (nickel-plated) - 1933-36. Art-deco, nickel-plated exterior. Zeiss Triotar f4.5/75mm lens. Compur shutter 1-300, B, T. $75-100 in U.S.A. (These bring about 30%-40% more in Germany.)

Rolleicord Ia

I (leather covered) - 1934-36. Black leather-covered exterior. Zeiss Triotar f3.8 lens. Compur shutter 1-300, B,T, no sync. $50-70 in U.S.A. (Nearly double that in Germany.)

Ia - 1936-47. Zeiss Triotar f4.5/75mm lens. No bayonet mounts on viewing or taking lenses. Rim-set compur shutter 1-300,B,T. No sync. Most have a frame finder in the focusing hood. Wide range of prices: $40-80. *(Illustrated bottom of previous column.)*

II - 1936-50. (#612,000-1,135,999) f3.5/75mm Zeiss Triotar or Schneider Xenar lens. Compur shutter 1-300,B,T or Compur Rapid 1-500, B. No. sync. Originally with no bayonet mounts, but bayonet added to the taking lens and then the viewing lens during the course of production. Version with bayonets on both the taking and viewing lenses sometimes referred to as the IIa. $40-60. (About 40% higher in Germany.)

III - 1950-53. (#1,137,000-1,344,050). f3.5/75mm Zeiss Triotar or Schneider Xenar lens. Compur-Rapid shutter 1-500,B. X sync. $45-60.

IV - 1953-54. (#1,344,051-1,390,999). Schneider Xenar or Zeiss Triotar f3.5/75mm lens. Synchro-Compur 1-500, B. MX sync. Double exposure prevention. $70-90.

V - 1954-57. (#1,500,000-1,583,999). Schneider Xenar f3.5/75mm lens. Synchro-Compur shutter, 1-500. Self-timer, MXV sync. LVS scale. Double exposure prevention. Large focusing knob with film speed indicator on right side. $60-100.

Va - 1957-61. (#1,584,000-1,943,999). Schneider Xenar f3.5 lens. Synchro-Compur shutter 1-500,B. Large focusing knob on left side. Non-removable focusing hood. $70-95.

Vb - 1962-70. (#2,600,000-on). Schneider Xenar f3.5 lens. Synchro-Compur 1-500 shutter. Large focusing knob on left side. Removable focusing hood. $90-145.

Rolleidoscop - 1926-41. The rollfilm version of the Heidoscop stereo camera. Actually, some of the very earliest production models of the Rolleidoscop still bore the name Heidoscop. Like the Heidoscop, this is a three-lens reflex. The center lens, for reflex viewing, is a triplet f4.2. Stereo Compound shutter 1-300. **45x107mm** - Tessar f4.5/55mm lenses. Much less common than the 6x13cm size. $750-1000.

6x13cm - Tessar f4.5/75mm lenses. For B11 or 117 rollfilm. Many converted for 120 rollfilm by users. $750-1200.

Rolleiflex - *TLR cameras for 6x6cm exposures on 120 film.*

I (original model) - 1929-32. (#1-199,999) The "little sister" of the already well-known Heidoscop and Rolleidoscop. Readily identified by the Rim-set Compur shutter, 1-300, B,T, and the film advance system, which, on this early model was not automatic; hence, no exposure counter.

With Zeiss Tessar f4.5/75mm, or more often, f3.8/75mm lens. This first model was made to take 6 exposures on No. 117 film, but some were converted to the standard 12 exposures on 120 film. Film winding knob, not lever. The earliest version of this model had no distance scale on the focus knob, and the back is not hinged, but fits into a groove. The second version has focus scale and hinge. $75-115.

Rolleiflex Automat models:

Automat (1937) - 1937-39. (#563,516-805,000). Zeiss Tessar f3.5/75mm lens. Bayonet mount for accessories on taking lens only. Compur-Rapid shutter 1-500, B,T, self-timer. Automatic film feed. No ruby window, no sportsfinder. Knurled wheels for setting lens stops and shutter speeds. $60-100.

Automat (1939) - 1939-49. (#805,000-1,099,999). Tessar or Xenar f3.5 lens. Like the 1937 model, but bayonet mounts on both the taking and the viewing lenses. $65-95. (About 50% higher in Germany.)

Automat (X-sync) - 1949-51. (#1,100,000-1,168,000). Called the Automat II in Germany. Tessar or Xenar f3.5/75mm lens. Synchro-Compur shutter, 1-500, B. Self-timer. X-sync. Sportsfinder. $125-175.

Automat (MX-sync) - 1951-54. (#1,200,000-1,427,999). Tessar or Xenar f3.5/75mm lens. Synchro-Compur 1-500, B. Self-timer. Lever for selecting M or X type sync. Very common. $70-120.

Automat (MX-EVS) - 1954-56. (#1,428,000-1,739,911). Tessar or Xenar f3.5/75mm lens. Synchro-Compur shutter, 1-500, B. Self-timer. MX sync and LVS scale on shutter. $80-120.

Rolleiflex 2.8A - 1950-51. (#1,101,000-1,204,000). Also known as Automat 2.8A.

Rolleiflex Old Standard

Zeiss Tessar f2.8/80mm lens. Synchro-Compur shutter, with X or MX sync. Self-timer. Sportsfinder. $80-100.

Rolleiflex 2.8B - 1952-53. (#1,204,000-1,260,000). Also known as Automat 2.8B. Zeiss Biometar f2.8/80mm lens. MX sync. $100-125.

Rolleiflex 2.8C - 1953-55. (#1,260,350-1,475,405). Also called Automat 2.8C. f2.8/80mm Schneider Xenotar or Zeiss Planar lens. Synchro-Compur shutter with MX sync. No LVS scale. $140-165. (Higher in Germany.)

Rolleiflex 2.8D - 1955-56. (#1,600,000-1,620,999). f2.8/80mm Zeiss Planar or Schneider Xenotar lens. Synchro-Compur shutter with MX sync and LVS scale. $200-225.

Rolleiflex E - 1956-59. Dual-range, non-coupled exposure meter. (Original distributor's advertising referred to this camera as the model "G" when sold without the meter.) MX sync. Two variations:
2.8E - (#1,621,000-1,665,999). f2.8/80mm Zeiss Planar or Schneider Xenotar. $210-250. (Higher in Germany.)
3.5E - (#1,740,000-1,787,999 and 1,850,000-1,869,999). f3.5/75mm Zeiss Planar or Schneider Xenotar. $185-230. (Higher in Germany.)

Rolleiflex E2 - No exposure meter. Flat, removable focusing hood. Two variations:
2.8E2 - 1959-60. (#2,350,000-2,356,999)

f2.8/80mm Xenotar. $245-270.
3.5E2 - 1959-62. (#1,870,000-1,872,010 and 2,480,000-2,482,999). f3.5/75mm Xenotar or Planar. $185-200.

Rolleiflex E3 - 1962-65. No exposure meter. Removable focusing hood. Planar or Xenotar lens. Two variations:
2.8E3 - (#2,360,000-2,362,024). f2.8/80mm lens. $225-250.
3.5E3 - (#2,380,000-2,385,034). f3.5/75mm lens. $175-225.

Rolleiflex F2.8 Aurum - 1983. Gold-plated commemorative model with alligator leather covering. Approximately 450 made. Schneider Xenotar f2.8/80mm. As new with original teak box, strap, etc.: $1200-1400.

Rolleiflex SL26 - 1968-73. Sophisticated SLR for 126 cartridge film. Interchangeable lenses; TTL metering. With Tessar f2.8/40mm normal lens: $65-85.

Rolleiflex Standard models:
Old Standard - 1932-38. (#200,000-567,550). Zeiss Tessar f4.5, f3.8, or f3.5/75mm lens. Compur 1-300,B,T or Compur-Rapid 1-500, B shutter. Lens mount accepts push-on accessories; no bayonet. Single lever below lens for tensioning and releasing the shutter. Lever-crank film advance. Exposure counter. $60-90. *(Illustrated top of previous column.)*

New Standard - 1939-41. (#805,000-927,999). Zeiss Tessar f3.5/75mm lens. Compur-Rapid, 1-500, B (no T or self-timer). Bayonet mount on viewing and taking lenses. Lens stops and shutter speeds set by levers. $60-90.

Studio - 1932-34. 9x9cm or 6x9cm. The only Rolleiflex in the 9x9cm size, this is the rarest of the Rolleiflexes. Prototypes only or possibly very limited quantities. Zeiss Tessar f4.5/105mm lens in Compur S shutter 1-1/250, T, B. Price negotiable. No known sales.

Rolleiflex T - 1958-75. (#2,100,000- on). Zeiss Tessar f3.5/75mm lens. Shutter with X or MX sync. Provision for built-in dual-range exposure meter. Available in black or grey. Grey: $200-250. Black, with meter: $200-300. Without meter: $135-160. (Higher in Germany.)

Tele Rolleiflex - intro. 1959. Zeiss Sonnar f4/135mm lens. Removable focusing hood. Later models allow use of 120 or 220 film. $500-650.

Wide-Angle Rolleiflex (Rolleiwide) - 1961-67. Distagon f4/55mm lens. Less than 4000 produced. $800-1200.

Rolleiflex 4x4 Cameras *TLR cameras for 4x4cm exposures on 127 rollfilm. Some variations called "Baby Rolleiflex", or "Rolleiflex Sport".*

Original - 1931-38. (#135,000-523,000). Zeiss Tessar f3.5 or f2.8/60mm lens. Compur shutter 1-300, B, T or Compur-Rapid 1-500, B,T. Earliest models (1931-33) have rim-set shutter. Later versions (1933-38) have levers for setting the lens stops and shutter speeds. Lens mount accepts push-on accessories (no bayonets). $125-225.

Sports Rolleiflex - 1938-41. (#622,000-733,000). Zeiss Tessar f2.8/60mm lens. Compur-Rapid shutter, 1-500, B,T. Bayonet mount on taking lens; some also have a bayonet mount on the finder lens. $275-425.

Grey Baby - 1957-68. (#2,000,000- on). Grey body. Xenar f3.5 lens. MXV shutter with LVS scale and self-timer. Double bayonet. Common. $150-200.

Post-War Black Baby - 1963-68. (#2,060,000-?). Black body. Zeiss Tessar or Schneider Xenar f3.5/60mm lens. Synchro-Compur MXV 1-1/500, B shutter. Rare. $250-375.

Rolleimagic - 6x6cm TLR cameras with automatic exposure control. Xenar f3.5/75mm lens.
(I) - 1960-63. (#2,500,000-2,534,999). $70-115. (50% higher in Europe.)
II - 1962-67. (#2,535,000-2,547,597). Manual override on the exposure control. $100-150. (50% higher in Europe.)

FRENNET (J. Frennet, Brussels) Stereoscopic Reflex - c1910. Graflex-style cameras for stereo exposures on 6x13cm or 7x15cm glass plates. $350-500.

FT-2 - c1955. Russian panoramic camera for 12 exposures 24x110mm on 35mm film. Industar f5/50mm lens. Shutter 100-400. $225-275.

FUJI KOGAKU SEIKI *Made cameras primarily before WWII, but the subminiature Comex was a post-war model.*
Baby Balnet - 1940's. Japanese copy of Zeiss Baby Ikonta, 3x4cm on 127 rollfilm. Balnet shutter. Nomular Anastigmat f2.9/50mm lens. Two styles: Early version has folding viewfinder and black trim. Later version, c1947, has rigid optical viewfinder, chrome trim, and accessory shoe. $75-125.

Baby Lyra - c1941. Folding camera for 3x4cm on 127 film. Terionar f3.5/50mm in Picco 25-100 shutter. Rare. $125-175.

Comex - Novelty subminiature for 14x14mm on rollfilm. Marked "Made in Occupied Japan". $175-225.

Lyra 4.5x6cm (Semi-Lyra) - c1936-40. Compact folding camera for 16 exposures 4.5x6cm on 120 rollfilm. Similar to Zeiss Ikonta A. Terionar f3.5/75mm anastigmat. Fujiko or Noblo shutter. Folding viewfinder. (Later c1952 version has optical rigid viewfinder.) $30-45.

Lyra Six, Lyra Six III - c1939. Horizontally styled folding cameras for 6x6cm on 120.

Lyrax

Similar to Zeiss Ikonta B. Less common than the "semi" model. Terionar f3.5/75mm lens, Fujiko shutter. $30-50.

Lyraflex - c1941. 6x6cm TLR. Terionar f3.5/75mm lens, Fujiko shutter. An uncommon "Rollei copy". $75-125.

Lyrax - c1939. Telescoping front camera for 4.5x6cm on 120. Uncoupled rangefinder. Terionar f3.5/75mm in Fujiko shutter. $100-150. *(Illustrated bottom of previous page.)*

FUJI PHOTO FILM CO. *Founded about 1934, the Fuji Photo Film Co. made film before WWII, but didn't begin camera production until after the war. The Fuji Photo Film Company is the manufacturer of Fujica cameras, many of which are still in use today. We are only listing a few of the more collectible models in this collectors guide.*
Fujica Drive - Half-frame 35mm with spring motor drive. Auto exposure. Fujinon f2.8/28mm in Seikosha-L shutter. $30-50.

Fujica Mini - c1964. Very small half-frame camera for 35mm film in special cartridges. Fujinar-K Anastigmat f2.8/25mm fixed-focus lens. Shutter coupled to meter. $75-125.

Fujicaflex - c1954. Twin lens reflex for 6x6cm on 120. Fujinar f2.8/83mm. Seikosha-Rapid B,1-400. $125-175.

Fujipet, Fujipet EE - c1959. Simple eye-level cameras for 6x6cm on 120 film. The EE model with built-in meter is somewhat similar in styling to the Revere Eyematic EE127. Mensicus lens, I,B shutter. $15-22.

Pet 35 - Inexpensive lightweight 35mm. Fujinar f3.5/4.5cm focusing lens. Copal shutter, B, 25, 50, 100, 200. $15-25.

FUJIMOTO MFG. CO. (Japan)
Semi-Prince, Semi-Prince II - c1935-36. Zeiss Ikonta A copies, 4.5x6cm. Various shutters. Schneider 4.5/75mm. $50-75.

FUJITA OPT. IND. LTD. (Japan)
Classic 35 IV - c1960. Inexpensive 35mm imported to the USA by Peerless Camera

Co., NY as one of a series of "Classic" cameras. f3.5/45, Fujita B,25-300. $15-20.

Fujita 66SL - c1958. Similar to the 66ST, but slow speeds to 1/5 sec. Block lettering on nameplate. $75-125.

Fujita 66SQ - c1960. Improved model of the 66SL with quick-return mirror. Fujita f2.8/80mm lens. $75-125.

Fujita 66ST - c1956. SLR for 6x6cm on 120 film. Interchangeable F.C. Fujita f3.5/80mm. Focal plane shutter B,25-500. Script lettering on nameplate. $75-125.

FUTURA KAMERA WERK A.G., Fritz Kuhnert (Freiburg)
Futura-S - c1950's. A very well constructed 35mm CRF camera. Interchangeable Kuhnert Frilon f1.5/50mm lens. Compur Rapid 1-400, B. $50-65.

GALILEO OPTICAL (Milan, Italy)
Associated with Ferrania, also of Milan.
Condor I - c1947. 35mm rangefinder camera, similar in style to Leica, but with front shutter. Eliog f3.5/50mm in Iscus Rapid shutter B,1-500. CRF with separate eyepiece. Collapsible front. $50-90.

Gami 16 - c1955's. Subminiature for 12x17mm exposures on 16mm film in cassettes. f1.9/25mm lens. Shutter 2-1000. Coupled meter, parallax correction, spring-motor wind for up to 3 rapid-fire shots. Original cost $350. These are not rare, yet are occasionally advertised at higher prices. Normal range: $250-275. Complete outfit with all accessories: f4/4x telephoto, flash, filter, 45 degree viewer, wrist strap, etc. sells for 2 to 3 times the cost of camera & case.

GALLUS (Usines Gallus, Courbevoie, France)

Bakelite - A streamlined folding camera made of bakelite plastic. Design based on the Ebner camera from Germany. Takes 6x9cm exposures on 120 film. Achromat f11 lens. P & I shutter. $25-40.

Derby - c1939-41. Folding strut camera for 3x4cm on 127 film. Som Berthiot Flor or Saphir f3.5 lens. Focal plane shutter. A French-made version of the Foth Derby. $30-50.

Derlux - c1952. Folding camera for 3x4cm on 127 rollfilm. Polished aluminum body. Very similar to the Foth Derby. Indeed some examples are identified as "Derby Lux" on the back. Gallus Gallix f3.5/50mm. FP shutter 25-500. $75-125.

Folding Rollfilm Camera - c1920. For 6.5x11cm. Gallus Anastigmat f6.3/120mm in Ibsor shutter. $20-35.

Stereo camera - c1920's. Rigid "jumelle" style all metal camera for stereo exposures in the two popular formats: 6x13cm or the smaller 45x107mm. Simple lenses, I&B shutter or more expensive versions with nickel-plated aluminum bodies, 1/300 jewelled shutters, and Goerz, Krauss, or Zeiss lenses. $100-150.

GALTER PRODUCTS (Chicago) *Founded in 1950 by Jack Galter, former president of Spartus Camera Co., and apparently in business for only a few years. Spartus Camera Co., meanwhile, became Herold Mfg. Co. at about the same time, having been bought by Harold Rubin, former Sales Manager for Spartus.*

Hopalong Cassidy Camera - c1950. Plastic box camera for 8 exposures 6x9cm on 120 rollfilm. Simple shutter and meniscus lens. The front plate depicts the famous cowboy and his horse. $15-25.

Majestic, Pickwik, Regal - Plastic "minicam" type cameras for 3x4cm on 127 film. $3-7.

Sunbeam 120 - Black bakelite box camera without flash sync. Body style identical to the Hopalong Cassidy camera. $4-8.

GAMMA (subminiature) - Novelty subminiature from "Occupied Japan". Shutter release on top of body. Angel f4.5 lens with rotating disc stops. $125-150.

GAMMA (Societa Gamma, Rome) Gamma (35mm) - c1947-1950. Leica copies. Model I c1947 has bayonet-mount lens, FP shutter with speeds B,20-1000 on one dial. Model III c1950 has screw-mount lens, and shutter speeds 1-1000. Gamma or Koristka Victor f3.5 lens. Rare. Estimate: $400-525.

Pajtas - c1955. Black bakelite camera for 6x6cm on 120 rollfilm. Achromat f8/80. $15-25.

GAMMA WORKS (Budapest Hungary) Duflex - c1947. 24x32mm. First 35mm SLR to have a metal focal plane shutter, instant return mirror and internally actuated automatic diaphragm. Extremely rare. $1000-1500.

GANDOLFI (London) *The history of the Gandolfi family in the camera business is already a legend, and 1985 marked the hundredth anniversary of the founding of the business by Louis Gandolfi. It has remained a family business since that time, with sons Thomas, Frederic and Arthur working with their father and eventually taking the reins after his death in 1932. The company has always specialized in hand-made wooden cameras. A large number of their cameras are custom-built to the specifications of clients. It would be difficult to give specific prices to such a wide range of individually crafted cameras, but as a point of departure, we can say that we have a number of recorded sales in the range of $175-450 and some reports of prices up to $1000. Obviously, since the cameras were made for 100 years in a traditional style, they are still very much in demand for use as well as for collections.*

GARLAND - (London, England)
Wet Plate camera - 8x10". c1865. Ross lens. $1300-1800.

GAUMONT (L. Gaumont & Cie., Paris)

Block-Notes *Compact folding plate cameras.*
4.5x6cm - c1904-24. f6.8 Tessar, Hermagis Anastigmat, or Darlot lens. $90-160.
6.5x9cm - c1909-24. f6.3 Tessar lens. Less common than the smaller model. $100-150.

Block-Notes Stereo - Compact folding cameras like the other Block-Notes models, but for stereo formats: 6x13cm and 45x107mm. f6.3 lenses. Variable speed guillotine shutter. For single plateholders or magazines. $200-225.

Klopic - Strut-folding focal plane camera, 10x15cm size. Copy of Deckrullo-Nettel. Berthiot Series I f4.5/165mm lens. Focal plane shutter 1-2000. $150-170.

Reporter - c1924. Heavy metal strut-folding camera for 9x12cm single plates or magazine. Flor f3.5/135mm lens. FP 1/25-1000 shutter. $200-300.

Spido - c1898. 9x12cm magazine camera in tapered front "jumelle" shape. Leather covered. Berthiot, Protar, or Dagor lens, pneumatic shutter. $125-150.

Stereo Spido Ordinaire - c1906-31. Black leather covered jumelle style stereo cameras for 6x13cm or 8x16cm stereo plates. Krauss Zeiss Protar f12.5/189mm or Tessar f6.3. Six speed Decaux Stereo Pneumatic shutter. $150-240.

Stereo Spido Metallique - c1920's. Panoramic version with 120 rollback: $300-500. Regular 6x13cm size without rollback: $200-300.

Stereo cameras - Misc. or unnamed models, 6x13cm. f6.3/85mm lenses; guillotine shutter. $200-300.

GEC

Transistomatic Radio Camera - c1964. Combination of a G.E. Transistor radio and Kodak Instamatic 100 camera. $150-175.

GENERAL PRODUCTS CO. (Chicago)
Candex Jr. - Black plastic minicam for 127 half-frames. $3-7.

Clix Miniature Camera - Marbelized brown plastic minicam for 3x4cm on 127 film. $5-10.

GENIE CAMERA CO. (Philadelphia, PA)
Genie - c1892. Focusing magazine-box camera for 3¼x4" plates. Push-pull action changes plates and actuates exposure counter on brass magazine. String-set shutter. $400-550.

GENNERT (G. Gennert, NYC)

Montauk - c1890. Detective style camera for plateholders which load from the side. Shutter-tensioning knob on the front next to the lens opening. Internal bellows focusing via radial focus lever on top of camera. $100-125.

Folding Montauk, Golf Montauk - c1898. "Cycle" style folding plate cameras. Leather covered wood bodies.

Gennert Folding Montauk

Wollensak Rapid Symmetrical, Ross Patent, or Rapid Rectilinear. 4x5" or 5x7". $45-85.

Long Focus Montauk - c1898. Like the Folding Montauk, but also has rear bellows extension. $60-100.

Montauk rollfilm camera - c1914 $20-30.

"Penny Picture" camera - c1890. A 5x7" studio camera with sliding back and masks to produce multiple small images on a single plate. $250-300.

Stereoscopic Montauk - c1898. Like the 5x7" Folding Montauk, but with Stereo lensboard. $250-350.

GENOS K.G. (Nurnberg. Germany)
Genos - c1949. Small black bakelite eye-level camera for 25x25mm on 127 film. f8 lens, Z&M shutter. $30-45.

Genos Fix - c1951-56. Two-tone 4.5x6cm bakelite rollfilm box camera, similar in style to the better known Bilora Boy. $30-35.

Genos Rapid - c1950. Plastic 6x6cm reflex camera for 120 film. $8-15.

GERSCHEL (Paris)

le Mosaic - c1906. An unusual camera designed to take 12 exposures, 4x4cm each, on a single 13x18cm plate. The camera is approximately the size and shape of a cigar box standing on end. A removable partition divides the camera interior into twelve chambers. The lens and shutter move horizontally and vertically on two tambours (like a roll-top desk) to allow for twelve separate exposures. The sliding front has index marks to indicate the proper lens position for each exposure. There is also a second set of index marks for making nine exposures per plate with a different interior partition. Oddly, it comes with a Rapid Rectilinear lens fitted in either a Wollensak or Bausch & Lomb shutter. $1800-2000. *(Illustrated on front cover.)*

Gevabox 6x9, eye level finder

GEVAERT *Founded in 1890 by Lieven Gevaert to manufacture calcium paper. Merged with Agfa in 1964. Although a leader in photographic* *materials, the company was never a major producer of cameras.*

Gevabox: *Box cameras in several variations for 120 film.*

Gevabox 6x6 - c1950. Black bakelite camera with white trim. Looks like an overgrown "Ansco Panda", and nearly identical to the Adox 66. $20-30.

Gevabox 6x9 (eye level) - c1955-56. Metal box camera with eye-level finder above body. Shutter 1/50 and 1/100. $8-15. *(Illustrated bottom of previous page.)*

Gevabox 6x9 (waist level) - c1951. Waist level brilliant finder. B,M shutter. $10-12.

Ofo - Bakelite camera with helical telescoping front. Similar to the Photax from France. Both cameras are designed by Kaftanski, whose creations were manufactured in Germany, France, and Italy. This one, however, is made by "SIAF Industria Argentina". Black or brown. $30-50.

Geymet Jumelle de Nicour

GEYMET & ALKER (Paris)
Jumelle de Nicour - c1867. An early binocular-styled camera for 50 exposures on 1¼x1¼" plates. A large cylindrical magazine contained the 50 plates, which were loaded and unloaded from the camera for each exposure by gravity. (Rather like a modern slide tray.) Rare. Estimate: $7500. *(Illustrated bottom of previous column.)*

GILLES-FALLER (Paris)
Studio camera - c1900. 18x24cm. Hermagis Delor f4.5/270mm lens with iris diaphragm. Finely finished light colored wood. $250-350.

GINREI KOKI (Japan)
Vesta - c1949. Novelty subminiature from "Occupied Japan". Two models: one has eye-level finder, the other has both eye and waist level finders. $50-75.

GLOBAL - Japanese 16mm "Hit" type novelty camera. $10-15.

GLOSSICK MFG. CO. (East Peoria, Illinois)

Direct Positive Street Camera - Leather covered wooden camera with a rear sleeve for manipulating the 6x9cm sheets of direct positive paper. Suitcase styling is typical of street cameras, but tapered in toward the top. $75-125.

GLUNZ (S. Glunz Kamerawerk, Hannover)
Folding plate camera, 6.5x9cm - c1920's. Double extension bellows. Tessar f4.5/120mm. Compur 1-250. $30-35.

Folding plate camera, 9x12cm - c1920's. Wood body, leather covered. Double extension bellows. Dial Compur shutter. Goerz Tenastigmat f6.8, or Zeiss Tessar f4.5 lens. $40-60. *(Illustrated top of next page.)*

Glunz 9x12cm Folding Plate Camera

Folding plate camera, 13x18cm -
c1905. Horizontally styled folding camera. Leather covered wood body. Triple extension bellows. Hemi-Anastigmat Series B f7.2 lens. Unicum double pneumatic shutter. $85-105.

Folding rollfilm models - f6.3 Tessar. Compur shutter. $30-40.

GNCO - Japanese novelty subminiature of the "Hit" type. $10-15.

GNOFLEX - c1956. Japanese Rolleicord copy. Horinor f3.5/75mm lens. NKS shutter B,1-300. $35-45.

GNOME PHOTOGRAPHIC PRODUCTS, LTD. (England)
Pixie - Metal box camera for 6x6cm on 620 film. Black crinkle-finish enamel. $10-15. *(Illustrated top of next column.)*

GOEKER (Copenhagen, Denmark)
Field camera - 18x24cm. Carl Zeiss Series II f8/140mm lens. $125-150.

Gnome Pixie

GOERZ (C. P. Goerz, Berlin, Germany)
Started in a single room in 1886, with the manufacturing of lenses as the main business. Became a major manufacturer with over 3,000 employees within the lifetime of the founder. In 1926, three years after the death of Carl Paul Goerz, the company merged with Contessa-Nettel, Ernemann, Ica, and Carl Zeiss Optical Co. to form Zeiss-Ikon. Some Goerz models were continued under the Zeiss name. In 1905, Mr. Goerz organized C.P. Goerz American Optical Co. to supply the steady demand for his products in the United States. This company is still in business, at the leading edge of space-age technology.

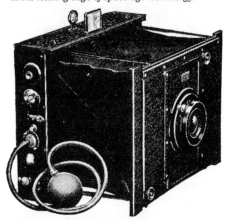

Ango - introduced c1899 and produced for at least 30 years. (An improved version of the Anschutz camera). Strut-type folding camera with focal plane shutter. Goerz Dagor f6.8, Dogmar f3.5, Syntor f6.8, Double Anastigmat f4.6, or Celor f4.8 are among the lenses you could expect to find. $95-150.

Goerz Anschutz Stereo

Ango Stereo - c1906. Similar to the above listing, but for stereo format. $225-275.

Anschutz (box form) - c1890. Dovetailed walnut box camera for 9x12cm plates. Cloth focal plane shutter. This was the first focal plane camera to achieve widespread popularity. Goerz Extra-Rapid Lynkeioscop lens. Folding sportsfinder. Uncommon. $1200-1500.

Box Tengor - c1925. 6x9cm exposures on 120 film. Goerz Frontar f11 lens. $20-30.

Anschutz (strut-type) - Introduced c1901 and quite common with the press during the early part of the century. A bedless "strut" type folding focal plane camera, designed by Ottomar Anschutz. Most often found in the 6x9cm, 9x12cm, and 4x5" sizes. $100-125.

Anschutz Stereo - c1890-1900. A focal plane strut-folding bedless stereo camera for paired exposures on 8x17cm plates. Panoramic views are also possible by sliding one lens board to the center position. With Goerz Dagor Double Anastigmat or Goerz Wide-Angle Aplanat lenses. A relatively uncommon camera. $175-250. *(Illustrated top of next column.)*

Folding Reflex - c1911. A compact folding single lens reflex camera for 4x5" plates. This camera competed for attention with the Bentzin, Goltz & Breutmann Mentor, and Ihagee Patent Klappreflex, all of which were designed to operate as an efficient full-size SLR, but be as portable as an ordinary press camera when folded. $225-275.

Folding rollfilm cameras - For 120 or 116 rollfilms. Various models with Goerz lens and Goerz or Compur shutter. $20-30.

Minicord - (C.P. Goerz, Vienna) - c1951. Subminiature TLR for 10x10mm exposures on 16mm film in special cartridges. f2/25mm Goerz Helgor lens. Metal focal plane shutter 10-400, sync. $225-325.

Minicord III - c1958. Brown leather covered. $225-375.

Photo-Stereo-Binocle - c1899. An unusual disguised detective binocular camera in the form of the common field glasses of the era. In addition to its use as a single-shot camera on 45x50mm plates, it could use plates in pairs for stereo shots, or could be used without plates as a field glass. f6.8/75mm Dagor lenses. $2000-2500. *(Illustrated top of next column.)*

Photo-Stereo-Binocle

Roll Tengor - c1925. Vertical folding rollfilm cameras. Cheaper lenses than the Roll Tenax.
4x6.5 cm - Vest Pocket size, 127 film. Goerz Frontar f9/45mm lens. Shutter 25-100, T, B. $35-50.
6.5x11cm - Tenaxiar f6.8/100mm in Goerz 25-100 shutter. $20-30.

Tenax Cameras *Listed by film type: plate cameras followed by rollfilm cameras.*

Vest Pocket Tenax (plate type) - c1909. Strut-type folding camera for 4.5x6cm plates. A smaller version of the "Coat Pocket Tenax". Goerz Double Anastigmat Celor f4.5/75mm, or f6.8 Dagor or Syntor lens. Compound shutter 1-250, B. $60-100.

Coat Pocket Tenax - c1912-25. 6.5x9cm on plates or film packs. Strut-type camera like the Vest Pocket Tenax. Goerz Dagor f6.8/90mm or Dogmar f4.5/100mm lens. Compound shutter 1-250, T, B. $50-80.

Tenax Folding Plate cameras, bed type
- (Tenax, Manufoc Tenax, Taro Tenax, etc.)
- Plate cameras c1915-1920. Folding bed
type in common square-cornered plate
camera style. Double extension bellows.
Ground glass back.
9x12cm size - Goerz Dogmar f4.5/150mm.
Dial Compur 1-150. $35-50.
9x12cm, Tropical - c1923. Teakwood
with brass fittings. Brown or red leather
bellows. Dogmar f4.5 or Xenar f3.5/135mm
in dial Compur. $250-450.
10x15cm - Goerz Dagor f6.8/168mm, or
Tenastigmat f6.3. Compound or Compur
shutter. $35-50.

Roll Tenax - c1921. Bed-type folding
rollfilm models similar to the American
cameras of the same period.
4x6.5cm - Vest pocket size for 127 film.
Similar to the folding vest pocket cameras
of Kodak & Ansco. f6.3/75mm Dogmar in
Compur shutter to 300. $50-75.
6x9cm - Tenastigmat f6.3/100mm in

Compur shutter 1-250. $20-40.
8x10.5cm - Tenastigmat f6.8/125mm.
$25-45.
8x14cm - Postcard (3¼x5½") size.
Dogmar f4.8/165mm or Dagor f6.8 in
Compur. $40-70.

Roll Tenax Luxus - c1925-26. Metal
parts are gold-plated. Wine red leather
covering and bellows. (Also made in blue/
green version.) Dogmar f4.5/75mm.
Compur 1-300. Rare. Only known recent
sale at auction in mid-1985 for about $800.

Stereo Tenax - c1912-25. Strut-type
folding stereo camera for 45x107mm plates
or packs. Goerz 60mm Dagor f6.8, Syntor
f6.3, or f4.5 Dogmar or Celor. Stereo
Compur or Compound shutter. $150-200.

Tengor - see Box Tengor, Roll Tengor

**GOLDAMMER (Gerhard Goldammer,
Frankfurt)**
Golda - c1949. 35mm camera with
uncoupled rangefinder. Trinar f3.5/45mm
in Prontor II or Radionar f2.9/50mm in
Prontor-S. $50-65.

Goldeck 16 - c1959. Subminiature for
10x14mm exposures on 16mm film.
Interchangeable "C" mount f2.8/20mm
Enna-Color Ennit lens. Behind the lens
shutter. Several models exist. Standard
model has fixed focus lens in Vario shutter.
Model IB is similar, but with focusing
mount. The Super Model has a 9-speed
Prontor shutter and front cell focusing. All
have rapid wind lever, bright frame finder.
While classified as a subminiature because
of its small film, the camera is about the
same size as a compact 35mm camera.
Although once considered more valuable,
a number of these have surfaced in the
last few years, and currently sell with
normal and telephoto lenses: $75-110.
With normal lens only: $60-90.

Goldix - c1950's. Unusual brick-shaped
camera for 4x4cm on 127 film. Eye-level
viewfinder is built into the far side of the
body. Goldeck f7.7/60mm. Singlo-2 shutter
30-100. $20-25.

GuGo - c1950. Low priced 6x6cm camera with telescoping front. Similar to the Welta Perle Jr. 120. Kessar f4.5/75mm in Vario 25-200. $12-18.

GOLDMANN (R. A. Goldmann, Vienna)
Amateur Field Camera, 9x12cm - c1895-1900. Wood body with brass trim. tapered bellows. Goerz Doppel Anastigmat f4.6/150mm. $125-150.

Field camera,13x18cm - c1900. Reversible back, Aplanat lens, mahogany body with brass trim. $125-150.

Reflex viewing, ground glass at rear, and adjustable wire frame finder. Black metal body, partly leather covered. $100-175.

Press camera - c1900. Bedless strut-folding 9x12cm plate camera. Zeiss Tessar f6.3/135. Focal plane shutter T, B, ½-90. Black wood body, leather bellows, nickel trim & struts. $150-175.

Universal Stereo Camera, 9x18cm - c1906. Strut-type focal plane stereo camera. Ebonized wood body. Tessar f6.3/136mm lens. Rare. $750-900.

GOLDSTEIN (France)
Goldy - c1947. Box camera of heavy cardboard with colored covering. Takes 6x9cm on 120 film. Built-in yellow filter. Made in black, blue, white, red, green, and maroon. Also available under such diverse names as Spring, Superas, Week-End, and Racing. Colors: $15-25. Black: $5-10.

GOLTZ & BREUTMANN (Dresden, Germany) *Later Mentor Kamerawerke. All Mentor cameras are listed here, including those manufactured by the "Mentor Kamerawerk", or Rudolph Grosser, Pillnitz.*
Klein-Mentor - c1913-35. A relatively simple SLR for 6x9cm and 6.5x9cm formats. Fold-up viewing hood. Measures 3½x4x4¾" when closed. This camera is a smaller version of the Mentor Reflex. Triotar f6.3/135mm in Compur 1-250. $125-175.

Mentor Compur Reflex - c1928. SLR box for 6.5x9cm plates. Zeiss Tessar f4.5/105 or f2.7/120mm lens. Compur shutter 1-250.

Mentor Dreivier - c1930. An eye-level camera for 16 exposures 3x4cm on 127 film. Styled much like a 35mm camera. Tessar f3.5/50mm lens in Compur shutter 1-300. Rare. $500-750.

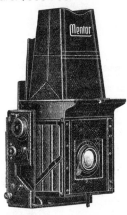

Mentor Folding Reflex (Klappreflex) - c1915-1930. Compact folding SLR in 6x9cm, 9x12cm and 4x5" sizes. Zeiss

Tessar lenses, usually f2.7 or f4.5. Focal plane shutter to 1000. $150-200.

Mentor Reflex - c1914-39. Like Graflex, basically a cube when closed. Fold-up viewing hood, bellows focus, focal plane shutter. Various styles with or without bellows or R.B. in three common sizes: 6.5x9cm, 9x12cm, and 10x15cm. For plates or packs. Most common lenses are f4.5 Tessar, Heliar, and Xenar. $135-200.

Mentor Sport Reflex, 9x12cm - c1936. Box-form SLR. Tessar f4.5/135mm lens. FP ⅛-1300. Rare. $175-200.

Mentor Stereo Reflex - c1913-25. Bellows focusing focal plane box reflex for stereo pairs in the two common European stereo sizes: 45x107mm, with Tessar f4.5/75mm lenses, and 6x13cm with Tessar f4.5/90mm lenses. Both sizes have focal plane shutter 15-1000. $300-450.

Mentor II - c1907. A strut-folding 9x12cm plate camera (NOT a reflex). Triplan f6/125mm or Tessar f4.5/120mm lens. Focal plane shutter. Wood body covered with black leather. Ground glass back. $75-125.

Mentorett - c1936. TLR for 12 exposures 6x6cm on 120 film. Mentor f3.5/75mm. Variable speed focal plane shutter, 1/15-600 sec. Film transport, shutter setting and

release are all controlled by a single lever. Automatic exposure counter. This is a very rare camera, as confirmed by an auction in December 1984. Against a pre-sale estimate of $480, the camera brought $850 in excellent condition with case. However, in March of 1985, another example failed to reach its $450 minimum, and in November, 1985, one sold at auction for the DM 950 minimum (about $435 including taxes, etc.)

GOMZ (USSR)
Sport (Cnopm) - c1935. 35mm SLR. Industar f3.5/50mm lens, shutter 1/25-500. 50 exposures 24x36mm in special 35mm cassettes. $400-700.

GOODWIN FILM & CAMERA CO. *Named for the Rev. Hannibal Goodwin, the inventor of flexible film, but taken over by Ansco. See Ansco for the listing of "Goodwin" cameras.*

GOYO CO. (Japan)

Rosko Brilliant 620, Model 2 - c1955. Black bakelite 6x6cm reflex style camera. 620 rollfilm. It is an export model of the Palma Brilliant Model 2 which used 120 film. $5-10.

G.P.M. (Giuseppi Pozzoli, Milano, Italy)
Fotonesa - c1945. Black bakelite
subminiature for 20x20mm exposures.
Frontar Periscop f8. I,T shutter. $125-175.

GRAFLEX, INC. *(Also including Folmer &*
Schwing and Folmer Graflex products from
1887-1973 except Cirkut cameras which are
listed under Eastman.)
Founded in 1887 as a partnership between Wm.
F. Folmer & Wm. E. Schwing and incorporated
in 1890 as the Folmer & Schwing Manufacturing
Co., it began camera manufacturing in 1897. It
incorporated in 1903 as the Folmer & Schwing
Manufacturing Co. of New York. George Eastman
purchased the company in 1905, moving it to
Rochester NY where it was called the Folmer &
Schwing Co., Rochester. The company dissolved
in 1907, becoming first the Folmer & Schwing
Division of Eastman Kodak and then in 1917
the Folmer & Schwing Department of Eastman
Kodak Co. The new Folmer-Graflex Corporation
took over the reins in 1926, changing its name to
Graflex Inc. in 1945. Graflex was a division of
General Precision Equipment Corp. from 1956
until 1968 when it became a division of Singer
Corporation. In 1973, Graflex dissolved and
Singer Educational Systems was formed, the latter
being bought by Telex Communications in 1982.

EXPLANATION OF SERIAL NUMBERS
RELATING TO GRAFLEX CAMERAS
The numbers on the attached chart have
been taken directly from the original
company serial number book. The first
existing page of that book starts somewhere in the year 1915. From observations
of actual cameras made previous to 1915
it would be safe to assume that the serial
numbers run sequentially at least back to
1905. Because of the purchase of Folmer
& Schwing in 1905 by Eastman Kodak, it
is not known at this time whether the
serial numbering was changed because
of that purchase. Furthermore, it must be
kept in mind that Folmer & Schwing did
not actually start manufacturing their own
cameras until 1897. Before that year, the
cameras that they offered under their own
name were manufactured by someone else.
The question is; was the serial numbering
started before 1897, or only after the
company began its own manufacturing?
Also, whenever the serial numbering
started did it begin with number 1?

The attached chart only takes the serial
numbers through the end of 1947. After
that year, a great deal of confusion
begins, and it would take more room than
the Price Guide allows to explain it all.
Basically, after 1947 different camera
models were assigned different serial
number blocks, and the blocks do not run
sequentially. In addition, several numbers
were repeated within the same camera
model line. The serial number list will be

printed in its entirety and the confusion
minimized in the forthcoming book on the
history of Graflex by Roger M. Adams.

The accompanying chart should also be
used only as an approximation, as it
reflects only the dates that the serial
numbers were entered in the book. The
cameras were actually made sometime
during the following 8-12 months. It
should NOT be used to figure the total
amount of cameras that were manufactured
as some cameras were scrapped and
others were never made, even though the
serial numbers had already been assigned.
The serial number book was never
changed to show any of these variations.
Actual production figures may never have
existed, and if they did, have not been
located as of this date.

Serial Numbers--------------Dates

Folmer & Schwing Division/Department
47,000- 87,976	1915-12/5/18
87,977-113,431	12/5/18-1920
113,432-122,949	1921-1922
122,950-147,606	1923-1925

Folmer-Graflex Corporation
147,607-159,488	1926-1927
159,489-175,520	1928-1930
175,521-183,297	1931-1933
183,298-229,310	1934-1937
229,311-249,179	1938-1939
249,180-351,511	1940-6/15/45

Graflex, Inc.
351,512-457,139	7/30/45-1947

A great deal of information in this section was
used with the kind permission of Mr. Richard
Paine, 10818 Green Arbor, Houston, TX 77089,
(713)-941-6937, from his 1981 book "A Review
of Graflex" published by Alpha Publishing Co.,
Houston, Texas. Collectors wishing more
detailed information on Graflex cameras
should consult this book.

We would also like to thank Roger Adams for
reviewing this section and adding notes and
corrections where necessary. Mr. Adams is
currently working on a book on Graflex
cameras, and he invites readers who are
interested in Graflex to contact him at: P. O.
Box 184, Arcadia, CA 91006, (818)-444-5239.
He is interested in everything related to the
Graflex companies, including apparatus,
literature, advertising, documents, records,
employee papers, awards, banners, etc. He will
be happy to field questions on any areas of
collecting, and would like to make contact
with anyone who has Graflex lore to share,
especially former employees.

NOTE: To keep major lines together, we have divided this section into three parts, each in alphabetic order:
1. **Graflex Single Lens Reflex Cameras.**
2. **Graphic cameras, including press and small format types.**
3. **Other cameras made by Graflex Inc.**

GRAFLEX SLR CAMERAS *All models have focal plane shutters to 1000, unless otherwise noted.*

Graflex (original) - c1902-05. (Earliest patent granted 11/5/01.) Boxy SLR with fold-up viewing hood. Stationary back. Top-hinged door covers the interchangeable lens. Focal plane shutter to 1200. Shutter controls on one piece plate. Normal lenses f4.5 to f6.8. Rare, negotiable. Estimates: 4x5" and 5x7": $250-500. 8x10": Find one first, then ask the price!

Graflex 1A - 1909-25. 2½x4¼" on 116 rollfilm. B&L Tessar f4.5 or f6.3, Zeiss Kodak Anastigmat f6.3, or Cooke f5.6 lens. Early cameras have an "accordian" style hood

Graflex 3A

with struts for support. Later ones have the more typical folding hood. Autographic feature available 1915-on. $75-100.

Graflex 3A - 1907-26. 3¼x5½" "postcard" size on 122 film. Minor body changes, including the addition of the autographic feature, in 1915. Various lenses, f4.5 to f6.8. $75-125. *(Illustrated bottom of previous column.)*

Early Auto Graflex with pleated hood

Auto Graflex - 1906/1907-1923. (Patented 2/5/07.) Stationary Graflex back. Extensible front with lens door hinged at top. Normal lenses f4.5 to f6.8. Design changes include: Pleated hood with front hinge, 1907-c.1910. Folding hood with front hinge c.1911-15. Folding hood with rear hinge 1916-23. 3¼x4¼": $60-80. 4x5": $75-125. 5x7": $150-200. *Add $50 for early model with pleated hood.*

Auto Graflex Junior 2¼x3¼" - 1914-24. Stationary Graflex back. Top door hinges at back. Bulge at rear for reverse-wind curtain. Extensible front. Same body later used in the 2¼x3¼" series B. $90-125.

Naturalists' Graflex

Compact Graflex - Stationary Graflex back. Top door hinged at front. Front bed. Double curtain to cap shutter.
3¼x5½" - 1915-24. $150-200.
5x7" - 1916-25. $200-250.

Home Portrait Graflex - 1912-42. 5x7". Revolving back. Focal plane shutter ½-500. Was also available as the "Special Press Model" with a high speed shutter to 1000.

The focal plane shutter could be set to pass one, two, or more of the aperture slits for a single exposure, thus allowing a very broad range of "slow" speeds. Normal lenses f4.5 to f6.3. This camera was used as the basis for "Big Bertha". $200-250.

National Graflex - SLR for 2¼x2½" on 120 rollfilm. Focal plane shutter to 500, B. B&L Tessar f3.5/75mm. Two models:
Series I - 1933-35. Non-interchangeable lens. Mirror set lever at operator's right of hood. $100-130.

Series II - 1934-41. Cable release. Mirror set lever at operator's left of hood. Ruby window cover. With normal f3.5/75mm lens: $125-200. (With additional B&L f6.3/140mm telephoto add $75-100.)

Naturalists' Graflex - 1907-21. One of the rarest of the Graflex cameras. It has a long body and bellows to accomodate lenses up to 26" focal length. 1907 model has a stationary viewing hood, set to the rear. After that, viewing hood could be positioned to view from top or back. Recent prices have ranged widely from $1500-2800. *(Illustrated top of this page.)*

Revolving Back Auto Graflex

Graflex, but reversible back. Focal plane shutter to 1200. Knob on the front standard raises/lowers the lensboard. $250-500.

Revolving Back Auto Graflex - Normal lenses f4.5 to f6.8. *(Illustrated top of previous column.)*
3¼x4¼" - 1909-41. Style of 1909-16 has front door which forms bed, unlike earlier 4x5" model; front hinged top lid, 3x3" lensboard. Style of c1917-41 has unique top-front curve, rear hinged top lid, and 3¼x3¼" lensboard. $110-150.
4x5" - 1906-41. Early models (1906-08) are styled like the original Graflex. Extensible front racks out on two rails; front flap covers lens. Later styles as with 3¼x4¼" size above, but with 3¾x3¾" lensboard. $125-175.

R.B. Graflex Junior - 1915-23. 2¼x3¼". Revolving back. Fixed lenses, normally f4.5 to f6.3. Lensboard suspended from focusing rails. Similar body style later used for the R.B. Series B. Rare. $100-135.

Press Graflex - 1907-23. 5x7" SLR. Stationary detachable spring back. Focal plane shutter 1/5-1500. Extensible front. No bed. Normal lenses f4.5 to f6.8. $250-350.

Reversible Back Graflex - c1902-05. 4x5" and 5x7" sizes. Very similar to the original

Graflex Series B - Stationary back. Kodak

Anastigmat f4.5 lens. Small front door opens allowing lens and small bellows to extend.
2¼x3¼" - 1925-26 only. Rare. $150-255.
3¼x4¼" - 1923-37. $50-80.
4x5" - 1923-37. $75-125.
5x7" - 1925-42. $150-200.

R.B. Graflex Series B - Revolving back. Kodak Anastigmat f4.5 lens.
2¼x3¼" - 1923-51. Same body style as earlier RB Graflex Junior. Small front door opens allowing lens and small bellows to extend. $75-125.
3¼x4¼" - 1923-42. Same body style as RB Tele Graflex. $60-90.
4x5" - 1923-42. Same body style as RB Tele Graflex. $75-125.

hardware. Later 4x5" models have black hardware and chrome trim.
3¼x4¼" - 1928-41. $60-110.
4x5" - 1928-47. $125-175.

R.B. Super D Graflex - Revolving back SLR. Flash synch on focal plane shutter. Automatic stop-down diaphragm. Minor variations made during its life.
3¼x4¼" - 1941-63. Kodak Anastigmat f4.5, Kodak Ektar f4.5 and f5.6. $175-225.
4x5" - 1948-58. f5.6/190mm Kodak Ektar or Graflex Optar. $300-350.

R.B. Graflex Series C - 1926-35. 3¼x4¼" only. Revolving back. Extensible front with hood over the lens. Fixed Cooke Anastigmat f2.5/6½" lens. Rare. $125-175.

R.B. Graflex Series D - Same body as the earlier RB Tele Graflex and RB Series B. Interchangeable lensboards. Extensible front with hood over the lens. Grey-painted

R.B. Tele Graflex - 1915-23. Revolving back. Designed with a long bellows to allow the use of lenses of various focal lengths. Same body used for RB Graflex Series B.
3¼x4¼": $75-125. 4x5": 110-140.

Stereo Graflex - 1904-05. 5x7" stereo SLR. Stationary back. Similar to style to the original Graflex, but wider to allow for stereo exposures. Two magnifiers in the hood. Quite rare. $1500-2000. *(Illustrated top of next page.)*

215

Stereo Graflex

No. 0 Graphic

Stereo Auto Graflex - 1906-23. 5x7" stereo SLR with only minor improvements having been made on the Stereo Graflex. Stereo prisms in the viewing hood resulted in one STEREO image on the ground glass. That has to be the ultimate composing aid for stereo photographers. Rising front. Very rare. $1000-1500.

Tourist Graflex - c1902-05. Stationary back. Extensible front. Sliding-door covers interchangeable lens. Shutter controls on one piece plate. 4x5" and 5x7" sizes. Very rare. Estimate: $300-600.

GRAPHIC CAMERAS:
Graphic camera - c1904. Simple plate cameras with single extension red bellows. No back movements. 4x5", 5x7", 8x10". $125-150.

No. 0 Graphic - 1909-23. 1⅝x2½" on rollfilm. Focal plane shutter to 500. Fixed-focus Zeiss Kodak Anastigmat f6.3 lens. $175-235.

Century Graphic - 1949-70. 2¼x3¼" press camera. Basic features of the Pacemaker Crown Graphic, but no body release, Graflock back only, and has a plastic body. Black or grey body with black or red bellows. With f4.5: $125-150. With Xenotar f2.8: $200-250.

Combat Graphic - c1942. 4x5" military camera made for the armed forces in WWII. Rigid all wood body, without bellows. Olive drab color. No tension knob on shutter. Sold as a civilian model "Graphic 45" in 1945. $175-275. *Note: the name "Combat Graphic" has been applied by collectors to other military models of conventional cameras, but we have listed those by their proper designation after the corresponding civilian models. See Anniversary Speed Graphic for KE-12(1), and*

Super Speed Graphic for KE-12(2). The 70mm model KE-4(1) is with the miscellaneous models at the end of the Graflex Inc. section.

Combat Graphic

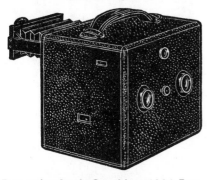

Deceptive Angle Graphic - c1904. Box camera for 3¼x4¼" exposures using double plate holders, magazine plate holder or cartridge rollholder. The 1904 Graflex catalog calls it "in every sense of the word a detective camera, being thoroughly disguised to resemble a stereo camera and so arranged as to photograph subjects at right angles to its apparent line of vision." Quite rare. Estimate: $2000-3000.

Graphic 35 - c1955-58. 35mm camera

designed and built in the U.S.A. by Graflex. Lens and shutter made in Germany and imported by Graflex for use on this camera. Graflar f3.5 or 2.8/50mm lens in helical mount with unique push-button focus. Prontor 1-300. Coupled split-image rangefinder. $30-45.

Graphic 35 Electric - c1959. 35mm camera with electric motor built into the takeup spool. Made by Iloca in Germany. Ysarex f2.8 or Quinon f1.9 in Synchro Compur shutter. Interchangeable front lens element. Coupled meter. In excellent working condition: $125-150. Often found with inoperative motor: $40-60.

Graphic 35 Jet - c1961. An unusual design, incorporating an auto advance mechanism powered by CO_2 cartridges. Made by Kowa. Quite prone to problems with both the shutter and the CO_2 advance system. Completely operational, with original case, box, and a few spare cartridges: $200-250. As normally found with the CO_2 system inoperative: $75-100. With shutter also bad: $40-60. *Note: Because of the problems with the CO2 advance mechanism, a completely manual model was also made.*

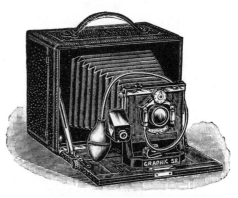

Graphic Sr. - c1904. Very similar to the Graphic camera of the same era, but with swing back. Red bellows. Polished brass trim. 4x5" or 5x7". $75-150.

Pacemaker Crown Graphic - Front shutter only. No focal plane shutter. Built-in body release with cable running along bellows. Metal lensboard. Hinged-type adjustable infinity stops on bed. Wide range of current prices.
2¼x3¼" - 1947-58. $150-175.
3¼x4¼" - 1947-62. $100-140.
4x5" - 1947-73. (Top mounted Graphic rangefinder with interchangeable cams added in 1955.) $150-250.

Reversible Back Cycle Graphic - c1900-06. "Cycle" style cameras with reversible back. Black leather, triple-extension red bellows, rising front. Interchangeable lensboards.
3¼x4¼" & 4x5" sizes - $100-125.
5x7" & 6½x8½" sizes - $100-150.

Reversible Back Cycle Graphic Special - 1904-06. Similar to the original R.B. Cycle Graphic, but sturdier design. Double-swing back. Rising/falling, shifting front. Drop-bed. Front and back focusing. Black leather, triple extension black bellows. Grey-oxidized brass trim. An accessory focal plane shutter was available. 5x7" and 6½x8½" sizes. Quite rare. $150-200.

Revolving Back Cycle Graphic - 1907-1922. Very similar to the Reversible Back Cycle Graphic (above), but revolving back,

no back focus or rear movements. An accessory focal plane shutter was available. 4x5": $75-125. 5x7", 6½x8½", 8x10": $200-250.

SPEED GRAPHIC CAMERAS *Many modifications and improvements were made in these cameras during their exceptionally long life-span (1912-68), so they are usually sub-divided for identification purposes into the following periods: Early (or top handle), Pre-anniversary, Anniversary, and Pacemaker. All models have focal plane shutters. The Speed Graphics are listed here in essentially chronological order.*

Early Speed Graphics - Top handle. Barrel lenses. Tapered bellows, almost double extension. Rising front. Folding optical finder with cross-hairs. Single focus knob on wooden bed.
3¼x4¼" - 1915-25. $70-115.
3¼x5½" - 1912-25. $110-150.
4x5" - 1912-27. (More compact style introduced in 1924, and called Special Speed Graphic.) $75-125.
5x7" - 1912-24. $135-185.

Pre-anniversary Speed Graphic - Side handle. Larger, straight bellows to

accomodate a larger lens standard and lensboard. Wooden bed with single focus knob. Hinged (not telescoping) sportsfinder. Early versions with folding optical finder, later changed to tubular finder. Grey trim.
3¼x4¼" - 1935-39. $60-100.
4x5" - 1928-39. $85-135.
5x7" - c1932-41. $150-200.

Miniature Speed Graphic - 1938-47. 2¼x3¼". Could almost be classified as an Anniversary model with its two focus knobs on the metal bed and chrome trim, but other features from the pre-anniversary years remain. The bed does not drop; the front does not shift. The sportsfinder is hinged, not telescoping. Earliest models with folding optical, later with tubular finder. $70-120.

knobs on the metal drop-bed. Metal lensboard. Built-in body release with cable running along the bellows. Single control on focal plane shutter. Hinged adjustable infinity stops on bed. Telescoping sportsfinder. Tubular viewfinder. Chrome trim. Prices vary widely. Most fall into the ranges listed, and there is no shortage of these cameras, but some vendors consistently advertise at higher prices.
2¼x3¼" - 1947-58. $150-195.
3¼x4¼" - 1947-63. $100-150.
4x5" - 1947-68. (Top mounted Graphic rangefinder witn interchangeable cams added in 1955.) $150-250.
Military model KE-12(1) - 4x5". Optar f4.5/127mm. Olive drab leather & enamel: $150-250. Full set KS-4A(1), with flash unit, film holders, tripod, etc. in Halliburton case. $200-300.

Stereo Graphic (35mm) - ca. mid-1950's for stereo pairs on 35mm film. Graflar f4/35mm lenses in simple shutter, 1/50, B. $60-90.

Anniversary Speed Graphic - 1940-47. Metal drop-bed with two focus knobs. Rising/shifting lens standard. Wooden lensboard. Telescoping sportsfinder. No body release for front shutter. All black (wartime models) or chrome trim. 3¼x4¼": $55-90. 4x5": $95-160.

Stereoscopic Graphic - c1902-21. Solidly built 5x7" stereo camera. Focal plane shutter. Rising front. Drop bed. Black bellows. Grey metal parts. Very rare. $1200-1500.

Pacemaker Speed Graphic - Two focus

Super Graphic - 1958-73. 4x5". All-metal press style camera. Built-in coupled rangefinder. Focusing scale for lenses from 90 to 380mm. Normal lenses include: Kodak Ektar f4.7/127, Schneider Xenar or Graflex Optar f4.7/135mm. Rise, swing, shift, tilt front movements. Revolving back. Electric shutter release. Although a few

Century 35

large dealers consistently advertise at higher prices, these are nearly always available in the range of: $250-350.

Super Speed Graphic - 1959-70. 4x5". Same as the Super Graphic (above), but with Graflex-1000 front shutter. No focal plane shutter. $300-400.
Military model KE-12(2) - with tripod, flash, etc. in olive drab Halliburton case: $300-400.

Graphic View - 1941-48. 4x5" monorail view camera. Without lens: $135-165.

Graphic View II - 1949-67. Improved version of the 4x5" monorail view camera. Has center asix tilts, not available on Graphic View I, and longer bellows. Without lens: $150-200.

MISCELLANEOUS CAMERAS FROM GRAFLEX INC.:
Century 35 - c1961. 35mm camera made by Kowa in Japan. Several models including A, N, NE. Prominar f3.5, 2.8, or 2.0 lens. Similar to the Kallo 35. $25-35. *(Illustrated top of next column.)*

Ciro 35 - c1950. 35mm RF camera, formerly sold by Ciro Cameras Inc. f4.5, 3.5, or 2.8 lens. Alphax or Rapax shutter. $15-30.

Crown View - 1939-42. Wooden 4x5" view camera. 4x4" lensboards interchangeable with 4x4" Speed Graphic. Rare. $185-250.

Finger-Print Camera - Special-purpose camera for photographing fingerprints or making 1:1 copies of other photos or documents. 2¼x3¼" Pre-focused lens is recessed to the proper focal distance inside a flat-black rigid shroud. To make an exposure, camera front opening is placed directly on the surface to be photographed. Four battery-operated flashlight bulbs provide the illumination. (Two similar cameras called the Inspectograph (see listing below) and

Graflex 22

220

Factograph were also made. The Factograph used special positive paper film on a roll. Later models of the Factograph became very specialized using bulk loads of film, motorized advance, and special lighting and bore no resemblance to the earlier models.) $75-125.

Graflex 22 - TLR for 6x6cm on 120 film. Optar or Graftar f3.5/88mm. Century Synchromatic or Graphex shutter. Fairly common. $25-40. *(Illustrated bottom of previous page.)*

Inspectograph Camera - Identical to the Fingerprint camera, but wired for 110V AC current instead of built-in batteries. Only about 500 made. $75-110.

KE-4(1) 70mm Combat Camera - c1953 Civilian black or Signal Corps Model in olive drab. For 5.5x7cm exposures on 70mm film. Designed by the late Hubert Nerwin, formerly of Zeiss Ikon, the camera resembles an overgrown Contax and is nicknamed "Gulliver's Contax". A few years ago, these were scarce and highly sought. Then Uncle Sam started disposing of them, and now they are very easy to find. Consequently, prices have dropped and they are harder to sell. Many are still advertised at higher prices, but one major dealer reported advertising an outfit with two lenses, flash, and case for 7 months at $495 before it finally sold. The f4.5/2½" Ektar wide angle is the least common lens. Camera set KS6-(1) with normal, tele, and W.A. lenses, case: $750-1000. Often found with f2.8/4" and f4/8" Ektar lenses, flash, and Halliburton case: $500-600 asking prices. Camera with normal lens only: $300-400.

Norita - c1969-73. Eye-level SLR for 6x6cm on 120 or 220 film. Three models: Deluxe, Professional (with front shutter), and Super Wide. Made by Norita Kogaku K.K. in Tokyo, imported by Graflex. Originally imported as the Warner. Noritar f2/80mm lens in interchangeable breech-lock mount. Focal plane shutter 1-500. $175-275.

Photorecord - Developed around 1934, introduced to the open market in 1936.

Made through the 1950's in many different forms and models, including civilian and military versions. Special purpose camera for microfilming, personnel identification, and copy work. All versions were designed around the same basic heavy cast metal camera and film magazine unit, and were offered as complete outfits including lights, stands, copy or I.D. apparatus. Designed for use with 100 ft. rolls of 35mm film, they were capable of 800 "double frame" or 1600 "single frame" exposures. Also capable of single exposures using Graflex plate or film holders. Camera with film magazine: $75-125.

GRAY (Robert D. Gray, NYC)
Vest Camera - c1885. All metal disc-shaped camera designed to be worn under a vest. Forerunner of the more common Stirn Vest Camera. Manufactured for Gray by the Western Electric Co. Takes 6 round exposures on an octagonal glass plate. $1300-1800.

View camera - 8x10". c1880. Periscope No. 4 lens with rotary disc stops. $175-200.

GREAT WALL SZ-1 - c1976. People's Republic of China 35mm spring-motor camera. CRF. f2.8/45mm coated lens, rotating 1/30- 1/300 shutter. Leather covered aluminum body. $50-60.

GRIFFIN (John J. Griffin & Sons, Ltd., London)
Pocket Cyko Cameras - c1902. Folding cameras of unusual book form, designed by Magnus Niell, the Swedish designer who is also responsible for the popular Expo and Ticka designs. Also sold on the continent under the name "Lopa". Several sizes and styles, including the No. 1 for 6.5x9cm plates, and the No. 2 with magazine back for 8x10.5cm plates. Despite higher prices a few years ago, more recent auction sales of the No. 1 have been in the $380-400 range, while we saw a No. 2 offered for $750 with original magazine back. *(Illustrated top of next page.)*

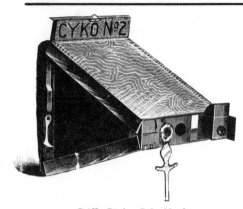

Griffin Pocket Cyko No. 2

GRIFFITHS (Walter M. Griffiths & Co., Birmingham, England)
Guinea Detective Camera - c1895. Leather covered cardboard camera in the shape of a carrying case. The top hinges to one side to change plateholders, and the front conceals a guillotine shutter. $200-250.

GROSSER (Rudolph Grosser, Pillnitz) *Manufacturer of Mentor cameras during the 1950's. However, all Mentor Cameras are listed in this edition under Goltz & Breutmann.*

GRUNDMANN
Leipzig Detective Camera - All wood box detective camera for 9x12cm plates. String-set shutter. $800-850.

GUERIN (E. Guerin & Cie., Paris)
Le Furet - c1923. Small, early 35mm camera for 25 exposures 24x36mm using special cassettes. This is the smallest of the pre-Leica 35mm cameras. While these sold a few years ago for $1500-1800, the current market indicates a more stable price of $800-1000.

GUILFORD - Polished walnut 5x7" English view camera with brass fittings. Brass-barreled Ross Extra Rapid lens. $150-175.

GUILLEMINOT (Guilleminot Roux & Cie., Paris)
Guilleminot Detective Camera - c1900. Polished walnut detective camera for 9x12cm plates. Brass knobs rack front panel forward and concealed viewfinders are exposed. Brass carrying handle and fittings. Aplanat f9/150mm lens. Eight speed rotary sector shutter. $800-900.

GUNDLACH OPTICAL CO., GUNDLACH MANHATTAN OPTICAL CO. (Rochester, N.Y.) *Originally founded by Ernst Gundlach for the production of optical*

goods, but for most of the company's history it was operated by H.H.Turner, J.C.Reich, & J.Zellweger. Gundlach Optical Co. acquired the Milburn Korona Company in 1896, which added a line of cameras to their line of lenses. Shortly thereafter, they joined with Manhattan Optical to become one of the leading sellers of dry-plate cameras well into the 1900's. The company was taken over by John E. Seebold in 1928 and the name changed to the "Seebold Invisible Camera Company."

Criterion View - c1909-1930's. Traditionally styled wooden view camera, virtually unchanged in appearance from its 1909 Gundlach catalog listing to the mid-1930s catalogs of Burke & James. Made in 5x7", 6½x8½", and 8x10" sizes. Current value is still as a good used view camera, depending on size and condition. $75-150.

Korona cameras - classified here by size:
3¼x4¼" and 3¼x5½" - Folding plate cameras, including "Petit" models. Cherry wood body, leather covered. Red bellows. $30-60.
4x5" - Folding bed view camera. $65-105.

5x7" - as above two listings. $75-125.

5x7" Stereo - Folding plate camera for stereo exposures on standard 5x7" plates.

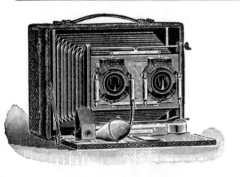

Leather covered wood body with polished wood interior. Simple stereo shutter. $300-360.

Korona 6½x8½" view - $100-150.
Korona 8x10" view - $125-175.

Korona 7x17", 8x20", and 12x20" Panoramic View - usually called "Banquet" cameras. With holder, without lens: $200-300. Add for lens, depending on type. A good working outfit with several holders and a good lens & shutter will bring $350-650.

Long Focus Korona - $125-175.

HADDS MFG. CO. - see Foto-Flex Corp.

HADSON - Japanese novelty subminiature of Hit type. $10-20.

HAGI MFG. (Japan)
Clover - c1939. Folding camera for 4.5x6cm on 120 film. Venner f4.5/75mm Anastigmat in Vester shutter, T,B,1-200. $50-75.

Clover Six - c1940. Folding camera for 6x6cm on 120 film. G.R.C. Venner f4.5/80mm in Oriental shutter T,B,1-200. $50-75.

HAKING (W. Haking, Hong Kong) *While Haking produces many cameras, most are not*

yet of collectible age. We are listing a few of the "novelty" types.

Halina 35 - c1982. Inexpensive plastic 35mm camera. Although a recent model, this is definitely a novelty camera. The same camera, of very inexpensive construction, appears under various names, often as a low-cost premium. $10-15.

Halina 35X - c1959. Inexpensive but heavy 35mm camera with cast metal body. $8-12.

Halina-Baby - Plastic novelty camera from Macau. $1-5.

Halina-Prefect Senior - Fixed focus TLR-style camera, 6x6cm. Stamped metal body with leatherette covering. Double meniscus f8 lens, B&I shutter. $10-15.

Halina Viceroy - Twin-lens box camera similar to the Halina-Prefect Senior. $10-15.

Kinoflex Deluxe - c1960. TLR style box camera, similar to the Halina-Prefect Senior. $10-15.

Roy Box - c1960's. For 4x4cm. Halimar 47mm lens. Single speed shutter. Built-in flash. $1-5.

Votar Flex - c1958. TLR style box camera, also similar to the Halina-Prefect Senior. $10-15.

Wales Reflex - TLR style camera similar to Halina-Prefect Senior (above). $10-15.

HALL CAMERA CO. (Brooklyn, NY) Mirror Reflex Camera - c1910. 4x5" Graflex-style SLR. f4.5/180mm lens. $75-125. *(Illustrated bottom of previous column.)*

Pocket Camera - c1913. Small focal plane strut camera. Goerz Celor f3.5 lens. $600-700.

HALMA-FLEX - 6x6cm TLR. Halmar Anastigmat f3.5/80mm. $12-18.

HAMAPHOT KG (Monheim, Germany) Modell P56L - c1952. Bakelite camera with telescoping front. Takes 6x6cm on 120. Available in black or dark green. $12-18.

Modell P56M - Similar to the above model, but green with gold-colored trim. $12-18.

Modell P56M Exportmodell - Dark green bakelite camera with helical telescoping front. Gold-colored metal trim. $12-18. *(Illustrated top of next page.)*

Hall Mirror Reflex

Hamaphot Model P56M Exportmodell

Modell P66 - c1950. Bakelite eye-level camera for 6x6cm on 120 rollfilm. Achromat f7.7/80mm. B,25,50,100. $8-12.

HAMCO - Japanese 14x14mm novelty camera of Hit type. $10-15.

HAMILTON SUPER-FLEX - c1947. Bakelite novelty TLR for 16 exposures on 127 film. Similar to Metro-Flex, etc. $5-10.

HANAU (Eugene Hanau, Paris)

le Marsouin - c1900. Rigid aluminum body stereo camera for 18 plates in magazine

back. No. 1 size for 45x107mm plates; No. 2 size for 6x13cm plates. Tessar or Balbreck lenses. Guillotine shutter. $175-225.

Passe-Partout - c1890. Unusual brass detective camera with conical front which moves in succession to four positions on a double 6x13cm plateholder, making a 6cm round exposure at each position. Quite rare. It's sales history shows cameras offered for sale in early 1982 at $6500, in October of 1984 for $2775, and in late 1986 for $2800.

HANEEL TRI-VISION CO. (Alhambra, CA)

Tri-Vision Stereo - c1953. Plastic and aluminum stereo camera for 28x30mm pairs on 828 rollfilm. f8 meniscus lenses with 3 stops. Usually found in excellent condition with original box, stereo viewer, etc. for $30-40.

HANIMEX
Holiday, Holiday II - c1960's. 35mm cameras with CRF. S-Kominar f3.5/45 in Copal. $12-18.

HANNA-BARBERA
Fred Flintstone, Huckelberry Hound, Yogi Bear (127 types) - Novelty cameras for 127 film, each featuring the image of a cartoon character printed on the side. Imitation light meter surrounds lens. $1-5.

Fred Flintstone, Yogi Bear (126 types) -

Similar small cameras, but for 126 cartridge film. On these, the front of the camera is in the shape of the character's head, with the lens in the mouth. $5-10.

HANSEN (J.P. Hasnsen, Copenhagen)
Norka - c1920's. Studio view camera for 2,3,4, or 6 portraits on one 12x16cm plate. Corygon Anastigmat f3.5/105mm or Cooke Aviar Anastigmat f4.5/152mm lens. With large Norca studio stand: $1000-1300.

HAPPY - Japanese Hit-type novelty camera. $10-15.

HARBOE, A. O. (Altona, Germany)

Wood box camera - c1870. For glass plates. Typical of the type of camera made in Germany during the 1870-1890 period. Although it pre-dated the "Kodak", it was made for the ordinary person to use. Brass barrel lens, simple shutter, ground glass back. Only one sale on record, in late 1976 at $600.

HARE (George Hare, London)
Stereo Wet-plate - c1860. For 3¼x6¾" wet collodion plates. Mahogany body with twin red bellows. Matching brass lenses with waterhouse stops. With ground glass back and wet-plate holder: $1000-1200.

Tailboard Camera - Full-plate size. Mahogany construction. Rack focus. Dallmeyer Rapid Landscape lens. $80-130.

Tropical Stereo Wet-plate camera - c1865. For stereo views on 5x8" wet plates. Polished teak body with brass fittings. Petzval lenses with waterhouse stops and flap shutter. $3000-3500.

Tourist camera - c1865. Half-plate. Fallowfield Rapid Doublet lens with iris diaphragm. Changing box. $350-600.

HARMONY - c1955. Inexpensive eye-level metal box camera from Japan for 6x6cm on 120. Focusing lens, 3 speed shutter, PC sync. $10-15.

HARTEX - Japanese subminiature of the Hit type. $10-15.

HARUKAWA (Japan)

Septon Pen Camera - c1953. A rare subminiature of unusual design. Camera combined with an oversized mechanical pencil. There are two major variations.
Deluxe Model - Has serial number on metal lens rim. Guillotine shutter. Variable f-stops controlled by knob under viewfinder. Back fastens with sliding latch. *(Illustrated above.)*
Simple model - Even more rare than the deluxe model. No serial number. No metal lens rim. Sector shutter. No f-stops. Back fastens with two thumb-screws.
Several years ago, a few new "Deluxe" models were discovered, complete with original box and instructions. These quickly sold for approximately $1250 each, and several recent transactions support that price. Used models, without the box and instructions have sold in the range of $500-800.

Septon Penletto - c1953. A name variant of the Septon. Features are like the simple model, except for the conical lens mount with narrow front. $600-900.

HASSELBLAD (Victor Hasselblad Aktiebolag, Goteborg, Sweden)
Founded by Fritz Victor Hasselblad in 1841 as F.W. Hasselblad & Co., the company opened a photo department in 1887. Due to expansion in that department, a separate company, "Hasselblads Fotografiska Aktiebolag", was founded in 1908 and became the Kodak general agent in Sweden. Although the early companies sold cameras made by other manufacturers, the real beginning was when "Victor Hasselblad Aktiebolag" was established in 1941 to manufacture aerial cameras for the Royal Swedish Air Force, as well as ground reconnaissance cameras. Dr. Victor Hasselblad retained his staff after the war and began the final designing of the Hasselblad 1600F, which was introduced in 1948. To ascertain the year of production, the two letters before the serial number indicate the year, with the code "VH PICTURES" representing the digits "12 34567890".

Aerial Camera HK7 - c1941-45. Hand-held aerial camera for 50 exposures on 70mm film. Tele-Megor f5.5/250mm. Shutter 1/150-400. $800-1200.

1600F - 1948-52. The world's first 6x6cm SLR with interchangeable lenses and film magazines. It is most easily distinguished by its focal plane shutter to 1/1600. Originally supplied with Kodak Ektar f2.8/80mm lens and magazine back for $548. Accessory lenses include Ektar f3.5/135mm and Zeiss Opton Sonnar f4/250mm. The shutter on the 1600F was not of the quality we have since grown to expect from Hasselblad, and often this model is seen for sale with an inoperative shutter for less. The prices given here are for cameras in VG-E condition, operational, with back and original lens: $450-650.

1000F - 1952-57. The second Hasselblad model, and still with a focal plane shutter, but with the top speed reduced to 1/1000 sec. This attempted to eliminate the accuracy and operational problems of the older shutter. Sold for $400 when new. Replaced the 1600F, but while supplies lasted, the 1600F continued to sell at $500.

Despite the improvements, these still are often found with inoperative shutters, for less than the prices quoted here. With back and normal lens: $300-400.

Super Wide Angle - 1954-59. Also called SW and SWA. Can be easily distinguished from the normal models, since it has a short, non-reflex body. "Super Wide Angle" is inscribed on the top edge of the front. The early SWA can be distinguished from the later SWC in several ways. The most obvious is that it has a knob for film advance rather than a crank, and shutter cocking is a separate function. The shutter release is on the lower right corner of the front, while the SWC has a top release button. Zeiss Biogon f4.5/38mm lens in MX Compur to 500. The value of this camera is not as a collectible, but as a usable camera. With finder and magazine back: $675-800.

500C - 1957-70. From a technical standpoint, the 500C is an innovative camera, since it replaced the focal plane shuttered 1000F with an entirely new Compur front shutter with full aperture viewing and automatic diaphragm. From a practical standpoint, however, the value of the camera is primarily as a very usable piece of equipment, despite the advanced age of some of the earlier ones. Collectors want cosmetically clean cameras, but generally the users will outbid the collectors for a clean 500C. That's the bottom line. Because of the wide range of lenses and accessories, it would not be practical to go into detail here, but as an example, you might pick up a nice 500C with back, finder, and f2.8/80mm Planar in the range of $650-750.

HEALTHWAYS

Mako Shark - c1957. Cylindrical plastic underwater camera. The entire working mechanism including shutter, lens, and film transport are identical to the Brownie Hawkeye Flash Model. Synchronized and non-sync models. $30-45.

HEILAND PHOTO PRODUCTS (Div. of Minneapolis-Honeywell, Denver, Colorado)
Premiere - c1957-59. 35mm non-RF camera made in Germany. Steinheil Cassar f2.8/45mm in Pronto to 200. $20-30.

HELIN-NOBLE INC. (Union Lake, Michigan)
Noble 126 - Miniature gold & black "snap-on" camera for 126 cartridges, with matching flash. Winding knob pivots for compactness. The world's smallest 126 cartridge camera. With tele and W.A. lenses in original plastic box: $50-75.

HELM TOY CORP. (New York City)
Bugs Bunny - c1978. Plastic camera with figure of Bugs Bunny. "Eh-Doc, Smile!". In Europe: up to $40. In the U.S.: $15-22.

Mickey Mouse - c1979. Blue plastic camera with white molded front. Mickey Mouse riding astradde a toy train. In Europe: $20-30. U.S.A.: $15-22.

Mickey Mouse Head (110 film) - c1985. Cheaply constructed camera in shape of Mickey Mouse head with red bow tie. Round camera mechanism for 110 film is based on the Potenza design. $10-15.

Punky Brewster - c1984. Red plastic 110 pocket camera. Added-on front with hinged top cover. Decals applied to the front, top, and carrying case. Retail price about $6. *(Illustrated top of next column.)*

Snoopy-Matic - A modern detective camera. The camera is shaped like a dog house, with Snoopy relaxing on the roof. The chimney accepts magicubes. This camera is less common than the others

Punky Brewster

from Helm, and is a more interesting design. It brings up to $100 in Europe and $50-60 in the U.S.

HENDREN ENTERPRISE

Octopus "The Weekender" - c1983. Named for its multiple functions, this device houses an AM-FM transistor radio, alarm clock with stopwatch functions, flashlight, storage compartment, and a 110 camera with electronic flash. It sold new for $70-80. This high price, coupled with quality problems, kept it from making great waves in the marketplace. $70-90.

HENNING (Richard Henning, Frankfurt/M, Germany) *The trade name Rhaco presumably stands for Richard Henning And Co.*
Rhaco Folding Plate Camera - c1930. 6.5x9cm. Ennatar Anastigmat f4.5/105mm. Ibsor 1-125 shutter. Radial lever focusing. $20-30.

Rhaco Monopol - c1933. 9x12cm folding plate camera. Radionar f6.3/135mm in Ibso 1-100. Radial lever focusing. $20-30.

HENSOLDT (Dr. Hans Hensoldt, Wetzlar) *The Henso cameras were actually made by I.S.O. in Milan, but sold with the Hensoldt, Wetzlar label for the Italian market.*

Henso Reporter - c1953. 35mm RF. Dr. Hans Hensoldt Iriar f2.8/5cm or Arion f1.9/50mm lens. FP shutter 1-1000. Folding rapid advance lever in base. $850-1150 in Germany.

Henso Standard - Similar, but knob wind rather than lever. $500-750.

HERBERT GEORGE CO. (Chicago)
Founded by Herbert Weil and George Israel c1945. Bought out in 1961 and name changed to "Imperial Camera Corp."

Davy Crockett - Black plastic box camera for 6x6cm. Metal faceplate illustrates Davy Crockett and rifles. $20-35.

Donald Duck Camera - c1946. Plastic 127 rollfilm camera for 1⅝x1⅝" exposures. Figures of the Disney ducks (Donald, Huey, Louie, and Dewey) in relief on the back. Meniscus lens, simple shutter. This was the first camera design patented by George L. Israel. The earliest models, ca. Sept 1946 were olive-drab color and without external metal back latches. This version brings about $10 more than the later ones. The body was soon changed to black plastic, and by November 1946, external back latches had been added. This is the most common version. With original cardboard carton: $35-50. Camera only: $15-25.

Flick-N-Flash - Twin lens box camera. $1-5.

Herco Imperial 620 Snap Shot

Happi-Time - Plastic camera for 127. Essentially the same design as the Donald Duck camera, but without the bas-relief back. $3-7.

Herco Imperial 620 Snap Shot - Cheap plastic box camera. $1-5. *(Illustrated on bottom of previous column.)*

Herco-flex 6-20 - Plastic twin-lens style. 2¼x2¼" on 620 rollfilm. $3-6.

Imperial Debonair - Bakelite box camera with interesting styling. Normally found in black color. $3-6.

Imperial Mark XII Flash - Plastic box camera, in colors. $1-5.

Imperial Reflex - ca. mid-1950's plastic 6x6cm TLR for 620 film. Simple lens and shutter. $1-5.

Imperial Satellite 127, Imperial Satellite Flash - $1-5.

Insta-Flash - Twin lens box camera. $1-5.

Roy Rogers & Trigger - Black plastic box camera for 620 film. Aluminum faceplate pictures Roy Rogers on Trigger. $15-20.

Savoy, Savoy Mark II, etc. - Common plastic box cameras. $1-3.

Official "Scout" cameras - Boy Scout, Brownie Scout, Cub Scout, Girl Scout. In black or in official scout colors. These cameras were based on many different "civilian" models, so quite a number of variations exist. Camera only: $5-10. In original box with flash unit: $10-15.

Stylex - An unusual design for the Herbert-George company. Plastic body with rectangular telescoping front. 6x9cm on 620 film. $5-10.

HERLANGO AG (Vienna)
Folding camera - For 7x8.5cm plates or rollfilm back. Tessar f4.5/105mm. Compur shutter 1-250. $30-40.

Folding Plate Camera, 10x15cm - Folding bed camera for 10x15cm plates. Double extension bellows. $25-35.

HERMAGIS (J. Fleury Hermagis, Paris)
Field Camera 13x18cm - Polished walnut camera with brass handle and inlaid brass fittings. Thornton-Pickard roller-blind shutter. Hermagis, naturellement, Aplanastigmat f6.8/210mm lens. Rotating maroon bellows for vertical or horizontal use. $175-250.

Micromegas - c1875. An unusual wooden box camera with hinged edges, designed to fold flat when the lensboard and viewing screen are removed. Nickel-plated lens with small slot for waterhouse stop in the focusing helix. $3500-4500. *(Illustrated on back cover.)*

Velocigraphe - c1892. Detective style drop-plate magazine camera for 12 plates 9x13cm in metal sheaths. Polished wooden body built into a heavy leather covering which appears to be a case. Front and back flaps expose working parts. $600-850.

Velocigraphe Stereo - c1895-97. Polished walnut magazine box camera for six 8x17cm plates. Matching, individually focusing Hermagis lenses in bright nickel-plated barrels. Shutter tensioning and plate changing mechanisms are coupled. And you thought the first idiot-proof cameras were made of plastic! $1000-1300.

HEROLD MFG. CO. (Chicago) *The Herold name was first used in 1951 when Harold Rubin, former Sales Manager for Spartus Camera Co., purchased the Spartus company and renamed it. This was about the same time that Jack Galter, former President of Spartus, had formed Galter Products. Herold Mfg. continued to produce Spartus cameras, changing its name to Herold Products Co. Inc. in 1956, and to "Spartus Corporation" about 1960. Check under the "Spartus" heading for related cameras.*

Acro-Flash - Black bakelite minicam for 127 film. Twin sync posts above the lens barrel. One of the few minicams with flash sync. $3-7.

Da-Brite - Brown bakelite minicam for 3x4cm on 127 film. $3-7.

Flash-Master - Synchronized minicam like the Acro-Flash. 3x4cm on 127 film. $3-7.

Herold 40 - Black bakelite minicam for 3x4cm on 127 film. $3-7.

Photo-Master - Economy model plastic minicam. "Photo Master" molded into the plastic shutter face rather than using a metal faceplate. $2-5.

Spartacord - x1958. Inexpensive 6x6cm TLR, but with focusing lenses. Nicely finished with brown covering and accessories. $10-15.

Spartus 35 - Low cost brown bakelite 35mm camera with grey plastic top. $10-15.

Spartus 35F, Spartus 35F Model 400 - Variations of the Spartus 35. $10-15.

Spartus 120 Flash Camera - c1953.

Brown bakelite box camera with eye level finder on side. $4-8.

Spartus Co-Flash - c1962. Small bakelite box camera with built-in flash reflector beside the lens. 4x4cm on 127. $8-12.

Sunbeam 120 - Bakelite box camera, either brown or black. Synchronized. Several variations. $1-5.

Sunbeam 127 - Two types:
Plastic box camera for 12 square pictures 4x4cm on 127 film. Styled like the more common Spartus Vanguard. $1-3.
Streamlined brown bakelite minicam for 16 exposures 3x4cm on 127 film. $3-7.

Sunbeam Six-Twenty - Plastic TLR style box camera. Several variations. $3-7.

HERZOG (August Herzog, New York City)
Herzog Amateur Camera - c1877. Very simple 2x2½" plate camera made of wood and cardboard. Dry plate slides into the back which is mounted on a baseboard. Pyramidal front holds brass lens that slides in and out for focusing. Rare. We have seen only one offered for sale in mid-1983 for $3500 in the original box with accessories.

HESEKIEL (Dr. Adolf Hesekiel & Co., Berlin)
Pompadour - Same camera that Lancaster sold as the Ladies' Gem Camera. See Lancaster.

HESS & SATTLER (Wiesbaden, Germany)
Field Camera, 9x12cm - c1895-1900. Tailboard style. Fine wood with brass trim. Tapered wine-red bellows. Hess & Sattler Universal Aplanat Extra Rapid lens with waterhouse stops. $125-175.

HESS-IVES CORP. (Philadelphia, PA)

Hicro Color Camera - c1915. Box-shaped camera for color photos 3¼x4¼" by the separation process via multiple exposures with filters. Meniscus lens. Wollensak Ultro shutter. (Made for Hess-Ives under contract by the Hawk-Eye Division of E.K.C.) $100-200.

HETHERINGTON & HIBBEN (Indianapolis)

Hetherington Magazine Camera - c1892. Magazine camera for 4x5" plates. Dark brown leather covered. Plate advancing, aperture setting, & shutter tensioning are all controlled by a key. This camera was once marketed by Montgomery Ward & Co. $450-550.

HG TOYS INC. (Long Island, New York) HG TOYS LTD. (Hong Kong)

Masters of the Universe He-Man 110 Camera - c1985. Green plastic camera shaped like "Castle Grayskull". Made in China under license from Mattel. $8-10.

Princess of Power She-Ra 110 Camera - c1985. Pink plastic camera shaped like "Crystal Castle". Made in China under

license from Mattel Toys. $8-10.

HI-FLASH - Novelty camera of Diana type. Synchronized. $1-5.

HILCON - Inexpensive metal eye-level camera for 4x5cm exposures on 120 film. Similar to the General, Rocket, and Palmer cameras from the Rocket Camera Co., but with a slightly longer body. $3-6.

HILGER (Adam Hilger, Ltd., London) Three-Colour Camera - Color separation camera with 2 small semi-silvered mirrors behind the lens. $700-1000.

HIT TYPE CAMERAS - *There are many small cameras which were made in post-WWII Japan. One class of these subminiatures is commonly called "Hit-types" because the Hit name (from Tougodo) was one of the first and most popular names found on this type of camera. Despite their overall similarity, there are many subtle differences in construction from one camera to the next, and there is a seemingly endless number of names which graced the fronts, tops, and cases. There may never be a complete list, but this is probably the most complete one to date. If you know of others not on this list, please write to the authors. This list is intended to include only the inexpensive, lightweight "Hit" type cameras. Heavier models, such as the Corona, Mighty, Mycro, Rocket, Tacker, Tone, Vesta, Vestkam, etc. are not included on this list.* **Name variations** - AHI, Amerex (Occupied Japan), Arcoflex, Arrow, Astra, Astropic, Atomy, Babymax, Barco, Beica, Bell 14, Betsons, Bluestar, Charmy, Click, CMA, CMC (in chrome or gold with a variety of colored coverings), Colly, Crown, Crystar, Dale, Diplomat, Electronic, Elite, Emson, Enn Ess, Francya, Global, Globe, GNCO, Hadson, Hamco, Happy, Hartex, Hit (Occupied Japan, chrome, and gold models), Homer, Homer 16 (rectangular body), Homer No. 1 (gray rectangular body), I.G.B., Jay Dee, Kassin, Kent, Lenz, Lloyd's, Lucky, Marvel, Midge, Midget, Mighty Midget, Minetta, Mini Camera (Hong Kong),

Miracle, Mity, Mykro Fine, Old Mexico, Pacific, Pamex, Peace, PFCA, Prince, Q.P, Real, Regent, Satellite, Shalco, Shayo, Sil-Bear, Sing 88, Siraton, Speedex, Spesco, Sputnik, Star-Lite, Stellar, Sterling, Swallow, Tee Mee, Toyoca (note: heavier "Toyoca 16" also exists), Traveler, Vesta (this is a heavier type, but not by much!), Walklenz. *PLEASE SEND ANY ADDITIONS AND CORRECTIONS TO: Jim McKeown; Centennial Photo; Box 1125; Grantsburg, WI 54840 USA. Please send your name and address if you wish to be on our "Hit list" and to cooperate in the research and enjoyment of these little cameras.*

HOEI INDUSTRIAL CO. (Japan)

Anny-44 - c1960. Inexpensive metal eye-level box camera for 4x4cm on 127 film. Designed to look like a 35mm camera. Fixed focus f8 lens, single speed shutter. $8-12.

Ebony 35 - c1957. Bakelite camera for 25x37mm exposures on 828 rollfilm. f11 meniscus lens. Simple B & I shutter. $10-15.

Ebony 35 De-Luxe - c1955. Like the Ebony 35, but metal trim on front and finder. f8 lens. $10-15.

Ebony Deluxe IIS - c1957. Metal front and top housing. PC sync accessory shoe. f8/50mm lens. $10-20.

HOFERT (Emil Hofert, EHO Kamera Fabrik, Dresden, Germany) see EHO-ALTISSA.

HOMER - Hit-type novelty subminature. $10-15.

HOMER 16 - c1960. Japanese novelty camera for 14x14mm exposures on 16mm film. Meniscus lens, simple shutter. Hit-type camera, but with rectangular top housing and thumb-wheel advance. (Similar to Bell 14 and Homer No. 1.) Chrome top body with black covering. "Homer 16" on viewfinder glass and shutter face. $15-20.

HOMER NO. 1: see Kambayashi & Co.

HONEYWELL
Electric Eye 35R - c1962. 35mm RF camera made by Mamiya with Honeywell name. Meter for auto diaphragm surrounds lens. $15-20.

HORIZONT - c1968. Russian 35mm panoramic camera with f2.8 pivoting lens for 120 degrees. $200-275.

HORNE & THORNTHWAITE (Newgate, G.B.)
Powell's Stereoscopic Camera - Patented in 1858 by T.H. Powell, the camera had a sliding back for two successive exposures on the same plate. The single lens camera could be positioned for the second exposure by sliding it along the tracks on the carrying case and its hinged lid. We have no recent sales recorded, but at least 2 examples sold in 1974 in the $3500-4000 range.

Wet-plate camera - c1860. Sliding box style for 12x16.5cm plates. $1000-1500.

HORSMAN (E. I. Horsman Co., N.Y.C.)

No. 3 Eclipse - c1896. Folding bed, collapsible bellows, polished cherry-wood view camera for 4½x6½" plates. Styled like the more common Scovill Waterbury camera. Brass barreled meniscus lens. Rubber-band powered shutter. $175-225.

Eclispe - c1895. An unusual box-plate camera for single exposures 4x5". Black papered wood body. Primitive meniscus lens. Wooden lens cap. $200-225.

HOUAY
Anny-35 - c1964. Inexpensive 35mm novelty camera. Looks convincing from a distance, but is only a box camera. $8-12. *Perhaps Houay and Hoei are variations in the*

English translation of the same manufacturer. Anny-35 has "Houay" stamped into its top. Anny-44 has "Hoei Industrial Co." on the lens rim. The two cameras are quite similar in construction.

HOUGHTON (London, England)

Houghtons dates back to 1834 when George Houghton joined Antoine Claudet as a glass seller. After the announcement of the Daguerreotype process in 1839, Claudet and Houghton secured the patent rights to the process in England and began selling Daguerreotype requisites. On Claudet's death in 1867 the firm became George Houghton and Son, George Houshton and Sons in 1892, and Houghtons Ltd. in 1904. The firm produced a vast range of cameras and accessories, notably after 1904 when it absorbed a number of smaller camera makers. From 1895 Houghtons was also responsible for producing the Sanderson camera.

The firm came together for manufacturing purposes with W. Butcher in 1915 and the two finally merged on January 1, 1926 as Houghton-Butcher (Great Britain) Ltd. Houghton-Butcher manufactured products and a selling arm, Ensign Ltd, was set-up in 1930. On the night of September 24-25, 1940 enemy action completely destroyed Ensign's premises at 88/89 High Holborn. Johnson and Sons, manufacturing chemists, took over Ensign forming Houghtons (Holborn) Ltd and sold apparatus including that manufactured by Johnsons. The "Ensign" name was retained by H-B which in 1945 joined forces with the long established Elliott and Sons to form Barnet-Ensign. Barnet Ensign Ross followed in 1948 and Ross-Ensign in 1954. George Houghton's sons and grandsons had continued in the business throughout all the mergers until the firm finally disappeared about 1961.

Throughout its history the firm produced cameras and accessories notably after 1926 for the mass-amateur market. During the inter-war period it was the largest producer of photographic equipment and was the most important in Britain.

All Distance Ensign Cameras - c1930. A euphemistic term for "fixed focus", this name was applied to box and folding model cameras for 2¼x3¼" (6x9cm) on rollfilm. Note: Colored models bring about twice

the prices listed here for black ones. Box models: $5-10. Folding models: $5-10. (Including Ensign Pocket Models I & II.)

Autorange 220 Ensign - c1941. Folding camera offering a choice of 12 or 16 exposures on 120 film. f4.5 Tessar in Compur 1-250. Focus by radial lever on bed. $40-60.

Empress - c1912-23. Mahogany field camera with extensive tilting movements. Made in ¼, ½, and full-plate sizes. Brass barrel lens in roller-blind shutter. $60-90.

Ensign Autospeed - c1933. 6x6cm format 120 rollfilm camera with FP 15-500. Film advance cocks the shutter. Aldis f4.5/4" lens. $250-350.

Ensign box cameras - Including E20, E29, 2¼A, 2¼B, Duo, etc. Black: $5-10. Colored: $15-25.

Ensign Cameo - c1927-38. Folding plate camera. Leather-covered wood body with metal front. Made in 2½x3½", 3¼x4¼", and postcard sizes. Aldis Uno Anastigmat f7.7 or Zeiss Tessar lens. $20-30.

Ensign Carbine - 1920's-1930's. A series of folding cameras originated by Butcher and continued after the merger. Primarily for rollfilm, but most models have a removable panel in the back which allows use with plates as well. Many models in a wide range of prices. $20-50.

Ensign Carbine (Tropical models) - c1927-36. Nos. 4, 6, 7, 12. Bronzed brass body, tan bellows. Tessar f4.5 lens in Compur shutter. $75-125.

Ensign Commando - c1945. Folding rollfilm camera for 6x6cm or 4.5x6 cm. Built-in masks at the film plane and in the viewfinder. Rangefinder coupled to the moving film plane. Ensar f3.5/75mm lens in Epsilon 1-300 shutter. $40-60.

Ensign Cupid - Introduced 1922. Simple metal-bodied camera for 4x6cm exposures on 120 film. The design is based on a 1921 prototype for a stereo camera which was never produced. Mensicus achromatic f11 lens. Available in black, blue, grey, and perhaps other colors. $35-50.

Ensign Double-8 - c1930-40. Strut-folding camera for 3x4cm on 120. Ensar

Anastigmat f4.5 lens in 25-100 shutter. $40-65.

Ensign Ful-Vue - c1940. Box camera with large brilliant finder. Several major styles. Rectangular box-shaped model c1941 is less common than the oddly shaped black or colored post-war model. Blue or red: $35-45. Black: $15-25.

Ensign Ful-Vue Super - Black cast metal body. Similar to Ful-Vue, but with hinged finder hood. Achromat f11 lens. Two-speed shutter. One unusual example marked "Made in India" brought $45 at a 1986 auction, but normal models sell for $15-25.

Ensign Greyhound - Folding bed 6x9cm rollfilm camera. Metal body with grey crackle finish. $12-18.

Junior Box Ensign - c1932. Simple box camera, identified as "J B Ensign" on the front. 6x9cm. Two-speed shutter. $8-12.

Ensign Mascot A3, D3 - c1910. Drop-plate magazine box cameras for 3¼x4¼" plates. $35-50.

Ensign Mickey Mouse - c1935. Box camera for six exposures 1⅝x1¼" on rollfilm. Mickey Mouse decal on front. Originally available alone or in the "Mickey Mouse Photo Outfit" complete

with darkroom equipment and chemicals.
Camera only: $60-90.

Pocket Ensign 2-1/4 B

Ensign Pocket E-20

Ensign Midget Model 55

Ensign Midget - 1934-40. Compact
folding cameras for 3.5x4.5cm exposures
on E-10 film.
Model 22 - Meniscus lens, T,I shutter.

Uncommon. $40-50.
Model 33 - Meniscus lens. Shutter 25-100.
Most common model. $35-50.
Model 55 - Ensar Anastigmat f6.3 lens.
Shutter 25-100. The most complex model.
$35-45.

Silver Jubilee models - 1935. Specially
finished in silver ripple enamel to
commemorate the silver jubilee of the
King and Queen. Model S/33 has fixed
focus lens; Model S/55 has Ensar f6.3
Anastigmat. These are the rarest of the
Ensign Midgets. $50-60.

Ensign Multex - c1936-47. Small
rangefinder camera for 14 exposures on
127. Coupled rangefinder in top housing
with viewfinder above. FP shutter T,
1-1000. Ross Xpres f3.5 or f2.9 lens.
$150-250.

Pocket Ensign 2-1/4 B - Strut-type folding
camera for 120 rollfilm. T & I shutter, 3
stops. $12-18. *(Illustrated in previous column.)*

Ensign Pocket E-20 - Self-erecting
camera for 6x9cm on 120 rollfilm. Fixed
focus lens, T & I shutter. $10-15. *(Illustrated
in previous column.)*

Ensign Ranger, Ranger II, Ranger Special - c1953, Folding cameras for 6x9cm on 120 or 620 film. $12-18.

Ensign Popular Reflex

Ensign Reflex, Deluxe Reflex, Popular Reflex, Pressman Reflex, Special Reflex - c1915-30. Graflex-style SLR cameras. 2½x3½" and 3¼x4¼" sizes. Focal plane shutter to 1000. Various lenses. $75-125.

Ensign Roll Film Reflex - c1920's. For 6x9cm exposures on 120 film. Several models. $75-125.

Ensign Roll Film Reflex, Tropical - c1925. Teak with brass trim. Aldis Uno or Dallmeyer Anastigmat lens. Focal plane shutter 25-500. $300-450.

Ensign Selfix 16-20 - c1950's. For 16 exposures 4.5x6cm on 120 film. (This style of camera was often called a "semi" at that time, because it took half-size frames on 120.) f4.5/75mm Ensar or f3.8

Ross Xpress. $35-45.

Ensign Selfix 12-20, 20, 220, 320, 820 - c1950's. Folding rollfilm cameras for 6x6cm or 6x9cm. Various inexpensive lenses and shutters. $10-20.

Ensign Selfix 420 - Self-erecting camera for 8 exposures 6x9cm or 12 exposures 6x6cm on 120 film. Folding direct frame finder and small pivoting brilliant finder. Ensar Anastigmat f4.5/105mm lens in Epsilon 1-150,B,T. $15-20.

Ensign Special Reflex, Tropical - c1930's. 6.5x9cm SLR. Teak body, brassbound. Brown Russian leather bellows. FP shutter 15-1000. $300-500.

Ensign Speed Film Reflex - Called "Focal Plane Rollfilm Reflex" for a time. Box-form SLR with tall folding hood. Similar to the "Roll Film Reflex" but with focal plane shutter, 25-500,T. For 6x9cm on 120 film. Ensar f4.5 Anastigmat is standard lens, but others were available. $75-125.

Ensign Speed Film Reflex, Tropical - c1925. 6x9cm SLR. Teak body, brassbound. Aldis Anastigmat f7.7/108mm. FP shutter 25-500. $400-450.

Ensign Super Speed Cameo - A special model of the Cameo. Cast metal body with leather-lined panels at the sides and top. Two variations: Brown crystalline enamel with bronze fittings and brown bellows. Black model has chrome plated fittings. Dallmeyer Dalmac f3.5 lens in Compur shutter. Brown: $75-100. Black: $30-40.

Vest Pocket Ensign - c1926-30. Body design is the same as the Ensignette, but takes ⅝x2½" exposures on 127 rollfilm. Enameled aluminum body. Achromatic f11 lens, 3 speed shutter. $40-60.

Ensignette - c1909-30. Folding rollfilm camera of the bedless strut type. Similar to the Vest Pocket Kodak camera but has extensions on both ends of the front panel which serve as table stands. Made in three sizes:No. 1 for 1½x2¼", No. 2 for 2x3", and Junior No. 2 for 2¼x3¼". Early No. 1 is brass. Later No. 1 and No. 2 are all-aluminum. Junior No. 2 is wood with metal back. Simple lens and shutter. $35-50.

Anastigmat Ensignette, Ensignette Deluxe - Versions of the No. 1 and No. 2 with focusing Anastigmat lenses such as Tessar f6.8 or Cooke f5.8 and better shutters. $40-60.

Holborn - c1900-05. Magazine box cameras, most common in ¼-plate size. Leather covered exterior, polished wood interior. $40-60.

Holborn Postage Stamp Camera - c1901. 9-lens copy camera. Makes 9 simultaneous stamp-sized copies of a photograph on a quarter plate. $250-300.

Klito, No. 0 - c1905. Magazine box camera, falling plate type, 3¼x4¼" size. Rapid Rectilinear lens. Rotating shutter. $30-45.

Folding Klito - 1910's-1920's. For 3¼x4¼" sheet films. Double extension bellows. Aldis Plano f6.8. $30-45.
(Illustrated top of next column.)

Folding Klito

Mascot No. 1 - Drop-plate box camera for 6.5x9cm plates. Fixed focus f11 lens with 4 stops on external rotating disc. T&I shutter. Identified on strap. $20-30.

May Fair - Metal box camera. T & I shutter. $12-18.

Royal Mail Stereolette - Polished wood stereo box camera for 45x107mm plates. Guillotine shutter. Small reflex finder. $600-750.

Sanderson cameras *Even though manufactured by Houghton, all Sanderson cameras are listed under Sanderson.*

Ticka - c1905-14. Pocket-watch styled camera manufactured under license from the Expo Camera Co. of New York, and identical to the Expo Watch Camera. For 25 exposures 16x22mm on special cassette film. Fixed focus f16/30mm meniscus lens. I & T shutter. $125-150.

Ticka Enlarger - Enlarges the 16x22mm Ticka negative to 6x9cm. Meniscus lens. $75-125.

Ticka, Focal plane model - With focusing lens. Rare. (Exposed works make it easy to identify.) $1000-1500.

Ticka, Watch-Face model - c1912. Hands on the face show the viewing angle. An uncommon model, and difficult to establish a price. Two sold at auctions several years ago for $70 and $460. Dealers have offered them for sale at prices

from $1500-2000. Confirmed sales are $1200-1500.

Triple Victo - c1890. ½-plate triple extension field camera. Mahogany body, brass trim. Taylor Hobson Cooke brass-bound lens. Thornton-Pickard roller-blind shutter. Front movements. $140-170.

Tudor - c1906. Folding bed camera for ¼-plates. Combined rising and swing front. Rack focus. Aldis Anastigmat or other lens in Unicum or Automat shutter. $30-50.

Victo - c1900. Half or full plate triple extension field cameras. Polished teak, black bellows. RR or Bush lens. Thornton-Pickard roller-blind or Automat pneumatic shutter. $125-175

HUNTER (R. F. Hunter, Ltd. London)
Gilbert - Steel box camera with brown lizard skin covering. $60-80. *(Illustrated on front cover.)*

Hunter 35 - Viewfinder 35. Made in Germany. Same as the Steinette. $15-20.

Purma Plus - c1951. A re-styled version of the Purma Special, 32x32mm on 127 rollfilm. Metal body. Purma Anastigmat f6.3/55mm. Metal FP shutter to 500, speeds are gravity controlled. $30-40.

Purma Special - c1930's. Bakelite & metal camera for 16 exposures 32x32mm (1¼" sq.) on 127 film. Three speed metal focal plane shutter. Speeds controlled by gravity. Fixed focus f6.3/2¼" Beck Anastigmat (plastic) lens. One of the first cameras to use a plastic lens. $25-35.

HURLBUT MFG. CO. (Belvidere, Ill.)

Velox Magazine Camera - c1890. An unusual magazine-plate detective camera. Plates are dropped into the plane of focus and returned to storage by turning the camera over. Focusing lever and plate changing lever are hidden in a recessed bottom. $550-750.

HUTTIG (R. Huttig, A.G., Dresden, R. Huttig & Son, Dresden) *Claimed in 1910 advertisements to be the oldest and largest camera works in Europe. Soon became Ica, then merged to form Zeiss-Ikon in 1926.*
Atom - c1908. 4.5x6cm plate camera. f8/90mm lens. Compound shutter 1-250. $150-200.

Cupido - Self-erecting 9x12cm plate camera with radial focusing. Rising front with micrometer screw. Extra Rapid Aplanat Baldour f8/125mm in Huttig shutter, B, T, 1-100. $25-35.

Fichtner's Excelsior Detective - c1892.

Polished wood body with built-in 12-plate magazine, 9x12cm. Goerz Lynkeioskop 125mm lens. 3-speed rotating shutter. 2 reflex viewfinders. $1000-1400.

Folding plate camera - c1906. 9x12cm plates. Black leathered wood body, aluminum bed. Red double extension bellows. Pneumatic shutter. $50-75.

Gnom - c1900. Falling-plate magazine box camera. Holds up to 6 plates 4.5x6cm. Meniscus lens. Rotary shutter. $125-200.

Helios - c1907. Strut-type folding plate camera, 9x12cm. 185mm Anastigmat lens. Focal plane shutter 6-1000. $75-125.

Ideal, 9x12cm - c1908. Folding-bed plate camera. Huttig Extra Rapid Aplanat Helios f8. Automat shutter, 25-100, B, T. Aluminum standard and bed. Red bellows. $35-45.

Ideal, 9x18cm - c1907. Helios f8/125mm. Sector shutter 1-250. $75-125.

Ideal Stereo - c1908. 6x13cm plates. Extra Rapid Aplanat Helios f8/105mm. Huttig Stereo Automat shutter 1-100, T, B. $130-170.

Lloyd, 9x12cm - c1905. Folding camera for 3¼x4¼" rollfilm or 9x12cm plates. Goerz Dagor f6.8/135mm lens. Compound shutter 1-250. Double extension red bellows. $50-90.

Lloyd, 13x18cm - c1905. Unusual in this large size. Double extension red bellows. Extra Rapid Aplanat f8 lens in Double pneumatic shutter. One example with focal plane and front shutters sold for about $200. Another with front shutter only brought $160.

Magazine cameras - c1900. 6.5x9 cm and 9x12cm drop-plate type box cameras, leather covered, including varied Monopol models. Focusing Aplanat lens and simple shutter. $50-60. (Polished wood models without leather covering $400-600.)

Record Stereo Camera - 9x12cm plates. Hugo Meyer Aristostigmat f6.8/120mm lenses. Focal plane shutter. $250-350.

Stereo Detective - c1900. Polished wood box camera for 9x18cm plates. Nickel trim. M&Z shutter. $400-500.

Stereolette - c1909. Small folding stereo camera for 45x107mm plates. Helios f8/ 65mm lens. I,B,T, shutter. $125-150.

Toska - c1907. Folding bed camera for 9x12cm plates. Leather covered mahogany body. Double extension aluminum bed. Rack focus. Universal Rapid Aplanat f7/ 130mm. $30-45.

Tropical plate camera - 6x9cm. Fine wood body with brass trim. Double extension brown bellows. Steinheil Triplan f4.5/135mm lens in Compound shutter 1-150. $450-600.

HYATT (H.A. Hyatt, St. Louis, MO)

Patent Stamp Camera - c1887. 16-lens copy camera for making 16 stamp-size photos on a 4x5" plate. $500-750.

ICA A.G. (Dresden) *Formed in 1909 as a merger of Huttig, Krugener, Wunsche, and the Carl Zeiss Palmos factory. Ica became a part of Zeiss-Ikon in 1926, along with Contessa-Nettel, Goerz, Ernemann, and Carl Zeiss Optical Co. Some models were continued under the Zeiss name. See also Zeiss-Ikon.*

Atom - c1912-25. Small folding camera for 4.5x6cm plates. In two distinctly different models, both in appearance and current value:

Horizontal-format Atom (Model B) -
Folding bed type with self-erecting front. Generally with f4.5/65mm Tessar or f6.8 Hekla. Compound shutter, 1-300. Unusual location of reflex brilliant finder. Viewing lens on front center of bed, but mirror and objective lens extend below the bed. $150-250. *(Illustrated top of next column.)*

Horizontal format Atom

Vertical-format Atom - (Including Models A, 50, 51.) In the more traditional folding bed style. Reflex finder is still on the front of the bed, but remains above the bed. $90-145.

Aviso - c1914-25. 4.5x6cm magazine box camera. Simple lens and shutter $70-90.

Bebe - c1913-25. Bedless strut-type folding plate camera. Bebe 40 for 4.5x6cm, Bebe 41 for 6.5x9cm. Tessar f4.5 lens in dial-set Compur shutter which is built into the flat front of the camera. $100-140.

Briefmarken Camera - c1910. Polished mahogany camera with brass trim. Takes 15 stamp-sized photos on a 9x12cm plate. Rare. Only one recorded sale, at an auction in October 1986 for $3800.

Cameo Stereo - c1912. Folding bed stereo for 9x18cm plates. Extra Rapid Aplanat Helios lenses. Automat Stereo shutter, ½-1000, T, B. Twin tapered bellows. Black covered wood body. $150-200.

Corrida - c1910. Folding 9x12cm plate camera. Helios f8/130mm in Automat shutter. $25-35.

Cupido 75 - Self-erecting camera for 6.5x9cm plates. Tessar f4.5/12cm in Dial Compur. Radial focus. Rising front with micrometer screw. Pivoting collapsible brilliant finder. "Cupido 75" on strap. $25-35.

Cupido 80 - c1914. Folding bed camera for 9x12cm plates or rollfilm back. Tessar f4.5/12cm lens. Compur dial-set shutter. $25-35.

Delta - c1912. Folding 9x12cm plate camera. Double extension bellows. Hekla f6.8/135mm in Compound shutter. $35-45.

Favorit 265, 425 - c1925. Folding-bed camera, 13x18cm (5x7") plates. Square black double extension leather bellows. f6.3/210mm Tessar. Compur dial-set 1-150. An uncommon size. $100-200. *(Illustrated top of next column.)*

Favorit Tropical - c1927-31. Polished teakwood body. Folding 9x12cm plate or filmpack camera. Tessar f4.5 lens in Compur shutter. $350-500.

Folding plate cameras - misc. models in 6x9 & 9x12cm sizes. $25-35.

Ica Favorit

Halloh 505, 510, 511 - c1914-26. Folding rollfilm cameras (also for plate backs) in the 8x10.5cm (3¼x4¼") size. Tessar f4.5/12cm or Litonar f6.8/135mm. Dial Compur shutter 1-250, B,T. $25-40.

Icar 180 - c1913-26. Folding bed 9x12cm plate camera. Ica Dominar f4.5/135mm. Compur dial-set shutter 1-200,T,B. $30-40.

Ica Icarette I

Ica Icarette C

Icarette - 1920's. Folding bed rollfilm cameras for 120 film. Two basic styles: the horizontally styled body for 6x6cm exposures such as the Icarette I *(illustrated bottom of previous page)* and A, and the vertical body style for 6x9cm such as the Icarette C, D, and L. Prices average the same for either style. $30-45.

Icarette 501, 502, 503 - c1919. 6.5x11cm image on rollfilm. Tessar f4.5 or Hekla f6.8/12cm in Compur, or Novar f6.8/135mm in Derval shutter. $25-40.

Ideal - c1920's. Folding-bed vertical style plate cameras. Double extension bellows. (See also Zeiss for the continuation of this line of cameras.) In three sizes:
6.5x9cm - (Model 111) Hekla f6.8/90mm, Tessar f6.3/90mm, or Litonar f4.5/105. Compur shutter 1-150. $35-45.
9x12cm - (Including models 245, 246) f4.5/150mm Tessar. Compur shutter. $50-80.
10x15cm - (Model 325) Tessar f4.5/165mm in Compur. $75-100.

13x18cm (5x7") - (Model 385) Tessar f4.5/210mm in dial Compur shutter. This larger size is much less common than the others. $90-120.

Ingo 395 - c1914-25. Folding camera for 13x18cm plates. Horizontal style. Novar Anastigmat f6.8/180mm. Ica Automat shutter. $60-80.

Juwel (Universal Juwel) - c1925. (Also continued as a Zeiss model after 1926.) A drop-bed folding 9x12cm plate camera of standard style, except that it has square format bellows and rotating back. It also incorporates triple extension bellows, wide angle position, and all normal movements. $200-275.

Lloyd - c1910. Folding camera for exposures 8x10.5cm on rollfilm or 9x12cm on plates. Dominar f4.5/135mm. Compur 1-200. $35-45.

Lloyd-Cupido 560 - c1922-25. Horizontally styled self-erecting rollfilm camera for 8.3x10.8cm. Hekla f6.8/100mm in Compound. Helical focus. Rare. $75-125.

Lloyd Stereo - c1910. Folding stereo or panoramic camera for plates or rollfilm. 8x14cm or 9x18cm sizes. A lever on the top moves the cloth roller septum in back for panoramic exposures. Compur 1-150 or Stereo Compound 1-100 shutter. Tessars f6.3 or Double Anastigmat Maximar f6.8 lenses. $200-250.

Lola 135, 136 - c1912-14. Folding bed, single extension camera for 9x12cm plates. Similar to the Sirene. Wood body with leatherette covering. Periskop Alpha f11, Ica Automatic shutter. $30-40.

Maximar - c1914-26. Folding bed double extension precision plate camera. Although the Zeiss-Ikon Maximar is much more common, it originated as an Ica model. 9x12cm size with Novar f4.5, Hekla f6.8, Litonar f4.5/135mm, in Compound, Compur, or Rulex shutter. $40-50.

Ica Nero

Most unusual feature is the focal plane shutter, T,B, 50-1000. The 4.5x6cm size is Ica's smallest focal plane camera. Zeiss Tessar f2.7 lens. 4.5x6cm: $300-500. 6.5x9cm: $175-250. 9x12cm (456): $100-150.

Nelson 225 - c1915. Folding bed double extension plate camera for 9x12cm. Tessar f4.5/150mm. Dial Compur T, B, 1-150. $35-45.

Nero - c1905. Magazine box camera for 9x12cm plates. Guillotine shutter, T & I. $40-60. *(Illustrated top of previous column.)*

Niklas 109 - c1920's. Folding bed plate cameras in 6.5x9 and 9x12cm sizes. f4.5 Litonar or Tessar lens in Compur shutter. $30-40.

Minimal 235 - c1912. 9x12cm folding bed double extension sheetfilm camera. f6.8/135 Hekla, or f6.8/120 Goerz Dagor lens. Ica Automat or Compound shutter. Leather covered wood body. $35-45.

Minimum Palmos - 1920's. Compact vertical format folding bed plate camera.

Nixe 555, 595 - c1920's. Folding bed camera. 9x12cm: $40-60. 9x14cm plates or 122 rollfilm. $40-70.

Orix 209 - c1924-25. Double extension folding 9x12cm plate camera. Double Anastigmat Litonar f4.5/135mm. Compur 1-200. $25-35.

Palmos Klapp-Stereo - c1911-26. (Originally from Zeiss Palmos Werk c1905.) Folding-bed stereo camera for 9x12cm plates. Aluminum body and bed, covered with leather. Focal plane shutter. Zeiss Tessar f6.3 or f4.5/9cm lenses. Some Zeiss and Ica models have the Dr. W. Scheffer inter-lens adjusting system. The two lenses are drawn closer together by stylus-type rods running in converging tracks on the camera bed. This allows for close-up work with automatic adjustment. This rare accessory dates from c1908-14. With close focus system: $450-550. Normal models: $300-475.

Periscop - 9x12cm plate camera. Alpha lens. $30-40.

Plaskop - c1925. Rigid-bodied stereo camera for plates or packfilm. Ica Novar Anastigmat lens in guillotine shutter, T & I. Black leather covered wood body with black painted metal parts. Reflex & wire frame finders. 6x13cm: $100-150. 45x107mm: $80-120.

Polyscop (rigid body) - c1910-25. Rigid-bodied stereo camera. Some models had plate backs; some had magazine backs. Could also be used as a panoramic camera by using one lens in the center position and removing the septum. Tessar f4.5 or 6.3 lenses. 6x13cm: $175-200. 45x107mm: $150-200.

Polyscop (strut-folding model) - For 45x107mm plates. Less common than the rigid models. $175-225.

Reflex 748, 750, 756, 756/1 - c1910-25. Graflex style SLR's, such as the Artists Reflex for 6x9cm, 8.5x11cm, or 9x12cm plates. Tessar f4.5 or Maximar f6.8 lens. Focal plane shutter to 1000. $150-175.

Folding Reflex - c1924. Very compact SLR which folds to about one-third the size of the box model. f4.5 Tessar or Dominar. $175-225.

Reporter (Record) - c1912. Strut-folding 9x12cm plate camera. Tessar f4.5/150mm. FP shutter to 1000. $100-150.

Sirene - c1914-26. Folding plate cameras, 6x9 or 9x12cm sizes. Economy models with f11 Periskop or f6.8 Eurynar lens. Ibso shutter. (Most common is Model 135 for 9x12cm.) $25-35.

Stereo Ideal (Type 650) - c1914-26. Folding stereo camera for 9x18cm plates. Twin f6.3 Tessar lenses. Compound shutter to 150. Twin black bellows. $150-250.

Stereo Ideal (651) - c1910. Folding bed stereo camera for 6x13cm plates. 90mm lenses (f4.5 or 6.3 Tessar or f6.8 Double Anastigmat) in Stereo Compound shutter. Magazine back. $200-300.

Stereo Minimum Palmos (693) - c1924-1926. Strut-folding stereo camera for 6x13cm plates or filmpack. Aluminum body with leather covering and leather bellows. Folding frame finder. Externally coupled focusing Tessar f4.5 or Triotar f3.5 lenses. Focal plane shutter 1/30 to 1000. $250-350.

Stereo Reicka - c1910-14. Folding bed stereo for 10x15cm plates. Various lenses in Stereo Compound shutter. $200-300.

Stereo Toska (680) - c1912. Folding-bed stereo for 10x15cm plates. Hekla f6.8/135mm. Compound shutter to 100. $150-200.

Stereolette 610, 611 - c1912-26. Compact folding-bed stereo camera for 45x107mm plates. Variety of available lens/shutter combinations. Model 610 has rack focus. Model 611 has radial lever. $175-225.

Stereolette Cupido (620) - c1912. Folding 45x107mm stereo. Hekla f6.8 or Tessar f4.5 lenses. Stereo Compound or Compur shutter. $125-175.

Stereofix - c1919. Simple rigid-body jumelle-style stereo camera for 45x107mm plates. Novar Anastigmat f6.8 in Ica Automatic shutter, T,B, 25-100. $150-175.

Teddy - c1914-22. 9x12cm folding plate camera. f8/130 Extra Rapid Aplanat Helios or f6.8/135mm Double Anastigmat Heklar. Automat shutter. $20-35.

Toska, 9x12cm - c1914-26. Folding plate camera. Zeiss Double Amatar f6.8/135 or f8/130 Rapid Aplanat Helios. Ica Automat or Compound shutter. $25-40.

Toska 330, 10x15cm - Horizontally-styled double extension plate camera. Extra wide lens standard allows use as a stereo camera with optional stereo lensboard. Zeiss Doppel-Protar Series VII f7/145mm in Compur 1-200. $75-100.

Trilby 18 - c1912. Magazine box camera for 6 plates 9x12cm or 12 exposures on sheet film. Ica Achromat lens. Guillotine shutter, T,I. Automatic exposure counter. $100-150.

Trix - c1915. Cut film camera. 4.5x6cm: $100-125. 9x12cm: $35-45. 10x15cm: $40-60.

Trona - c1912-26. 6x9 or 9x12cm double extension plate/rollfilm cameras. Tessar f4.5. Compur shutter. $35-55.

Tropica 285 - c1912-26. Tropical model folding-bed 9x12cm plate camera. Square back style. Double extension bellows, finely finished wood body with brass trim. $400-600.

Tudor Reflex - c1919-26. 9x12 SLR. Dominar f4.5/105mm or Tessar 150mm lens. FP shutter. $130-195.

Victrix - c1912-25. Folding bed camera for 4.5x6cm plates. Ica Dominar f4.5/75mm or Hekla f6.8/75mm. Automat or Compur shutter. Focus by radial lever on bed. $75-125.

Volta 125, 146 - c1914. Folding-bed 9x12cm plate camera. Novar Anastigmat f6.8/105mm. Shutter 25-100, T,B. $20-30.

IDAM (Societe d'Appareils Mecaniques IDAM, Colombes, France)

Belco - Cast metal camera for 36x36mm exposures on 127 rollfilm. Similar to the Clic camera, but with extinction meter incorporated in finder housing. Since the camera is not adjustable, the meter serves only to let the user know if it is practical to take a picture. The same camera was also sold with the name Roc. $40-50.

Clic - c1953. Cast metal camera for 3x3cm on special film similar to Kodak 828. Single speed shutter. Bilux f8 lens. $40-50.

Roc - Specifications and prices as Belco, above.

IDEAL TOY CORP. (Hollis, NY)

Kookie Kamera - c1968. Certainly in the running for the most unusual camera design of all time, from the plumbing pipes to the soup can. It looks like a modern junk sculpture, but takes 1¾x1¾" photos on direct positive paper for in-camera processing. With colorful original box, instructions, disguises etc. : $85-125. Camera only: $60-90.

I.G.B. Camera - Japanese novelty subminiature of the Hit type. $10-15.

IHAGEE KAMERAWERK, Steenbergen & Co., Dresden, Germany

(The name derives from the German pronunciation of the initials "IHG" from the full company name "Industrie und Handels Gesellschaft" which means Industry and Trading Company.

Duplex cameras - *Ihagee used the name "Duplex" for two distinctly different cameras:*
Two-shuttered Duplex - c1920's. Folding bed plate camera. Square body. Focal plane shutter in addition to the front inter-lens shutter. This was the camera which inspired the name. 6.5x9cm and 9x12cm sizes. $100-150.

Vertical format Duplex - c1940's. Folding bed plate camera. f3.5 or 4.5 Steinheil lens, Compur shutter. Double extension bellows. $30-40.

Elbaflex VX1000 - 35mm SLR. Same as Exakta VX1000. FP shutter 12-1000. Body with waist-level finder: $50-65.

Exa - c1950's. 35mm focal plane SLR. Models I, Ia, II, IIa, IIb. Normal lenses: Meritar f2.8 or Domiplan f2.9. $25-45.

Exa System - Similar to the Exa, but marked "System Exa, VEB Rheinmetall Soemmerda" on the faceplate. Tessar f2.8/50mm. $85-125.

Exakta (A) (original) - Introduced in 1933. The first small focal plane SLR. For 8 exposures 4x6.5cm on 127 rollflm. f3.5 Exaktar or Tessar. Focal plane shutter 25-1000. Black finish. (Some models with slow speeds to 12 sec. Some models not synched.) $125-175.

Exakta B - c1935. Similar to the model (A) above. Main body still black leather covered, but some models have chrome finish on metal parts. Focal plane shutter 25-1000, and slow speeds to 12 sec. Self-timer. f2.8 or f3.5 Tessar or Xenar normal lens. $150-225.

Exakta C - c1935. Much less common than the A & B. Accepts plate back adapter with ground glass for using plates or cut film. $150-200.

Exakta Jr. - c1936. Similar to the model B, but speeds only 25-500. "Exakta Jr" on

the front. Non-interchangeable lens. No self-timer. $100-150.

Night Exakta - c1936. Similar to the model B, but wider lens flange size for special fast lenses. Not a common model, probably because of a non-standard lens mount. It was available in all-black or in black and nickel. Biotar f2.0/80mm or Xenon lens. $250-350. *The easiest way to make a quick identification is that the serial number is on the viewing hood and not on the lens flange.*

Kine Exakta I (original type) - 1936. Identifiable by the round magnifier in the non-removable hood. The world's first single lens reflex for 35mm film. Similar in appearance to the larger "VP" model from which it was derived. Focal Plane shutter 12 to 1000 sec. Bayonet mount

Kine Exakta I, rectangular magnifier

interchangeable lenses include Exaktar f3.5/50, Primotar f3.5/50, Tessar f3.5/50, Tessar f2.8/50, Primoplan f1.9/50, and Biotar f2/58mm. Historically important and rare. $450-600.

Kine Exakta I (rectangular magnifier) - c1937-46. Like the original type, but with a rectangular focusing magnifier. No cover on the magnifier. Non-removeable finder. Most models say "Exacta", not "Exakta". $125-150. *(Illustrated bottom of previous page.)*

Exakta II - c1949-50. 35mm SLR. Rectangular focus magnifier with hinged protective door. Most say "Exakta", some "Exacta". Interchangeable bayonet-mount lenses: f2.8 or 3.5/50mm Tessar, f2.8/50 Westar, f2/50 Schneider Xenon. $60-100.

Exakta V - c1950. 35mm. Normal lenses as listed above. $65-90.

Exakta VX (Varex) - c1950's. 35mm. Same normal lenses as Exakta II. Very common. With normal lens: $65-100. Body only: $40-55.

Exakta VX IIA - c1960's. Very common. With normal lens, prism finder in Excellent condition: $60-100. Body only: $40-50.

Exakta VX IIB - c1960's. Similar to the VX IIA with minor cosmetic changes. With normal lens: $50-90.

Exakta VX 1000 - c1967. Same as VX IIB, but with instant return mirror. With normal lens: $65-95.

Exakta 66 - Single lens reflex for 12 exposures 6x6cm on 120 rollfilm. f2.8 Xenar or Tessar. Two distinct body styles:

Pre-war model - c1938. Horizontal body sytle and film transport (like an overgrown Exakta A, B or C). Focal plane shutter, 12 sec to 1/1000. $500-700.
Post-war style - c1954. Vertical style, much like the twin-lens reflex shape, but with only one lens. $450-650.

Ihagee folding plate cameras - 6x9cm size with f4.5/105mm Tessar in Compur shutter. 9x12cm size has similar lens/shutter. $30-40. *(Illustrated top of next column.)*

Ihagee Folding plate camera

Ihagee folding rollfilm cameras - For 8 exposures 6x9cm on 120 film. Anastigmat f4.5 lens in Compur or Prontor shutter. $20-30.

Newgold - c1927. Tropical folding plate camera. 6.5x9cm or 9x12cm sizes. Polished teak, brass fittings. Brown leather bellows. U-shaped brass front standard. Rising/ falling, cross front. Huttig f8 or Tessar f5.6 lens in Compur shutter. $400-600.

Parvola - c1930's. Also called Klein-Ultrix. For 127 rollfilm, plates or packs. Telescoping front. Three models:3x4cm, 4x6.5cm, and the twin or "two-format" model for either size. $50-80.

Patent Klapp Reflex - c1920's. Compact folding SLR for 6.5x9 or 9x12cm. Focal plane shutter to 1000. f4.5 Dogmar, Tessar or Xenar. $250-350.

Photoklapp Derby - c1924-34. Single extension folding bed camera for 9x12cm plates. Luxar f7.7/135mm in Vario 25-100. $25-35.

Photoknips - c1924-35. Compact 4.5x6cm plate camera. Front supported by cross-swinging struts. Wire frame finder. Achromatic lens. Front wheel with 3 stops. Shutter ¼-100,Z. Uncommon. $175-200.

Plan-Paff - c1928-30. Box style SLR for 6.5x9cm plates. Trioplan f6.3/105mm lens. Z,M shutter. $75-125.

Roll-Paff-Reflex - c1920's. SLR box camera for 6x6cm on 120 film. Simple meniscus Achromatic or Meyer Trioplan f6.8/90mm lens. Z,M shutter. $75-100.

Stereo camera - Folding bed style for 6x13cm plates. Meyer Trioplan f6.3/80mm lens. Stereo Prontor shutter. $175-250.

Ultrix (Auto) - c1930. Folding bed camera. Small size for 4x6.5cm on 127 rollfilm: $60-90. Larger size for 6x9cm on 120 film: $20-35.

Ultrix (Cameo, Weeny) - c1931. Models with telescoping screw-out lens mount like the Parvola, above. $50-75.

Ultrix Stereo - c1925-37. Folding bed rollfilm camera for 7x13cm stereo exposures. Doppel-Anastigmat f4.5/80mm. Compur shutter 1-300. Leather covered. Black enamelled baseboard. Brass and nickeled parts. $175-250.

IKKO SHA CO. LTD. (Japan)
Start 35 - c1950. A simple bakelite eye-level camera for 24x24mm on 35mm wide Bolta-size rollfilm. "Start 35" molded into top. Top removes to load film. Fixed focus f8, B,I shutter. Original box says "Start Junior Pen Camera" and instructions call it "Start Junior Camera". This model is much less common than the later ones. $35-50.
Start 35 K - Similar, but with hinged back. $20-25.

Start 35 K-II - c1958. A deluxe version with metal top housing and front trim plate. PC sync post on front. "Start 35 K-II" on top. An attractive camera. $30-45.

ILFORD LTD. (England)
Advocate - c1953. Cast metal 35mm. Ivory enameled finish. Dallmeyer Anastigmat f3.5/35mm. Shutter 25-200. $75-95.

Sporti 4 - An inexpensive plastic eye-level

camera for 127 film. Styled like a 35mm camera. Black & tan body with brass-colored trim. Made by Dacora for Ilford. $12-18.

Sportsman - c1967. Viewfinder 35mm. Made for Ilford by Dacora. Like the Super Dignette. Dignar f2.8/45mm. Pronto LK 15-500 shutter. $10-20.

Sprite - 4x4cm gray plastic eye-level box camera. $4-8.

Sprite 35 - Inexpensive grey plastic 35mm. Fixed focus f8 lens, with f11 and f16 stops. Single speed shutter. Lever advance. DEP. Identical to Agilux Agiflash 35. $8-12. *(Illustrated top of next column.)*

Witness - c1951. Coupled rangefinder 35mm. Dallmeyer Super-Six f1.9/2" lens in interrupted screw-thread mount. FP shutter 1-1000. It is rumored that only about 500 were made. Uncommon. $500-700 asked in the U.S., but several have sold at auction in England between $225-$325.

IMPERIAL CAMERA CORP. (Chicago)

Deluxe Six-Twenty Twin Lens Reflex - Inexpensive plastic TLR box camera. $1-5.

Plastic 4x4cm cameras - c1964. Such as: Cinex, Cubex IV, Delta, Deltex, Lark, Mark 27, Matey 127 Flash, Mercury Satellite 127, Nor-Flash 127, Satellite II. $1-5.

Ilford Sprite 35

Plastic 6x6cm cameras - c1956. Such as: Adventurer, Mark XII Flash,Reflex, Savoy, Six-twenty, Six-Twenty Reflex. $1-5.

Special models - Scout cameras, Rambler

Flash Camera (AMC preminum), etc. $5-10.

IMPERIAL CAMERA & MFG. CO. (LaCrosse, WI)

Magazine camera - c1902. Falling-plate magazine box camera for twelve 4x5" plates. $30-45.

IMPULSE LTD. (Maryland Heights, MO. USA)

Voltron Starshooter 110 - c1985. A working 110 camera forms part of the body of the Voltron robot. The robot itself converts to the shape of a 35mm camera, with the taking lens of the real 110 camera appearing to be the viewfinder of the dummy 35mm camera. Made in Macau. Retail $25.

INDO (Lyon & Paris, France) *The name is an abbreviation of Industrie Optique, and the camera line is a continuation of the cameras from Fex. Most cameras with the Indo name are low-priced models, often used as premiums and found frequently with promotional messages printed on them.*

Impera 4x4 - Black plastic eye-level box camera for 127 film. $1-5.

INDRA (Frankfurt, Germany)
Indra-Lux - c1949. Streamlined black bakelite camera for 4x4cm on 127 film. Fixed focus f7.7/60mm lens. Z&M shutter. Rare. $75-125.

INDUSTRIEA BRASILEIRA (Brazil)

Plik - 127 plastic box camera. Similar in style to the Bilora Boy. $35-45.

INETTE - Folding 6x9cm rollfilm camera, made in Germany. Inetta f6.3/85mm in Embezit shutter. $15-20.

INFLEX - c1950. Unusual German cast-metal camera for 4x4cm on 127 film. Reflex styling, but viewer is a simple brilliant finder. Zeyer Anastigmat f3.8/50mm in Vario shutter. Rare. $150-175. *(Illustrated top of next page.)*

INGERSOLL (Robert Ingersoll Brothers, New York City)
Shure-Shot - Tiny all-wood box camera for single exposures on glass plates. Simple

Inflex

rotary shutter. 2½x2½" size: $150-225. 3¾x3¾" size, less common: $200-300. *Note: This is not to be confused with the later model "Shur-Shot" box cameras by Agfa and Ansco for rollfilms.*

INTERNATIONAL METAL & FERROTYPE CO. (Chicago, Ill)

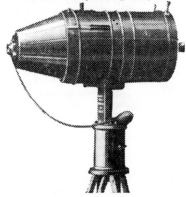

Diamond Gun Ferrotype - Large nickel cannon-shaped street camera. $800-1200.

IRWIN (U.S.A.)

Cheap 3x4cm cameras - c1940's. Such as: Dual Reflex, Irwin Reflex, Irwin Kandor, Kandor Komet. Metal sardine-can shaped novelty cameras. $10-20.

ISE (Germany)
Edelweiss Deluxe - Folding camera for 6.5x9cm plates. Brown leather, tan double extension bellows. Tessar f4.5/120mm lens in Compur. $75-100.

ISGOTOWLENO: *Translates as "Made in the U.S.S.R."*

ISING
Isoflex I - c1952. Heavy cast metal reflex box, 6x6cm. Focusing lens. Large brilliant finder. Same as Pucky I. $10-20.

Puck - c1948. Telescoping 3x4cm rollfilm camera. Cassar f2.8/50mm in Prontor II. $15-25.

Pucky - c1949-50. Twin-lens box camera. Bakelite body. Large brilliant finder. M&Z shutter. $20-30.

Pucky I, Ia, II - c1950-54. Like Pucky but with cast aluminum body. Model I is found with or without hinged finder hood. Models Ia & II have hood. $10-20.

ISO (Milan, Italy)
Bilux - c1950. 35mm with coupled rangefinder. Essentially the same camera as the Iso and Henso Reporter cameras. Lever advance in baseplate. Interchangeable Iriar f3.5/50mm lens. Focal plane shutter 1-1000. $450-500.

Duplex 120, Super Duplex 120 - c1950. Stereo camera for 24 pairs of 24x24mm exposures on 120 film. The 24x24 format was the common format for 35mm stereo, but putting the images side-by-side on 120 film advanced vertically was a novel idea. $150-225.

Standard - c1953. Rangefinder 35mm. Iadar f3.5/50mm. FP shutter 20-1000. Quite similar to the Hensoldt "Standard", a knob-advance version of the more interesting Henso Reporter. $450-500.

ISOPLAST GmbH (Germany)
Filius-Kamera - c1954. Black plastic novelty camera for 32x40mm on 828 film. $15-25.

IVES (F.E. Ives, Philadelphia, Penn.)
Kromskop Triple Camera - c1899. First American camera making tri-color separation negatives in a single exposure. Three plates exposed simultaneously through 3 colored filters, by the use of prisms. Plates were arranged vertically in the camera body. Rare. Price negotiable. Estimate: $3000-5000 or more.

JAK-PAK
Kiddie Camera - Novelty camera for 126 cartridges. A boy's or girl's face covers the camera front. $1-5.

JAPY & CIE. (France)
le Pascal - c1898. Box camera with spring-motor transport. 12 exposures, 40x55mm on rollfilm. Meniscus lens, 3 stops. 2-speed shutter, B. Leather covered wood and metal body with brass trim. The first motorized rollfilm camera. Several sales in the early 1980's for $500-650. However, one was passed at auction in mid-1985 when bidding failed to reach its $280 estimate.

JAY DEE - "Hit" type Japanese novelty subminiature. $10-15.

JEANNERET & CIE. (Paris)

Monobloc - c1915-25. Stereo camera for 6x13cm plates. f4.5 Boyer Sapphir or f6.3 Roussel Stylor 85mm lenses. Built-in magazine. Pneumatic shutter. Metal body, partly leather covered. $150-175.

JEM (J. E. Mergott Co., Newark, N.J.)

Jem Jr. 120 - c1940's. All metal box camera. Simple lens and shutter. $4-8.

Jem Jr. 120, Girl Scout - All metal, green-enameled box camera. Girl Scout emblem is on the front below the lens. $8-12.

JEWELL 16 - Plastic camera for half-frame exposures on 127 rollfilm. $5-10.

JONTE (F. Jonte, Paris, France)
Field camera - c1895-1900. 5x7" mahogany camera with brass binding. Rotating bellows for vertical or horizontal use. $100-150.

JOS-PE GmbH (Hamburg & Munich)
The company name comes from one of the owners, JOSef PEter Welker, a banker. The other owners were photographer Koppmann and engineer Gauderer.

Tri-Color Camera - c1925. All-metal camera for single-shot 3-color separation negatives. Coupled focusing via bellows to each plate magazine. Scarce.
4.5x6cm size - Quinar f2.5/105mm lens. Compound shutter: $1300-2000.
9x12cm size - Cassar f3/180mm in Compound 1-50 shutter. $1000-1500.

JOUGLA (J. Jougla, Paris, France)
Sinnox - c1901-06. Magazine-box camera with tapered body. Magazine holds 6 plates, 9x12cm. Rapid Rectilinear lens in Wollensak pneumatic shutter. $150-175.

JOUX (L. Joux & Cie. Paris, France)
Alethoscope - 1905. All-metal stereo plate camera. Rectilinear Balbreck lenses. 5-speed guillotine shutter. Newton finder. 45x107mm or 6x13cm sizes. $150-200.

Ortho Jumelle Duplex - c1895. Rigid-bodied "jumelle" style camera. Magazine holds 6.5x9cm plates. f8/110 Zeiss Krauss Anastigmat. Five speed guillotine shutter. An uncommon camera. $150-200.

Steno-Jumelle - c1895. Rigid, tapered body, magazine camera for 18- 6.5x9cm or 12- 9x12cm plates. The magazine is built into the camera body, and is loaded through a panel on top. Raising the hinged top when the lens is pointed upward moves the push-pull plate-changing mechanism. $150-250.

Steno-Jumelle Stereo - c1898. Similar design to the Steno-Jumelle, but with 2 lenses for 8x16cm stereo exposures. 12-plate magazine. $300-375.

JULIA - c1900-05. Horizontally styled folding bed rollfilm camera for 9x9cm. Leather covered wood body. Shutter built into wooden lensboard. $175-225.

JUMEAU & JANNIN (France)
Le Cristallos - c1890. Folding bed camera for darkroom-loaded rollfilm. 9x12cm or 6x9cm size. Black leather with gold outlines. Lens has external wheel stops. $200-250.

JUMELLE *The French word for "twins", also meaning binoculars. Commonly used to describe stereo cameras of the European rigid-body style, as well as other "binocular-styled" cameras where one of the two lenses is a viewing lens and the other takes single exposures. See French manufacturers such as: Bellieni, Carpentier, Gaumont, Joux, Richard.*

JUNKA-WERKE

Junka - c1938. 3x4cm exposures on special paper-backed rollfim. Achromat f8/45mm lens in single speed shutter. $50-75. *The same basic camera was sold by Adox adter WWII and was named Juka.*

JURNICK (Max Jurnick, Jersey City, New Jersey)
Ford's Tom Thumb Camera - c1889. Similar body style to the Photosphere camera. All metal. Camera is concealed in a wooden carrying case for "detective" exposures. Later models are called the Tom Thumb camera, dropping Ford's name from the camera name. With original wooden case: $2500-3500. *(Illustrated top of next column.)*

JUSTEN PRODUCTS
Justen - Plastic novelty camera of the "Diana" type. $1-5.

KAFTANSKI (Fritz Kaftanski)
Banco Perfect - Plastic bodied rollfilm camera with telescoping front. 2¼x3¼"

Jurnick Ford's Tom Thumb Camera

exposures. Focusing lens, built-in yellow filter. $10-15.

KALART CO. (New York City)

Kalart Press camera - 1948-53. 3¼x4¼". Dual rangefinder windows to allow for use

Kalimar A

with either eye. f4.5/127mm Wollensak Raptar in Rapax 1-400 shutter. Dual shutter release triggers controlled by Electric Brain. $140-160. *(Illustrated on back cover.)*

KALIMAR (Japan)
Kalimar A - c1955. 35mm non-rangefinder camera. f3.5/45mm Terionon lens. Between-the-lens synchro shutter to 200. $15-25. *(Illustrated bottom of previous page.)*

Colt 44 (Kalimar 44) - c1960. Made for Kalimar by Hoei Industrial Co. Both names, "Colt 44" and "Kalimar 44" appear on the camera. 4x4cm on 127 rollfilm. Kaligar f8/60mm lens. Single speed shutter. $15-25.

Kali-flex - c1966. Simple, plastic, TLR-style camera. Kalimar f8 to f22 lens. Between-the-lens shutter. 6x6cm exposures on 120 film. $8-12.

Kalimar Reflex - c1956-62. Made for Kalimar by Fujita Optical Ind. SLR. Interchangeable Kaligar f3.5/80mm lens,

Kalimar TLR 100

focuses to 3½". FP shutter 1-500, B, X sync. Instant return mirror. Export version of the Fujita 66. With normal lens: $60-90.

TLR 100 - Black plastic TLR. Copy of Voigtlander Brillant body, but viewing lens is externally coupled to the taking lens. Lomo T-22 f4.5/75mm. Shutter B, 15-250. Also sold as Lubitel 2. $10-15. *(Illustrated bottom of previous column.)*

KAMBAYASHI & CO. LTD. (Japan)

Homer No. 1 - c1960. Novelty subminiature. Construction similar to "Hit" type cameras, but style is different. Gray metal exterior. Black plastic interior. 14x14mm exposures on 16mm rollfilm. Meniscus lens. Single speed shutter. $40-60.

KAMERA & APPARATEBAU (Vienna, Austria)
Sport-Box 2, Sport-Box 3 - c1950. Black bakelite eye-level box cameras. Folding frame finder. f8/50mm. M,T shutter. $25-35.

KAMERAWERKE THARANDT (Germany)
Vitaflex - c1949. TLR-style, 6x6cm on 120 film. f4.5 lens. $25-40.

KAMERETTE JUNIOR No. 1, No. 2, No. 4 - c1930. Japanese "Yen" box camera for 1¼x2" cut film. $10-15.

KAMERETTE No. 1, No. 2 - Small Japanese "Yen" box camera with ground glass back. Uses sheet film in paper holders. $10-15.

KAMERETTE SPECIAL - Japanese folding "Yen" camera for single sheet films in paper holders. Wood body, ground glass back. $15-20.

KASHIWA (Japan)
Motoca - c1949. 35mm Leica copy. Lunar Anastigmat f3/45mm. This lens is interchangeable, but Kashiwa made no other lenses to fit this camera. Shutter 25-300,B. $200-250.

KASSIN - Japanese novelty subminiature of the Hit type. $10-15.

KEITH CAMERA CO.

Keith Portrait Camera - c1947. 5x7" wooden studio camera. Silver hammertone finish. 17" bellows extension. Swing back. $150-200.

KEMPER (Alfred C. Kemper, Chicago)
Kombi - intro. 1892. The mini-marvel of the decade. A 4 oz. seamless metal miniature box camera with oxidized silver finish. Made to take 25 exposures 1⅛" square (or round) on rollfilm, then double as a transparency

viewer. (From whence the name "Kombi".) Sold for $3.00 new, and Kemper's ads proclaimed "50,000 sold in one year". Although not rare, they are a prized collector's item. $150-175. (Add $25 for original box, often found with the camera.)

KENFLEX - Japanese 6x6cm TLR. First Anastigmat f3.5/80mm lens. $15-25.

KENNEDY INDUSTRIES (London, England)
K.I. Monobar - c1950. 35mm monorail camera, with full movements. 24x36mm exposures on cut film. $600-900.

KENNGOTT (W. Kengott, Stuttgart)
6x9cm plate camera - c1920's. Folding-bed style. Double extension bellows. f4.8/105mm Leitmeyr Sytar lens in Ibsor 1-125 shutter. $25-35.

10x15cm plate camera - Leather covered wood body. Revolving back. Triple extension bellows. Kengott (Paris) Double Anastigmat f6.8/180mm lens in Koilos shutter 1-300. $50-75.

10x15cm plate camera, Tropical - Lemonwood body. Gold-plated brass trim. Light brown leather bellows. Steinheil Unifocal f4.5/150 lens in Kengott Koilos 1-100, T, B shutter. $500-750.

Matador - c1930. 6.5x9cm folding plate camera. Self-erecting front. Spezial Aplanat f8/105mm in Vario. $20-30.

Phoenix - c1924. Tropical camera with gold-plated metal parts. Brown bellows. Sizes: 6x9cm, 9x12cm, or 9x14cm. Most common in 9x12cm size with Tessar f4.5/135mm in dial Compur. Earlier sales peaked in 1979 at about $500-800 in Germany. The most recent auction figures from England have been in the $100-200 range. The long-term stable price should end up at about $300-500.

Supra No. 2 - c1930. Double extension folding camera for 6.5x9cm plates. Xenar f4.5/105mm in Compur 1-250. $20-35.

KENT - Japanese novelty camera of the "Hit" type. 14x14mm. $10-15.

KERN (Aarau, Switzerland)
Bijou - c1925. Aluminum-bodied hand and stand camera. Inlaid leather panels on sides. Rounded corners. Kern Anastigmat f4.5 lens in Compur 1-200 shutter. 6.5x9 or 9x12cm size. $300-400.

Stereo Kern SS - 1930-35. Early 35mm stereo camera, 20x20mm exposures. Kern Anastigmat f3.5/35mm lenses, with 64mm inter-lens separation (larger than the Homeos). All controls are located on the top of the camera. Leica-style viewfinder. $800-1000. (A complete outfit with camera, case, transposing table viewer, etc. could nearly double this price.)

KERSHAW(A. Kershaw and Sons Ltd.)
Abram Kershaw established his firm in 1888 and by 1898 was making camera parts for trade manufacturers. During the early 1900's the photographic side expanded. Field cameras, studio cameras and tripods were being made. From 1905 the Kershaw Company started in earnest to produce the Soho Reflex which was based on Cecil Kershaw's patent of 1904. These were being made for Marion and Co., London Stereoscopic Co., Ross, Watsons, and others who sold them under their own name. Kershaw also produced cameras for other manufacturers.

Kershaw joined APM in 1921 and Soho Ltd. in 1929 where it was the dominant partner. In both companies Kershaw produced most of the cameras and equipment marketed under the APeM and Soho names. At the same time Kershaw

pursued its own projects, notably cine equipment through its associated company of Kalee Ltd. The firm produced a range of cameras until the 1950's when production ceased because the Rank Organisation, which had acquired Kershaw in 1947, wished to direct production to other products.

Most of the Kershaw cameras were named after birds because company directors were avid bird-watchers.

Curlew I,II,III - c1948. Self-erecting folding camera for 6x9cm on 120 film. Sturdy construction but poor sales. Production is estimated at less than 300 for all models combined. $100-125.

Eight-20 Penguin - c1953. 6x9cm rollfilm camera. $10-20. *(Illustrated in previous column.)*

Kershaw Patent Reflex - c1920. Graflex-style single lens reflex. Revolving back. 6x9cm exposures. $100-150.

KEYS STEREO PRODUCTS (U.S.A.)

Trivision Camera - c1950's. For 6 stereo pairs or 12 single shots on 828 film. Fixed focus f8 lenses. Single speed shutter. Similar to Haneel Tri-Vision, but large black decal covers aluminum back. $20-30.

KEYSTONE (Berkey Keystone, Division of Berkey Photo, Inc.)
Wizard XF1000 - c1978. Rigid-bodied instant camera for Polaroid SX-70 film.

Kershaw Eight-20 Penguin

f8.8/115mm lens. Electronic shutter. Production of this camera resulted in a legal confrontation between Keystone and Polaroid. $10-15.

KEYSTONE FERROTYPE CAMERA CO. (Philadelphia, PA)

Street camera - Suitcase style direct-positive street camera with ceramic tank inside. Various masks allow for taking different sized pictures. $125-175.

KIDDIE CAMERA (Made in Taiwan)
A series of cameras, all employing a basically round body similar to that originated by the Potenza tire camera from Japan. Although the basic structure is copied, there is plenty of imagination on the exterior design, and some even include electronic music boxes which play when the shutter is released. The lens is hidden under the nose which doubles as a lenscap. Practicality is not the main concern. I would wager that most children would either lose the lenscap or forget to remove it. Nevertheless, it is a cute series of novelty cameras. "Kiddie Camera" is the brand name used on the packaging of most that we have seen.

Bear Camera - Camera shaped like a bear's head. Uses 110 film. Removable nose is lens cap. Several variations of color and equipment. Colors include "Brown Bear" with brown face and yellow nose and ears; "Panda" in black and white; Tan with panda markings; Orange with white nose and red eyes, etc. Some have hot shoe; others have plugged top. $25-35.

Clown Camera - The same round camera with the facade of a clown's head. The lens is still under the removable nose, but the clown's hat is the shutter release. Some have plugged top, others have electronic music box which plays "Home Sweet Home". $25-35. *(Illustrated on front cover.)*

Dog Camera - Basically round camera with facade of Dog's head. Head is brown with orange around mouth; nose and tongue are red. $25-35.

Santa Claus - The same round camera, but this time with the visage of the famous man from the North Pole. Molded in white plastic, with red hat and lips. $25-35.

KIGAWA OPTICAL (Japan) *Before about 1940, the company was called Optochrome Co.*
Tsubasa Baby Chrome - c1937. Bakelite bodied eye-level camera for 16 exposures, 3x4cm on 127. Optical eye-level finder. New Gold f6.3/50mm in New Gold shutter B,25-100. $50-75.

Tsubasa Chrome - c1937. Dual format eye-level camera for 4x6.5cm or 3x4cm on 127 film. Lucomar f6.3/75mm in Wing Anchor shutter T,B,25-150. Spring-loaded telescoping front. $35-50.

Tsubasa Semi - c1952. Vertical folding bed camera, 4.5x6cm on 120. Bessel f3.5/75mm lens. KKK shutter 10-200,B. $25-35.

Tsubasa Super Semi - c1938. Horizontal folding bed camera, 4.5x6cm on 120. Lucomar Anastigmat f4.5/75mm. New Gold shutter 25-150, T,B. $35-45.

Tsubasaflex Junior - c1951. Inexpensive 6x6cm TLR. Lenses externally gear-coupled. Lause Anastigmat f3.5/80mm. Shutter 10-200,B. $20-25.

KIKO 6 - Japanese 120 rollfilm camera. $15-25.

KIKO-DO CO. (Japan)
Superflex Baby - c1938. Single lens reflex, 4x4cm on 127 film. Design similar to Karmaflex. This was the first 4x4cm SLR from Japan. Super Anastigmat f4.5/70mm. Behind the lens shutter B,25-100. $100-200.

KILFITT (Heinz Kilfitt, Munich, Germany; Heinz Kilfitt Kamerabau, Vaduz, Liechtenstein; Metz Apparatebau, Nuernberg, Germany)
Mecaflex - c1953. A well-made 35mm SLR in an odd 24x24mm format for 50 exposures on regular 35mm cartridge film. Interchangeable bayonet mount lenses, f3.5 or 2.8/40mm Kilar. Prontor-Reflex behind-the-lens shutter. Entire top cover of camera hinges forward to reveal the waist-level reflex finder, rapid-wind lever, exposure counter, etc. When closed, the

matte-chromed cast metal body with its grey leatherette covering looks somewhat like a sleek, knobless Exakta. Not too many were made, and it was never officially imported into the United States. $250-375.

KINDER COMPANY (So. Milwaukee, Wisconsin)

Kin-Dar Stereo camera - c1954. Stereo camera for 5-perforation format on 35mm film in standard cassettes. Steinheil Cassar f3.5/35mm lenses. Five speed shutter, 1/10-1/200 plus Bulb. Advancing the film cocks the shutter, but the shutter can also be cocked manually. Viewfinder and rangefinder combined in single eyepiece, located near the bottom of the camera. Design by Seton Rochwite, whose first major success had been the Stereo Realist Camera. Original price in 1954 was $99.50. $65-95.

KING CAMERA - c1930's. Japanese miniature cardboard "Yen" box camera for single sheet film in paper holder. Single speed shutter with separate cocking lever. Ground glass back. This is one of the better quality "Yen" cameras. $15-25.

KING (Bad Liebenzell, Germany)
Dominant - Postwar German 35mm. Cassar f2.8/45mm in Prontor 500LK shutter. $10-20.

Regula IA above, Regula Gypsy below

Regula - 35mm cameras, introduced in 1951. Various models: IA through IF, IP, IPa; IIIa, b, bk, c, d; Cita III, IIId; Gypsy; KG, PD, RM, etc. f2.8 Cassar, Gotar, Ennit, or Tessar lens. $10-20.

KING SALES CO. (Chicago, Illinois)
Cinex Candid Camera - Bakelite minicam for half-frame 127. Identical to the Rolls Camera Mfg. Co.'s Rolls camera. $3-7.

KING'S CAMERA - Plastic novelty camera for half-127. Made in Hong Kong. $3-6.

KINGSTON - c1960. Small novelty TLR from Hong Kong. Takes 4x4cm on 127 film. Plasicon f8/65mm lens. $5-10.

KINN (France)
Kinax (I) - c1949. Folding camera, 8 exposures on 120 film. Berthiot f4.5/105mm lens. This model does not have parallax corrected finder. Colored: $25-35. Black: $15-20.

Kinax II - c1950. Folding camera for 120 rollfilm, 6x9cm. Parallax correction in viewfinder. Variations include: black or gray leather with black or gray bellows, red metal with red leather bellows. f4.5/105 Som Berthiot or Major Kinn lens in Kinax shutter. Red or grey: $25-35. Black: $15-20.

Kinax Alsace - c1952. Folding rollfilm camera for 6x9cm on 620 film. Berthiot f6.3/100mm lens. Kinax shutter 25-100. Burgundy: $25-40. Black: $15-25.

KIYABASHI KOGAKU (Japan)

Kinax Baby - c1950. Low-priced version of the Kinax with Meniscus lens. 6x9cm on 120 film. $15-20.

Kinax Junior - c1950. One of the better-equipped of the Kinax series. Kior Anastigmat f6.3/100mm in 25-150 shutter. $15-20.

KINON SC-1 - c1986. Novelty 35mm camera from Taiwan, styled like rangefinder type. $1-5.

KINUSA K-77 - c1986. Novelty 35mm camera from Taiwan, styled with small pseudo prism. $1-5.

KIRK Stereo camera, Model 33 - Brown bakelite body. Same body style as Haneel Tri-Vision. Takes six stereo pairs, 26x28mm on 828 film. Three variations: 1. Has aperture numbers 1,2,3 on front but no name on back. 2. Has "Kirk Stereo" on back, but no aperture numbers on front. 3. Has neither name nor numbers. $40-60.

Autoflex - c1957. 6x6cm TLR for 120 film. f3.5 Tri-Lausar lens. $50-75.

K.K. - *Found after the name of many Japanese camera companies, the initials K.K. stand for "Kabushiki Kaisha" meaning "Joint Stock Co."*

KLAPP - *Included in the name of many German cameras, it simply means "folding". Look for another key reference word in the name of the camera.*

KLEER-VU FEATHER-WEIGHT - Plastic novelty camera made in Hong Kong. Half-frame on 127. $1-5.

KLEFFEL (L. G. Kleffel & Sohn, Berlin) Field camera - c1890. 13x18cm horizontal format. Brown square-cornered bellows. Wood body with brass trim. Brass barrel lens. $150-200.

KNIGHT & SONS (London) Knights No. 3 Sliding-box camera - c1853. From the transition period between Daguerreotypes and wet plates, which first were used about 1851. Sliding box-in-box style camera of dovetailed mahogany. Rising front. Two positions for plateholder. Brass landscape lens with waterhouse stops. Full-plate size: $900-1200.

KOBLIC (P. Koblic, Prague) Epifoka - c1946. Hand-held aerial camera for 120 rollfilm. One model for 6x9cm, another for 6x6cm or 4.5x6cm. Tessar or Dagor lens. Compur or Prontor II shutter. Folding frame finder. $125-175.

KOCH (Paris, France) Stereo wet-plate camera - c1860. Wooden stereo box camera for 9x21cm wet plates. Jamin f11/125mm lenses mounted on a tamboured panel for adjustment of lens separation. Rare. $3000-4000.

KOCHMANN (Franz Kochmann, Dresden)

Enolde - c1931. Folding 6x9cm self-erecting rollfilm camera with an unusual detachable telescope-viewer which mounts on the side. The front of the telescopic finder attaches to the lens standard while the rear portion is fixed to the camera body. It serves for focusing and as a viewfinder, especially for close-ups. Rack & pinion focusing to 3 feet. f4.5 Enolde Anastigmat in 3-speed shutter or f4.5 Zeiss Tessar in Compur. $200-250.

Enolde I,II,III - c1930. Folding bed cameras for 6.5x9cm plates. Models I and II are single extension; Model III has double extension. Model I has a small reflex brilliant finder; Model II has reflex and wire frame finders. $20-40.

Korelle cameras - *There are several basic types of Korelle cameras which appear regularly on today's market. The most common of these by far is the reflex. All types, even if not identified by model name or number on the camera, are easily distinguished by size and style. For this reason, we have listed the Korelle cameras here in order of increasing size.*

18x24mm (Korelle K) - c1933. Compact 35mm half-frame camera in vertical format. Thermoplastic body is neither folding nor collapsing type. Shutter/lens assembly is a fixed part of the body. Front lens focusing. Trioplan f2.8/35mm in Compur 1-300 shutter. $200-300.

3x4cm (style similar to the model K, or like a Wirgin Klein-Edinex) - c1932. For 16 exposures on 127 film. This model has telescoping front like the Edinex. Schneider Radionar f2.9/50mm. Compur 1-300, T, B. $50-75.

3x4cm (strut-folding type) - For 16 exposures on 127 film. E. Ludwig Vidar

f4.5/50mm lens in Vario or Compur shutter. $50-75.

4x6.5cm (strut-folding rollfilm type) - c1930. For 8 exposures on 127 film. Schneider Radionar f3.5/75mm or Xenar f2.8/75mm. Compur or Compur Rapid shutter. Basically the same as the Korelle "P" below, but with rounded ends added to the length of the body to house the film rolls. $40-55.

4.5x6cm (Korelle P) - c1933. Strut-folding type for plates, similar to the above rollfilm model, but shorter and with square ends. A fine quality vest-pocket plate camera. Tessar f2.8/75mm or f2.9 Xenar. Compur shutter 1-250. Leather covered metal body. Uncommon. $200-350.

6x6cm (strut-folding rollfilm type) - c1937. Strut-folding type with hinged lens shade/cover. Various lenses f4.5 to f2.8. Prontor I,II; Compur, Compur Rapid; Ibsor shutters. $50-75.

Reflex Korelle (also called **Meister Korelle** and **Master Reflex**) - Introduced c1934. Single lens reflex for 12 exposures 6x6cm on 120 film. (Probably the earliest 6x6cm SLR.) The first model is identifiable by the focal plane shutter 1/25 to 1/500 only, + B. Later models (Models II, IIa, III) with self-timer and shutter speeds extended from 2 secs to 1000. $75-125.

KOEDA (Japan)
Colly - Hit-type subminiature for 14x14mm exposures on 17.5mm rollfilm. Meniscus lens. $10-15.

KOGAKU - *Japanese for "Optical". This term is found in the name of many Japanese firms, usually preceded by the key name of the manufacturer. (However, if you are reading the name from a lens, it may only be the maker of the lens and not the camera.)*

KOEHNLEIN (Konrad Koehnlein, Nuernberg, Germany)
Wiko Standard - c1936. Bakelite subminiature for 13x17mm on special 16mm rollfilm. Laack Poloyt f4.5/30mm. Focal plane shutter 20-200. $125-150.

KOLAR (V. Kolar, Modrany & Prague, Czechoslovakia)
Box Kolex - c1932. Brown leathered metal box camera for 4.5x6cm plates. Rekolar f6.3/75mm lens in Pronto or Vario. Rare. $100-150.

Kola - c1936. An unusual box-shaped camera for various formats on either of two film types. Takes 4x4cm or 3x4cm exposures on 127 film, or 24x36mm exposures on 35mm film with different masks. Zeiss f2.8/60mm Tessar or f2.9/50mm Xenar. Compur shutter. Early model has folding optical finder; later model has tubular finder. $200-325.

Kola (folding rollfilm) - c1934. Folding camera for 16 exposures 4.5x6cm on 120 rollfilm. Rekolat f6.3/75mm in Vario 25-100. $40-50.

Kola Diar - c1933. "Diary" camera for children and beginners. Small camera for r12- 32x32mm exposures on special rollfilm. Simple construction with fixed focus f11/50 Achromat, two stops. Siko shutter, I,T. Folding direct frame finder. $125-175.

Kolex - c1932. Small self-erecting camera for 4.5x6cm plates. (Similar to the vertical Ica Atom.) Rekolar f4.5/75mm in Vario or Pronto; or with Trioplan f3.5/75mm in Compur. Rare. $150-200.

KOMLOSY - Metal-bodied 70mm camera. Rapid advance. $75-125. *(Illustrated bottom of previous column.)*

KONISHIROKU KOGAKU *Konishiroku and its predecessors have been involved in the photographic business since 1873 when Konishi-ya sold photographic and lithographic materials.*
1873 - Konishi-ya
1876 - Konishi Honten
1902 - Rokuoh-sha factory founded.
1921 - Reorganized as corporation "Konishiroku Honten".
1936 - Incorporated as a limited company "Kabushiki Kaisha Konishiroku" (Konishiroku Co. Ltd.).
1943 - Name changed to "Konishiroku Shashin Kogyo Kabushiki Kaisha" (Konishiroku Photo Industry Co. Ltd.).
1944 - Merger with Showa Photo Industries Co. Ltd.

Konica I

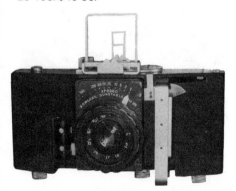

Komlosy

Baby Pearl - c1935. Folding camera for

16 exposures on 127 film. f4.5/50mm Hexar or Optar lens. Rox shutter B, 25-100. $75-125.

Konica - c1948-54. 35mm RF. Hexar or Hexanon f2.8 or 3.5 lens in Konirapid or Konirapid-S 1-500 shutter. Earliest models were made in Occupied Japan, and had no sync. No double exposure prevention. $35-50. *(Illustrated on previous page.)*

Konica II - 1951-58. 35mm RF. Hexanon f2.8/50mm in Konirapid-MFX 1-500 shutter. Double exposure prevention. $30-40.

Konica III - 1956-59. 35mm RF. Hexanon f2/48mm lens in Konirapid-MFX 1-500 shutter. $35-50.

Konica IIIA - 1958-61. Similar to the Konica III, but large center viewfinder window and larger rangefinder windows. Hexanon f2/48mm lens. $40-55.

Konica IIIM - 1959-60. 35mm RF with meter (usually not working). Hexanon f1.8/50mm lens in Seikosha SLV 1-500 shutter. Takes full or half frame exposures. $75-125.

Konica Autoreflex - c1967. First 35mm SLR with focal plane shutter to feature automatic exposure control. Full or half-frame. Also marketed as Autorex. $100-175.

Konica F - c1960. Konishiroku's first 35mm SLR. Coupled selenium meter. Shutter to 1/2000. Scarce in the U.S.A. $175-225.

Konilette 35 - c1959. 35mm viewfinder

camera. Konitor f3.5/45mm lens. Shutter to 1/200, B, sync. $15-25.

Pearl No. 2 - c1920's. Typical folding-bed rollfilm camera for 6x9cm on 120 film. Shutter 25-100,T,B. $30-45.

Pearl I - c1949-50. Folding camera 4.5x6cm "semi" or half-frames on 120 film. Hexar f4.5/75mm in Durax shutter T,B, 1-100. Uncoupled rangefinder. $75-125.

Pearl II - c1952-55. Similar to Pearl I, but coupled rangefinder and Konirapid-S to 500. "Pearl II" on top housing. $75-125.

Pearl IV - c1958. Folding 120 rollfilm camera, 4.5x6cm. CRF. Elaborate system of projected frames in viewfinder. Hexar f3.5/75mm. Seikosha-MXL, B,1-500. $175-225.

Pearlette - c1925-46. Trellis-strut folding camera for 4x6.5cm exposures on 127 film. Various models. Most commonly found with Rokuohsha Optar f6.3/75mm in Echo shutter 25-100. Deluxe models have f4.5 lens, folding optical finder. $60-80.

Rokuoh-Sha Machine-gun Camera Type 89 - World War II vintage training camera for machine gunners. Size, shape, and weight comparable to a machine gun, but holds 35mm film to make moving picture of targeted subject. Camera runs while trigger is squeezed, making 18x24mm images. Hexar f4.5/75mm lens. $250-350.

Sakura (Vest Pocket Camera) - c1931. Not related to the Sakura Seiki Co. which made the Petal camera. Small brown or maroon bakelite camera for ten exposures 4x5cm on 127 film. One of very few cameras to use the 4x5cm format on 127 film. Rokuoh-Sha fixed focus lens. B,I shutter. $75-100.

Semi-Pearl - c1938-1948. Folding bed camera for 16 exposures, 4.5x6cm, on 120 film. Hexar f4.5/75mm lens. Shutter to 100. RF. $30-45.

Snappy - c1949. Subminiature camera for 14x14mm exposures. Interchangeable Optar f3.5/25mm lens. Guillotine shutter behind the lens: B, 25, 50, 100. Made in Occupied Japan. With normal lens: $100-150. With f5.6/40mm Cherry Tele lens (illustrated above) add: $50-75.

KORSTEN (Paris)
Litote - 1902-1904. Rigid-bodied jumelle-style stereo for plates. 4.5x10.7cm or 6x13cm sizes. Aplanat or Krauss lenses. 3-speed guillotine shutter. Newton finder. $50-100.

KOSSATZ (Konstantin Kossatz, Berlin, Germany)
Spiegel-Reflex - c1920. Single lens reflex of the Graflex style. Leather covered body with nickel-plated metal parts. 13x18cm exposures on plates. Goerz Dogmar f4.5/240mm lens. Focal plane shutter. $350-375.

KOWA OPTICAL (JAPAN)
Kallo - c1955. Rangefinder 35, some models with uncoupled meter. Prominar f2.8 or f2 lens. Seikosha shutter, B,1-500. $20-30.

Kalloflex - c1954. 6x6cm TLR, 120 film. Prominar f3.5/75mm lens in Seikosha 1-500 shutter. $60-90.

Komaflex-S - c1960. One of the very few 4x4cm SLR's ever made. 127 film. Die-cast body. Gray anodized finish. Gray covering. Kowa Prominar f2.8/65mm. Seikosha SLV between the lens shutter, 1-500, B. $75-125.

Kowa E - 1962-66. 35mm SLR. Coupled selenium meter. Prominar f2/50mm non-interchangeable lens (with telephoto and wide-angle attachments available). Seikosha SLV shutter, 1-500, B. $20-35.

Kowa H - 1963-67. 35mm SLR. Coupled selenium, automatic, shutter preferred. Kowa f2.8/48mm lens in Seikosha 30-300 shutter. $25-40.

Ramera - intro. 1959. Plastic six-transistor radio with 16mm sub-miniature camera. 10x14mm exposures. Also sold under the name Bell Kamra. Prominar f3.5/23mm. 3-speed shutter, 50-200, B. Available in: black, blue, red, white. Generally found new in box for $50-75.

Super Lark Zen-99 - c1960. Gray 127 camera with imitation light meter and rangefinder windows. 4x6cm or 4x4cm on 127 rollfilm. Prominar f11/70mm fixed focus. I,T shutter. $10-20.

Zen-99 - Inexpensive eye-level camera for 8 or 12 exposures on 127 film. Dark grey enamel with light grey covering. $10-20.

KOZY CAMERA CO.
Pocket Kozy - c1895. Flat-folding bellows camera. Bellows open like the pages of a book. This early model has a flat front, not rounded as the on later model. 3½x3½"

exposures on rollfilm. Meniscus f2.0/5"
lens. Single speed shutter, T. Waist-level
viewfinder. $1200-1500.

Pocket Kozy, Improved - c1898. Similar
to the first model, but front end with lens
is rounded, not flat. $600-750.

KRANZ (L.W. Kranz)
Sliding-box Daguerreotype Camera -
c1856. Wood body. 9x12cm. $5000+

KRAUSS (G. A. Krauss, Stuttgart;
E. Krauss, Paris)

Eka - (Paris, c1924) For 100 exposures,
30x44mm on 35mm unperforated film.
Krauss Zeiss Tessar f3.5/50mm lens in
Compur 1-300 shutter. $550-850.

Peggy I - (Stuttgart, c1934) 35mm strut-
folding camera. Tessar f3.5/50mm lens.
Compur shutter 1-300. $250-400.

Peggy II - (Stuttgart, c1934) Basically the
same as Peggy I, but with coupled
rangefinder. Early model automatically
cocked the shutter by pushing in the front
and releasing it, but this meant that the
camera was stored with the shutter

tensioned. Later model (scarcer) had
manual cocking lever. Often with Xenon
f2 or Tessar f2.8. $250-400.

Photo-Revolver - (Paris, c1920's) For
18x35mm exposures on 48 plates in
magazine or special rollfilm back. Krauss
Tessar f4/40mm lens. 3-speed shutter,
25-100, T. $1800-2200.

Polyscop - (Paris, c1910) Stereo camera
for 45x107mm plates in magazine back.
$150-200.

Rollette - (Paris, c1920's) Folding rollfilm
cameras, with Krauss Rollar f6.3/90mm
lens in Pronto 25-100 shutter. Focus by
radial lever on bed. $40-50.

Rollette Luxus - c1928. Similar, but with
light brown reptile covering and brown
bellows. $145-160.

Stereoplast - (Stuttgart, c1921) All-metal
rigid body stereo, similar to the Polyscop.
45x107mm exposures. f4.5/55mm lenses.
Stereo-Spezial shutter to 300. Magazine
back for glass plates. $150-200.

Takyr - (Paris, c1906) Strut-folding camera
for 9x12cm plates. Krauss Zeiss Tessar
f6.3/136mm lens. Focal plane shutter.
$125-175.

KREMP (Wetzlar, Germany)

Kreca - c1930. Unusual 35mm with prismatic telescope for rangefinder. Identical to Beira II camera from Woldemar Beier, but rarer still. "Kreca" embossed on front leather. "Kremp, Wetzlar" logo embossed on back. Kreca f2.9 lens in rim Compur to 300. $250-350.

KRUGENER (Dr. Rudolf Krugener, Bockheim/Frankfurt, Germany)

Delta (plate camera) - c1905. Vertically styled 9x12cm folding plate camera. Black leather covered wood body. Aluminum standard, nickel trim. f6.8/120mm Dagor or Euryscop Anastigmat lens. Delta shutter 25-100. $50-75.

Delta (plate & rollfilm) - Horizontal style rectangular body. Folding bed. Early models c1900 have wooden lensboard with built-in shutter or external brass "Delta" shutter. Later types c1905 have Unicum shutter and large metal frame finder. Wine red or light brown bellows. 9x9cm and 9x12cm sizes. Early types with built-in shutter or Delta shutter: $200-300. Later types with Unicum shutter: $125-175.

Delta (rollfilm) - c1900-1903. Horizontally styled folding bed 6x9cm camera with rounded ends. Leather covered wooden body and aluminum bed. Leather-covered wooden lensboard with built-in M,Z shutter and reflex finder. Wine-red bellows. $75-100.

Delta Detective - c1890. Small polished mahogany box camera. Leather changing bag for 12 plates, 6x8cm. Shutter cocked and released by pulling on 2 strings on top of the camera. $400-600.

Delta Magazine Camera - c1892. For 12 exposures 9x12cm on plates which are changed by pulling out a rod at the front of the camera. Achromat lens in simple spring shutter. $400-500.

Delta Periskop - c1900. Folding bed camera for 9x12cm plates. Leather covered wood body. Red bellows. Krugener Rapid Delta Periscop f12 lens in delta shutter 25-100. $75-100.

Krugener Simplex Magazine

Delta Stereo - c1898. Folding bed stereo camera for 9x18cm exposures on plates or rollfilm. Earliest models with wooden lensboard, later made of metal. Periplanat or Extra-Rapid Aplanat lenses. Red bellows. Polished wood interior. $175-275.

Electus - c1889. Non-focusing TLR-style magazine box camera. Similar to the Simplex Magazine camera, but only holds 18 plates. Steinheil lens. Single speed shutter. $800-1200.

Jumelle-style magazine camera - For 18 plates 6x10.7cm. Brass-barrel Periscop lens, leather covered wood body. Built-in changing magazine. $175-250.

Million - c1903. Leather covered stereo. 9x18cm on rollfilm, single or stereo exp. Looks like a box camera, but has a short bellows extension. Red bellows. Periskop lenses. Guillotine shutter. $150-200.

Normal Simplex - c1892. Polished mahogany magazine camera for 12 plates, 9x12cm. Small box with waist-level viewfinder retracts into the top of the camera body when not in use. Antiplanat lens, 3 diaphragm stops. $1200-1600.

Plaskop - c1907. Compact strut-folding

camera for 45x107mm stereo plates. Unusual hinged frame finder incorporates lenscaps. Metal body available with or without leather covering. Various lenses. Four speeds plus time. Rare. $250-325.

Plastoscop - c1907. Strut-folding stereo camera for 45x107mm plates. $125-175.

Simplex Magazine - c1889. Non-focusing TLR-style with changing mechanism for 24 plates, 6x8cm. Polished mahogany. Steinheil or Periscop f10/100mm lens. Single speed sector shutter. $1200-1400. *(Illustrated top of previous column.)*

Taschenbuch-Camera - c1889-1892. Leather covered camera, disguised as a book. Achromatic f12/65mm lens is in the "spine" of the book. Guillotine shutter, T, I. Shutter is cocked and released by pulling on 2 strings. Internal magazine holds 24 plates for 40x40mm exposures. $2500-2900.

K.S.K.
Corona - Subminiature made in Occupied Japan. 14x14mm exposures. Rim-set leaf shutter, iris diaphragm. Red leather covering with gold-colored metal parts. $200-250. *(Illustrated on back cover.)*

KUGLER (Earl Kugler, U.S.A.)
Close Focus Camera - Unusual vertically styled polished wood folding bed camera for 2½x4¼" exposures on rollfilm. Rack and pinion focusing to 12". Symmetrical 4x5 lens in Unicum shutter. Rigid wood handle on top. $100-150.

KULLENBERG, O. (Essen, Germany)
Field camera, 5x7" - Vertical format field camera with red tapered bellows, brass-barreled Universal Aplanat f8 lens with iris diaphragm. Rouleau shutter. $175-225.

KUNIK, Walter KG. (Frankfurt)

Foto-Fueller (Luxus) - c1956. The German version of the French Stylophot, designed by Fritz Kaftanski. This luxus version has a crudely applied covering of imitation snakeskin. Hardly in competition with the Luxus Leica, but still not often found. $200-250.

Mickey Mouse Camera - c1958. Subminiature, like the Ompex, but with the Mickey Mouse name on the faceplate. 14x14mm exposures on 16mm Tuxi film. Red hammertone body. Meniscus lens, single speed shutter. $75-100.

Ompex 16 - c1960. Subminiature similar to the Tuxi. Black or red body. Meniscus lens, single speed shutter. Red: $50-75. Black: $40-50.

Petie with gold trim

Petie - c1958. Subminiature for 16 exposures 14x14mm on 16mm film. Meniscus f11/25mm lens in simple shutter. Gray crinkle finish enamel with gold-colored trim: $45-65. Black with silver parts: $30-50.

Petie Lighter - c1956. Petie camera in a special housing which also incorporates a cigarette lighter. Art-deco enamel finish or leather covered. $450-500.

Petie Vanity - c1956. Petie camera housed in a make-up compact. Front door opens to reveal mirror and powder. One top knob contains a lipstick, another provides storage for an extra roll of film. Art deco enameled finish in red, green, or blue. $450-500.

Petitax - c1962. Novelty camera for 14x14mm exposures on rollfilm. f11/25mm lens. Simple shutter. $30-50.

Tuxi - c1960. For 14x14mm on 16mm film. Achromat Roeschlein f7.7/25mm lens in synched shutter, B, M. $30-50.

Tuximat - c1959. 14x14mm on 16mm film. Meniscus lens f7.7/25mm. Synched

Tuximat

shutter. Simple built-in meter. $90-120.

KURIBAYASHI CAMERA WORKS, PETRI CAMERA CO. (Tokyo) *Kuribayashi*

Camera Works was established in 1907 as a small workshop producing photographic accessories such as plate holders and wooden tripods. Its first production camera was the Speed Reflex of 1919. Most pre-WWII models were sold under the "First" brand name by Minagawa Shoten, a trading firm. During the Occupation, the name "Petri" was chosen, contracted from "Peter the First". This was hoped to improve acceptance in non-Japanese markets. The company name was changed to Petri Camera Company in 1962. After seventy years, the company went bankrupt in 1977.

None of the pre-WWII models were marketed outside of Japan. Though Kuribayashi was a leading domestic manufacturer, most models were still made in small lots and are now quite rare and highly sought in Japan. During the Occupation, nearly all Japanese cameras, including Petri models, were sold to Allied forces and western markets.

Cameras in this section are listed in chronological order.

PLATE CAMERAS
1919 Speed Reflex - Similar to the English Thornton large format SLR's. Two models with either quarter-plate or 6x9cm formats. German Tessar lens, cloth focal plane shutter with speeds to 1/1000. Very rare. $600+

HAND PLATE CAMERAS
Folding hand plate cameras with interchangeable ground glass focusing backs and plate holders for 2¼x3¼" formats. Initially fitted with imported European shutters and optics, by the early 1930's Kuribayashi's plate models mounted some of the very first all-Japanese made shutters and lenses (Seikosha and Tokyo Kogaku).

Mikuni - c1926. One of the leading Japanese-made cameras during the late 1920's. Tessar f4.5-6.3/105mm lens, Vario shutter. No known example in any Japanese collection. Value unknown.

First Hand - 1929, new model 1932.
Kokka Hand - 1930, new model 1932.
Tokiwa Hand - 1930.
Romax Hand - 1934.
All models are similar, fitted with Tessar or Trinar 105mm lenses and Vario or Compur shutters. The 1929 First Hand was the initial model to bear the name "First". In 1934 the majority of the factory's models mounted Toko and State (Tokyo Kogaku) 105mm Anastigmat lenses and the Vario-inspired Seikosha Magna shutter. All models rare, available only in Japan. Collectors' price $75-300.

First Etui Camera - 1934. Patterned after the KW Patent Etui. Very compact folding camera fitted with Toko Anastigmat 105mm, Magna shutter. $75-250.

PRE-WAR ROLLFILM MODELS
Starting in the early 1930's with the increasing supply of rollfilm in Japan, the hand plate camera gave way to the compact and easy to use rollfilm models.

First Roll - 1933. Folding metal body camera fitted with Radionar, Trinar or Toko (State) 105mm and a variety of shutters of Japanese and German make. Full frame exposures on 120 rollfilm. $75-250.

Semi First - 1935. 4.5x6cm on 120 rollfilm.
Baby Semi First - 1936. 4.5x6cm on 120 rollfilm.
First Six - 1936. 6x6cm on 120 rollfilm. The first Japanese-made camera for the 12-on-a-roll format.
First Center - 1936. 6x9cm on 120 rollfilm.
First Speed Pocket - 1936. The first Japanese camera to take both Vest and Baby formats. 127 film.

BB Semi First - 1940. 4.5x6cm on 120 rollfilm. The first camera to be made in Japan with a built-in exposure meter (extinction type).
Baby BB Semi First - 1940. 4.5x6cm on 120 rollfilm.
Auto Semi First - 1940. 4.5x6cm on 120 rollfilm.
All are self-erecting folding bellows designs fitted with a variety of Japanese made lenses/shutters, dominated for the most part by Toko Anastigmats and Seikosha's copy of Vario or rim-set Compur shutter. In fact, the 1936 model of Semi First sported the first Compur-type Seikosha shutter. All presently rare with current values starting about $75 for Semi First and over $300 for Speed Pocket and Auto Semi First.

First Reflex - 1937. One of the first Japanese-made 120 twin lens reflex cameras, fitted with First Anastigmat 75mm and First shutter, 1-200. Very rare, with less than five examples known. Collector's value unknown.

POST-WAR ROLLFILM MODELS

After the war, Kuribayashi introduced its own line of shutters and lenses. Carperu leaf shutters in a variety of speeds with Orikon and Orikkor lenses.

Kuri Camera - 1946.
Lo Ruby Camera - 1947. Improved versions of the pre-war Semi First. Made in small quantities mounting First or Kokka 75mm Anastigmats; First or Wester Compur type shutters. Collector's value unknown.

Petri Semi, II, III - 1948. First use of the word "Petri". Fitted with Petri and Orikon 75mm lenses and Petri 1-200 shutter. Built-in uncoupled rangefinder. Majority marked MIOJ on back cover latch. $75 and up.

Petri RF - 1952. Compact version of the larger Petri Semi type. Orikon f3.5/75mm and Carperu 1-200 shutter. Uncoupled rangefinder. $50 and up.

Petri RF 120 - 1955. Very similar to the Petri RF, but with coupled rangefinder. Uncommon. Price unknown.

Petri Super - 1955.
Petri Super V - 1956. Last Kuribayashi rollfilm self-erecting models. Very similar to pre-war Auto Semi First with coupled rangefinder. Fitted with Tessar-type Orikkor 75mm lens and Carperu or Seiko Rapid shutter. Uncommon, high quality folding camera. $100 and up.

Karoron - 1949.
Karoron S - 1951. Popular models of the more expensive and feature-laden Petri Semi. Neither fitted with rangefinders. Orikon 75mm lens and Carperu shutter to 200. $35 and up.

Karoron S-II, Karoron RF - 1951-52. Both exactly alike and different from the Petri RF in nameplate alone. Orikon f3.5/75mm, Carperu shutter. Uncommon. $75.

Petri Flex - 1955. The only post-war TLR camera to be manufactured by Kuribayashi Camera. Rolleicord-inspired with matched Orikkor f3.5/75mm taking and viewing lenses; Carperu shutter to 200. Rare. $150.

PETRI 35mm MODELS

Petri 35 - 1954. First 35mm rangefinder camera from Kuribayashi. Orikkor f3.5 or f2.8/45mm lens, Petri-Carperu shutter, 1/10-200. Uncommon. $35 and up.

Petri 35X, MX - 1955.
Petri Automate - 1956.
Petri 35 2.0 - 1957.
Petri (35) 2.8 - 1958.
Petri 35 1.9 - 1958.
These models were based on the original 1954 Petri 35. Fitted with Orikkor 45mm f2.8, 2.0, 1.9 lenses. Copal and Carperu shutters with speeds of either 1/300 or 1/500. All have coupled rangefinders. Common, with prices starting at $10.

Petri 2.8 Color Super - 1958.
Petri 1.8 Color Super - 1959.
Petri 1.9 Color Super - 1960.
The Petri Color Super series were improved models with a projected bright line viewfinder with automatic parallax correction. High quality taking lenses. Sold in vast numbers. Common. $10 and up.

Petri EBn - 1960. Built-in selenium cell exposure meter fitted in Petri Color Super body. Orikkor 45mm f1.9 or 2.8 lens. Copal or Carperu shutter in geometrical progression to 500. $35.

Petri Seven - 1961.
Petri Seven S - 1962.
Petri Pro Seven - 1963.
Petri Racer - 1966.
Petri Seven S-II - 1977.
All are coupled rangefinder models with selenium cell (CdS on Racer) mounted inside of lens ring, called "Circle Eye" by the factory. All available with either f1.8 or 2.8 Petri lenses (f1.8 only on Petri Pro Seven) and shutters to 500. Exposure readout in viewfinder and on the top cover with the exception of the Petri Seven fitted only with finder meter scale. Very popular camera with user prices starting at $5.

Petri Prest - 1961.
Petri Hi-Lite - 1964.
Petri Computor 35 - 1971.
Petri M 35 - 1973.
Petri ES Auto 1.7 - 1974.
Petri ES Auto 2.8 - 1976.
Petri 35 RE - 1977.
With the exception of the selenium-celled Petri Prest and Hi-Lite, these models contain fully automatic CdS photometers. All have coupled rangefinders with projected bright line frames. Petri lenses in 40 and 45mm focal lengths in a range of apertures to f1.7 using Petri and some Seiko-made shutters. Prices start at $10.

Petri Half, Junior, Compact - 1960.
Petri Compact E - 1960.
Petri Compact 17, Petri Half - 1962.
Kuribayashi was the second Japanese camera maker to market a line of half-frame models. All equipped with projected bright line viewfinders and Petri-Orikkor f2.8/28mm lenses. The 1960 Petri Half was

fitted with a rapid advance lever and Carperu shutter to 250. Compact E was the same as the Petri Half, but with a built-in uncoupled selenium exposure meter. The 1962 half-frame models sported electric eye photometer for fully automatic exposure and revised body design. All still available both for the user and collector. Compact and high quality. Prices start at $35.

Petri Color 35 - 1968.
Petri Color 35E - 1970.
Petri Micro Compact - 1976.
Full frame, compact 35mm cameras with a retractable Petri f2.8/40mm lens patterned after the Rollei 35. One of Petri's most successful models, the original 1968 Petri Color 35 had a coupled CdS photometer with shutter speeds to 250. The Color 35E and Micro Compact were very similar but with fully automatic exposure mechanism. Prices start at $25.

PETRI SINGLE LENS REFLEX MODELS
Most models supplied with 55mm f2 or f1.4 normal lens in Petri breech mount. All share the same basic body design and front-mounted shutter release. Most models common and still available on the used market.

Petri Penta - 1959.
Petri Penta V2, Petri Flex V - 1961.
Petri Penta (Flex) V3 - 1964.
Petri Penta (Flex) V6 - 1965.
Petri Penta (Flex) V6-II - 1970.
Petri Penta was Kuribayashi's first modern SLR camera with focal plane shutter ½-500 and pre-set screwmount Petri Orikkor f2/50mm lens. Later improvements include automatic lens aperture and introduction of Petri breech lens mount system with the Petri Penta V2 (called Petri Flex series in non-Japanese markets). Clip-on CdS photometer on the Petri Penta V3 and later Petri V6. User prices start at $20.

Petri Flex Seven - 1964.
Petri FT - 1967.
Petri FT-II - 1970.
Petri FTX - 1974.
Petri FT 1000, FT 500 - 1976.
Petri MFT 1000 - 1976.
Petri Micro MF-1 - 1977.

With the exception of the Petri Flex 7 (external CdS cell), these Petri models featured TTL photometers with stop-down aperture, match-needle meters. Cloth focal plane shutter of 1-1000 (500 on the FT 500). Breech lens mount used on Petri Flex 7, FT, and FT-II; universal 42mm screw-type lens mount on all other models. Petri MFT 1000 and Micro MF-1 are compact models. FT 100 and 500 also sold under different brand names. User prices range from $30 and up. Petri Flex Seven is rare and highly sought after by Japanese collectors, with prices starting at $200.

Petri FT EE - 1969.
Petri FTE - 1973.
Petri FA-1 - 1975.
All shutter speed priority, fully automatic reflexes. TTL meter sets f stop with full aperture metering. Cloth focal plane shutter in FT EE and FTE similar to Petri Flex V (½-500), and 1-1000 with FA-1. FT EE and FTE nearly alike, except for designation. FA-1 is most deluxe and advanced model of its type from Petri Camera. All use standard Petri breech lens mount. $35 and up.

RAPID FILM SYSTEM MODELS

Petri Auto Rapid - 1965.
Petri Instant Back (AKA Anscomatic 726) - 1966.
Petri Pocket 2 - 1975.
Petri Grip Pak 110 - 1977.
Petri Push-Pull 110 - 1977.
All these feature quick loading film systems; Petri Auto Rapid (Agfa Rapid), Petri Instant Back (Eastman Kodak 126), and Petri Pocket 2, Grip Pak, and Push-Pull (Eastman Kodak 110 cartridge load). Leaf shutter and fixed Petri lenses. All common with user prices starting at $5.

Fotochrome Camera - 1965. Made by Petri Camera for USA firm of Fotochrome Inc. Using mirror-type image reversing system, special drop-in film packs allowed for direct color prints without negative with factory processing. Unusual plastic body with flip-up reflector for built-in bulb flash. Petri f4.5/105mm lens and Vario-type shutter. Still available new in boxes, usually for $20-30.

K.W. (Kamera Werkstatten A.G., Dresden, Germany) *After WWII, K.W. became part of the "V.E.B. Pentacon" group, but cameras continued to bear the KW trademark.* **Happy** - c1931. Folding 6.5x9cm plate camera. Similar to the Patent Etui. Black leather covered metal body. Schneider Radionar f6.3/105mm lens in Vario shutter. $50-75.

Jolly - c1950. Subminiature for 10x15mm exposures. T & I shutter. One of the first post-war subminiatures from Germany, and the only one from K.W. Rare. $200-250.

Kawee - *Apparently this was the American marketing name for the "Patent Etui". See the next four entires.*
Patent Etui, 6.5x9cm - Black leather and bellows. Focus knob on bed. Tessar f4.5/ 105mm or Radionar f6.3/105mm lens. Vario, Ibsor or Compur shutter. $40-80.

Patent Etui, 6.5x9cm Luxus - Tastefully finished in brown leather with light brown bellows. $150-175.

K.W. Pilot, TLR model

Patent Etui, 9x12cm size - The most common size. f4.5 or f6.3 Rodenstock Eurynar, Schneider Radionar, Isconar, Erkos Fotar, or Zeiss Tessar or Trioplan. Shutter: Ibsor, Vario, or Compur. $35-50.

Patent Etui, 9x12cm Luxus - c1928. Brown leather covering; light brown bellows. $150-175.

Pilot (TLR) - 1932-37. TLR for 16 exposures 3x4cm on 127 film. With f2 Biotar: $400-500. With Xenar f2.9, f3.5; or Tessar f2.8, f3.5: $150-225. *(Illustrated top of next column.)*

Pilot 6 - 1936-39. SLR for 12 exposures 6x6cm on 127 film. KW Anastigmat f6.3/ 75mm or Laack Pololyt f3.5/75mm or 80mm lens. Metal guillotine shutter 25-100, later 20-150. Last models c1938-1939 have interchangeable lenses, and 20-200 shutter. $60-100. *Replaced in 1939 by the Pilot Super.*

Pilot Super - 1939-41. SLR for 12 exposures 6x6cm on 120 film. Could also take 16 exposures 4.5x6cm with mask. Built on the same chassis as the Pilot 6, but easily distinguished by the addition of a small extinction meter attached to the viewing hood. Interchangeable lens, such as: Ennastar, Pilotar, or Laack, f2.9, 3.5, or 4.5. Shutter 20-200,T,B. $60-90. *(Illustrated top of next page.)*

Pocket Dalco (blue) - An unusual name variation of the Patent Etui 6x9cm. Blue leather covering with blue bellows. Tessar f4.5/105mm in Compur. $200-250.

Pilot Super

Praktica FX2

Praktica FX3 - c1957. Like FX2, but with internal automatic diaphragm stop-down. $30-50.

Praktica - c1952. 35mm SLR. Waist-level viewing. Interchangeable lens: f2.8 or 3.5. Focal plane shutter 2-500, B. $25-50.

Praktica Nova - c1965. 35mm eye-level SLR. Domiplan f2.8 lens. Focal plane shutter 2-500. $30-50.

Praktica FX - 1952-57. 35mm SLR with waist-level finder. Westanar or Tessar f2.8 or 3.5 lens. Focal plane shutter 2-500. $30-50.

Praktica FX2 - c1956. Same as FX, but with accessory pentaprism for eye-level viewing. With normal lens and prism finder: $30-50. *(Illustrated top of next column.)*

Praktiflex - c1938. 35mm waist-level SLR. Victor f2.9/50mm, Tessar f3.5 , or Biotar f2.0 lens. Focal plane shutter 20-500. Grey lacquered with brown leather: $100-200. Normal: $45-65.

Praktiflex II - c1940. Victor f2.9/50mm lens. $30-50.

Waist-level or prism finders. $125-175.

Praktiflex FX - c1955. Tessar f2.8 or Primoplan f1.9 lens. $35-50.

Praktina FX - c1956-66. 35mm SLR. FP shutter 1-1000, B. Interchangeable Biotar f2/58mm lens. Interchangeable pentaprism. $75-100 without motor. Add $40-60 each for spring motor drive or bulk film back.

Reflex-Box - c1933. Boxy SLR for 8 exp. 6x9cm on 120 rollfilm in horizontal format. KW Anastigmat f6.3/105mm, or Steinheil f4.5/105mm. Three speed shutter 25-100, B. Folding top viewing hood. $80-125.

Rival Reflex - c1955. 35mm SLR made in USSR occupied Germany. Praktica body with crude name change. Wetzlar Vastar f2.8/50mm lens. FP shutter, sync. $30-45.

Praktina IIa - c1959-74. 35mm SLR. Jena T 2.8/50mm. Focal plane shutter to 1000. $50-90 without motor. Add $40-60 each for spring motor drive or bulk film back.

Praktisix, Praktisix II - c1957-62. 6x6cm SLR. Also sold as Pentacon Six. Focal plane shutter 1-1000. Interchangeable bayonet mount Meyer Primotar f3.5/80mm.

KYOTO SEIKI CO. (Japan)
Lovely - c1948. Japanese subminiature taking 14x14mm exposures on paper-backed rollfilm. Simple fixed-focus lens, shutter 25-100,B. Rare. $500+.

LA CROSSE CAMERA CO. (LaCrosse, Wisc.)

Snapshot - c1898. Miniature cardboard and brass box camera. 28x28mm exposures. (Identical to the Comet Camera made by Aiken-Gleason Co. of LaCrosse.) $350-450.

LA ROSE (Raymond R. La Rose & Sons, Culver City, USA)
Rapitake - c1948. Unusually designed 35mm for 18x24mm exposures. Metal body. Tubular viewfinder. Fixed focus f7.5/35 lens. Single speed shutter. Plunger at back is the shutter release and also advances the film. $200-300.

LAACK (Julius Laack & Sons, Rathenow)
Ferrotype camera - c1895. Metal "cannon" camera for 25mm dia. ferrotypes. f3.5/60mm lens. $700-900.

Merkur - 10x15cm folding plate camera. Polyxentar f6.8/150mm lens in Koilos shutter. $20-30.

Padie - 9x12cm folding plate camera. Laack Pololyt f6.8/135mm. Rulex 1-300 shutter. $25-35.

Tropical camera - Folding plate camera, 9x12cm. Wood exterior, brown bellows. Laack Pololyt f4.5/135 lens in Ibsor shutter or Laack Dialytar f4.5 in Compur. With gold plated metal parts: $500-600. With brass trim: $200-300.

Wanderer - 6.5x9cm plate camera. $25-40.

LACON CAMERA CO., INC. (Shinano Camera Works, Japan)
Lacon C - c1954. 35mm viewfinder camera. S-Lacor f3.5/45mm lens, shutter 25-300,B. $15-20. *(Illustrated top of next column.)*

Lacon C

LAMPERTI & GARBAGNATI (Milan)
Detective camera - c1890. 9x12cm. Polished wood body. Leather changing sack. $250-350.

Wet-plate camera - c1870. Polished walnut body, square blue bellows. 18x18cm. Tilting back. Brass barrel Darlot Petzval lens, waterhouse stops. $1500-2000.

LANCART (Etablissements Lancart, Paris)

Xyz - c1935. Nickel-plated subminiature. Roussel Xyzor f7/22mm lens. Shutter 25, B,l. 12x15mm exposures. $500-650.

LANCASTER, (J. Lancaster, Birmingham, England)
Brass Bound Instantograph - c1908. Mahogany view, with brass binding. Lancaster lens and shutter. $175-250.

Gem Apparatus - c1880. 12-lens camera, taking 12 exposures on a 9x12cm ferrotype plate. Polished mahogany body. Front panel is slid sideways to uncover the lenses and back again to end the exposure. $1000-1500.

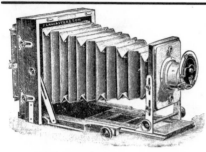

Instantograph ¼-plate view - c1886-1910. Brass barrel Lancaster f8 or f10 lens in Lancaster rotary shutter. Iris diaphragm. Wood body, tapered red bellows. $100-175. **-- ½ or full-plate size** - $100-200.

International Patent - c1892-1905. Tailboard style mahogany camera with reversible back. Most commonly found in ¼ and ½-plate sizes. Wine-red square bellows. Lancaster brass barrel lens with iris diaphragm. $80-185.

Kamrex - c1900. ¼-plate camera. Red leather bellows. Mahogany with brass trim. R.R. lens. $75-150.

Ladies Cameras: Note there are several cameras with similar names.

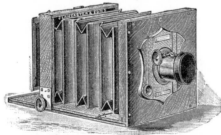

Ladies Camera - c1880's. Folding tailboard style view camera of polished mahogany. Not to be confused with the handbag style "Ladies" cameras. $150-250.

Lancaster Le Meritoire

Ladies Camera - c1890's. ½-plate reversible-back camera. Achromatic lens, iris diaphragm. Single speed pneumatic shutter. When closed, the case resembles a ladies' purse with tapered sides. In the early variation, c1894, the front door hinges 270 degrees to lay flat under the body. The rear door forms a tailboard for rearward entension of the back. Later models use the front door for a bed on which to extend the front with tapered bellows. $1000-1500.

Ladies Gem Camera - c1900. Lyre-shaped body covered in alligator skin. Same camera as the Certo "Damen-Kamera". Looks like a stylish woman's handbag when closed. ¼-plate size. Rare. Negotiable. Estimate: $7500+. (One reported sale for about $18,000.)

Le Meritoire - c1882. Wooden view. Brass trim. Brown or blue double extension bellows. Lancaster lens. Sizes from ¼-plate to 10x12". $175-250. *(Illustrated top of previous page.)*

Le Merveilleux - c1890's. ¼-plate field camera. Aplanat lens. Quite common on auctions in England for $75-125.

Omnigraph - c1891. ¼-plate detective box camera. Achromatic lens. See-Saw shutter. One sold at auction in Germany in 1978 for over $500. Another reportedly sold at auction in England in 1986 for $25. You figure it out.

Postage Stamp Cameras - c1896. Wood box cameras of various designs, having 4 or 6 lenses, for "gem" exposures. $1500-2500.

Rover - c1891. Detective box camera, holding 12 plates. Rectilinear lens, See-Saw shutter. $450-650.

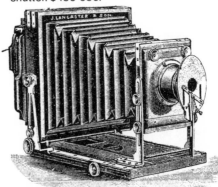

Special Brass Bound Instantograph - c1891. Folding tailboard camera, double swing. Brass bound. Red or black square leather bellows. Rectigraph or Lancaster lens. Patent See-Saw shutter. ¼ and ½-plate sizes. $100-150.

Stereo Instantograph - c1891. Folding 8x17cm stereo. Red bellows. Rectograph lenses. $350-450.

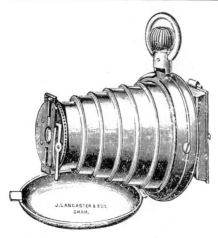

Watch Camera - c1890's. Designed like a pocket watch. Self-erecting design consists of six spring-loaded telescoping tubes. Men's size (1½x2" plates) or Ladies' size (1x1½" plates). Rare. Price negotiable. Estimate: Men's: $13,000. Ladies': $15,000. Beginning about 1982, reproductions of this rare camera have been offered for sale. Recent auction sales have been in the range of $1100-1200.

LAURIE IMPORT LTD. (Hong Kong)

Dick Tracy - c1974. Miniature plastic novelty camera as described below. The camera has no special markings, but the box has the name and picture of Dick Tracy. $8-12.

Miniature Novelty Camera - c1974. Small plastic novelty for 14x14mm exposures on Mycro-size rollfilm. Originally could be obtained for 10 Bazooka gum wrappers. $1-3.

LAVA-SIMPLEX INTERNATIONALE
Simplex Snapper - c1970. Novelty camera for 126 cartridge. The film cartridge becomes the back of the camera. 28x28mm exposures. $5-10.

LAVEC INDUSTRIAL CORP. (Taipei, Taiwan)
Lavec LT-002 - Inexpensive 35mm novelty camera styled like a pentaprism SLR. $1-5.

LAWLEY (London)
Wet-plate camera - c1860. Bellows-type wet-plate camera for plates up to 13x13cm. Brass Petzval lens, waterhouse stops. $1000-1500.

LE DOCTE (Armand Le Docte, Brussels, Belgium)
Excell - 1890. Twin-lens reflex style box camera. Teak body, brass fittings. Rapid Rectilinear f8 lenses are on a recessed board, behind the front door. Bag-type plate changer. Magazine holds 20 plates, 8x10.5cm. Mirror system allows for either horizontal or vertical viewing. $900-1200.

LEADER CAMERA - Beige and black plastic camera of the "Diana" type. Made in Hong Kong. $3-6.

LECHNER
Hand Camera, 9x12cm - c1905-07. Folding camera with single-pleat bellows and gate struts. Ebonized wood body with trim. Focal plane shutter. Goerz Doppel Anastigmat Series III f6/120mm. Accessory reflex finder fits in shoe. $320-360.

LEE INDUSTRIES (Chicago, IL)
Leecrest - Bakelite minicam, 3x4cm on 127 rollfilm. $6-10.

LEECH & SCHMIDT
Tailboard camera, 13x18cm - Walnut construction. Bellows and focusing screen revolve as a unit to change orientation. $125-200.

LEHMAN (Gebr. Lehman, Berlin)
Pelar-Camera - c1947. One of the very first post-war cameras made in Germany.

General body style resembles Leica A (actually more like Leica B, since it has no FP shutter). Ludwig Pelar f2.9/50mm lens in 25-100 front shutter which resembles Vario or Stelo. Extremely rare. One known auction sale in Sept. 1986 for $350.

LEHMANN (A. Lehmann, Berlin)

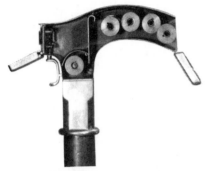

Ben Akiba - c1903. Cane handle camera. Obviously, a rare camera like this cannot be shackled with an "average" price. Two known sales were for $5,000 and $8,000.

LEIDOLF (Wetzlar)
Leidox, Leidox II - c1951. 4x4cm. Triplet f3.8/50mm lens in Prontor-S shutter to 300. $25-35.

Lordomat, Lordomat C-35, Lordomat SLE, Lordomatic - c1954. 35mm cameras with interchangeable Lordonar f2.8/50mm. Prontor-SVS shutter. CRF. Some models have built-in meter. Two-stroke film advance. Early models: $30-40. With meter and multi-lens viewfinder: $60-100.

Lordox - c1953. Compact 35mm viewfinder camera. Lordon f2.8 or f3.8/50mm lens. Pronto shutter, sync. Body release. $25-40.

LEITZ (Ernst Leitz GmbH, Wetzlar) *The history of Ernst Leitz in the optical industry began in 1849, only a decade after Daguerre's public announcement of his process. It was not until 75 years later that the first Leica camera was put on the market. If that seems like a long time for research and development it must be pointed out that the Leica was not the raison d'etre of the company. In 1849, Ernst Leitz began working in the small optical shop of C. Kellner at Wetzlar, whose primary business was the manufacturing of microscopes and telescopes. After Kellner's death, Ernst Leitz took over the company in 1869, and the operation continued to grow, becoming one of the world's major manufacturers of microscopes. Oskar Barnack, who worked for Zeiss from 1902-1910, joined the Leitz firm in 1911 and built the first Leica model in 1913. (Some historians indicate that he had proposed a similar camera to his former employer before joining the Leitz firm.) This first prototype had a fixed speed of 1/40 second, the same as movie cameras. Several 35mm still cameras were marketed at about this time by other companies, but without great success. At any rate, the "Leica" was mothballed for 10 years before finally being placed on the market in 1925. The immediate popularity of the camera coupled with improved quality of production and service catapulted the Leitz company into a strong position in the camera industry which continues to this day.*

LEICA COLLECTING - Leica collecting is a fascinating field which has attracted collectors of all ages, from those who used the Leica cameras when they were youngsters to those who have just acquired their first camera within the last few years. Hence, there is an international demand worldwide for cameras of all ages, from the first Leica I with fixed lens to the latest limited edition of the Leica M4P.

During the late 1970's, the prices of rare or unusual Leica cameras had increased to such an extent that speculators joined the bandwagon and the ensuing unselective buying sent the prices sky high for even the most mundane items. Fortunately, the speculators have now left the field of collecting and the price structure is now a more adequate reflection of demand.

TWO GOLDEN RULES that apply to Leica Collecting are:
1. That all items in excellent or like-new condition should be acquired.
2. That items of extreme rarity be acquired regardless of condition.
Thus, common items in less than excellent condition should be acquired only for use or for parts. For some of the more specialist items such as the Leica M Anniversary cameras, it is now essential for them to have their certificates, as of late some forgeries have been circulating. On the

whole, the price structure has not changed, although rarer items have seen their values increase disproportionately to common ones. The five most desirable Leica cameras are the following: Leica I with Elmax, Leica Compur, Leica 250, Leica 72, and Leica MP. These items will always demand very high prices, and the condition is important but not essential. More important is the authenticity and the originality of these cameras. It is better to have a camera in lesser but all original condition than a like-new specimen that has been renovated at great cost.

Leica cameras: *All models listed are for full-frame (24x36mm) exposures, and all are listed in chronological order by date of introduction. Although we have included a few basic identification features for each camera, these are meant only for quick reference. For more complete descriptions, or history of each model, we would suggest that you refer to a specialty book on Leica cameras. There are a number of good references, among which are: "Leica, The First Fifty Years" by G. Rogliatti, published by Hove Camera Foto Books in England; "Leica Illustrated Guide" by James L. Lager, published by Morgan & Morgan in New York; or "Leica, A History Illustrating Every Model and Accessory" by Paul-Henry van Hasbroeck, published by Sotheby Publications in London.*

SERIAL NUMBERS: *In most cases, concurrent camera models shared the same group of serial numbers. Therefore, where a serial number range is listed for a particular model, it does not belong exclusively to that model.*

This guide presents the basic information to help a novice collector to determine the probable value range of most common Leica cameras. It is not intended to be complete or extensive. That would require much more space than our format will allow. Our intention with this guide is not to give Leica specialists a price list, but rather to report to our more general audience the current price ranges which are being established by those specialists. There are many specialists in Leica cameras. One of them has been especially helpful in reviewing all of the prices in this section. A "blind" survey comparing his separate price estimates with our data proved to be surprisingly close on most items. We should caution, however, that the Leica market fluctuates more than many of the other areas of collecting, and you should consult with several respected authorities before making any major decisions about which you are unsure. Our primary Leica consultant is a well-known dealer in the field who would be happy to help you with questions on important cameras. Of course, he would also be interested in hearing about Leica cameras

you have for sale. Contact: Don Chatterton, P.O. Box 3960, Santa Barbara, CA 93130 (805-682-3540).

CONDITION OF LEICA CAMERAS:
Leica collectors are generally extremely conscious of condition. The spread of values is quite great as condition changes from MINT to EXC to VG (Range 2 to 6). With the exception of some of the very early and rare Leicas which are collectible regardless of condition, it would be wise to assume that EXCELLENT CONDITION (5) should be considered the MINIMUM condition which collectors seek. Therefore we are using figures in this section of the book only which represent cameras in at least EXCELLENT but not quite MINT condition (Range 3-4). Cameras which are truly MINT or NEW (Range 0-2) would bring higher prices and be easier to sell. Cameras in less than excellent condition (Range 6-9) are difficult to sell and often must be discounted considerably below these figures. Even the rare models, where less than perfect condition is tolerated, must be complete and in the ORIGINAL state.

For further information, or if in doubt about authenticity of rare models, contact: Leica Historical Society of America, 10590 N.W. 27th St. #101, Miami FL 33172. Phone: 305-477-7300. Memberships $25.00/yr.

Except where noted, prices are given for body only. A separate list of add-on prices for normal lenses is at the end of the Leica section.

Ur-Leica (Original) - The Ur-Leica, with only 21 specimens produced and most of them already in private or public collections, will command a substantial price. Up to $50,000 has been estimated, but we have no sales records.

Ur-Leica (replica) - Non-functional display model of Oscar Barnack's original 1913 prototype, reproduced by Leitz for museums, etc. Cosmetic condition is the important consideration, since these are inoperative cameras. $500-750.

Leica O-Series - Preproduction series of 31 cameras, Serial #100-130, hand-made in 1923 & 1924. Since the focal plane shutter was not self-capping on the first seven examples, they required the use of a lens cap which was attached with a cord to a small bracket on the camera body. This feature was retained on the second batch even though they had a self-capping shutter. The viewfinder (either folding or telescope type) is located directly above the lens. Leitz Anastigmat f3.5/50mm lens in collapsing mount. Extremely rare and highly desirable. $15,000-25,000.

Leica I (A) - 1925-1930. The first commercially produced Leica model, and the first mass produced 35mm camera of high quality. These facts make the Leica I a highly sought camera among not only Leica collectors, but general camera collectors also. Black enameled body. Non-interchangeable lenses, all 50mm f3.5 in collapsible mount with helical focus. "Hockey stick" lens lock on the front of the body is the most obvious identification feature. Body serial numbers listed are approximate and may overlap between the variations. Value depends on lens and serial number.

Anastigmat f3.5/50mm (1925) - The earliest and rarest. Perhaps 100-150 made. (#130-260?) Shutter speed 1/25-1/500. Up to $10,000 for unmodified example.

Elmax f3.5/50mm (1925-1926) - (#260?-1300?) $4,000-6,000. Originality and completeness of original fittings is an important consideration with this camera. There are lots of fakes, perhaps as many as the real ones. Current value opinions differed widely on this, from about $4,000 to $6,000 as the TOP price for a very nice one.

Elmar f3.5/50mm (1926-1930) -

(#1300?-60000) Priced by Serial #. 4-digit: $400-600. 5-digit: $300-500. Most examples found are in less than excellent condition and would bring $200-300, while a truly mint example could reach $1000. The close focusing model (to 20" rather than 1m.) used to add $25-50 to above prices, but that price distinction generally has disappeared.

Hektor f2.5/50mm (1930) - (#40000-60000) Relatively rare, but not as appealing to some collectors as the other early Leicas. In Exc + condition: $1300.

I Luxus - Gold-plated A-Elmar camera with lizard skin covering. Only about 95 were made by the factory, but many imitations abound. Authenitc models have serial numbers between 28,692 and 68,834. Check with a specialist for exact numbers. Only a handful of original authentic specimens have been recorded. Authentic, with verified serial number, not modified: Prices of $15,000 are asked, but probably not achieved. Realistically, they have been known to bring $12,000. With original crocodile case, add $1000-2000.

Luxus Replica - A gold-plated model which is not factory original. A number of replicas or "counterfeit" Luxus models have been made from other Leica I cameras, and while these resemble the real thing for purposes of display, they are not historically authentic. High quality conversions (some of the best conversions are being imported from Korea), if beautifully Mint condition have sold for $1,000-$1,500. Many replicas are offered in lesser condition for $1000, most of which are only worth half that amount. While they serve a good purpose for decoration, they are not necessarily considered to be a good investment item.

Leica Mifilmca - c1927. Microscope camera with permanently attached microscope adapter tube with a Mikas beam splitter and an Ibsor shutter. Body design is like the Compur Leica (B) but without a viewfinder or accessory shoe. The design was modified about 1932 to accomodate the standard lens flange fittings. Early Mifilmca camera with fixed tube is quite rare, but not as highly sought as non-technical models, so despite rarity, when encountered they sell for: $2000-3000. The later models with detachable tube might bring $1600-1800.

Leica I (B) - 1926-1930. The "Compur" Leica. Approximately 1500 were made in two variations, both with Elmar f3.5/50mm.

Dial-set Compur - (1926-1929) is extraordinarily rare, especially if in excellent condition. About $5000.

Rim-set Compur - (1929-1930). Although not as rare as the dial-set version, this is still a highly sought camera. $3500-4000.

Leica I (C) - 1930-1931. The first Leica with interchangeable lenses. Two variations:
Non-Standardized lens mount - Lenses were custom fitted to each camera because the distance from the lens flange to the film plane was not standard. The lens flange is not engraved, but each lens is numbered with the last three digits of the body serial number. With matching engraved Elmar lens: $900-1000 if very clean. A very few (first couple hundred made) had the full serial number on the lens. These bring an extra $100. Most which do not have a swing-down viewfinder mask were fitted with Hektor lenses: $1200-1400. It is difficult to locate an outfit with two lenses, let alone three lenses. With swing-down mask and 35mm, 50mm, and 135mm lenses, all with matching number; full set: $3000-4500.

Standardized lens mount - The lens mount on the body has a small "o" engraved at the top of the body flange. Lenses now standardized and interchangeable from one body to another. With f3.5/50mm: $250-300 maximum.

Leica II (D) - 1932-1948. The first Leica with built-in coupled rangefinder. This is a desirable camera, but only if in exceptional condition.
Black body - Quantity-wise, there are more black ones, but condition is harder to maintain on black. If exceptionally fine condition: $150-200.
Chrome body - Less common in number than black, but retails for less. $75-125.
Body & lens - Together with a matching lens in the correct serial number range, the set will bring a slight premium. Serial numbers for lenses up through the early post-war models should be approximately 50% above the serial number of the body. This is because about three lenses were made for every two bodies. So a nice clean outfit with a black body and a nickel Elmar lens would bring $250-350. A chrome body and lens in similar condition: $150.

Leica Standard (E) - 1932-1948. Similar to the standardized "C", but with smaller (12mm dia.) rewind knob, which pulls out to make rewinding easier. A rare camera, especially if found in black and nickel finish, complete with rotating range finder and nice nickel lens. Such a set would be expected to bring $300-500. A similar set in chrome with Elmar lens, excellent condition: $200. Black body: $200-250.

Leica III (F) - 1933-1939. The first model with slow-speed dial, carrying strap eyelets, and diopter adjustment on rangefinder eyepiece. Shutter to 500. Black body: $175-225. Chrome body: $135-150. (As with most Leica cameras, one in exceptionally fine condition could bring twice the prices listed, which are for cameras between excellent and mint condition.)

Leica 250 Reporter - 1934-1943 - The early model (FF) is like Model F, but body ends extended and enlarged to hold 10 meters of 35mm film for 250 exposures. Only about 950 were made. Later model (GG) is built on a model G body and has shutter speed to 1000. These were designed for heavy use, and most were used accordingly, so there are not many which are very clean. They are difficult to sell if restored. Very clean, original examples would sell in these ranges: FF: up to $6000, GG: up to $4500. More commonly available in lesser condition for $2500-3000. Probably the rarest but not the most expensive is the chrome version of the 250. A motorized version camera would probably bring twice as much.

Leica IIIa (G) - 1935-1950. Basically like the "F", but with the addition of 1/1000 sec. shutter speed. Chrome only. (There are rumors of a small number of black finished IIIa's, but to date none with any sort of pedigree have appeared.) The IIIa was the most produced of all pre-war Leicas, and therefore is not highly rated as a collectible. However, an early example in mint condition

Leica IIIa (G)

might prove to be a wise purchase, since they can be bought with Elmar lens for $75-125.

Leica IIIa "Monte en Sarre" - Assembled after WWII (between 1950 and 1955) in the French occupied German state of Saarland, from pre- and post-war parts. Very few were made. The top of the body is engraved "Monte en Sarre" below the normal "Ernst Leitz, Wetzlar" engraving. Down considerably from earlier sales figures. Realistically: $600-900.

Leica IIIb (G) - 1938-1946. Similar to the IIIa, but rangefinder and viewfinder eyepieces are next to each other. Diopter adjustments lever below rewind knob. Hard to find in excellent condition, but worth: $125-175. This was the last pre-war camera produced by Leitz, and the first to have batches allocated to the military. Luftwaffen Eigentum specimens would fetch about two or three times the price of a normal civilian model.

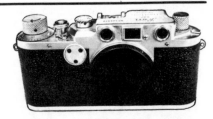

Leica IIc

Leica IIIc - 1940-1946. Die-cast body is ⅛" longer than earlier models. One-piece top cover with small "platform" for advance-rewind lever. This is a difficult camera to locate in fine condition, due to the poor quality of the chrome during wartime Germany. An exceptionally clean example would be worth $200. Early model with red curtain (one curtain has red side facing forward): $200-250. A regular body in excellent condition: $75-125. Less than excellent: $40-60.

Leica IIIc "K-Model" - The letter K at the end of the serial number and on the front of the shutter curtain stands for "kugellager" (ball-bearing), or perhaps "kaltefest" (cold weather prepared). The ball-bearing shutter was produced during the war years, primarily for the military. Chrome model: $650. Often blue-grey painted. $450-650, depending on condition.

Leica IIIc Luftwaffe & Wehrmacht - Engraved with "Luftwaffen Eigentum", "W.H.", eagle, or other military designations. Most have "K" shutter. The most interesting military markings are worth more. Grey or chrome body: $500-650. Up to $1200 for truly MINT condition with lens.

Leica IIId - 1940-42. Similar to the IIIc, but with the addition of an internal self-timer. This was the first Leica to include the self-timer. Factory and other conversions exist, and considering the elevated price of this camera, it would be wise to verify authenticity before paying the going rate of: $3000-3500.

Leica 72 - 1954-57. Similar to the IIIa but for 18x24mm format. Identifiable by exposure counter for 75 exposures, half-frame masks on viewfinder and at film plane. Most were made in Midland, Ontario. $4500-6000. A very small quantity was made in Wetzlar. A Wetzlar model with verified serial number: $5000-7000. There have been fakes of the Wetzlar model.

Leica IIc - 1948-1951. Like the IIIc, but no slow speeds. Top shutter speed 500. Not a hot selling camera. Body only, MINT: $125-150. *(Illustrated top of next column.)*

Leica Ic - 1949-1951. No slow speeds. No built-in finders. Two accessory shoes for mounting separate view and range finders. Difficult to find in Mint condition, but will bring: $200-250.

Leica IIIf - 1950-1956. Has MX sync. Three variations, all common, so prices are for MINT.
"Black-dial" - shutter speed dial is lettered in black, with speeds 30, 40, 60. $80-100.

"Red-dial" - shutter speed dial is lettered in red, with speeds 25, 50, 75. $100-140.
"Red-dial" with self-timer. - $200-225.

Leica IIIf (Swedish Army) - An all black version, made for the Swedish Army, if complete with matching black lens: $3,500-4,500.

Leica IIf - 1951-1956. Like the IIIf, but no slow speeds. Black dial and red dial models. Body only, MINT: $100-135. Excellent: $50.

Leica If - 1952-1956. No slow speed dial nor finders. Separate finders fit accessory shoes. Flash contact in slow speed dial

Leica If

location. Black dial body is rare, and used to bring much higher prices. Difficult to find in really clean condition, they sell currently for $300-600. Red dial body: $200-250.

Leica If Swedish 3 crown - Chrome body. Actually engraved by Swedish military, not Leitz. Not a legitimate Leica model.

Leica IIIg - 1956-1960. The last of the screw-mount Leicas. Bright-line finder and small window next to viewfinder window which provides light for finder illumination. MINT could sell in $500-600 range. EXC or less sells with difficulty for $200-250.

Leica IIIg Swedish Crown Model - 1960. A batch of 125 black-finished cameras for the Swedish Armed Forces were among the very last IIIg cameras produced. On the back side of the camera and on the lens are engraved three crowns (the Swedish coat-of-arms). With lens: $4000-4500.

Leica Ig - 1957-1960. Like the IIIg, but no finders or self-timer. Two accessory shoes accept separate range & view finders. Top plate surrounds the rewind knob, covering

the lower part when not extended. Only 6,300 were made. Body only: $400-600.

Leica Single-Shot - ca. 1936. Ground glass focus. Single metal film holder. Ibsor shutter. Should be complete with lens, shutter, film holder, and ground glass for $600-700. Add $250 for rare viewfinder.

Leica M3 - 1954-1966. This is a classic Leica in itself and much sought after, being one of the leading cameras of the 1950's. Fine specimens will reach good prices especially if boxed and in Mint condition. Two variations in film advance:
Single-stroke advance - There is a price differential based on serial number ranges. Prices listed are for body only.
Serials below 1,000,000: $275-325.
Serials 1,000,000 to 1,100,000: $350-450.
Serials above 1,100,000: $450-600.
Double-stroke advance - Body only, Mint: $300-450. Excellent: $125-175.

Leica MP, black (above) and chrome (below)

Leica MP - 1956-57. A variation of the M3. Normally identifiable by the MP serial number, but authenticity should be verified as counterfeit examples have reached the market. Chrome: $4000-4500. Black:

$5000-5500. *The Leica MP must not be confused with Leica MP2 which is an extremely rare motorized Leica M3.*

Leica M2, chrome - 1957-1967. Like the single-stroke M3, but with external exposure counter. Finder has frame lines for 35, 50, & 90mm lenses. All early models and some later ones were made without self-timer. Existence of self-timer does not affect price. Body only. Button rewind: $250. Lever rewind, serials under 1,100,000: $325 Serials over 1,100,000: $375.

Leica M2, black - Mint body: $1500-2000. EXC+: $600-1000.
Leica M2, Grey finish - Much rarer than green M3 or M1. $3000-4500.

Leica M2 MOT, M2M - Motorized versions. $1500-2000.

Leica M1 - 1959-64. Simplified camera for

scientific use, based on the M2. Lacks rangefinder, but has automatic parallax correcting viewfinder. $300-400.
Leica M1 Military Green - $4000-5000.

Leica MD - 1965-66. Replaced the M1, and further simplified. Based on the M3 body, but has no rangefinder or viewfinder. Allows insertion of identification strips to be printed on film during exposure. $375-450.

Leica MDa - 1966-75. Similar to the MD in features, but based on the M4 body (slanted rewind knob). $300-400.

Leica M4 - 1967-73 (plus a later batch in 1974-75 in black chrome). Similar to M2 and M3, but slanted rewind knob with folding crank. Frames for 35, 50, 90, and 135mm lenses.
Silver Chrome - Excellent: $525. Mint to $1000.
Black Chrome - Excellent condition. Canadian: $550. Wetzlar: $625. *These can be identified by the wax seal in a small hole at 12 o'clock on the lens mounting flange. New cameras have excised letters: "C" for Canada or "L" for Wetzlar. Factory serviced cameras have incised letters: "Y" for Rockleigh, "51" for Vancouver, "T" for Toronto, "L" for Wetzlar.*

Black Enamel - $700.
Fiftieth Anniversary model - Must be NEW in box with warranty cards. These have dropped in price in the last few years. Wetzlar model: $1250. Midland: $1450.

Leica M4M, M4 Mot - Should be complete with electric motors, and MINT condition. M4M: $3,500. M4 Mot: $3000. In Exc+ condition: $1800-2000.

Leica KE-7A - A special rendition of the M4, made for the U.S. Millitary and using their designation "KE-7A Camera, Still

Picture". With Elcan f2/50mm lens. Military version with federal stock number, or "Civilian" model without back engraving: $2000-$3000.

Leica M5, chrome (above) and black (below)

Leica M5 - 1971-85. Rangefinder camera with TTL metering. Black: $700-800, MINT. Chrome: $700-1000 MINT. *If absolutely like new, in box with cards, the silver chrome model will bring more than the anniversary model, because most were used and fewer remain in truly mint condition. On any M-camera, the condition of the strap lugs is often an indicator of the amount a camera has been used. Any scratch can knock the price down by 50%.*
Fiftieth Anniversary - Must be NEW. Black chrome: $1200. Silver chrome: $1450

Leica CL, 50th Anniversary

Leica CL - 1973-75. Designed by Leitz Wetzlar, made in Japan by Minolta. $200-350. Fiftieth Anniversary model: $550-700.

Leicaflex, chrome (above) and black (below)

Leicaflex - Original model introduced 1964. A landmark in the development of reflex cameras, due to its very bright prism system. Chrome: up to $500 if MINT; EXC+: $175-200. Black: $500-600 normally, but up to $850 MINT.

Leicaflex SL - Chrome: $200, up to $500 Mint. Black Enamel: $200, up to $700 Mint. Black chrome: $300. *(Black version illustrated on next page.)*
Leicaflex SL Olympic - NEW in box with cards: $800-900.

289

Leicaflex SL, black

Leicaflex SL2, black 50 Jahre

Leicaflex SL Mot - With motor, nice condition: $700-750.

Leica R3 - Black: $200. Chrome: $400 if MINT. *This camera was produced in Portugal. A small number have German baseplates as though made in Germany and not Portugal. One source indicates that this may have been done to avoid problems with customs for Photokina. At any rate, the "German" models in either black or chrome bring about the same price as the normal chrome model or perhaps just slightly more.*

Leica R3 Gold - Must be complete with gold Summilux-R f1.4/50mm lens, in original wood case, with box, strap, etc. AS NEW: $3000.

Leica R3 Safari - c1972. About 2500 made. Olive green body. With original box, as new: up to $1000.

Leica R3 Mot - With winder: $400.

Leica R4 - Although people collect them, these are primarily usable cameras, and an important word of warning comes from one of our consultants. Due to the high cost of repairs, Leitz only repairs the R4 under its "Signature Service" which costs $235. There are four generations of R4 cameras, the first three of which were subject to electronic problems. Try to avoid a used R4 which is out of warranty

Leicaflex SL2 - Important in that it is the last mechanical Leitz reflex camera and sought after by both collectors and users. This accounts for the high prices. Black or Chrome: $750. MINT: $1000-1200.
Anniversary Model (50 Jahre) - Only collectible if NEW. Black: $1200. Chrome: $1650. *(illustrated top of next column.)*

SL2 Mot - With motor: $1500-1800.

Leica R4

21mm f4 Super Angulon: $325 MINT CHROME.
28mm f6.3 Hektor: $100 MINT.
28mm f5.6 Summaron: $225-250 MINT.

or with serial number below 1,600,000. Black or Chrome: $300-350.

R4 Mot (incorrectly engraved) - Over 1000 were made, and they are not rare, but they may bring slightly more than the normal ones.

Leica R4S - A limited version of the R4. Same warnings apply, and not much different in price.

SCREWMOUNT LENSES - The following lens prices are "add-on" values to the body prices listed above. Condition is extremely important in buying a used Leica lens. Because of the age of these lenses, and the type of balsam glue used to cement the elements together, a large number of these lenses are showing signs of separation, crazing, or cloudiness. They should be carefully checked by shining a flashlight through from the rear of the lens and examining closely. If the lens shows signs of deterioration, forget it. Not only would it be costly to repair, but it would be virtually impossible to match the original optical quality.

33mm f3.5 Stemar: $1200 with viewfinder and beamsplitter in case.
35mm f3.5 Elmar: $40 MINT.
35mm f3.5 Summaron: $60 MINT.
35mm f2.8 Summaron: $115 MINT.
35mm f2 Summicron: $300 MINT. *Note: Many fakes converted from lower-valued bayonet-mount lenses.*
50mm f3.5 Elmar (pre-war uncoated or postwar, black scale, coated): $40 MINT.
50mm f3.5 Elmar (postwar, red scale, coated): $120-150 MINT.
50mm f3.5 Wollensak Velostigmat: $50
50mm f2.8 Elmar: $100.
50mm f2.5 Hektor: $100.
50mm f2 Summar (collapsible mount): $10.
50mm f2 Summar (rigid mount): $750.
50mm f2 Summicron (collapsible mount) - Inspect carefully. About 90% have scratches on front element, and they are also subject to haze and crystallization. Unscratched and crystal clear: $125.
50mm f2 Summicron (rigid mount): $500.

15mm f8 Zeiss Hologon: $2000-2500, MINT with filter and finder.

50mm f2 Summicron (in Compur Shutter): $1500-2500 with arm.
50mm f2 Summitar: $18.
50mm f1.5 Summarit: $50.
50mm f1.5 Xenon: $50.

50mm f1.4 Summilux: $700.
65mm f3.5 Elmar: $125.
73mm f1.9 Hektor: $125.
85mm f1.5 Summarex (black): $650.

85mm f1.5 Summarex (chrome): $350.
90mm f4.5 Wollensak Velostigmat: $85.
90mm f4 Elmar: $60.
90mm f2.8 Elmarit: $300.
90mm f2.2 Thambar (with shade & caps):
   $800-1000.
90mm f2 Summicron: $375.
105mm f6.3 Elmar ("Mountain" Elmar):
   $375-475.
125mm f2.5 Hektor: $225.
127mm f4.5 Wollensak Velostigmat: $75.
135mm f4.5 Hektor: $60.
135mm f4 Elmar: $200.
180mm f2.8 Elmarit (for Visoflex): $350.
200mm f4.5 Telyt (for Visoflex): $90.
200mm f4 Telyt (for Visoflex): $170.
280mm f4.8 Telyt (for Visoflex): $200.
   (New in box: $300.)
400mm f5 Telyt (attached shade): $450.
400mm f5 Telyt (removable shade): $550.

LENINGRAD - c1950. Russian 35mm RF Leica copy. f3.5/50mm lens in Leica mount. FP shutter, 1-1000. Motor drive. $225-295.

LENNOR ENGINEERING CO. (Illinois)
Delta Stereo - c1955. 35mm stereo camera, 23x25mm pairs. Blue enamel and leatherette covered. La Croix f6.3 lens in guillotine shutter 25-100, B. Scale focus 5,8,10,12' to infinity. Camera and case only: $40-60. With matching viewer: $90-100.

LENZ - "Hit" type novelty camera for 16mm film. $10-15.

LEONAR KAMERAWERK (Hamburg)

Filmos - c1910. Folding camera for 8x10.5cm on rollfilm or 9x12cm plates. Leonar Aplanat f8 or Periscop Aplanat f11/130mm. $30-45.

Leonar, 10x15cm - c1910. Similar to the 9x12cm, but with Leonar Anastigmat f8/140 or f6.8/170 lens. Dial Compur 1-200 shutter. Triple extension. Uncommon in this size. $70-100.

Perkeo Model IV - c1910. Simple folding camera, 9x12 plates or 8x10.5cm filmpacks. Achromat f16, Aplanat f11, or Extra-Rapid Aplanat f8. B&L Auto shutter. $25-35.

LEREBOURS (Paris)
Gaudin Daguerreotype - c1841. Cylindrical all-metal daguerreotype camera. Fixed-focus. Rotating diaphragm. One recorded sale, Oct. 1982: $8350.

LEROY (Lucien LeRoy, Paris)
Minimus - c1924. Rigid body 6x13cm stereo. $175-215.

Stereo Panoramique - 1905-11. Black, all-metal camera for 6x13cm plates in stereo or, by rotating one lens to center position, panoramic views. Krauss Protar f9/82mm or Goerz Doppel Anastigmat f8.5/80mm. Five speed shutter. $175-215.

LESUEUR & DUCOS du HAURON
Melanochromoscope - c1900. Color separation camera, three exposures on one plate. Also served as a chromsoscope, for viewing the pictures. Despite considerably higher estimates, one failed to attract bids over $1800 at a November 1982 auction, and remained unsold.

LEULLIER (Louis Leullier, Paris)

Summum - c1925. Roussel Stylor f4.5/75mm lenses. Focusing and fixed-focus models. Stereo shutter 25-100. Rising front. Changing magazine for six 6x13cm stereo plates. $100-150.

Summum Sterechrome - c1940. 24x30mm stereo exposures on 35mm film. Berthiot Flor f3.5/40mm lens. Shutter to 300. $300-400.

LEVI (S.J. Levi, London, England)
Leviathan Surprise Detective - c1892. Polished walnut box camera which holds six 3¼x4¼" plates on the three vertical sides of a revolving drum. $800-900.

Minia Camera - ¼-plate. Black leather covered body, maroon leather bellows. Ross Goerz Patent Doppel-Anastigmat f7.7/5". T-P rollerblind shutter. Rack focus. $50-75.

Pullman Detective - c1896. Satchel style-detective for 5x7" plates. The bottom becomes the bed of the camera, when the leather case is placed on its back. Single or stereo lensboards available. Archer & Sons lens. Roller blind shutter. $1200-1800.

LEVY-ROTH (Berlin)

Minnigraph - c1915. 18x24mm exposures on 35mm film in special cassettes. The first European still camera to use cine film. Minigraph Anastigmat f3.5/54mm lens. Single speed flap shutter. $900-1000.

LEWIS (W. & W.H. Lewis, New York)
Daguerreotype camera - c1852. Initiated the so-called "Lewis-style" daguerreotype cameras later made by Palmer & Longking. Collapsible bellows daguerreotype camera for ½-plates. Ground glass focusing. $6000-6500.

Wet Plate camera - c1862. Large size, for plates up to 12x12". Folding leather bellows. Plates and ground glass load from side. A rare camera. $900-1100.

LEXA MANUFACTURING CO.
(Melbourne, Australia)

Lexa 20 - c1950. Metal box camera for 6x9cm on 120 film. $8-12.

L.F.G. & CO. (Paris, France)

Francais - c1910. Small metal box camera for two 4x5cm plates which pivot into position for exposure. Meniscus f11/55mm lens in simple shutter. $100-125.

Franceville - c1908. Simple black box camera made of plastic or cardboard. Takes 4x4cm exposures on plates. Meniscus lens, guillotine shutter. Plastic version is unidentified. Cardboard type has gold lettering on back. $90-120. *(Illustrated top of next column.)*

LIEBE (V. Liebe, Paris)
Monobloc - c1920. For stereo or panoramic views on 6x13cm plates. Tessar f6.3 or Boyer Saphir f4.5/85mm lenses in pneumatic spring shutter. Metal body is partly leather covered. $150-175. *See also Jeanneret Monobloc.*

LIFE-O-RAMA CORP.
Life-O-Rama III - c1953. German 6x6cm on 120 film. f5.6/75 or f3.5 Ennar lens. Vario shutter, sync. $15-20.

L.F.G. Franceville (rear view)

LIFE TIME
Life Time 120 Synchro Flash - All metal box camera identical to the Vagabond 120. $1-5.

LIGHT - c1934. Japanese Maximar copy. 6.5x9cm. Heliostar f4.5/105mm lens in Neuheil rim-set 25-150 shutter. $45-60.

LIGHT INDUSTRIAL PRODUCTS
(China)

Seagull 4 - c1970's. TLR for 6x6cm on 120 rollfilm. f3.5/75mm lens. 1-300 shutter, x-synch. Collectible because few Chinese cameras are imported to the U.S.A. $35-45.

Seagull No. 203 - 6x6cm folding bed camera. Copy of Zeiss Ikonta IV. 12 or 16 exposures on 120 film. f3.5/75mm lens. $50-75. *(Illustrated top of next page.)*

Seagull No. 203

LINA, LINA-S - 4x4cm plastic novelty cameras of the "Diana" type. $1-5.

LINDEN (Friedrich Linden, Luedenscheid, Germany)
Lindar - c1950. Metal box camera, leather covering. 6x6cm on 120. Meniscus f9.5/80mm lens. T, I shutter. Large waist-level brilliant finder. Built-in yellows filter. $5-10.

Lindi - c1950. Metal 6x6cm box camera with large reflex brilliant finder. Black or grey hammertone finish. Meniscus f10.5/80mm lens. A lower priced version of the Lindar. Grey: $30-40. Black: $15-25.

Reporter 66 - c1952. Metal 6x6cm box camera with leather covering. Similar to the Lindar and Lindi. Meniscus f9.5/80mm lens. $20-30.

LINHOF PRAZISIONS KAMERAWERK (V. Linhof, Munich) *While we are presenting a selection here of cameras which could be considered "collectible", generally the Linhof line tends to be a family of cameras which fall more into the category of usable equipment.*

(early folding cameras) - c1910-1930. (pre-"Technika" models.) Folding plate cameras in standard sizes, 6.5x9cm to 13x18cm. Front and back extensions. Ground glass focus. $75-150.

Multi-Speed Precision Camera - c1925. Folding bed camera for 9x14cm plates. Spring-loaded back accepts single metal holders in front of ground glass. Emil Busch Multi-Speed Leukar f6.8/6½" lens in General T,B, 5-100 shutter. $60-90.

Precision View - c1930. Triple extension hand camera. Rise/cross front. Tessar f4.5/135mm in Compur. $150-200.

Stereo Panorama - c1920. For 6x13cm exposures (stereo or panoramic). Two Reitzschel Sextar f6.8/120mm lenses and one Reitzschel Linar f5.5/150mm lens. Compound shutter. Metal body, leather covered. $250-300.

Technika I - c1930. With Tessar f4.5 in Compound or Compur shutter. 6.5x9cm: $425-525. 5x7": $400-600.

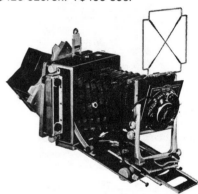

Technika III - 1946-50. Despite the fact that these are old enough to be considered collectible, their primary value lies in their usability. Price dependent on lens and shutter accessories. Commonly found with f4.5 Xenar. 2¼x3¼" or 4x5": $300-450. 5x7": $400-550.

Technika Press 23 - 1958-1963. Press camera for 6x9cm exposures. Accepts cut film, film packs and rollfilm. Interchangeable lenses. Compur shutter to 400. The high prices are due to usability, not rarity. $325-425. *(Illustrated top of next page.)*

LIONEL MFG. CO. (The train people)
Linex - ca. late 1940's. Cast metal subminiature for stereo pairs of 16x20mm exposures on rollfilm. f8/30mm lenses. Guillotine shutter, synched. Camera only: $40-60. Outfit with case, flash, viewer: $60-85.

295

Linhof Technika Press 23

Lippische Flexora

LIPPISCHE CAMERAFABRIK (Barntrup)

Flexo - c1950. Twin lens reflex for 6x6cm on 120 film. Helical focus operated by lever below lens. Identical taking and viewing lenses include Ennar f3.5 or f4.5 and Ennagon f3.5. Prontor-S, Pronto-S, Prontor II, or Vario shutter. $35-50.

Flexo Richard - c1953. Unusual name variation of the Flexo. "Flexo Richard" on nameplate at front of finder hood. $60-90.

Flexora - c1953. 6x6cm TLR. Ennar f3.5 or 4.5/75 or Ennagon f3.5/75mm lens. Vario, Pronto-S, or Prontor-SV shutter. $35-50. *(Illustrated top of next column.)*

Optimet (I) - c1958. TLR for 6x6cm on 120 film, similar to Rollop. Rack and pinion focus with left-hand knob. Ennagon f3.5/ 75mm lens in Prontor-SVS shutter. $60-80.

Rollop - c1954. TLR for 6x6cm on 120 film. Ennagon f3.5/75mm lens. Prontor-SVS shutter 1-300. $60-90.

Rollop Automatic - c1956. TLR for 6x6cm on 120. Called Automatic because shutter is tensioned by film advance. Ennit f2.8/ 80mm lens. Prontor SVS 1-300. $70-100.

LITTLE WONDER - c1922. (Not related to the c1900 "Little Wonder" box camera.) All metal camera for 40x64mm on 127 rollfilm. Folding frame finder, external T & I shutter. Lens housing extends via helix. Meniscus lens. Sold by L. Trapp & Co., London, but may have been made in Germany. $40-60.

LIZARS (J. Lizars, Glasgow)
Challenge - c1905. 3¼x4¼" plates. Leather covered mahogany construction. f6 or f8 Aldis or Beck lens, or f6.8 Goerz. $150-175.

Challenge Dayspool, 3¼x4¼" - c1905. For rollfilm. Leather covered mahogany construction. f6 or f8 Aldis or Beck lens, or f6.8 Goerz. $150-175.

Challenge Dayspool Tropical - Similar to the above model, but polished Spanish mahogany body, rather than leather covered. Red leather bellows. $400-550

Challenge Dayspool No. 1, 4¼x6½" - c1900. For rollfilm. Leather covered. Red bellows. Beck Symmetrical lens. $175-225.

Challenge Dayspool Stereoscopic Tropical - c1905. Mahogany camera for 2¼x6¾" plates or rollfilm. $650-900.

Challenge Junior Dayspool - c1903-11. Horizontally styled folding-bed rollfilm camera. Identical to the No. 1 Dayspool but with B&L single valve shutter, 25-100. Three sizes: A: 2¼x2¼". B: 2¼x3¼". C: 2½x4¼". "A" size, rare: $225-275. "B" or "C": $175-225.

Challenge Magazine Camera - c1903-1907. Box camera for 12 plates or 24 films, 3¼x4¼". Beck Symmetrical lens. Unicum shutter. $35-60.

Challenge Stereo Camera, Model B - c1905. 3¼x6¾" plates. Leather covered wood body. B&L RR or Aldis Anastigmat lenses in B&L Stereo shutter. $450-500. Wooden "Tropical" model, teak with brass trim. $750-900.

LLOYD (Andrew J. Lloyd & Co., Boston)
Box camera - 4x5" glass plates. $40-60.

LLOYD (Fred V.A. Lloyd, Liverpool, England)
Field camera - c1910. ½-plate folding camera. $100-150.

LOEBER (Eugene Loeber, Dresden)
Field Camera, 13x18cm - c1895-1900. Tailboard style field camera with fine wood and brass trim. Tapered green bellows with wine red corners. Rodenstock Bistigmat 13x18 brass lens with revolving stops and built-in manually operated shutter blade. $150-200.

Klapp camera - c1915. Strut-folding 9x12cm plate camera. Anastigmat f6.8/135mm lens. $75-125.

Magazine Camera - c1905. Leather covered box camera, holding 12- 9x12cm plates. f8 lens, 3-speed shutter. Rapid wind lever. Two large brilliant finders. $75-125.

LOEBER BROTHERS (New York) *The Loeber Brothers manufactured and imported cameras c1880's-1890's.*
Folding bed plate camera - British full-plate camera. Fine polished wood, black bellows, brass trim. Brass-barreled lens with waterhouse stops. $150-200.

LOGIX ENTERPRISES (Montreal, Canada & Plattsburgh, NY)
Kosmos Optics Kit - 35mm SLR with interchangeable lenses in an optical experimment kit. $15-20.

Logikit - Kit of plastic parts to build your own 35mm SLR. $15-20.

LOLLIER (X. Lollier, Paris)

Stereo-Marine-Lollier - c1903. An unusual instrument which combines the features of a stereo camera and binoculars. Unidentified lenses. Two-speed guillotine shutter. Its general appearance and operation are somewhat similar to the more common Goerz Photo-Stereo-Binocle, but it uses standard 45x107mm stereo plates. Very rare. $3000-4000.

LOMAN & CO. (Amsterdam)
Loman's Reflex - c1892. Box-style SLR. Polished wood, brass fittings. Loman

Aplanat f8/140mm lens. FP shutter 3-200. Made in sizes ¼ to ½ plate. $600-900.

Loman Reflex - c1906. Leather covered SLR with tall folding viewing hood. Rack focusing front with bellows. Focal plane shutter ⅛-1300. Eurynar Anastigmat f4/135mm. $100-125.

LOMO (Leningrad)
135 BC - Spring-wound 35mm. f2.8 lens, shutter to 250. $35-50.

LONDON & PARIS OPTIC AND CLOCK CO.
Princess May - c1895. Half-plate mahogany and brass field camera. Ross Anastigmat f8/7½" lens. $125-175.

LONDON STEREOSCOPIC & PHOTO CO. *This company imported and sold under their own name many cameras which were manufactured by leading companies at home and abroad.*

Artist Hand Camera - c1889. Twin lens reflex style box camera. Mahogany body, brass lens. Identical to the Francais Kinegraphe. 9x12cm plates. $900-1400.

Artist Reflex, Tropical - c1910. SLR for

¼-plates. Very similar to the Marion Soho Tropical. Mahogany or teak body, green or red leather hood and bellows. Brass trim. Heliar f4.5/150 lens. FP shutter to 1000. Despite sales in the early 1980's for $1500-1800, there were two examples sold at auction in England for $250-400 in 1985.

Binocular camera - c1898. Rigid-bodied, jumelle style stereo. Two sizes: 6x9cm with an 18-plate magazine; 5x7" with a 12-plate magazine. Krauss-Zeiss Anastigmat f6.3 or f8/110mm lens. Guillotine shutter. $200-250.

Carlton - c1895. Box-TLR for 12 plates or 12 films. Sizes: ¼-plate, 4x5", ½-plate. Euryscope f5.6 or Rapid Rectilinear or Ross Goerz Double Anastigmat f7.7. Shutter 1-100, T,I. $325-350.

Dispatch Detective - c1888. Wooden-box style detective camera covered in dark green leather. Camera is in the front half of the box, the 9x12cm plates store in the back half. Side-hinged lid. $600-800.

Field camera - c1885. Mahogany body, brass trim, red double extension bellows. RR f8 lens. Full and half plate sizes. $100-200.

King's Own Tropical - c1905. Folding bed camera for 2½x4¼" plates or rollfilm. Teak with brass fittings. Goerz Dagor f6.8/120mm lens in Koilos pneumatic shuter, 1-300. $700-1000.
--4¼x6½" - Similar to the smaller size, but with Goerz Doppel Anastigmat f9/180mm in B&L shutter. $800-1200.

Tailboard stereo camera - c1885. 3½x6¼" plate. Swift & Son 4" lenses. Side board panel. Thornton rollerblind shutter. Dark maroon bellows. $450-550.

Twin Lens Artist Hand Camera - c1889. Large twin lens reflex. Front door covers the recessed lenses. Leather covered. 9x12cm, 4x5", ½-plate sizes. Magazine holds 24 sheets or 12 plates. $350-450.

Wet plate camera - c1855. 4x5" sliding box style. Light colored wood body (7x7½x6¼" overall) which extends to 10". London Stereoscopic Petzval-type lens in brass barrel. $1800-2000.

LORENZ (Ernst Lorenz, Berlin)
Clarissa - c1929. Small strut-type focal plane camera, 4.5x6cm. Polished ebony-wood body with brass trim and brown bellows. Helioplan f4.5 or Trioplan f3/75mm. Rare. $1300-1500.

LORILLON (E. Lorillon, Paris)
Field camera - c1905. 13x18cm, tailboard style. Wood with brass trim, square red bellows. Taylor, Taylor & Hobson lens in roller-blind shutter. $150-200.

LUBITEL, LUBITEL 2 - c1949. TLR, 12 exposures, 6x6cm on 120 film. Copy of Voigtlander Brillant. f4.5/75mm T-22 lens. Variable speed shutter, 10-200. $20-30.

LUCKY - Japanese novelty subminiature of the Hit type. $10-15.

LUETTKE (Dr. Luettke & Arndt, Wandsbek, Hamburg, & Berlin, Germany)
Folding plate camera - 9x12cm, horizontal format. Black leathered wood body. Red-brown bellows. Luettke Periscop lens with rotary stops. Brass shutter. $50-75.

Folding plate/rollfilm camera - c1900-1902. Unusual folding camera for either rollfilm or 9x12cm plates. Wooden body with nickel trim. Rare. $200-225.

Folding rollfilm camera - 8x10.5cm. Black leathered body with red cloth bellows. Nickel trim. Luettke Periplanat lens. $40-50.

Linos - c1898. 9x12cm folding plate camera. Walnut body, brass trim. Aplanat f8/165mm lens. Pneumatic shutter. $400-450.

LUMIERE & CIE. (Lyon, France)

Box camera - Simple lens and shutter, 127 rollfilm. $5-10.

Box camera, No. 49 - for 122 film. $5-10.

Eljy, Super Eljy - c1937-48. 24x36mm exposures on special 30mm wide paper-backed rollfilm. Lypar f3.5/50mm lens in Eljy shutter. Fairly common. $45-65.

Eljy Club - c1951. 24x36mm exposures on special 35mm film. Lypar f3.5/40mm. Synchro shutter 1-300. Chrome top housing incorporates optical finder and extinction meter. (Last model is without extinction meter.) $100-125.

Lumibox - c1934-38. Metal box camera for 6x9cm on 120. Focusing lens. $5-10.

Lumix F - simple folding 6x9cm rollfilm camera. Meniscus lens. $15-25.

Scout-Box - c1935. Painted metal box camera. 6x9cm on 120 rollfilm. $10-15.

Sinox - 6x9cm folding rollfilm. Nacor Anastigmat f6.3/105mm lens. Central shutter 25-100. $15-25.

Sterelux - c1920-37. Folding stereo camera for 116 rollfilm, 6x13cm. Spector Anastigmat f4.5/80mm lens. Shutter 1/25-1/100, later models have 1-100. $180-230.

LUNDELIUS MFG. CO. (Port Jervis, N.Y.)
Magazine camera - c1895. For 12 plates in vertical format. Leather covered wood body. Measures 10x8x4½ overall. $100-150.

LURE CAMERA LTD. (Los Angeles, CA)

Lure - c1973. Plastic 110 cartridge camera. Camera was sent in for processing of film; pictures and new camera were mailed back. The same camera also appears as "Lure X2" in Hawaii, "Blick" in Italy, "Rank" in England and Europe, and "Love" which is made in Brazil. $1-5.

MACKENSTEIN (H. Mackenstein, Paris)
Field Camera - c1900. 13x18cm tailboard style folding view camera. Polished wood with brass trim and brass handle. Tapered wine-red bellows. Carl Zeiss Anastigmat lens in Mattioli roller-blind shutter. $200-325.

Folding camera - c1890. Hinged mahogany panels with round cutout support front standard, like the Shew Eclipse. Maroon bellows. Brass Aplanat f9/150mm lens. $250-275.

Francia, 9x12cm - c1910. Strut-folding plate camera with focal plane shutter 15-2000. Wine red single pleat bellows. Leather covered wood body. With Dagor f6.8/120mm lens and magazine back: $175-225.

Francia Stereo (folding) - c1906. Strut-folding stereo cameras for 45x107mm or 6x13cm plates. Max Balbreck or Sumo Aplanat lenses, guillotine shutter with variable speeds. Red leather bellows. $175-200.

Francia Stereo (rigid) - c1900-10. Jumelle-style stereo cameras in 6x13cm and 9x18cm sizes. Goerz Doppel Anastigmat or Dagor f6.8 lenses. Guillotine shutter. Large Newton finder. With magazine back: $225-265.

Jumelle Photographique - c1895. Rigid jumelle-style camera for single (non-stereo) exposures. Leather covered wood body. 6.5x9cm and 9x12cm sizes. Goerz Doppel Anastigmat f8 lens. Six-speed guillotine shutter. With magazine back: $125-175.

Photo Livre - c1890. The French edition of the popular Krugener Taschenbuch-Camera. A leather-covered camera disguised as a book. Achromatic f12/65mm lens is in the "spine" of the book. Guillotine shutter. Internal magazine holds 24 plates for 4x4cm exposures. $2300-2700.

Pinhole camera - c1900. Polished walnut ¼-plate tailboard camera. Maroon bellows. 6 "pinhole" openings on the lensboard, take 6 exposures per plate. One offered in Nov. 1982 for $750.

Stereo Jumelle - c1893. For 18 plates 9x18cm in magazine. Goerz Double Anastigmat 110mm lens, variable speed guillotine shutter. $150-200.

MACRIS-BOUCHER (Paris)

Nil Melior Stereo - c1920. A wide-angle stereo camera, based on the theory that short focus wide angle lenses gave more natural stereo vision and allowed 6x13cm exposures in a camera just slightly larger than most 45x107mm stereos. Boyer Sapphir or E. Krauss Tessar f4.5/65mm

Macvan Reflex 5-7 Studio Camera

lens in seven-speed spring shutter. Large newton finder. 12-plate magazine for 6x13cm plates. $100-150.

MACVAN MFG. CO.
Macvan Reflex 5-7 Studio camera - c1948. Large studio-style TLR. 5x7" plates or cut film. Revolving, shifting back. Parallax correction. Ilex Paragon f4.5/8½" in Ilex #4 Universal. Reflex or ground glass viewing. $225-275. *(Illus. bottom of previous column.)*

MACY ASSOCIATES

Flash 120 - Metal box camera, 6x9cm. Black crinkle enamel finish. Art-deco faceplate. $5-10.

Supre-Macy - c1952. Japanese 6x6cm TLR made by Hachiyo Optical Co. for Macy's. Similar to Alpenflex I. Alpo f3.5/75mm in Orient II 1-200 shutter. $65-95.

MADER (H.Mader, Isny, Wuerttemberg)
Invincibel - c1889. All-metal folding bed camera for 5x7" plates. Aplanat f6/180mm lens. Iris diaphragm. $600-700.

MADISON I - Folding camera for 6x6cm on 620 film. f4.5 lens. Shutter to 200. $15-25.

MAGIC INTRODUCTION CO. (N.Y.)

Photoret Watch Camera - c1894. For 6 exposures ½x½" (12x12mm) on round sheet film. Meniscus lens. Rotating shutter. $300-450. (Original box and film tin would add to this price.)

Presto - c1896. All-metal, oval-shaped camera, invented by Herman Casler. 28x28mm exposures on rollfilm or glass plates. Meniscus lens with rotating front stops. Single speed shutter. $350-550.

MAGNACAM CORP. (New Jersey)

Wristamatic Model 30 - c1981. Short-lived plastic wrist camera. 6 circular exposures on 9mm dia. film. Fixed focus. $35-50.

MAL-IT CAMERA MFG. CO. INC. (Dallas, TX)

Mal-It Camera - Factory-loaded disposable cardboard camera, pre-addressed to the processing lab. The original price of the camera included processing and printing of 8 Jumbo pictures. $25-35.

MAMIYA CAMERA CO. (Tokyo)

Camex Six - c1950. Horizontally styled folding bed rangefinder camera for 6x6cm on 120. Similar to the Mamiya 6, with movable film plane for focusing. Takatiho Zuiko f3.5/75mm in Seikosha-Rapid 1-500. Unusual. $100-150.

Family - c1962. 35mm SLR. Behind-the-lens Copal shutter B,15-250. Sekor f2.8/48mm interchangeable lens. Uncoupled exposure meter with cell on front of prism. $75-125.

Korvette - c1963. Name variant of Mamiya Family camera, marketed in England by B.Bennett & Sons Ltd. $75-125.

Magazine 35 - c1957. 35mm rangefinder camera. Non-interchangeable Mamiya/Sekor f2.8/50mm. Seikosha-MXL, 1-500,B. Interchangeable film magazines. $75-125.

Mamiya 6 - c1946-1950's. Basically a horizontal folding-bed camera for 12 square exposures, 6x6cm, on 120. Some featured the option of 16 vertical exposures, 4.5x6cm, as well. About a dozen models were made. Zuiko f3.5/75mm lens in Copal or Seikosha shutter. Coupled rangefinder. Unusual feature:Knurled focusing wheel just above the back door of the camera moves the film plane to focus while the lens remains stationary. $50-75.

Mamiya-16 - c1950's. Subminiature for 20 exposures 10x14mm on 16mm film. Various models including: Original model, Deluxe (with plain, smooth body), Super (like original but with sliding filter), Automatic (built-in meter). No significant price difference among these models. $25-35.

Mamiya-16 Police Model - c1949. This was the first Mamiya 16 camera, made in black finish. Has no serial number. Shutter B,25,50,100 only. No built-in filter. Detachable waist-level brilliant finder. $350-375.

Mamiyaflex Automatic-A - c1949. This was the first Japanese TLR with automatic film stop (not requiring use of red window). Zuiko f3.5/75mm in Seikosha-Rapid shutter. The earliest version does not have a sports finder. $100-150.

Mamiyaflex II - c1952. TLR for 6x6cm on 120 film. Setagaya Koki Sekor f3.5/7.5cm. Merit B, 1-300. Front element focus; viewing lens externally gear-coupled. Self-timer. ASA synch post. Film advance cocks shutter. $50-75. *(Illustrated on front cover.)*

Mamiyaflex Junior - c1948. Mamiya's first

TLR, of relatively simple design especially when compared with the sophisticated models of the next two decades. At least three variations, all with Towa Koki Neocon f3.5/75mm lens in Stamina shutter. The first model has the winding knob low on the right side, while the others place it near the top. First two have speeds to 200, third goes to 300. All have front-element focusing with externally gear-coupled taking and viewing lenses. Uses 120 film for 6x6cm images. First model: $100-150. Later variations: $50-75.

Mammy - c1953. Small bakelite camera for 24x28mm exposures on 828 film. Cute Anastigmat f3.5/45mm lens. Shutter 25-100,B. Unusual design. $60-85.

Myrapid - c1967. Automatic half-frame 35mm with meter cell surrounding lens. Tominon f1.7/32mm in Auto Copal 30-800. $10-20.

Pistol camera - c1954. Half-frame 35mm camera, shaped like a pistol. Sekor fixed focus f5.6/45mm lens. Single speed shutter. Only 250 believed to have been made for police training. $1000-1200.

Saturn - c1963. A name variant of the Mamiya Family camera. Marketed in England by Dixons Photographic Ltd. $75-125.

Mamiya/Sekor Auto XTL - c1971. 35mm SLR. Advanced design but limited production due to poor sales. TTL automatic exposure. Auto Mamiya-Sekor f1.8/55mm interchangeable lens. $100-125.

MANHATTAN OPTICAL CO. (New York)
(See also Gundlach-Manhattan)

Bo-Peep, Model B, 4x5" - c1898. Folding plate camera. Red bellows, brass shutter. (Similar to other brands of the same period.) $50-75.

Bo-Peep, Model B, 5x7" - c1898. Double extension bellows. Brass lens with rotating stops. $60-90.

Night Hawk Detective - c1895. For 4x5" plates. Polished oak body, or leather covered. String-set shutter, T & I. Ground glass or scale focus. Rapid Achromatic lens. All wood: $300-350. Leather covered: $200-275.

Wizard Duplex No. 1, No. 2 - c1902. Folding bed rollfilm camera for 3¼x4¼" exposures. Focusing similar to the Screen Focus Kodak: ground glass focusing where back is removed. Dark slide on back prevents exposures of film. $250-300.

Wizard folding plate cameras:
4x5" size - Including Baby, Cycle, Wide Angle, Senior, Junior, A, and B. $45-65.
5x7" size - Including Cycle, B, and Senior models. $60-85.

Long-Focus Wizard - 5x7", including Cycle and Senior models. Triple extension maroon bellows, RR lens, Unicum shutter. $100-140

MANIGA - Small die-cast metal subminiature, similar to the Aiglon and Bobby. Takes 13x14mm exposures on rollfilm. Oversized round or oval shutter. Uncommon. $125-175.

MANIGA MANETTA - c1930. Small metal camera for 3x4cm on rollfilm. Body shaped like sardine can with tubular finder on top. Laack Poloyt f4.5/50mm on lens in Manetta (Pronto-style) shutter 25-100,B,T. Uncommon. $200-250.

MANSFIELD (A division of Argus, Inc.)

Mansfield Automatic 127 - Horizontally styled black plastic box camera for 4x4cm on 127 film. Styling like the Tower Camflash 127, Tower Automatic 127, and USC Tri-matic. Automatic exposure. Selenium meter controls diaphragm. Single speed shutter. Built-in AG-1 flash beside lens. $1-5.

MANSFIELD HOLIDAY
Skylark - c1962. 35mm camera with coupled meter. Luminor Anastigmat fixed focus lens. Shutter 10-200, X-sync. $15-20.

MAR-CREST MFG. CORP.

Mar-Crest - Bakelite novelty camera for half-frame 127. $3-7.

MARION & CO., LTD. (London) *Marion was established in 1850 as an offshoot of the Parisian firm of A. Marion and Cie. and was set up to exploit the carte-de-visite craze. It expanded to deal in photographic materials and as photographic dealers it sold cameras. In 1887 it set up its own plate manufacturing plant at Southgate, North London.*
The Soho range of cameras (named after Marion's Soho Square address) was sold by Marion but most were probably made by Kershaw of Leeds. This arrangement was formalized in 1921 when the two firms joined with five others to form APM. Marion was also a part of the 1930's regrouping that resulted in the formation of Soho Ltd.
Academy - c1885. TLR-style camera. Eye-level viewfinder. 4 sizes: 1¼x1¼" to 3¼x4¼". Magazine holds 12 plates. Petzval-type lens. Rotary shutter, T,I. Finished wood, brass fittings. Rack and pinion positioning of plates for exposure. In 1887, a mirror

was added to the finder of the larger models to make it usable as a waist-level camera. This improved version was called the "New Academy". Estimate: $2000-3000.

Cambridge - c1901-04. Compact folding field camera. Mahogany with brass trim. Made in ¼, ½, and full-plate sizes. RR lens and rollerblind shutter. $100-150.

Krugener's Patent Book Camera - The English edition of the better known Krugener's Taschenbuch Camera. Its cover gives the story, embossed in leather: "Manufactured in Germany for Marion & Co. The Sole Agents." One auction sale, late 1986: $2500.

Metal Miniature - c1884. Tiny, all-metal plate camera. Back moved into focus by a rack-and-pinion. Petzval-type f5.6/55mm. Guillotine shutter. 3x3cm plates. Later versions were more streamlined, with a sliding lens tube for focusing. Made in 5 sizes from 3x3cm to ½-plate. Despite higher prices a few years ago, more recent auction sales indicate a range of $1250-1500.

Parcel Detective - 1885. A box detective camera, neatly covered with brown linen-lined paper and tied with string to look like an ordinary parcel. Fixed focus lens. It used standard 3¼x4¼" plates which could be loaded into the camera in daylight from flexible India-Rubber plateholders. No known sales. Estimated value: $5000+.

Perfection - c1890. Folding field camera, full plate or 10x12" size. Find polished wood. Dallmeyer f8 RR lens in brass barrel with iris diaphragm. $175-225.

Radial Hand camera - c1890. Mahogany magazine camera for 12 ¼-plates. Plates were held in radial groves to be moved into position for exposure and then moved

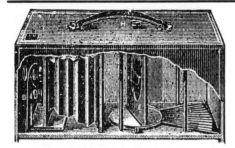

Marion Radial Hand camera

back again. Guillotine shutter. $700-900.

Soho Pilot - c1932. Bakelite folding rollfilm camera. $10-20.

Soho Reflex - Graflex-type SLR cameras. Focal plane shutter.
2½x3½" - Tessar f4.5/4". $75-150.
3¼x4¼" - Ross Xpres f3.5/5½". $75-150.
3½x5½" - Ross Xpres f4.5. $75-125.
4¾x6½" - Dagor f6.8/210mm. $75-125.

Soho Stereo Reflex - c1909. Similar to the Soho Reflex, but for stereo exposures. Goerz lenses. FP shutter. 9x14cm plates. $500-750.

Soho Tropical Reflex - 2½x3½" or 3¼x4¼" size. Dallmeyer f3.5 Dalmac, Ross Xpres f3.5 or other popular lenses. Revolving back. Fine polished teak wood. Red or green leather bellows and viewing hood. Brass trim. A beautiful tropical camera. $1700-2300.

MARKS (Bernard Marks & Co., Ltd., Canada)
Marksman Six-20 - Metal box camera, 6x9cm. $5-10.

MARLOW BROS. (Birmingham, England)
MB, No.4 - c1900. Mahogany field camera, with brass fittings. Various sizes 3¼x4¼" to 10x12". $400-500 with appropriate lens.

MARTAIN (H. Martain, Paris)
View Camera - 13x18cm size. Bellows and back swivel for vertical or horizontal format. Sliding lensboard. With Darlot lens: $175-200.

MARUSO TRADING CO. (Japan)
Spy-14 - c1965. Actually, the Spy-14 is not a camera, but rather an outfit which includes a Top II camera with case, film, and developer in an attention-getting display box. $30-40.

Top Camera - c1965. Bakelite Japanese subminiature camera with metal front and back. The entire camera is finished in grey hammertone enamel so it looks like an all-metal camera. Rectangular shape is similar to the Minolta-16, but construction quality is more like the Hit-types. Takes 14x14mm exposures on standard "Midget" size rollfilm. Meniscus lens, single speed shutter. One version has a reflex finder. $35-50.

Top II Camera - c1965. Nearly identical to the Top Camera, above. Some examples have black front and back; others are all grey. $20-25.

MARVEL - Half-127 camera similar to the Detrola. Extinction meter and uncoupled rangefinder in top housing. $12-18.

MASHPRIBORINTORG (Moscow, USSR)

Chaika II - c1968. (Cyrillic letters look like YANKA-II.) Half-frame 35mm for 18x24mm exposures. Industar-69 f2.8/28mm interchangeable lens. Shutter 30-250. $30-40.

Bera - see Kiev-Vega below.

Kiev - c1945-1970's. 35mm RF cameras, including Models 2, III, 4, 4A. Contax copies. f2/50mm Jupiter lens. $70-140.

Kiev-Vega, Kiev-Vega 2 ("Bera" in cyrillic lettering) - Subminiature for 20 exposures on 16mm. Copies of Minolta-16, but with focusing lenses. Industar f3.5/

Kiev-Vega 2

23mm. Shutter 30-200. $40-60.

Kiev 30 - c1960. Subminiature for 13x17mm exposures on 16mm film. Third in the series following Kiev-Vega, Kiev-Vega 2. All black body. $30-50.

Kneb - see Kiev.

Narciss - c1960. Cyrillic-lettered versions look like "Hapyucc". Subminiature SLR for 14x21mm on 16mm unperforated film. White or black leather covering. Industar-60 f2.8/35mm lens. Previously peaked at $750-1000, but now stabilized at $450-550.

Smena - c1952. Cyrillic letters look like Cmeha. Black plastic 35mm cameras, models 1 to 8. Shutter 10-200,T. f4.5/40mm lens. $10-20.
Smena Symbol - c1970's. $12-18.

Yanka-II - see Chaika-II, above.

MASON (Perry Mason & Co., Boston)

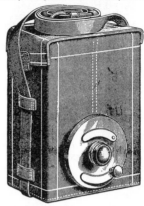

Argus Repeating Camera - c1890. Metal bodied camera in leather case giving the appearance of a handbag. Vertical style. 12-plate magazine. 3" dia. image on 3¼x4¼" plates which drop into plane of focus when lenstube assembly is turned. $1500-2000.

Companion - c1886. 4x5" polished mahogany tailboard view. Brass Achromatic lens, rotating disc stops. $100-150.

Harvard camera - c1890. For 2½x3½" plates. Meniscus lens. All metal. Black with gold pin-striping. A few years ago these sold in the $150 range, but recent trends put it at $60-90.

MASTER REFLEX - The anglo version of the pre-war Meister-Korelle. *See Kochmann.*

MAWSON (John Mawson, Newcastle, England)
Wet-plate camera - c1860. Sliding-box style. Petzval type lens. $1000-1500.

Wet-plate stereo camera - c1865. Bellows style for 3¼x6½" stereo exposures on wet-plates. Ross Achromatic lenses. $1000-1500.

MAXIM MF-IX - c1986. Novelty Taiwan 35 styled with a small pseudo-prism. $1-5.

MAY, ROBERTS & CO. (London, England)
Sandringham - c1900. 8x10.5cm field camera. Wood body, brass fittings, black bellows. Wray 5" lens. $125-150.

MAZO - (E. Mazo, Paris)
Field & Studio camera - c1900. For 13x18cm on plates. Fine wood body, GG back, double extension bellows. Horizontal format. Mazo & Magenta Orthoscope Rapid f8 in Thornton-Picard shutter. $175-225.

Stereo camera - Polished mahogany tailboard stereo. Brass-barrel Mazo lenses in Thornton-Pickard shutter. Red leather bellows. $400-600.

McBEAN (Edinburgh)

Stereo Tourist - 9x18cm. Steinheil Antiplanat lens. Thornton-Picard shutter 1-225. $350-450.

McCROSSAN (Glasgow, Scotland)
Wet-plate camera - Sliding-box style. Petzval-type lens. $600-800.

McGHIE and Co. (Glasgow, Scotland)
Studio View - c1890. Polished mahogany, folding bed camera. Square bellows. Brass barrel lens, focused by rack and pinion. Swing/tilt back. GG back. Pneumatic shutter. $200-250.

McKELLEN (S.D. McKellen, England)
Treble Patent Camera - c1884. Mahogany field camera. First folding field camera to feature the double-stay lensboard support system which was later improved by Sanderson. Also the first with built-in tripod head in the base of the camera, which became a common feature of the English cameras. Dallmeyer R.R. lens with waterhouse. Full plate size. $200-250.

MEAGHER (London, England)
Tailboard camera - Dovetailed mahogany. Dry plate sizes ¼-plate to full plate. Brass trim. Brass barrel lens with wheel stops. $100-125.

Tailboard Stereo camera - c1870. Polished mahogany, 9x18cm exposures. Brass-barrel Dallmeyer or Ruby f6 lenses. Thornton-Pickard shutter. $350-500.

Wet-plate bellows camera - c1860. Made in front bed and tailboard styles. Half or full plate size. Polished mahogany, maroon bellows. Dallmeyer, Wollensak, or Ross lens. Waterhouse stops. $250-400.

Wet-plate sliding-box camera - c1860. Polished mahogany. Sliding box moves by rack and pinion. Made in sizes ¼-plate to 5½x7½" sizes. Petzval-type brass barrel lens. $1300-1800.

MECUM - c1910. Stereo box camera for 9x12cm plates. Leather covered. Ground glass or waist-level viewing. Meniscus lenses. T,B,I shutter. Either lens can be capped for single exposures. $100-140.

MEGO MATIC - Blue and black plastic camera of the "Diana" type. $1-5.

MEGURO KOGAKU KOGYO CO. LTD. (Japan)

Melcon - c1955. Leica-copy. Collapsible Hexar f3.5/50mm lens. FP 1-500,T,B. $400-600.

MENDEL (Georges Mendel, Paris)
Detective camera - for 12 plates 3¼x4¼". RR lens, rotating shutter, iris diaphragm. $125-150.

Triomphant - c1900-1905. Magazine box camera for 9x12cm plates. Brown leather covered wood body. Ortho-Symmetrical lens. Extra Rapid shutter. $125-150.

MEOPTA (Prerov, Czechoslovakia)

Flexaret - c1953-62. 6x6cm TLR. Models (I), II, III, IV. Mirar or Belar f3.5/80mm in Prontor II shutter. Crank advance on early models, changed to knob advance in model IV. $30-50.

Mikroma - c1949. 16mm subminiature. Mirar f3.5/20mm lens. Three-speed shutter 25-200. Rapid-wind slide. $40-60.
(Illustrated top of next page.)

Meopta Mikroma

Mikroma II - c1964. Similar to the above, but with 7-speed shutter, 1/5-400. One recorded sale of a beige-leather example for $100. With normal leather covering: $50-65.

Milono - c1950. Unusual folding-bed camera for 6x6cm on 120 film. Mirar f4.5/80mm in Compur Rapid 1-500. $35-45.

Opema - c1951. Leica copy. Opemar f2 or Belar f2.8 lens. Rare. $75-150.

Stereo Mikroma (I) - c1961. For stereo exposures on 16mm film. Mirar f3.5/25mm lenses. Shutter 1/5-100. Sliding bar cocks shutter. $115-150.

Stereo Mikroma II - Similar to the Stereo Mikroma, but advancing film automatically cocks shutter. Grey or black leather. $125-175.

Stereo 35 - c1960's. 12x13mm stereo exposures on 35mm film. Mirar f3.5/25mm fixed focus in Special shutter 1/60, B. Stereo slides fit into View-Master type reels. Diagonal film path allows 80 stereo pairs to be exposed in two diagonal rows on a single pass of the film. MX sync. Plastic and metal. Camera only: $100-150. Add $50-75 for cutter and viewer.

MERIDIAN INSTRUMENT CORP.
Meridian - c1947. 4x5" press/view. Linhof copy. f4.5/135mm lens. $150-250.
(Illustrated top of next column.)

MERIT - Plastic Hong Kong novelty camera of the "Diana" type. 4x4cm on 120 film. $1-5.

Meridian

MERKEL (Ferdinand Merkel; Tharandt, Germany)
Elite - c1924. Double extension camera for 6.5x9cm plates. Novar Anastigmat f6.8/120mm. 1-100 shutter. $35-50.

Minerva - c1925. Tropical style folding bed camera for 9x12cm plates. Mahogany body with brass trim. Brown double extension bellows. Rack focus. Meyer Trioplan Methan's Anastigmat, or Steinheil Unofokal f4.5/135mm lens in Compur or Ibsor shutter. $500-700.

Phoenix Tropical, 9x12cm - c1920's. Folding bed camera. Fine wood body, brass trim, brown double extension bellows. Tessar f4.5/135mm in Compur shutter. $300-500.

MERTEN (Gebr. Merten, Gummersbach, Germany)
Merit Box - c1935. Brown or red and black bakelite box for 4x6.5cm on 127

Metro Flash No. 1 Deluxe

film. f11/75mm Rodenstock lens. T & I shutter. $20-30.

METASCOFLEX - 6x6cm Rolleicord copy from Japan. Metar f3.5/80mm lens. $75-125.

METRO MFG. CO. (New Jersey)
Metro Flash No. 1 Deluxe - Self-erecting, rollfilm camera with art-deco covering. 6x9cm. $20-30. *(Illustrated on bottom of previous page.)*

METROPOLITAN INDUSTRIES (Chicago, Ill.)
Clix 120 - All metal box camera, 6x9cm on 120. $1-5.

Clix Deluxe - Black plastic minicam for half-127. $3-7.

Clix Miniature - Black plastic minicam for 828 film. $3-7.

Clix-Master - Black plastic minicam for 127 film. $3-7.

Clix-O-Flex - c1947. Reflex style plastic novelty camera. Half-frame 127. $5-10.

Metro-Cam - Black plastic minicam for 3x4cm on 127 film. $3-7.

Metro-Flex - Plastic, TLR-style novelty camera. Half-frame 127. Several variations in body styling. $5-10.

METROPOLITAN SUPPLY CO. (Chicago, Ill.)
King Camera - Small 2x2x3½" cardboard camera for glass plates. Back fits on like a shoe-box cover, similar to Yale and Zar. Not to be confused with the Japanese King Camera of the WWII era. $75-100.

MEYER (Ferd. Franz Meyer, Blasewitz-Dresden, Germany)
Field Camera (English style) - c1900. Self-casing field camera of the compact "English" folding type. Solid wood front door becomes bed. Front standard hinges forward and lensboard pivots on horizontal axis. Tapered red or green bellows with accented corner reinforcements. Rapid Rectilinear lens in brass barrel. $150-200.

Field Camera (revolving bellows) - c1900-1905. Tailboard style folding camera for 13x18cm plates. Fine wood with brass trim, brass handle. Tapered green bellows with black or red corners. Back and bellows rotate as a unit to change orientation. Rise and cross front. Meyer Lysioskop #2 lens. $125-180.

Field Camera (square bellows) - c1900-1905. Tailboard style 13x18cm view camera with square black bellows. Fine wood with brass trim. Meyer Universal Aplanat f7.8 brass barrel lens. $100-125.

MEYER (Hugo Meyer & Co., Goerlitz)

Megor - c1931. Strut-folding 3x4cm rollfilm camera, similar to the Steinheil and Korelle models. Leather covered aluminum body. Trioplan f3.5/50mm lens. Compur 1-300, T,B shutter. $75-100.

Silar - c1930. For 10x15cm plates. Triple extension bellows. Meyer Aristostigmat f5.5/180mm lens in Compound shutter 1-150. $75-125.

MF Stereo Camera - 45x107mm plates. f6.8 Luminor lenses. $125-175.

MICRO 110 - c1986. Miniature novelty camera which snaps onto a 110 film cartridge. Same camera also sold as "Mini 110" and "Baby 110". Retail about $7.

MICRO PRECISION PRODUCTS (England)

Microcord - c1952. Rolleicord copy, 6x6cm. Ross Xpres f3.5/75mm lens. Prontor SVS 1-300 shutter. $50-75.

Microflex - c1959. Rolleiflex copy, 6x6cm. F3.5/77mm lens in Prontor SVS shutter. $50-75.

MIDGET - Japanese Hit-type novelty camera. $10-15.

MIGHTY MIDGET - Japanese Hit-type novelty camera. Red leather covering. $15-25.

MIKUT (Oskar Mikut, Dresden)

Mikut Color Camera - c1937. For three color-separation negatives 4x4cm on a single plate 4.5x13cm. Mikutar f3.5/130mm lens. Compur shutter 1-200. $2000-2500.

MILBRO - c1938. Simple Japanese folding bed "Yen" camera for 3x5cm sheet film. Meniscus lens, simple shutter. $15-25.

MIMOSA AG (Dresden)
Mimosa I - c1947. Compact 35mm. Meyer Triplan f2.9/50mm lens. Compur Rapid shutter. Unusual boxy style for 35mm camera. $50-75. *There were isolated earlier sales for higher prices, but recent confirmed sales have all been in the $40-80 range.*

Mimosa II - Trioplan f2.9 lens. Velax shutter 10-200. $75-100. *see note above.*

MINETTA - "Hit" type Japanese 16mm rollfilm novelty camera. A relatively late and common model. $5-10.

MINI-CAMERA - Common "Hit" type novelty camera from Hong Kong. Much poorer quality than the earlier Japanese types. $3-6.

MINOLTA (Osaka, Japan) *The Minolta Camera Company was established by Mr. Kazuo Tashima in 1928 under the name of "Nichi-Doku Shashinki Shokai" (Japan-Germany Camera Company). The company's history is more easily followed by breaking it into five distinct periods. The brand names of the cameras made during each period follow in parentheses.*
1928-31 Japan-Germany Camera Company (Nifca cameras)
1931-37 Molta Company (Minolta cameras)
1937-62 Chiyoda Kogaku Seiko (Minolta, Konan, and Sonocon cameras)
1962-82 Minolta Camera Co. Ltd. (Minolta cameras)
1982- Minolta Camera Co. Ltd. (Minolta cameras)

Nifca period - 1928-31. The newly formed company produced cameras which were of the latest designs of their day, using Japanese made bodies and German made lenses and shutters.
NIFCA= (NI)ppon (F)oto (CA)meras.

Molta Period - 1931-37. As the company grew it was reorganized as a joint stock firm under the name of the Molta Company. It was during the early years of this period that the name Minolta was adopted as a trade name on the cameras.
MOLTA= (M)echanismus (O)ptik und (L)insen von (TA)shima.

Chiyoda Period - 1937-62. As expansion and progress continued the company went through another reorganization emerging as Chiyoda Kogaku Seiko, K.K. This expansion saw Chiyoda become the first Japanese camera company to manufacture every part of their own cameras.

Minolta Period - 1962-82. Began with a change of the company name to The Minolta Camera Company, Ltd. Marketing areas were expanded; so were the products that were manufactured. It was during this period that Minolta entered the fields of office copy machines, planeteria, and manufacturing for other companies.

Modern Minolta Period - 1982-. Signified by the new Minolta logo. To date, Minolta has produced in excess of 40 million cameras.

MINOLTA (cont.)

Many arguments exist regarding which of Minolta's many "firsts" was most significant to photography. My nomination is Minolta's founder, the late Mr. Kazuo Tashima, who remained at the head of his company from 1928-82. "The first founder of any camera company to remain its president for 54 years." (His son, Hideo Tashima, became Minolta's president at that time, and Kazuo Tashima stepped into the role of "Chairman of the Board" of the Minolta Camera Co.)

Most of the information and photographs in this section have been provided by Jack and Debbie Quigley of Quigley Photographic Services. Both are particularly fond of Minolta equipment, which led them to study Minolta cameras and history. If you have any questions on Minolta, Nifca, or Molta cameras, particularly rare or unusual models, the Quigleys will be happy to help. Contact them in care of Quigley Photographic Services, 1120 NE 155 St., N. Miami Beach, FL 33162. You may also wish to have a free copy of their newsletter. See details in their display ad in the back of this book.

Prices are as estimated by the Quigleys in consultation with Minolta collectors worldwide. Many of the early cameras are not often seen for sale, so estimates of experts are our best guide. For the cameras which are common, we used price statistics from our data base.

The cameras in the Minolta section have been arranged in a somewhat unusual manner. Generally we have followed a chronological order, but usually we have listed second and third generation models immediately after their predecessor to aid collectors in identification and comparing of features. For the same reason, we have listed all of the twin-lens reflex models together, and likewise the subminiatures. These two groups are toward the end of the Minolta section.

Nifcalette - 1929. Folding camera for 4x6.5cm on 127 film. Hellostar Anastigmat

f6.3/75mm. Koilos 25-100,T,B shutter. There were 5 models of Nifcalette A, 4 models of Nifcalette B and 2 models of Nifcalette D. Some have Compur 1-300,T,B shutters with Zeiss Anastigmat lenses. Others had Vario shutters with Wekar lenses. The camera itself was marked Nifca Photo. New price: 39 Yen. Current value: $350+.

Nifca-Klapp - 1930. 6.5x9cm folding plate camera. f6.3/105mm Zeiss Anastigmat or Wekar Anastigmat. Vario 25,50,100,T,B or Compur 25-200 shutter. New price: 39 Yen. Current value: $225+.

Nifca-Sports - 1930. 6.5x9cm folding plate camera. Wekar Anastigmat f4.5/105, Compur 1-200,T,B. There were three models of this camera. Some had Vario and Koilos shutters with Zeiss Anastigmat lenses. New price: 85 Yen. Current value: $225+.

Nifca-Dox - 1930. 6.5x9cm strut folding camera. One model had Nifca Anastigmat f6.8/105mm in Koilos 25-100,T,B. The other had a f6.3/105 lens, details uncertain.

Semi-Minolta I

Nifca-Dox

New price: 29 Yen. Current value: $500+.

Happy (Molta Co.) - 1931. 6.5x9cm

folding plate camera. Earliest models were equipped with Zeiss and Wekar Anastigmat f4.5 lenses in a Compur shutter 1-200. Later models had Coronar Anastigmat f4.5/105mm, Crown 5-200,T,B. New price: 40 Yen. Current value: $175+.

Semi-Minolta I - 1932. Folding camera for 4.5x6cm on 120 rollfilm. Coronar Anastigmat f4.5/75mm in Crown 5-200,T,B shutter. New price: 15 Yen. Current value: $125. *(Illustrated top of previous column.)*

Semi Minolta II - 1937. Folding camera, for 16 exposures, 4.5x6cm on 120 rollfilm. Coronar Anastigmat f3.5/75mm in Crown 5-200,T,B. New price: 120 Yen. Current value: $45-55.

Auto Semi Minolta - 1937. Folding camera for 6x4.5cm on 120 rollfilm. Promar Anastigmat f3.5/75mm in Crown II-Tiyoko 1-400,T,B. CRF. Self-stop film counter and advance. The body is almost identical to the Welta Weltur. New price: 248 Yen. Current value: $100-150.

Minolta - 1933. (Note: This was the first use of this brand and model name.) 6.5x9cm strut folding camera. Coronar

1933 Minolta camera

Anastigmat f4.5/105mm, Crown 1-200,T.B. Featured a built-in footage scale. New price: 97 Yen. Current value: $175.

Baby Minolta

Minolta Best (Also called **Vest** and **Marble; Best** is the official name.) - 1934. Collapsing dual format 127 rollfilm camera. Formats 4x6.5cm and 4x3cm obtained by inserting a plate at the film plane. The Minolta name was embossed in the leather. There were three different models. Model I: f8/75mm fixed focus. Model II: f5.6/75mm front element focus. Model III: f4.5/80mm front element focus. All were Coronar Anastigmat lenses in Marble 25-100 shutters. The body and back door were made of a plastic which was not widely known at that time. It was only in the experimental stage in Germany. The telescoping plastic sections were reinforced with bright stainless steel. New prices: Model I- 19.5 Yen; Model II- 28.5 Yen; Model III- 37.5 Yen. Current value: $65-80.

Baby Minolta - 1935. Bakelite 127 rollfilm camera; 4x6.5cm or 4x3cm formats were changed by a removable plate at the film plane. Coronar Anastigmat f8/80mm fixed focus, fixed f-stop, pull-out lens in bakelite housing. Japanese-made Vario-type 25-100,T,B shutter. New price: 9.5 Yen. Current value: $60-75. *(Illustrated top of next column.)*

Minolta Six - 1935. Collapsible folding camera for 6x6cm on 120 follfilm. Horizontally styled bakelite body without bed or struts. Front standard pulls out with telescoping stainless steel snap-lock frames around bellows. Coronar Anastigmat f5.6/80mm. Crown 25-150,T,B. New price: 50 Yen. Current value: $85.

Auto Minolta - 1935. 6.5x9cm strut folding

plate camera. Actiplan Anastigmat f4.5/ 105, Crown 1-200,T,B. Top mounted CRF. Footage scale on the face of the camera. New price: 135 Yen. Current value: $225.

Minolta Autopress - 1937. 6.5x9cm strut folding plate camera, similar in style to the Plaubel Makina. Promar Anastigmat f3.5/ 105. Crown Rapid 1-400,T,B, synched at all speeds. CRF on the top aligns with a folding optical finder on the camera face. Coupled automatic parallax correction. Footage scale on the face. This camera has commonly been referred to as a Plaubel Makina copy; however, it had features not found in Plaubel Makina until many years later. Complete outfit includes ground glass focusing panel, three single metal plate holders, flashgun, and FPA. New price for body and flashgun: 310 Yen. Current value for complete outfit: $275-325. Camera only: $150-200.

Aerial camera - 1939. 11.5x16cm format. Designed for military use. Never commercially sold. Unmarked Minolta f4.5/200mm lens with f4.5, f5.6 settings. Shutter speeds 200, 300, 400. Current value: $375.

Minolta 35 (first model) - intro. 3/1947. 35mm rangefinder camera, styled like Leica, first for 24x32mm and later

24x36mm on standard 35mm cassettes. Interchangeable (Leica thread) Super Rokkor f2.8/45mm lens. Horizontal cloth focal plane shutter 1-500,T,B, ST. This was Minolta's first 35mm camera. It went through six minor model changes:
- (Type A): 2/48. Serial #0001-4000. Image size of 24x32mm. "Chiyoda Kogaku Osaka" on top. First marketed 2/48.
- (Type B): 8/48. Serials to about 4800. Image size 24x33.5mm, otherwise like the Type A.
- (Type C): 2/49. Serial range uncertain. "C.K.S." stamped on top. Image 24x34mm.

- (Type D): 8/49. Begins with serial #9001. Exact physical changes not yet determined, but this is probably the first with front grooved for focusing tab, and with repositioned rewind lever.
- Model E: 2/51. Begins with Serial #10,001. "Model-E" engraved on front. Has strap lugs.
- Model F: 2/52. Begins with serial #20,000. "Model-F" on front.
None of these were exported, although some were brought back by soldiers. New price: 35,000 Yen. Current values: Early type A: $100-125. Later types: $70-80.

Minolta Memo - 1949. 35mm viewfinder camera. Rokkor f4.5/50mm lens. Between-the-lens 25-100,B shutter. Helical lever focusing. Rapid advance lever. This was Minolta's low priced 35mm camera of the day. Steel body and basic mechanism, bakelite top and bottom plates. New price: 8,000 Yen. Current value: $95-125.

Minolta 35 Model II - 1953. 35mm rangefinder camera. Interchangeable Super Rokkor f2.8/45mm or optional f2.0/50mm lens. Horizontal cloth focal plane shutter, 1-500,T,B, ST. New price: 47,200 Yen. Current value: with f2.0, $125; with f2.8, $100.

Minolta A - 1955-57. 24x36mm rangefinder. Early models had Optiper MX, Chiyoda Kogaku, and Citizen MV between-the-lens shutters set by wheel on camera top. Non-interchangeable Chiyoko Rokkor f3.5/45mm lens. New price 14,800 Yen. Current value: $35-40.

Minolta A2 - 1955-58. 35mm rangefinder. Non-interchangeable Chiyoko Rokkor f3.5 or f2.8/45mm lens. Between-the-lens shutter set by wheel on camera top. Citizen in 1955-56, Citizen MV and MVL in 1957, and Optiper MXV in 1958. New price: 17,900 Yen with f3.5, 20,100 with f2.8. Current value: $35-40.

Minolta A3 - 1959. 35mm rangefinder. Non-interchangeable Minolta Rokkor f2.8/45mm lens. Shutter 1-500, B. $25-35.

Minolta A5 - 1960. 35mm rangefinder camera. Rokkor fixed mount lens in Citizen MVL shutter.
- Two Japanese models: f2.8/45mm or f2.0/45mm lens. Both have shutter 1-1000, B. New price: 14,000 and 17,500 Yen. Current value: $60.
- U.S.A. model: f2.8/45mm lens, shutter 1-500, B. New price: $69.50. Current value: $15-30.

Minolta Sky - 35mm rangefinder camera designed by Minolta for release in 1957 but was never introduced into the public marketplace. About 100 made. Built-in bright-line viewfinder, auto parallax correction. Used interchangeable Minolta M-mount lenses. It could also use screw mount lenses from the Minolta 35 and 35 Model II by use of an M-mount/SM adapter. New price was to be about $325 with Rokkor f1.8/50mm. Current value estimate: $8,000-10,000.

Minolta Super A - 1957. 35mm rangefinder camera. Seikosha-MX 1-400, B between-the-lens shutter. Single stroke lever advance. Most commonly found with Super Rokkor f1.8/50mm lens. (New price: 36,500 Yen.) Other normal lenses were f2.0/50mm (New: 34,500 Yen) and f2.8/50mm (New: 31,300 Yen). Current value of the body with 1 normal lens: $45-70. *(Illustrated top of next page.)*
- Coupled selenium meter: $20-25. (The meter clipped into the accessory shoe and coupled to the shutter speed control.)

Minolta Super A

Current values on other Super Rokkor lenses:
- 35mm/f3.5: $40.
- Lenses with auxillary finders and case:
- 85mm/f2.8: $65.
- 100mm/f3.8: $65.
- 135mm/f4.5: $50.

Minolta Autowide - 1958. 35mm rangefinder camera, similar to the Super A, but with Rokkor fixed mount f2.8/35mm lens. Between-the-lens Optiper MVL 1-500, B,ST shutter. Film advance and rewind on the bottom of the camera. CdS match needle metering. New price: 21,000 Yen. Current value: $40-60.

Minolta SR-2 - 1958. 35mm SLR. Quick return mirror, auto diaphragm. Horizontal cloth FP shutter 1-1000, B. Minolta bayonet lens mount. Most common lens is the f1.8/55mm Minolta Rokkor PF. New price: 51,500 Yen with lens. Current value: $90-110.

Minolta SR-1, early style - 1959. 35mm SLR. Minolta bayonet lens mount. Most common lens is the Minolta Rokkor PF f2.0/55mm. Horizontal cloth focal plane shutter, 1-500, B. There were five different models of the first style SR-1. The first 3 models, 1959-61, did not have the bracket for the coupled meter. The bracket was added in 1962. Other changes include the addition of depth of field preview button. On very early models the name "SR-1" was placed to the left of the word Minolta. New price: 36,000 Yen. Current value of any of the five models, with lens: $70-90.

Minolta SR-1, new style - 1964. Same features as the early SR-1 of 1962, but body styling is more squared in appearance around the top cover edges. Viewfinder eyepiece was squared rather than rounded as on the early model. A new set of accessories were introduced with this model such as a slip on CdS meter. $70-90.

Minolta SR-1S - 1964. Same features as the SR-1 of 1964, but top shutter speed now 1000, not 500. $70-90. *(Illustrated top of next page.)*

317

Minolta SR-1S

Minolta SR-3 - 1960. 35mm SLR. Minolta bayonet lens mount. Most common lens is the Minolta Auto Rokkor PF f1.8/55mm. Horizontal cloth focal plane shutter, 1-1000, B. Detachable coupled CdS exposure meter. New price: 41,500 Yen with lens. Current value: $75-100.

Minolta V2 - 1958. 35mm rangefinder camera. Rokkor f2.0/45mm, between-the-lens Optiper HS (High Speed) 1-2000, B shutter. New price 23,000 Yen. Current value: $85. *Note: Usually found with loose lens and shutter assembly due to the loosening of screws. They should be replaced, not just tightened, to be worth the value shown.*

Minolta V3 - 1960. Like the V2, but with selenium metering. Rokkor f1.8/45mm lens,

Optiper HS 1-3000,B shutter. New price: 23,000. Current value: $115. *Note: These also are usually found with a loose lens and shutter assembly. The screws should be replaced, not just tightened, to be worth the value shown. It costs about $40 to have this done professionally.*

Uniomat - 1960. 35mm rangefinder with built-in coupled selenium meter. Minolta Rokkor f2.8 lens. Shutter speeds determined automatically by the light readings. New price: 16,000 Yen. Current value: $45.

Uniomat III - 1964. 35mm rangefinder. Built-in meter on the lens front. The camera only says "Uniomat" not "Uniomat III". Non-interchangeable Rokkor f2.8/45mm. Shutter automatically controlled by the meter and ASA settings. New price 14,000 Yen. Current value: $30-50.

Variation: Anscoset III - 1964. Identical to the Uniomat III, but says "Anscoset III". Made for export to the USA. New price: $89.95. Current value: $30-45.

Minolta AL - 1961-65. 35mm rangefinder. Built-in selenium meter. Non-interchangeable f2.0/45mm Rokkor PF lens. Citizen shutter 1-1000, B, MX sync, ST. New price: 19,500 Yen. Current value: $30-40. *(Illustrated top of next page.)*

Minolta AL-2 - 1963. 35mm rangefinder. Built-in CdS meter. Non-interchangeable Rokkor f1.8/45mm lens. Shutter 1-500, B. New price: 21,800 Yen. Current value: $65.

Minolta AL

Minolta AL-S - 1965. 35mm rangefinder with meter. Non-interchangeable Rokkor QF f1.8/40mm. Shutter 1-500, B. Made for the USA market. New price: $92,90. Current value: $40.

Minolta AL-F - c1968. 35mm rangefinder camera. Automatic, CdS controlled, shutter-priority metering. Shutter 30-500. Rokkor f2.7/38mm lens. $35.

Minolta SR-7, early style - 1962. First 35mm SLR with built-in CdS meter and scale. Minolta bayonet lens mount. Most common lens is the Rokkor PF f1.4/58mm. Horizontal cloth focal plane shutter, 1-1000, B. ASA dial settings from 6 to 3200. New price: 28,500 Yen with lens. Current value: $75-100.

Minolta SR-7, new style - 1964. Same features as the early SR-7, but with squared off body styling. $75-100.

Minolta Repo - 1962. Half-frame 35mm rangefinder. Built-in meter automatically sets shutter speeds on Citizen L shutter. MX sync. Non-interchangeable Rokkor f2.8/30mm lens. New price: 10,300. Current value: $30.

Minolta Repo-S - 1964. Half-frame 35mm rangefinder. Built-in match needle metering. Rokkor PF f1.8/32mm. Shutter ⅛-500, B. New price: 14,500. Current value: $50-70.

Minolta Hi-Matic - 1962. 35mm rangefinder camera with built-in selenium meter. Rokkor PF f2.0/45mm lens in Citizen shutter to 500, ST, sync. New price: 19,800 Yen. Current value: $35.

Minoltina-P

Variation: Ansco Autoset - 1962. Made by Minolta for Ansco in the USA. Identical to the Hi-Matic but has Rokkor f2.8/45mm lens, and auto metering is slightly different. New price: $90. Current value: $20-35.

shutter 1/30-250, B, ST, MX sync. New price: 13,700. Current value: $20-30.

Minolta Hi-Matic 7 - 1963. 35mm rangefinder with built-in meter. Non-interchangeable Rokkor PF f1.8/45mm. Shutter has manual speeds ¼-500, B. Could also be used on auto. New price: 22,900 Yen. Current value: $30-50.

Minoltina-S - 1964. 35mm rangefinder. Built-in meter. Rokkor QF f1.8/40mm lens. Shutter 1-500, B. New price: 20,000 Yen. Current value: $30-45.

Minolta 24 Rapid - 24x24mm on 35mm. Rangefinder; built-in CdS meter. Rokkor f2.8/32mm. Manual shutter speeds 1/30-250, B. Could also be used on automatic. New price: 15,800 Yen. Current value: $80.

Minolta ER - 1963. 35mm SLR. Fixed mount Rokkor f2.8/45mm lens in 30-500, B shutter. Wide angle and tele auxiliary lens sets available. New price: $119.50. Current value: $45.

GAF Ansco Autoset CdS - 1964. 35mm rangefinder. Built-in CdS meter. Made for the USA market. Ansco Rokkor f2.8/45mm, shutter 1/30-500 auto, B. New price: $79.95. Current value: $20-35. *(Illustrated top of next page.)*

Minoltina-P - 1964. 35mm rangefinder. Match needle metering. Rokkor PF f2.8/38mm non-interchangeable lens. Citizen

GAF Ansco Autoset CdS

Electro Shot - 1965. Auto 35mm rangefinder. Non-interchangeable Rokkor QF f1.8/40mm. Auto shutter 1/16-1/500. This was the first electronically controlled 35mm lens/shutter camera. New price 22,140 Yen. Current value: $25-35.

Minolta SR-M - 1970. First 35mm SLR with integrated motor built in the body. Power supply was a grip on the side of the body. Minolta SR/SRT bayonet mount. Most common lens is Minolta Rokkor MC RF f1.7/55mm. Horizontal cloth focal plane shutter, 1-1000, T,B. Sync at 1/60. There was no meter built into the body or provision for adding one. New price 129,000 with body and grip. Current value: $250-325.

Minolta XD-7, XD-11, XD - 1977. Made in black and chrome, this camera was

marketed in Europe as the XD-7, in North America as the XD-11, and in Japan as the XD. This is the world's first multimode exposure 35mm. Shutter or aperture priority and metered manual modes. X-sync at 1/100. Mechanical speeds "O", 1/100, B. Minolta bayonet mount for the shutter priority mode MD lens. Vertical traverse metal focal plane shutter with electomagnetic release. Electronic stepped or stepless speeds 1-1000, B. Black: $200-275. Chrome: $150-225.

MINOLTA 6X6cm TWIN LENS REFLEX CAMERAS
There are 24 different models of Minolta 6x6cm

Minoltaflex (1937), Minoltaflex (1950's), Minoltacord,
Minolta Miniflex, Minolta Autocord (non-metered), Minolta Autocord CdS

TLRs. Any internal or external change is considered to be a new model of that camera. All use either 120 or 220 rollfilm and have f3.5/75mm lenses. The shutters are Konan, Citizen, Seikosha and Optiper.

1937 Minoltaflex (I) (two models)
1939 Minolta Automat (two models)
1950-54 Minoltaflex II, IIB, III (three models)
1953-54 Minoltacord (three models)
1955 Minoltacord Automat (one model)
1955 Minolta Autocord L (one model)
  (selenium metered)
1955 Minolta Autocord LMX (one model)
  (selenium metered)
1955-65 Minolta Autocord (seven models)
  (non-metered)
1957 Minolta Autocord RA (one model)
  (non-metered)
1965 Minolta Autocord CdS (three models)
  (CdS metered)

Minoltaflex (I) - 1937. First Japanese TLR. 6x6cm on 120 rollfilm. Says "Minolta" on front, not "Minoltaflex". Promar Anastigmat f3.5/75mm taking lens, Minolta Anastigmat f3.2/75mm viewing lens. Crown II-Tiyoko 1-300,B. Main body is identical to Rolleicord, top of the hood is identical to Ikoflex. Had a unique side lock and shutter release to avoid double exposure. Also available with Zeiss lenses and Compur shutters. New price: 305 Yen. Current value: $125-175. *(Illustrated bottom of previous page.)*

Minolta Automat - 1939. TLR for 6x6cm on 120 rollfilm. Promar f3.5/75mm taking and viewing lenses. Crown 1-300,B. Crank advance like early Rolleiflex. Hood like Ikoflex. New price: 493 Yen. Current value: $150-225.

Minoltaflex II, IIB, III - 1950-54. 6x6cm TLR. Rokkor f3.5/75mm lens in S-Konan Rapid 1-500 shutter, B. $50-80.

Minoltacord, Minoltacord Automat -

c1955. TLR predecessors of the Minolta Autocord. Rokkor f3.5/75mm lens. Citizen 1-400 shutter. $60-90. *(Illustrated bottom of previous page.)*

Minolta Autocord, Autocord RA - 1955-1965. Non-metered models. Rokkor f3.5/75mm lens. Optiper MX 1-500 shutter. $60-90. *(Illustrated bottom of previous page.)*

Minolta Autocord L, LMX - Selenium meter. $90-110.

Minolta Autocord CdS I, II, III - CdS meter. $110-150. *(Illustrated bottom of previous page.)*

Minolta Miniflex - 1959. TLR, for 4x4cm on 127 film. Minolta Rokkor f3.5/60mm lens. Optiper or Citizen MVL shutter 1-500, B. Less than 5000 made. New price 12,700 Yen. Current value: $300+. *Note: There have been reports that the Miniflex has sold for thousands of dollars in Japan. However this has not been confirmed. Most reports around the USA/Canada and Europe have reported the sale of this limited production camera to be $300-450. (Illustrated bottom of previous page.)*

MINOLTA SUBMINIATURE CAMERAS

Konan 16 - 1950 (Chiyoda Kogaku). 16mm subminiature, 10x14mm exposures. Chiyoko Rokkor f3.5/25mm lens. 25-200, T,B shutter. Push-pull advance and shutter cocking. New price: 7,750 Yen. Current value: $60-90.

Minolta 16 Model I - 1957-60. Subminiature taking 10x14mm exposures on 16mm film in special cassettes. Rokkor f3.5/25mm lens. Shutter has only three speeds, 25,50,200. No bulb. Push-pull advance. New price: 6,900 Yen. Blue: $100-150. Green: $75-100. Red: $60-90. Gold: $50-75. Black: $35-50. Chrome finish is very common: $15-25.

Minolta 16 Model II - 1960-66. Identical in appearance to the Model I, but with f2.8 lens and shutter has five speeds 30-500, plus B. New price: 7,300 Yen. Prices for colored models same as the Model I, above. Very common: $15-25.

Minolta 16 Model P - 1960-65. Rokkor f3.5/25mm, shutter 1/100 only, sync. New price: 4,100 Yen. Very common: $15-20.

Sonocon 16mm MB-ZA - 1962. 16mm subminiature, 10x14mm exposures. Black body. Rokkor f2.8/22mm, shutter 30-500,B.

Minolta 16 EE

This is actually a Minolta 16-II combined with a 7 transistor radio. New price: 6,900 Yen. Current value: $100-150.

Minolta 16 EE - 1962-64. Rokkor f2.8/25mm; shutter 30-500. Auto exposure using selenium cell. New price: 9,500. Current value: $20-30. *(Illustrated bottom of previous column.)*

Minolta 16 EE II - 1963-65. Rokkor f2.8/25mm, shutter speeds H (High) and L (Low) (200 and 50). Auto exposure CdS metering. New price: 12,400 Yen. Current value: $20-30.

Minolta 16PS - 1964-74. Identical in appearance to the Model P, but shutter 30-100. Made only for export to the U.S.A. New price: $26.90. Very common. Usually found like new, with case, box, and instructions for $15-25. Camera with case only: $10-18.

Minolta 16-MG - 1966-71. Rokkor f2.8/20mm, shutter 30-250. Match needle metering. Very common. Kit with case, chain, and MG flash: $25-35. Camera with case and chain only: $20-25.

Minolta 16 MG-S - 1969-74. Made in black or silver. Rokkor f2.8/23mm, shutter 30-500. Auto match needle metering. With case, flash, strap, instructions in presentation box: $35-50. Camera and case only: $25-35.

Minolta 16 QT - 1972-74. Rokkor f3.5/23mm, shutter 30-250. Auto metering.

Black or chrome. Very common. Often found with case, electronic flash, etc. in presentation box. Like new: $35-50. Camera and case only: $20-30.

Maxxum - 1985. *Technical details/prices from your Minolta dealer. This is new merchandise. We're including it only because of its name.* This is a story of the mid-1980's world business atmosphere: International trade agreements, grey-market dealing, import/export restrictions, warranty contracts... all symbols of the times. Separate brand names for different countries led to the name Maxxum for the North American version of the camera called "7000 AF" in Europe and "Alpha 7000" in Japan. In spelling the name Maxxum, the decision was made to use an interlocking double X. That all sounds like a great idea, until giant Exxon sees the advertising. Exxon, of course, has used the interlocking double X in their trademark for some time. Now nobody at either Minolta or Exxon is worried that people will put cameras in their gas tank or tigers in their cameras, but from a legal viewpoint, if any infringements on a trademark are allowed, the protected design could soon become generic, unprotectable, and useless as an identifiable symbol for the original product. So, now the innocent new baby, Maxxum, with cameras, lenses, and advertising materials already in distribution, faces a change. Minolta agreed to change the design of the Maxxum logo. Exxon agreed to allow a gradual phasing in of the changes to avoid disrupting Minolta's production schedules. Now that's a reasonable way to conduct business. After all "we all make misteaks."

Will the double-crossed Maxxum be collectible? Of course, if you can afford to buy one and let it sit around. Will it be rare? Probably not. There were many produced and shipped.

MINOX *Subminature cameras for 8x11mm exposures on 9.5mm film in special cassettes. The original model, designed by Walter Zapp,*

was made in 1937 in Riga, Latvia.

Original model - (stainless steel body) - Made in Riga, Latvia by Valsts Electro-Techniska Fabrika. Guillotine shutter ½-1000. Minostigmat f3.5/15mm lens. Historically significant and esthetically pleasing, but not rare. Readily available in the $400-500 range, they sell well in the $300-400 range. The original zippered blue, brown, or black case with "Riga" markings will fetch an additional $25.

Minox "Made in USSR" - Stainless steel model made during the short time the Russians held Latvia before the German occupation. (Approximately Spring to Fall, 1940.) $700-850.

Minox II - 1949-51. Made in Wetzlar, Germany. Aluminum body. $60-85.

Minox III - 1951-56. Export model of the Minox A for the USA. $60-80.

Minox III, gold-plated - With design pattern in metal, gold-plated, in crocodile case with gold chain. $1200-1800.

Minox III-S - c1954-63. Gold: $1000-1300. Black: $200-400. Chrome model, with case and chain: $50-70.

Minox A - c1948. Wetzlar. Complan f3.5. Gold: $1500-2000. Chrome: $80-100.

Minox B - c1958-71. Built-in meter. Black: $150-200. Chrome: $50-70. *(Illustrated top of next page.)*

lens, single-stroke winding lever, and rapid-rewind crank. $50-65.

Minox B

Minox BL - c1971-76. CdS meter. Gold: $600-800. Chrome: $100-150.

Minox C - c1969-79. Black: $80-120. Chrome (extremely common): $70-100.

Minox Accessories:
Binocular attachment - $15.
Daylight Developing Tank - with thermometer. $15.
Flashgun for Model B - with case. $7.50
Reflex finder for Model B - $10.
Right angle finder for Model B - $7.50
Tripod adapter - $15.

M.I.O.M. (Manufacture d'Isolants et d'Objets Moules)

Lec Junior - Rigid, light brown bakelite body. 4x6.5cm exp. on rollfilm. $10-20.

Loisir - c1938. Plastic rollfilm camera for 8 or 16 exposures on 120 film. Radior lens, simple shutter, T & I. $10-20.

Miom - Rigid black bakelite body. 4x6.5cm on rollfilm. $15-25.

Photax - Streamlined black bakelite body. Helix lens mount. 6x9cm on rollfilm. $10-20.

MIRACLE - Japanese novelty subminiature of the Hit type. $10-15.

MIRAGE - Deluxe "Diana" type camera for 6x6cm on 120 film. Built-in AG-1 flash with hinged reflector. Imitation meter cell. $1-5.

MIRANDA CAMERA CO. LTD. (Tokyo)
Miranda A - c1958. Same body design and features as the Miranda T, except: FP shutter 1-1000, Miranda Soligor f1.9/50mm

Miranda C - 1958-60. 35mm SLR. Soligor f1.9/50mm interchangeable lens. FP shutter 1-500, B. Instant return mirror. $50-75.

Miranda D - 1960-62. 35mm SLR. Auto Soligor f1.9/50mm interchangeable lens. FP shutter 1-500,B. Instant return mirror. $45-60.

Miranda F - c1963-66. Similar to the "C" and "D". Same lens and FP shutter. $45-65.

Miranda G - c1966-68. Similar, but FP shutter 1-1000, B,ST. $65-85.

Miranda S - c1959. Unusual Miranda SLR because it has a fixed waist-level finder. Soligor Miranda f2.8/50mm. FP shutter B,1-500. $75-125.

Miranda T (Standard) - c1955. First Miranda-made 35mm SLR, and the first Japanese SLR with a pentaprism (and a removable one at that)! Zunow f1.9/50mm interchangeable lens. FP shutter 1-500, B. Non-return mirror. Marked "Orion Camera Co." $150-200.

Miranda TII - c1955. Similar to T, but Arco f2.4/50mm; FP shutter 30-1000,B. Marked "Miranda Camera Co." $60-100.

MISUZU TRADING CO. (Japan)
Midget Jilona cameras - *A series of subminiature cameras. Similar in style to the cheap "Hit" cameras, but heavy cast metal construciton. The earliest models were from the late 1930's, but the most commonly found ones in the U.S.A. are the post-war models.*

Midget Jilona (I) - c1937. This earliest of the Midgets is easily identifiable by the folding finder. It initiated a style which led the way for the Mycro and Hit types. Takes 14x14mm exposures on 17.5mm paper-backed rollfilm that eventually became known as "Mycro-size" rollfilm. $75-100.

Midget Jilona Model No. 2 - c1949. Identified on the top. Shutter B,I (1/50). $40-60.

Midget Model III - c1950. "Model III Midget" on top. Body release. Shutter B, 25-100. $50-75.

MITHRA 47 - c1950. Brown plastic box camera for 6x9cm on 120 film. Meniscus lens. M&Z shutter. Made in Switzerland. $15-25.

MITY - Japanese novelty subminiature of "Hit" type. $10-15.

MIYAGAWA SEISAKUSHO (Tokyo)

Boltax I, II, III - c1938. Small viewfinder 35mm, 24x24mm on Bolta film. Picner Anastigmat f4.5/40mm, Picny-D 25-100, B shutter. $75-100.

Picny - c1935. Compact camera for 3x4cm exposures on 127 film. Very similar in size and shape to the Gelto-D by Toakoki Seisakusho but rounded ends and better finish almost make it look like a stubby Leica. Even the collapsing lens mount is a direct copy of the Leica styling. Picny Anastigmat f4.5/40mm lens. Picny shutter 1/25-1/100, T,B. $60-80.

MIZUHO KOKI (Japan)
Mizuho-Six - c1952. Folding two-format camera for 120 film, 6x6cm and 4.5x6cm. Militar Speciial f3.5/80mm lens. NKS shutter 1-200,B. $30-45.

Moeller Cambinox

MOCKBA 5 (U.S.S.R) - c1938. Folding rollfilm rangefinder camera, copy of Super Ikonta C. 6x9cm or 6x6cm exposures. Netar Anastigmat f3.5/105mm lens. $80-100.

MOELLER (J. D. Moeller, Hamburg, Germany)
Cambinox - c1956. A combination of high quality 7x35 binoculars and a precision camera for 10x14mm exposures on 16mm film. Interchangeable f3.5/90mm lenses. Rotary focal plane shutter 30-800. $500-750. *(Illustrated bottom of previous page.)*

MOLLIER (Etablissements Mollier, Paris)
Le Cent Vues - c1925-30. An early camera for 100 exposures 18x24mm on 35mm film. Several variations. Early ones have a square cornered, vertically oriented metal body. The metal front has rounded corners. 'Le "Cent Vues"' (100 views) written above the lens. Second c1926 has leather covered body with rounded ends. Hermagis Anastigmat f3.5/40mm in Compur shutter 1-300. $1100-1600.

MOLTENI (Paris, France)
Detective camera - c1885. Wooden body, 9x12cm plate camera of an unusual design. Front portion of body hinges up 180 degrees to rest on the top of the camera body, becoming the front of the viewfinder. Back of the body lifts up to form the back of the viewfinder. Brass fittings. Brass barrel Molteni Aplanat lens. Brass lens cap acts as the shutter. $1000-1400.

MOM (Magyar Optikai Muvek (Hungarian Optical Works), Budapest)
Fotobox - c1950. High quality 6x6cm metal box camera. Large built in eye-level finder on top. Achromat f7.7/75mm lens, shutter 1/25-100. $45-55.

Mometta - 35mm. Coupled RF with single eyepiece. Non-interchangeable Ymmar f3.5/50mm. FP shutter, Z, 25-500. Bottom loading. $60-75.

Mometta II - c1953. Rangefinder Leica copy. Ymmar f3.5/50mm lens. FP shutter 1/25-500. $75-125.

Momikon - c1950. Rangefinder 35. Ymmar f3.5/50mm lens. FP shutter 25-500. $75-100.

MOMENT (MOMEHM) - Russian copy of Polaroid 95. f6.8/135mm. "BTL" shutter, 10-200, B. Black bellows. Rare. $100-150.

MONARCH MFG. CO. (Chicago) *Also spelled Monarck.*

Plastic novelty cameras - c1939. Half-frame, 127. Minicam-style, horizontal or reflex-type bodies. Various names: Fleetwood, Flash Master, Flex-Master, Kando Reflex, Pickwik, Remington. $3-7.

Monarch 620 - c1939. Simple, cast aluminum camera for 4.5x6cm on 620 film. Also sold as the Photo-Master Twin 620. $8-12.

MONARCK MFG. CO. (Chicago) *Also spelled Monarch.*
Monarck - Plastic novelty cameras for full or half frames on 828 film. Minicam-style. $3-7.

MONO-WERK (Rudolph Chaste, Magdeburg, Germany)
Mono-Trumpf - c1914. 9x12cm folding bed plate camera. Mono Doppel Anastigmat f6.3/136mm lens. Ibsor shutter. $30-45.

MONROE CAMERA CO. (Rochester, N.Y.) *(Incorporated in 1897, merged in 1899 with several companies to form Rochester Optical & Camera Co.)*
Folding plate cameras (bed types) - "cycle" style folding cameras. 4x5": $40-60. 5x7": $60-90.

Folding plate cameras (strut types) - c1898. They fold to a very compact size, only about 1½" thick including brass double plateholder. Sizes:

Vest Pocket Monroe (left),
Pocket Monroe No. 2 (right)

Vest Pocket Monroe - 2x2½". $175-250.
Pocket Monroe No. 2 - The medium-sized version of the compact Monroe cameras, made for 3½x3½" plates. $150-200.

Pocket Monroe A - 3¼x4¼". The last of the series by Monroe before the merger. $100-150.

Monroe Model 7 - 5x7" "cycle" style plate camera. Double extension maroon bellows. RR lens, Gundlach shutter. This camera looks like the Rochester it is about to become. $75-125. *(Illus. top of next column.)*

Monroe Model 7

MONROE SALES CO.
Color-flex - c1947. Pseudo-TLR aluminum camera. Cream colored enamel and burgundy leatherette covering. $35-50.

MONTANUS (Solingen, Germany)
Montana - c1956. Basic 35mm camera. Deltanon Anastigmat f3.5/45mm in 50-200 shutter. $20-30.

Montiflex - 6x6cm TLR. Steinheil Cassar f2.8/80mm. Prontor-SVS shutter. $75-100.

Rocca Super Reflex - c1955. 6x6cm TLR. Steinheil Cassar f2.8/80mm lens. Prontor 1-300 shutter, MX sync. $75-100.

MONTGOMERY WARD & CO.
Model B - 4x5" folding plate camera. Leather covered wood body. Rapid conv. lens. Wollensak shutter. $40-60. *Note:Most of the cameras sold through Montgomery Ward were not marked with the company name. Sears was one step ahead of Wards in that respect.*

MW - Horizontally styled bakelite folding camera. Similar to Vokar A,B and Voigt Jr. Probably sold by Montgomery Ward, but we can find no catalog references. $15-20.

Thornward Dandy - Detective-type box-plate camera for 4x5" plates. Same camera as the Gem Poco box camera made by Rochester Camera Mfg. Co. $40-60.

Wardflex (metal) - c1955-59. Metal-bodied TLR for 6x6cm on 120 film. Made by Taiyodo for Wards. Biokor f3.5/80mm lens. TKK shutter B,1-200. Rack and pinion focus. $20-30.

Wardflex (plastic) - c1941. Black plastic 6x6cm TLR for 120 film. An Argoflex E with the Wardflex name. Argus Varex f6.3/75mm lens, extrenally gear-coupled to finder lens. Shutter 25-150,T,B. $15-20.

Wards 35 - c1956. An Adox Polo 1S with the Wards 35 name. Adoxar f3.5/45mm lens. Shutter 1-300. $15-20.

Wards xp400 - Simple 35mm camera with automatic diaphragm. Made in Japan. Meter cell surrounds the lens. $15-25.

MONTI (Charles Monti, France)
Monte Carlo, Monte Carlo Special - c1948. Folding rollfilm cameras for 6x9cm on 120 film. f3.5 or 4.5/90mm lens. $15-25.

MOORE & CO. (Liverpool, England)

Aptus Ferrotype Camera - 1895-1930's. Black leather covered wood body, for 4.5x6.3cm plates. Meniscus lens. Suction bulb takes unexposed plate and swings it into position for exposures. $150-250.

MOORSE - (H. Moorse, London)
Single-lens Stereo - c1865. Unusual stereo camera for 9x18cm exposures on wet-plates. Camera sits in a track on the top of its case. Between the two exposures, the camera is moved along the track to give the proper separation for the stereo exposures. Meniscus lens. $3000-3500.

MORITA TRADING CO. (Japan)

Gem 16, Model II - c1956. Novelty subminiature, 14x14mm on paper-backed rollfilm. Mensicus lens. B,I shutter. $65-85.

Kiku 16, Model II - c1956. Same as Gem 16, Model II, above. $65-85.

MORLEY (W. Morley, Ltd., London, England)
Wet-plate camera, ¼-plate - c1860. Bellows camera. Jamin-Darlot lens, waterhouse stops. $550-650.

Wet-plate camera, full plate - c1860-70. Bellows type camera for 16x18cm wet plates. Fine wood with brass trim. Square red bellows. With original Jamin brass lens: $1000-1500.

Wet-plate stereo camera - c1860. Negretti & Zambra brass-barrel lenses. Waterhouse stops. $1800-2200.

MOSCOW (MOSKWA) - Russian copies of the Zeiss Super Ikonta C. Models (1)-5. Industar f3.5/105 or f4.5/110mm. Moment shutter 1-250. $75-125.

MOUNTFORD (W.S.Mountford Mfg., NY)
Button tintype camera - Leather-covered cannon-style button tintype camera, taking 100 1" dia. tintypes. $800-1200.

MOURFIELD
Direct Positive Camera - Large brown-leathered camera. Prism mounted in front of lens. $120-140.

MOZAR (Dr. Paul Mozer, Duesseldorf, Germany)
Diana - c1950. Bakelite box camera for 6x9cm on 120 film. f11 lens. M&Z shutter. $30-45.

MUELLER (Conrad A. Mueller, Strengenberg, Germnay)
Noris - Folding camera for 4.5x6cm on 120 film. Cassar f2.9/75mm lens in Compur shutter. $25-35.

MULTIPLE TOYMAKERS (N.Y.C.)

Camera Kit, Wonderful Camera - c1973. Small plastic half-frame 127 camera in kit form. Simple assembly of 5 large pieces and a few small ones yields a camera named "Wonderful Camera" with f8 lens in 1/50 sec. shutter. The kit comes bubble packed on a card. Made in Hong Kong. $1-5.

MULTISCOPE & FILM CO. (Burlington, Wisc.) *Multiscope & Film Co. manufactured the Al-Vista cameras from 1897 through 1908. At the end of 1908, the company sold all the rights, patents, and equipment for the panoramic cameras to the Conley Camera Co. of Rochester, Minnesota.*
Prices quoted are for complete camera, normally with 3 diaphragms, set of 5 fans, and viewer.

Baby Al-Vista (left), and Al-Vista 5D (right)

Al-Vista Panoramic Cameras - patents 1896, 1901, and 1904. Takes panoramic pictures (model number gives film height in inches) The standard five-format models take pictures in lengths of 4, 6, 8, 10, or 12 inches on rollfilm. The dual-format models take a standard proportion picture or double-width panoramic view.

Baby Al-Vista - c1906-08. For 2¼x6¾" pictures on 120 film. Actually, there are two models. No. 1 was a simple model without viewfinder or speed adjustment. It sold originally for $3.50. Baby Al-Vista No. 2, which originally cost $5.00, had a viewfinder and a fan to slow down the swinging shutter. $250-350.

Model 3B - c1900-08. Dual-fomat model. Picture 3½" high by either 4½ or 9" long. $250-300.

Model 4B - c1900-08. Standard five-format model. Pictures 4" high by 4,6, 8,10, or 12" long. $200-250.

Model 4G - c1904. Dual format, 4" high by 5 or 10" long. Takes snapshots only. $225-275.

Model 5B - c1900-08. Standard five-format model. Pictures 5" high by 4,6, 8,10, or 12" long. $225-275.

Model 5C - c1900-03. Five panoramic formats on rollfilm or standard photos on glass plates with lens tube locked in center position and rear lens hood detached. A "semi-convertible" model. $250-350.

Model 5D - c1900-08. Like the 5B, but lengths of 6,8,10,12, and 16". $225-275.

Model 5F - c1900-08. The convertible model. This camera has two fronts which use the same back. One front is the swinging lens panoramic, and the other is a folding-bed front which looks like the typical folding plate cameras of the day. An unusual and rare set. $400-500.

Model 7D - c1901. Dual format, 7" high by 7½ or 15" long. Uncommon. $300-400.

Model 7E - c1901-08. Dual format, 7" high by 10½ or 21" long. Uncommon. $300-400.

Model 7F - c1901-07. Large size convertible model, similar to 5F above.

The standard front has extra long bellows for use with convertible lenses, such as the 8½" rectilinear lens originally supplied. Complete: $600-700.
Note: Other models and variations of Al-Vista cameras generally sell in the $225-275 range. Some of these include: 3A, 4, 4A, 4C, 5, and 5A.

MUNDUS (France)
Mundus Color - c1958. Beige vertical camera for 8x14mm exposures on double 8 movie film. Resembles a movie camera. Interchangeable Berthiot f2.8/20mm lens. Shutter 1-300. $200-250.

MURER & DURONI (Milan, Italy)
Newness Express - c1900. Magazine box cameras for various sized plates: 4.5x6cm, 6x9cm, 7x8cm, 8.5x11cm (3¼x4¼") and 9x12cm. Murer Anastigmat f4.5 or 6.3, focal length depending on size of camera. Focal plane shutter. $50-70.

Folding plate cameras, focal plane - c1905-30. Strut folding style. In all the sizes listed above. $100-125.

Muro - c1914. Vertical 4.5x6cm strut-folding camera. Suter Anastigmat f5/70mm. FP shutter to 1000. $150-200.

Reflex - c1912. SLR for 6.5x9cm plates. Murer Anastigmat f4.5/120mm. Focal plane shutter 15-1000. $100-125.

SL - c1900. Small leather covered wooden 4x5.5cm box camera. Three stops: 10,20,40. P&L shutter. Two brilliant finders. $75-100.

SL Special - c1910. Strut-folding camera for 45x107mm stereo plates. Murer Rapid Aplanat f8/56mm lenses. Newton finder has lenscaps attached. In retracted position, lenses are protected. $125-150.

Sprite - c1915. Vertical 4.5x6cm strut-folding cameras. Made in 127 rollfilm and

plate versions. Rapide Aplanat f8/70mm lens. Shutter 25-100. $100-125.

Stereo - c1920. 45x107mm folding camera. Murer Anastigmat f8 or f4.5/60mm. Focal plane shutter, 15-1000. $150-200.

Stereo Box - c1905. Magazine box camera for stereo exposures. 6x13cm or 8x17cm sizes. Rapide Rectilinear f10 lenses. $175-225.

Stereo Reflex - c1929. SLR for 45x107mm plates. f4.5 lenses. $400-450.

UF - c1910. Strut-folding camera for 4.5x6cm filmpacks in special back. Aplanat lens. Between-the-lens shutter 25-100. $75-125.

UP-M - c1924. Strut-folding camera for 4.5x6cm plates. Rapid Aplanat f8/70mm. Between-the-lens shutter. $75-100.

MUSASHINO KOKI
Rittreck IIa - c1956-60. SLR for 6x9cm on sheetfilm or 120 rollfilm. Historically, this was the first 6x9cm SLR from Japan. Professionally, it was a very competent studio camera. Close focusing bellows. Interchangeable lensboards and backs. FP shutter, T,B,1/20-500. With normal lens and back: $150-250.

Optika IIa - c1956-60. Essentially a name variant of the Rittreck IIa, but shutter to 400, not 500. With f3.5/105mm Luminor and rollback: $150-250.

MUSE OPTICAL CO. (Tokyo, Japan)
The Muse Optical Co. name was used by Tougodo for various cameras.

Museflex, Model M - c1949. TLR for 3x3cm on paper-backed 35mm rollfilm. f5.6/55mm. Automatic shutter. We have seen several offered at prices $250-350, but have confirmed sales in the $50-75 range.

MUTSCHLER, ROBERTSON, & CO.
Manufacturer of the "Ray" cameras, which were later sold & labeled under the "Ray Camera Co." name. See Ray.

MYKRO FINE COLOR 16 - Japanese subminiature for 13mm wide exposures on 16mm film in special cassettes. Body style similar to the Whittaker Pixie. $35-65.

MYSTIC PLATE CAMERA CO. (New York)
Mystic Button Camera - Button tintype camera. Spring loaded tube advances buttons for exposure. $250-350.

NAGEL (Dr. August Nagel Camerawerk, Stuttgart, Germany)
Formed by Dr. Nagel in 1928, when he left Zeiss Ikon. Sold to Kodak A.G. in 1932.
Anca (10,14,25,28) - 1928-34. Folding plate cameras in 6.5x9cm and 9x12cm sizes. Most commonly found with Nagel Anastigmat f4.5, 6.3, 6.8 lenses in Pronto 25-100 shutter. $60-110.

Fornidar 30 - 1930-31. 9x12cm folding plate camera. Nagel Anastigmat f6.3/135, f4.5, or Laudar f4.5/135mm lens. Compur shutter 1-200. $75-100.

Librette (65,74,75,79) - 1933. 6x9cm folding rollfilm cameras. Most commonly found with Nagel Anastigmat f4.5, f6.3, or f6.8 lens in Pronto 25-100 shutter. $75-125.

Pupille - 1931-35. (Also called "Rollaroy" in England). 16 exposures, 3x4cm on 127 film. With Leitz Elmar f3.5/50mm lens: $200-300. Normally equipped with Schneider Xenon f2, Xenar f2.9, or f3.5/50mm in Compur 1-300 shutter. $125-175.

Ranca - 1930-31. 3x4cm on 127 film. Similar to Pupille, but cheaper. Has front-lens focusing. Nagel Anastigmat f4.5/50mm in Pronto or Ibsor 1-150 shutter. $125-200.

Recomar 18 - 1928-38. Folding-bed plate camera, 6x9cm. Compur shutter 1-250. With Leitz Elmar f4.5: $125-150. With normal lens; Nagel Anastigmat, Xenar, Tessar f3.8, f4.5, f6.3/105mm: $50-85.

Recomar 33 - 1928-39. Folding 9x12cm plate camera, double extension bellows. Compur 1-250, T, B. With Leitz Elmar f4.5/135mm: $150-250. With normal f4.5/135mm lens: $50-85.

Vollenda, 3x4cm - 1931-37. Horizontal style folding bed rollfilm camera. Pronto or Compur shutter. With Elmar f3.5/50mm: $150-200. With normal lens, such as Xenar or Radionar f3.5 or f4.5/50mm: $50-75.

Vollenda, 4x6.5cm, 5x7.5cm, 6x9cm - c1930-37. Folding bed rollfilm cameras for 127, 129, or 120 film. With normal f4.5 lens: $25-45.

NATIONAL (Osaka, Japan)

Radio/Flash CR-1 - c1978. 110 cartridge camera with built-in flash and radio. $75-100.

NATIONAL CAMERA (England)
Folding field camera - c1900-1905. ½-plate. Fine mahogany finish. Reversible back, tapered black bellows, Ross f6.3/7" homocentric lens. Thornton-Pickard roller-blind shutter. $100-150.

NATIONAL CAMERA CO. (N.Y.C.)
Baldwin-Flex - TLR-style minicam for 3x4cm on 127 film. $5-10.

NATIONAL CAMERA CO. (St. Louis, Missouri)

Naco - Horizontal folding rollfilm, 8x14cm. Similar to the #3A Folding Hawk-Eye. Rapid Rectilinear f4 lens. Ilex 25-100 shutter, B.T. $30-45.

NATIONAL INSTRUMENT CORP. (Houston, Texas)

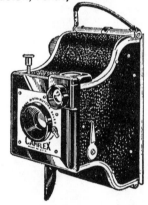

Camflex - 6x6cm aluminum box camera. $15-25.

Colonel - c1947. Aluminum 6x6cm box camera. $15-25.

NATIONAL PHOTOCOLOR CORP. (New York, NY)

One-Shot Color Camera - c1939. 9x12cm exposures on plates, sheet film or film packs. Goerz Dogmar f4.5/8¼" lens. Compound shutter 1-100, T,B. Single extension bellows. $350-500.
--- 5x7" size - c1939. Similar to above, except for size. $350-500.

NATIONAL SILVER CO.
National Miniature - Black plastic minicam for half-frame 127. $3-7.

NEGRA INDUSTRIAL, S.A. (Barcelona, Spain)
Nera 35 - Low cost 35mm. Two speed shutter, Speed Acrinar lens. Hot shoe. $10-15.

NEGRETTI & ZAMBRA (London, England)
Field Camera - 4¾x6½". Mahogany ½-plate camera. Tessar f4.5/210mm in dialset Compur Rollerblind shutter. $100-150.

One-Lens Stereo Camera - c1865-70. Wet-plate sliding-box camera, 8x8cm. For stereo exposures, camera is mounted on top of its stoarge case and moved in its mount between exposures. Negretti & Zambra lens. Rare and desirable. Price negotiable. Estimate: $10,000+.

Stereo Camera - c1862. Mahogany sliding-box wet-plate camera. Brass-barrel Negretti & Zambra lenses. $3000-3500.

NEIDIG (Richard Neidig Kamera-Werk, Plankstadt, Germany)
Perlux - c1950. 35mm camera for 24x24mm exposures. Many shutter and lens combinations, including Kataplast f2.8/45mm in Vario 25-200. $40-60.

NEMROD CO. (Spain) *Named for Nemrod the hunter, King of Babylonia.*

Siluro - c1960-62. Underwater camera molded from "Novodur" plastic. Takes 12 exposures, 6x6cm, on 120 film. Styled like the Healthways Mako-Shark camera, but built for use at depths to 40 meters. Lead weights inside back. Valve on front to pressurize interior. Fixed focus f16 lens, 1-2.5 meters. Single speed shutter 1/55 sec. Battery and capacitor for external flash are contained within the camera body. $30-50.

NEO FOT - Bakelite 120 rollfilm camera made in Denmark. $30-40.

NEOCA CO. (Japan)
Neoca IS - c1955. 35mm with coupled rangefinder. Neokor f3.5/45mm lens. Ceres shutter 5-300, B. $30-40.

Neoca IIS - c1955. 35mm with coupled rangefinder. Neokor f3.5/45mm lens. Rectus shutter 1-300,B. $30-40.

Robin - Rangefinder 35. Neokar f2.8/45mm lens. Citizen MV shutter to 500. A number of different models, but all in the same price range. $20-30.

NETTEL KAMERAWERK (Sontheim-Heilbronn, Germany) *Formerly Sueddeutsches Camerawerk- Koerner & Mayer. Later became Contessa-Nettel in 1919 and Zeiss-Ikon in 1926.*
Argus - c1911. Monocular-styled camera, the precursor to the Contessa-Nettel Ergo. Right angle finder in monocular eyepiece. An unusual disguised camera, less common than the later Contessa and Zeiss models. British catalogs called it the "Intimo". $850-1250.

Deckrullo - c1908. A series of strut-folding focal plane "klapp" cameras for glass plates. Focal plane shutter ½-2800.
9x12cm size - Zeiss Tessar f6.3/135mm or Dogmar f4.5/150mm. $100-150.
10x15cm size - Tessar f4.5/165mm or 180mm. $125-175.
13x18cm size - Zeiss Anastigmat f8/210mm lens. $100-150.
18x24cm size - Xenar f4.5/210mm. FP shutter. $150-200.

Folding plate camera, 9x12cm - Double extension bellows. Tessar f6.3/135mm lens. Dial Compur 1-250. $40-60.
--5x7" - Zeiss Anastigmat f8/210mm. $75-125.

Sonnet - c1913. 10x15cm folding plate camera. Single extension. Tessar f6.3/165mm, Compur 1-200. $80-100.

Sonnet (Tropical model) - 4.5x6cm. Tessar f4.5/75mm. Compound shutter 1-300. Teakwood with light brown bellows. $400-600.
- 6x9cm size - Tessar f4.5/120mm in Compound shutter. $200-400.

Stereo Deckrullo Nettel, Tropical - c1912. Teakwood with brass trim. Tessar f4.5/120mm lenses. Focal plane shutter. $700-900.

Tropical Deckrullo Nettel, 10x15cm - c1910-15. Teakwood camera with nickel struts and trim. Brown bellows. Nettel Anastigmat f4.5/165mm. Focal plane ½-2800. $500-650.

NEUMANN (Felix Neumann, Vienna, Austria)
Magazine camera - c1895. Wood box for 12 plates 9x12cm. Leather changing bag, meniscus lens. $175-225.

NEUMANN & HEILEMANN (Japan)
Condor - Folding 120 rollfilm camera, half-frame. $35-50.

NEW HIT - 16mm subminiature made in Occupied Japan. $30-45.

NEW IDEAS MFG. CO. (New York)
Manufacturing branch of Herbert & Huesgen.

Magazine camera - c1898. Polished wood box detective camera. String-set shutter. $250-375.

Tourist Multiple - c1913. One of the earliest cameras to use 35mm motion picture film for still pictures, and the first to be commercially produced. Vertically styled body, leather covered. Tessar f3.5, Goerz Hypar f3.5, or Steinheil Triplar f2.5 lens, guillotine shutter. Film capacity of about 50 feet for 750 exposures 18x24mm. The outbreak of WWI slowed the tourist

New Taiwan Yumeka 35-R5

market for which this camera was intended, and probably only about 1000 were ever made. $1500-2200.

NEW TAIWAN PHOTOGRAPHIC CORP.
Yumeka 35-R5 - c1983. A poor quality transistor radio built into a poor quality 35mm camera. New in box: $15-25.
(Illustrated bottom of previous column.)

NEW YORK FERROTYPE CO.
Tintype camera - c1906. Professional model with three-section plateholder for postcards, 1½x2½" tintypes, and "button" tintypes. Two-speed Wollensak shutter. With tank and black sleeve. $150-200.

NEWMAN & GUARDIA (London)

Deluxe - c1896. Box-style camera with bellows extension. Zeiss Protar f9/220mm lens. $225-325.

Folding Reflex - c1921. A single-lens-reflex which takes 6.5x9cm plates. Ross Xpress f2.9 or f4.5 lens. Folds to compact size. $150-200.

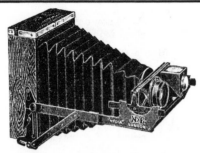

Nydia - c1900. Tapered bellows, folding plate camera. Unusual design for folding. Bellows detach from lensboard, which then swings to the end of the body. 9x12cm and 10x13cm sizes. Wray Rapid Rectilinear or Ross f8 or f6.3 lens. Guillotine shutter 2-100. $300-400.

Sibyl Cameras - *Early models without names seem to be pre-1912, when the company began assigning names to the various sizes. Each name defines a specific size.*

Baby Sibyl (4.5x6cm) - c1912-35. 4.5x6cm on plates or filmpacks. Rollfilm model gives 1⅝x2⅜" images. Tessar or Ross Xpress f4.5/75mm. N&G shutter 2-200. $225-300.

New Special Sibyl (6.5x9cm) - c1914-1935. For 2½x3½" plates or 2¼x3¼" filmpacks. Rollfilm model gives 2-5/16x3⅝" image. Ross Xpress f4.5/112mm. N&G Special shutter. $175-225.

New Ideal Sibyl (3¼x4¼") - c1913. For 3¼x4¼" plates or filmpacks. Rollfilm model gives 3x4⅝" image. Tessar f4.5/135mm. N&G shutter. $175-225.

Excelsior (2½x4¼") - c1933. Rollfilm size. Ross Xpres f4.5/136mm lens. N&G patent shutter. $150-200. *(Illustrated bottom of next column.)*

Sibyl - c1907-1912. Folding-bed rollfilm or plate cameras. Tessar f6.3/120mm, Ross f3.5 or 4.5 lens. N&G Special shutter. 6.5x9cm: $60-110. 3¼x4¼": $100-125.

Sibyl Deluxe - c1911. 9x12cm. Double extension bellows. Zeiss Protar f6.3/122mm. N&G shutter. 2-100. $250-300.

Newman & Guardia Trellis

Sibyl Excelsior

Sibyl Stereo - c1912. 6x13cm filmpack camera. Trellis struts like other Sibyl cameras. Zeiss Tessar f4.5/120mm lens. Shutter 2-100. $1000-1400.

Trellis - c1930. Folding-bed plate camera in ¼ and ½-plate sizes, with typical N&G struts. Protar lens, N&G shutter. $250-350. *(Illustrated on previous page.)*

Twin Lens Pattern - c1895. 9x12cm, box-TLR. Viewed through a chimney-like extension in the viewing hood. $300-400.

Universal Pattern B, Universal Special Pattern B - c1905-13. Box magazine camera for 3¼x4¼" plates. Internal bellows allow front of box to slide out for copy work or close-ups. Zeiss f6.3 lens. N&G pneumatic shutter 2-100. $100-150.

NEWTON PHOTO PRODUCTS
(Los Angeles, CA)

Newton New Vue - c1947. All-metal bi-rail view. Gray enamel, nickel trim. Rotating back. Rapid front focus, micro focus at rear. With appropriate lens/shutter. $150-250.

NIAGARA CAMERA CO. (Buffalo, NY)
Niagara #2 - Box camera for 3½x3½" plates in double plateholders which load

Niagara #2

through hinged door on top. $25-35.

NICCA L-3 - c1986. Novelty 35mm camera from Taiwan. Simple styling without phony prism found on many such cameras. This one sold at a retail price of $8. $1-5.

NICCA CAMERA WORKS (Japan)
Kogaku Seiki Co. 1940-1947
Nippon Camera Works 1948-1948
Nicca Camera Works 1949-1958
see Yashica for post-1958
Production began under the Kogaku Seiki Co. name with two models of Nippon camera in 1942, with and without rangefinder. The Nicca Original, produced by Nippon Camera Works in 1948, is essentially identical to the Nippon except for top plate engraving and Nikkor rather than Kol Xebec lens. The Original Nicca was followed by Type 3, IIIA, IIIB, IIIS, IIIL, 3S, 3F, 4, 5, and 33. Nicca also made cameras for Sears under the "Tower" name. Flash sync, lever wind, hinged backs and projected frame lines were added over the course of the production. The company was absorbed by Yashica in 1958 and the final two Nicca models were the Yashica YE (a Leica IIIc copy) and YF (similar in appearance to Leica M2).

Nippon - $750-1000.
Nicca Original - $450-600.
Other knob wind models - $100-150.
Lever wind models - $110-175.

NICHIRYO TRADING CO. (Japan)
Nicnon Binocular Camera - c1968-78. Binocular camera for half-frame on 35mm. Nicnon f3.5/165mm. 3-speed shutter, 60-250. Viewing is done as with regular binoculars. A beam-splitting device in the right side enables the viewed object to be photographed. The camera body is the Ricoh Auto Half. Motorized film transport. This camera was later distributed by Ricoh under the name "Teleca 35". $250-350.
(Illustrated on top of next page.)

Nichiryo Nicnon Binocular Camera

NIELL & SIMONS (Cologne)
Lopa - c1902. Same as the Griffin Pocket Cyko. See Griffin (page 221).

NIHON KOKI CO.
Well Standard Model I - c1939. Rollfilm camera with telescoping front. Styled like a 35mm camera. Takes unusual image size of 4x5cm for 10 exposures on 127 film. Eye-level and waist-level finders. Well Anast. f3.5/65mm in NKK shutter, T, B, 25-150. $60-90.

NIHON PRECISION INDUSTRY(Japan)
Zany - c1950. Subminiature for 10x14mm on 16mm film in special cassettes. Fixed-focus Gemmy Anastigmat f4.5/25mm. Internal shutter. Some examples are marked "N.S.K." on top and others are labeled "N.D.K.". A rare subminiature. $200-300.

NIHON SEIKI (Japan)
Nescon 35 - c1956. 35mm viewfinder camera. Body very similar to the Soligor 45. Nescor f3.5/40mm. Shutter 25-200,B. $15-25.

NIKO - Plastic body. 16 exposures, 3x4cm on 127 film. $2-8.

NIKOH CO. LTD. (Japan)
Enica-SX - c1983. Subminiature for 8x11mm on Minox cassette film. Built-in butane lighter. Similar to the Minimax-Lite, but has built-in electronic flash. Tortoise-shell covering; gold edges. Suzunon f3.8/14.3mm fixed focus. Single speed shutter. $60-75.

Minimax-lite - c1981. Subminiature

8x11mm camera with built-in butane lighter. Fixed focus, single speed. $50-60.

Supra Photolite - Identical in the Minimax-lite, but with a different name. $55-65.

NINOKA NK-700 - c1986. Novelty 35mm camera styled like an SLR. Originally offered as a free premium by a travel club, which followed up by offering the companion flash for the inflated price of $21. (Similar camera and flash outfits retail at less than $15.) Collectible value with flash: $5-10. Camera only: $1-5.

NIPPON KOGAKU K.K. (Tokyo)
Nippon Kogaku K.K. was formed in 1918 by the merger of some smaller optical firms. During the pre-war years, they made a large variety of optical goods for both the military and scientific communities. These included microscopes, telescopes, transits, surveying equipment, binoculars, periscopes, aerial lenses, sextants, microtesters and other related equipment. Because of the types of items produced, they were virtually unknown to the general public and to the world outside of Japan. With the advent of WWII, they were chosen to be the primary supplier of optical ordnance for the Japanese military establishment and grew to over twenty factories and 23,000 employees. Most of the optical equipment used by the Japanese Army, Air Force, and Navy was produced by Nippon Kogaku. After the end of the war they were reorganized for civilian production only and were reduced to just one factory and 1400 employees. They immediately began to produce some of the fine optical equipment they made before the war for the scientific and industrial fields, but had yet to produce any cameras for general use. Before the war they had begun to make photographic lenses, including those for the famous Hansa Canon, and actually made all of Canon's lenses up to 1947. They also produced their lenses in a Leica-type screw mount as well as the early Canon bayonet. Sometime in 1945 or 1946, they decided that they should get into the camera field in an attempt to expand their product line. Since they were making lenses for 35mm cameras, it was a logical step to make a camera to use these same lenses. By September of 1946, they had completed the design of what was to become their first camera and decided on the name NIKON, from NIppon KOgaku. They studied the strong points of the two leading 35mm cameras of the day, the Contax and Leica, and combined many of the best features of both in the new Nikon design.

The majority of the information and photographs in the Nikon section are the work of Mr. Robert Rotoloni, a prominent collector and avid user of Nikon cameras. His interest in the field led him to write and publish a book entitled "The Nikon - An Illustrated History of the Nikon Rangefinder Series", ©1981. Although his first book is out of print, Mr. Rotoloni has written a new edition entitled "Nikon Rangefinder Camera" published in 1983 by Hove Foto Books, England. In the U.S.A., autographed copies are still available directly from the author at the address below. Since Mr. Rotoloni is also a respected dealer in collectible Nikon cameras, readers are invited to contact him with regard to buying or selling Nikons as well as exchanging information on the subject. Serious Nikon enthusiasts should write to him for full information on The Nikon Historical Society and its newsletter. As a courtesy, please include a stamped self-addressed envelope with queries. He may be reached at: P.O. Box 3213; Munster, IN 46321 USA. Tel. 312-895-5319.

Our second Nikon consultant is Dr. Burton Rubin, a well-known collector of Nikon and 35mm cameras. Dr. Rubin writes a column, "The Collectible 35" for *Shutterbug.* You may write to him at 4580 Broadway, New York, NY 10040.

Nikkorex Zoom 35 - c1963. The first still camera with a non-interchangeable zoom lens. Zoom Nikkor Auto f3.5/43-86mm. Selenium meter. $125-175.

Nikon I - 1948. Focal plane shutter to 500. Bayonet lens mount which continued to be used for later models. Unusual image size of 24x32mm. Despite printed information to the contrary, the exposure counter is NOT numbered past 40 in any case. Made for a little over one year, with a total production of about 750 cameras. Originally supplied with Nikkor 50mm f3.5 or f2.0 lens. Serial numbers 609-1 to 609-758, of which the first 20 or 21 were pre-production prototypes. Rare. Price negotiable. Estimate: $3000+.

Nikon M - August 1949-December 1951. Total production of about 3,200 cameras. The 24x34mm format is a compromise between the 24x32 of the Nikon I and the standard 24x36. It is the only Nikon rangefinder camera to be identified on the camera. The letter "M" precedes the serial number on the top plate. Current value with normal f2.0 or f1.4 lens: 1949 type (no synch) $800-1200. 1950 type (with synch) $400-600. *Note: Late M's with*

flash sync are considered by the factory to be S's, even though they have the M serial number.

Nikon S - 1951-54. The first Nikon to be officially imported into the USA. Identical to the later Nikon M with flash sync (which the factory already called "S"). The only difference is that the serial number no longer has the "M" prefix. (#6094100- on) 24x34mm format. Replaced in December 1954 by the S2. Quite common, and often seen advertised above and below this normal range. With f2 or f1.4 lens: $125-175.

Black Nikon S2

Chrome Nikon S2

Nikon S2 - Dec.1954-early 1958. New features include rapid wind lever, shutter to 1000, crank rewind, and a larger viewfinder window permitting 1:1 viewing. The top plate steps up over the new larger viewfinder, but the accessory shoe remains on the lower level, unlike the later S3. Over 56,000 produced, which is more than any other Nikon rangefinder camera. It was the first to have the 24x36mm format, be available in black, and the first to take a motor drive accessory. Current prices include f2.0 or f1.4 lens. Chrome: $160-210. Chrome with black dials: $175-230. Black: $500-750. *Note: Chrome model is very common and often seen advertised above and below the normal range.*

Chrome Nikon SP

Black Nikon SP, with motor drive

Nikon SP - Sept.1957-at least 1964. The most famous and significant Nikon rangefinder camera, again showing innovation in camera design. It offered a removable back which could be replaced with a motor-drive back. Universal finder for six focal length lenses 28-135mm. Approximately 23,000 produced. The popular motor-drive back led the way for Nikon's dominance of motor-driven photography in the following two decades. Easily recognized by the wide viewfinder window which extends over the lens. The "Nikon" logo, no longer fitting above the lens, was moved off center below the shutter release. Prices include f2 or f1.4 lens. Chrome: $400-550. Black: $500-800. Add $400-500 for motor drive. *Note: Chrome model is very common and often seen advertised above and below the normal range.*

Nikon S3 - Introduced in 1958, this popular version of the SP could also be motorized. At least 14,000 were made

Nikon S3

during its production run which continued at least until 1960. Styled similar to the SP, but with a rectangular viewfinder window, and the Nikon logo again centered over the lens. Two major features distinguish it from the earlier S2: The viewfinder window is larger on the S3. The top plate steps up in the center (accessory shoe is on the high side). Prices with f2 or f1.4 lens. Chrome: $275-400. Black: $500-800. Black "Olympic" with "Olympic" lens: $600-1000.

Nikon S4 - Announced in 1959, this simplified version of the S3 was never imported into the USA, so they are seen less frequently in the USA than in Japan. At least 5900 were made, all in chrome finish. With f2 or f1.4 lens: $450-650.

Nikon S3M - 1960. A modified S3 for half-frames, permitting 72 exposures per load. It was Nikon's first half-frame camera, and was made in black or chrome. Only 195 were reportedly made, although more may exist. Most were motorized. With f2 or f1.4 lens. Chrome or black: $4500-5500. Motor drive for S3M: $1500.

NIKON RANGEFINDER LENSES *All are Nikkor lenses in bayonet mount.*

21mm f4 black only, with finder: $600+.
    Add $50-75 for shade.
25mm f4 chrome, with finder: $300+.
25mm f4 black, with finder: $350+.
28mm f3.5 chrome Type 1 or 2: $110-175.
28mm f3.5 black: $150-200.
35mm f3.5 MIOJ: $100-150.
35mm f3.5 chrome Type 1 or 2: $55-70.
35mm f3.5 black: $70-95.
35mm f3.5 Stereo Nikkor: Outfit with lens,
    prism attachment, UV filter, shade, and
    finder in leather case. Very rare.
    $2500-3500.
35mm f2.5 chrome: $50-75.
35mm f2.5 black Type 1: $75-100.
35mm f2.5 black Type 2 (An f2.5 lens, but
    in f1.8-type barrel. Not easily found):
    $150-200.
35mm f1.8 all black: $300-400.
35mm f1.8 black and chrome: $125-170.
50mm f3.5 Micro Nikkor: $300-500.
50mm f3.5 collapsible: Looks very much
    like the Leitz Elmar, but in Nikon mount.
    Sold only on Nikon I. $400-500.
50mm f2.0 collapsible: $150-250.
50mm f2.0 chrome: $35-55.
50mm f2.0 black: $45-65.
50mm f2.0 all black: $150-250.
50mm f1.5: $200-275.
50mm f1.4 chrome: $40-60.
50mm f1.4 aluminum: $250-350.
50mm f1.4 black and chrome: $50-65.
50mm f1.4 all black (early): $200-250.
50mm f1.4 Olympic: $250-300.
50mm f1.1 Internal bayonet: $350-400.
    Add $75-100 for matching shade.
50mm f1.1 External bayonet: $400-475.
    Add $75-100 for matching shade.
85mm f1.5: $250-375.
85mm f2 chrome: $60-80.
85mm f2 black: $90-150.
105mm f4: $125-200.
105mm f2.5: $70-110.
135mm f4 Short mount for bellows: $125-175.
135mm f4 Serial #611x: $250-275.
135mm f4 Serial #904x: $125-200.
135mm f3.5 chrome: $55-70.
135mm f3.5 black: $60-80.
180mm f2.5: $250-350.
250mm f4 manual: $200-250.
250mm f4 preset: $150-200.
350mm f4.5: $300-400.
500mm f5: $600-750 with original
    wooden case.
1000mm f6.3: $1000-2000 or more.

NIKON RANGEFINDER ACCESSORIES
Finders
21mm optical: $75-100.
25mm optical: $50-75.
28mm optical: $35-50.
35mm mini for S2: $100-125.
35, 85, 105, 135mm chrome optical: $20-35.

Chrome 24X32 Variframe: $500-600.
Chrome MIOJ Variframe: $100-150.
Chrome Variframe: $50-75.
Black Variframe, with shoe: $150-175.
Black Variframe, no shoe: $200.
28mm adapter for black Variframe: $250.
Varifocal: $50-75.
28mm adapter for Varifocal: $100.
Bright line; 35, 85, 105, 135mm: $60.
Bright line 50mm: $200.
Bright line, stereo: $300.
Folding Sports finder: $150.

Reflex Housings
Early type, copy of Leica PLOOT: $350-500.
Second type, 45 degree: $325-400.
Second type, 90 degree: $500-600.

Flash Equipment
BCB: $40.
BCB II: $30.
BCB-3: $20.
BC 4, BC 5, BC 6: $10.

Closeup Attachments
For S with f2: $75.
For S with f1.4: $85.
For S2, either lens: $75.
For SP, either lens: $75.

Copy Stands
Model S: $250.
Model SA: $225.
Model P: $350.
Model PA: $325.

Motor Drives:
Black: $400.
Chrome: $500.
Chrome S 72 for S3M: $1500.

NISHIDA KOGAKU (Japan)
Mikado - c1951. Copy of Kodak Duo 620, 6x6cm. Westar Anastigmat f3.5/75mm lens.

Nomar No.1

Northter Model II shutter to 200. $30-45.

Wester Autorol - c1956. Folding bed camera for 6x6cm on 120 film. Wescon f3.5/75mm in NKK shutter 1-400, B. CRF. $25-35.

NITTO SEIKO (Japan)
Elega-35 - c1952. Leica-styled 35mm camera. Eleger or Elega f3.5/45mm screwmount lens (not interchangeable with the Leica lenses). Rotary shutter 1-200,B. $250-350.

NOMAR No. 1 - Metal box for 127 film. Film spools behind plane of focus. Black or green enameled. $15-25. *(Illustrated bottom of previous page.)*

NORISAN APPARATEBAU GmbH (Nuernberg, Germany)

Afex - Small bakelite camera for 25x25mm on standard 828 film. Similar to the Hacon and Nori, but with metal top and bottom plates. $20-30.

Hacon - c1935. Small bakelite camera for 25x25mm on rollfilm. The same design also appears under the name "Genos", probably after WWII. $20-30.

Nori - c1935. Black bakelite camera for 25x25mm exposures on 35mm wide rollfilm. Early version has folding finder.

Later version has rigid optical finder. A postwar version was sold under the name "Ernos" by Photoprint A.G. $20-30.

NORTH AMERICAN MFG. CO.

Namco Multi-Flex - c1939. Plastic twin-lens novelty camera for 16 exposures on 127. Similar to "Clix-O-Flex". $5-10.

NORTHERN PHOTO SUPPLY CO.
Liberty View - c1913. Same camera as the New Improved Seneca View, 8x10". $100-150.

NORTON LABORATORIES *In 1933, Universal Camera Corp. had Norton Labs design a camera. After a falling out between the two companies, Norton continued with the "abandoned" joint project, while Universal set about modifying and producing their own version, the Univex A. See Universal Camera Corp. for related models, including the Norton-Univex.*

Norton - c1934. Cheap black plastic camera for 6 exposures 1⅛x1½" on No. 00 rollfilm on special film spools. The end of the film spool extends outside the camera body and functions as a winding knob. Stamped metal viewfinder on back of body. $20-25.

NOVA - c1938. 3x4cm on 35mm wide rollfilm. Front extends via telescoping boxes. Special Anastigmat f4.5, shutter 25-100. $225-275.

NYMCO FOLDING CAMERA - c1938. Low-cost Japanese folding "Yen" camera for 3x5cm cut film in paper holders. Leatherette covered. Simple lens, single-speed shutter. $25-35.

OBERGASSNER (Munich)
Oga - 35mm viewfinder camera. Built-in meter. f2.8/45 lens. $10-15.

Ogamatic - c1960's. 35mm camera with coupled meter. Color Isconar f2.8/45mm in Prontormat shutter. $10-15.

OCEAN OX-2 - c1986. Novelty 35mm from Taiwan, styled with small pseudo-prism. $1-5.

OEHLER (B.J. Oehler, Wetzlar, Germany)

Infra - c1951. Plastic 35mm with metal top and bottom. Extinction meter incorporated in top housing. Punktar f2.8/35mm lens in Prontor 25-200 shutter. 24x24mm. $25-45.

OKADA KOGAKU (abbreviated *OKAKO*) **Japan**
Gemmy - c1950. Pistol-shaped

subminiature for 10x14mm exposures on 16mm film in special cassettes. Trigger advances film. Fixed focus f4.5/35mm lens. Three-speed shutter, 25,50,100. Current estimate: $500-750.

Kolt - c1950. 13x13mm subminiature from Occupied Japan. Kolt Anastigmat f4.5/25mm. Iris diaphragm. Shutter, B, 25, 50, 100. $145-165.

OKAM - Czechoslovakia. c1935. 4.5x6cm box camera for plates. Meyer Helioplan f6/105mm in Patent 2 disc shutter 5-1000. Rare. Known sales range from $175-500.

OLBIA (Paris)
Clartex 6/6 - Bakelite camera for 6x6cm on 620 film. $20-35.

Olbia BX - Black or maroon bakelite eye-level camera for 6x6cm on 620 film. Identical to the Clartex. Meniscus lens in two-speed shutter. $20-35.

OLYMPIC CAMERA WORKS (Japan)

Olympic - c1934. Bakelite half-frame 127. f6.3/50mm helical focus lens. Olympic shutter 25,50,B. $65-95.

New Olympic - c1938. Bakelite rollfilm camera for 4x4cm on 127. Ukas f4.5/50mm lens. Shutter 25-150, T,B. $40-60.

Semi-Olympic - c1937. 4.5x6cm on 120. Bakelite body. Ukas f4.5/75mm lens. Shutter 25-150, T,B. $40-60.

Super-Olympic - c1935. The first Japanese 35mm. Bakelite body. f4.5/50mm lens. Shutter 25-150, T,B. $65-95.

Vest Olympic - c1938. Half-frame on 127 rollfilm. Ukas f4.5/75mm Anastigmat. Shutter 25-150,T,B. $40-60.

Olympus 35 IV

OLYMPUS KOGAKU (Japan)
Olympus 35 - c1948-59. Several variations, some with rangefinder. Commonly found with f2.8/48mm Zuiko, shutter 1-500. $30-40.

Olympus M-1 - c1972. 35mm SLR. Original model designation "M-1" was quickly changed to "OM-1". Very few were marked "M-1". FP shutter 1-1000,B. $300-400.

Pen, original - c1959-66. For 18x24mm "half" frame exposures on 35mm film. Zuiko f3.5/28mm lens. 5-speed shutter 25-200,B. $30-45.

Pen D - c1962-65. Zuiko f1.9/32mm.

Copal-X shutter ⅛-500,B. Built-in meter. $40-60.

Pen F - c1963-66. Single lens reflex. Zuiko f1.8/38mm. Rotary FP shutter, 1-500,B. Common. $75-125.

Pen FT - c1966-72. With f1.8/38mm normal lens. Black model: $150-175. Chrome model is very common: $100-150.

OMI (Ottico Meccanica Italiana, Rome)

Sunshine - c1947. Small three-color camera/projector. A few years ago, these

OMO Global 35

sold for about $3000, since only a few were known to exist. Since that time, more have surfaced and we have seen them offered as new, in box, for as low as $500 from 1984 to 1986. Auction sales have been in the $240-500 range.

OMO (U.S.S.R.)
Global 35 - Black bakelite 35mm camera of simple but attractive design. f4/40mm lens; B, 15-250 shutter. Also sold as Smena 6. $15-25. *(Illustrated bottom of previous page.)*

O.P.L.-FOCA (Optique et Precision de Levallois S.A., France)

Foca - c1945-55. 35mm rangefinder cameras. Sometimes called Leica copies, but not really very close. Four models with 0, 1, 2, or 3 stars and a few other models as well. Optar f3.5 or f2.8/50mm lens. FP shutter 1-1000. $80-110.

Foca Marly - Simple plastic camera for 4x4cm on 127 film. Built-in flash. Fixed focus Meniscus lens. Single speed shutter. $10-20.

Focaflex - c1960. Unusually styled 35mm SLR. By using a mirror instead of a prism, the top housing does not have the familiar SLR bulge. Styling is very much like the rangefinder cameras of the same era, but without any front windows on the top housing. Oplar Color f2.8/50mm lens. Leaf shutter B, 1-250. $60-95.

OPTIKOTECHNA (Prague and Prerov, C.S.S.R.)
Flexette - c1938. TLR for 6x6cm on 120 film. This is the renamed Kamarad II, formerly manufactured by Bradac. Trioplan f2.9/75mm lens in Compur 1-250. $75-115.

Spektareta - c1939. Three-color camera, for 3 simultaneous filtered exposures on 35mm film. Body is styled like a movie camera. Spektar f2.9/70mm. Compur 1-250 shutter. $3000-3500.

ORION CAMERA, No. 142 - Plastic novelty camera from Hong Kong. 3x4cm on 127. $4-8.

ORION WERK (Hannover)
Daphne - Vest pocket rollfilm camera. F.Corygon Anastigmat f6.3/85mm in Pronto. $15-25.

Orion box camera - c1922. For 6x9cm glass plates. Meniscus f17 lens, simple shutter. $50-60.

Rio 84E, 8x10.5cm

Rio folding rollfilm cameras - Individual models are difficult to identify, since many variations were produced but not generally marked with model number. Most common in the 6x9cm and 8x10.5cm sizes. $25-35.

Rio folding plate cameras - c1923. 6.5x9cm, 9x12cm, and 10x15cm sizes. Leather covered wood body with metal bed. f4.5 or f6.3 Meyer Trioplan, Helioplan, or Orion Special Aplanat. Vario or Compur shutter. $25-35.

Rio 44C - c1921-25. Horizontally styled folding bed camera for 9x12cm plates. Typically with Corygon f6.3 in Vario or Helioplan f4.5/135mm in Compur 1-200. Uncommon. $50-75.

Tropen Rio 2C, 5C - c1920. Folding-bed 9x12cm plate cameras. Teak and brass. Brown double extension bellows. Model 5C is like 2C but with slightly wider front standard to accomodate faster lenses in larger shutter. Model 2C normally with f6.3 or f6.8 lens. Model 5C typically with Tessar or Xenar f4.5/150mm lens in Compur shutter 1-150. $350-500.

O.T.A.G. (Vienna, Austria)
Amourette - c1925. Early 35mm for 24x30mm exposures using special double cassettes. Trioplan f6.3 lens. Compur shutter 25, 50, 100. Down from earlier high prices to $175-300.

Lutin - Nearly identical to the better known Amourette. $250-350.

OTTEWILL (Thomas Ottewill, London)
Sliding-box camera - c1851. Mahogany wet-plate camera in 9x11" size. Camera is completely collapsible when front and back panels are removed. Ross or Petzval-type lens. $3000-3500.

OWLA KOKI (Japan)
Owla Stereo - c1958. For stereo pairs 24x23mm on 35mm film. Owla f3.5/35mm lenses. Shutter 10-200,B. $125-175.

PACIFIC - Japanese novelty subminiature of the "Hit" type. $10-15.

PACIFIC PRODUCTS LTD. (Hong Kong, Los Angeles, Taipei)

Lynx PPL-500XL - c1986. Behind this pretentious name and smart styling lurks an inexpensive novelty 35mm camera. It sold new, complete with electronic flash for under $15. I would hate to assess its value as a photographic instrument, but as a collectible, it brings $1-5.

PALMER & LONGKING

Lewis-style Daguerreotype camera - c1855. ½-plate. $5000-6000.

PANAX - Plastic novelty camera of the "Diana" type. $1-5.

PANON CAMERA CO. LTD. (Japan)

Panon Wide Angle Camera - c1952. 140 degree panoramic camera. 2x4½" exp. on 120 rollfilm. Hexar f3.5/50mm or Hexanon f2.8/50mm. Shutter 2, 50, 200. $650-825.

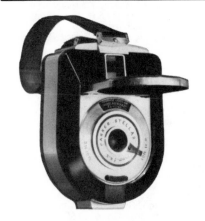

Parker Camera

Widelux - c1959. Panoramic camera for 24x59mm images on standard 35mm film. Lux f2.8/26mm lens. Also sold under the Kalimar label. Various models. $400-500.

PAPIGNY (Paris)
Jumelle Stereo - c1890. For 8x8cm plates. Magazine back. Chevalier f6.5/100 lenses. Guillotine shutter. $175-225.

PARIS (Georges Paris) *Cameras used the name GAP, from the manufacturer's initials.*

GAP Box 3x4cm - ca late 1940's. Small box camera shaped somewhat like the Zeiss Baby Box. Available black painted, black leather covered, or with decorative front panels in gold, blue & gold, or red & gold. $20-35.

GAP Box 6x9cm - c1947. Metal box camera, normally with black leatherette covering but occasionally found with marbled colors. 6x9cm on 120 film. $12-20.

PARK (Henry Park, London)
Tailboard camera - c1890. ½ plate field camera. Rapid Rectilinear f8. $200-225.

PARKER PEN CO. (Janesville, Wisc.)
Parker Camera - c1949. Plastic subminiature for 8 images, 13x16mm on a 147mm strip of unperforated 16mm film in a special sylindrical cassette. Parker Stellar f4.5/37mm lens in rotary shutter, 30-50. At least 100 cameras were used in a test marketing study by Parker and a Chicago advertising firm. At one time they were presumed to have been destroyed, and only a few examples were known to exist. The collectible value reached a $750-1000 range. Within the last few years a significant number have surfaced and the price has again dropped to $400-500. *(Illustrated top of previous column.)*

PDQ CAMERA CO. (Chicago)
PDQ Photo Button Camera - c1930. All-metal button tintype camera. Echo Anastigmat lens. $750-900.

Mandel Automatic PDQ, Model G - c1935. Large street camera for 6x9cm exp. rolls of direct positive paper. Built-in developing tank with tubes to change solutions. RR f6/135mm lens. $150-200.

PEACE - c1949. Early "Hit-type" camera with cylindrical finder. Simple fixed-focus lens; B & I shutter. $150-225.

PEACE III - c1950. Similar to the earlier version, but with Kowa f4.5 lens, R.K. shutter, different back latch. $125-175.

PEACE, PEACE BABY FLEX - c1949. Japanese reflex style subminiatures for 12x14mm on rollfilm. Fixed focus lens, B,I shutter. $500-600.

PEARSALL (G. Frank E. Pearsall, Brooklyn, NY)
Compact - c1883. First camera to use the basic folding camera design, used by most American folding plate cameras into the 1920's. Full plate size. Only one known sale, in 1981, for $3200.

PECK (Samuel Peck & Co., New Haven, Conn.)
Ferrotype, 4-tube camera - c1865. Takes 1/9 plate tintypes. $800-1200.

Wet-plate camera - c1859. Full plate size. $900-1200.

PEER 100 - Camera disguised as a package of cigarettes. The camera is a Kodak Instamatic 92 or Instamatic 100 camera within a plastic outer housing which resembles a package of Peer 100 cigarettes. $200-250.

PEERLESS MFG. CO.
Box camera - Early paperboard box camera for single 2½x2½" glass plates. $50-75.

PENROSE (A.W. Penrose & Co. Ltd.)
Studio camera - c1915. 19x19". $250-350.

PENTACON (VEB Pentacon, Dresden, Germany) *The Dresden factory of Zeiss Ikon was destroyed in 1945, and in 1948 the main offices were moved to the former Contessa factory in Stuttgart. Meanwhile, the Dresden operation became a public "Volks Eigener Betrieb", using the name "Zeiss Ikon VEB". This causes a certain confusion, especially with similar camera names and designs. After much dispute with the West German operation at Stuttgart, the Zeiss Ikon and Contax names were relinquished completely and the "VEB Pentacon"* name became the banner for the combine which also included Balda and KW. Eventually, the VEB combine marketed cameras from Balda, Beier, Certo, Exa, Exakta, Praktca, Pentacon, KW, etc.

Belmira - Unusual 35mm RF camera of Beier origin. Trioplan or Tessar f2.8/50mm. Rapid wind lever at back. $20-40.

Consul - c1955. Rare name variation of the Pentacon (Contax-D). Identical except for the factory-engraved Consul name. $100-125.

Contax "No-Name" - c1963. Rangefinder camera based on the Zeiss Contax II, redesigned to look more like the IIa or IIIa. In reality, it is a Russian Kiev camera, made for the U.S.A. market without any name. With normal lens: $150-200.

Contax D - c1953. 35mm SLR. Standard PC sync on top. Zeiss Jena Biotar f2, or Hexar or Tessar f2.8. FP shutter to 1000. Four or five variations. Last version has auto diaphragm like Contax F, but is not marked F. Clean and working: $75-135.

Contax E - c1955. Like the Contax D, but with uncoupled selenium meter built onto prism. $100-150.

Contax F - c1957. Same as the Contax D, but with semi-automatic cocking diaphragm. Clean & working: $75-125.

What's in a name?
Trademark usage and export/import regulations led to various names being used on the East-German Contax SLR cameras. The Contax S was the earliest model (c1949-51) and does not exist with other name variations, because it was out of production before the trademark and name changes began. It is recognizable by sync. in tripod socket. There are three or four versions. Generally the earliest are finished best.
The following chart compares the original "Contax" model with name variants.

CONTAX Model (VEB Zeiss-Ikon)	FEATURES	NAME VARIATIONS of PENTACON MODELS
Contax S	Sync. in tripod socket	NONE
Contax D	Standard PC sync. on top	Pentacon, Consul, Hexacon*, Astraflex*, "No name"*
Contax E	Meter built onto top of prism	None known.
Contax F	Auto diaphragm	Pentacon F, Ritacon F
Contax FB	Auto diaphragm plus meter	Pentacon FB
Contax FM	Auto diaphragm plus interchangeable finder screen	Pentacon FM
Contax FBM	Auto diaphragm, meter, RF	Pentacon FBM

The model letters are based on the camera's features. F=Automatic Diaphragm, B=Built-in meter, M=Split-image finder screen

*Note: Hexacon and Astraflex are "House brands". The original Pentacon name has been obliterated and the store name riveted or glued on. The "No name" version has the Pentacon Tower emblem, but no camera name engraved.

Contax FB - Zeiss Biotar f2/58mm. Focal plane shutter 1-1000. $90-135.

Contax FM - c1957. Zeiss Biotar f2/58mm. Automatic diaphragm. Interchangeable finder screen. $100-150.

Contax S - 1949-51. One of the first 35mm prism SLR's, along with the Rectaflex which appeared in 1948. Identifiable by sync connection in tripod socket. Biotar f2 lens. FP shutter 1-1000, B. Early models

Ercona II

have no self-timer. Later models have a self-timer with lever below shutter release. Early models are well-finished with typical Zeiss quality. Clean and working: $175-225.

Ercona, Ercona II - c1954. Folding bed rollfilm camera. 6x9cm or dual format 6x9cm and 6x6cm. Ludwig Meritar f4.5/105mm in Prontor-S 1-250, B. $25-35. *(Illustrated bottom of previous column.)*

Hexacon - c1948. Same as the Contax D. Clean & working: $50-100.

Orix - c1958. Half-frame (18x24mm) on 35mm film. Precursor of the Penti. $25-50.

Pentacon - c1948-62. Same as the Contax D. 35mm SLR. Tessar f2.8/50mm lens. Focal plane shutter 1-1000. $55-95.

Pentacon "No-Name" - Like Pentacon, and has Pentacon tower emblem, but no name engraved. This should not be confused with the "No-Name Contax" which is a rangefinder camera. $200-300.

Pentacon F - c1957-60. Meyer Primotar f3.5/50mm or Tessar f2.8/50mm. $60-80.

Pentacon FB - c1959. Built-in exposure meter. Tessar f2.8/50 or Steinheil f1.9/55 lens. $75-125.

Pentacon FBM - c1957. Built-in exposure meter. F2 or f2.8. $75-125.

Pentacon FM - c1957. Built-in exposure meter. Tessar f2.8/50mm lens. $50-100.

Penti - c1959. 18x24mm on 35mm film. Meyer Triplan f3.5/50mm lens. Gold colored body with enamel in various colrs: blue-green, red, cream, etc. $25-40.

Penti II - c1961-62. Similar to Penti, but with built-in meter and bright-frame finder. Colors include: black & gold, black & silver, or ivory & gold. $25-40.

Pentina, Pentina E, Pentina FM - 1960's. Tessar f2.8 in breech-lock mount, similar to Praktina mount. 35mm leaf-shutter SLR. Rarely in working order. Repairmen hate them according to one source. Normally $25-40; more if clean & working.

Pentona, Pentona II - Low-priced basic 35mm viewfinder camera. Meyer f3.5/45mm lens. Bright frame finder. $15-25.

Prakti - c1960. Domitron or Meyer lens. Electric motor drive 35mm camera, but motor drive rarely working. $25-50.

Ritacon F - c1961. Name variant of the Pentacon F. Very rare with this name. $125-175.

Taxona - c1950. For 24x24mm exposures on 35mm film. Novonar or Tessar f3.5 lens. Tempor 1-300 shutter. (This is the DDR successor to the pre-war Zeiss Tenax, made partly from pre-war Tenax I parts.) $25-50 in Germany. Somewhat higher in U.S.A.

Werra - c1955. 35mm. Models I-IV. Jena

Tessar f2.8/50mm lens. Compur Rapid 1-500 shutter. Film advanced and shutter cocked by turning ring around lens barrel. Lens shade reverses to encase shutter and lens. Olive green or black leather. $25-50 in Germany where common. $50-70 in U.S.A.

PEPITA - c1930. For 3x4cm images. Rapid Aplanat f7.7/50mm in 25-100 shutter. $40-55.

PERFECT CAMERA - c1910. Simple cardboard box camera for 6x9cm single plates. $75-125.

PERKA PRAZISIONS KAMERAWERK (Munich, Germany)

Perka - c1922. Folding-bed plate camera. Double extension bellows. Lenses include: Symmar f5.6/135mm, Staeble Polyplast-Satz f6/135mm, and Tessar f4.5/150mm. Compound, Compur, or Compur-Rapid shutter. Construction allows tilting of back and lens standard for architectural photos. $150-250.

PERKEN, SON, & RAYMENT (London)
Folding camera - c1890. Mahogany with brass trim. Optimus lens. ½-plate size. $150-225.

Optimus Camera DeLuxe - c1894. Black

leather-covered folding camera ¼-plate. Opens like an early Folding Kodak. Extra Rapid Euryscope lens. Rack and pinion focus. Roller-blind (Thornton-Pickard) shutter. Iris diaphragm. Estimate: $300-500.

Optimus Detective - c1888. ¼-plate mahogany bellows camera inside of a black leather covered box. External controls. Brass RR lens, waterhouse stops, rotary shutter. Nearly identical to the Detective Camera of Watson & Sons. Estimate: $300-500.

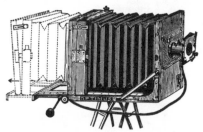

Optimus Long Focus Camera - c1892-1899. Tailboard style field camera. Mahogany body, brass trim. Square red-brown double extension bellows. Rack and pinion focus. $175-250.

Studio camera - c1890's. Full-plate (6½x8½") size. $200-225.

Tailboard camera - c1886. ¼ and ½ plate sizes. Mahogany body with brass fittings. Ross lens, waterhouse stops. Maroon leather bellows. $150-225.

PFCA - Japanese novelty subminiature camera of the Hit type. Unusual streamlined top housing. Large flat advance knob. $10-15.

PHO-TAK CORP. (Chicago)
Eagle Eye - c1950-54. Metal box camera with eye-level optical finder. Precision 110mm lens. T&I shutter. $3-7.

Foldex - c1950's. All metal folding camera for 620 film. Octvar or Steinheil lens. $5-10.

Macy 120, Marksman, Spectator Flash, Trailblazer 120, Traveler 120 - c1950's. Metal box cameras for 6x9cm. $5-10.

Reflex I - c1953. TLR-styled box camera. $8-12.

PHOBA A.G. (Basel, Switzerland)
Diva - 6x9cm folding-bed plate camera. Titar f4.5/105mm lens. Compur shutter. $25-35.

PHOCIRA - Small box camera for 3x4cm on 127 film. Similar to Eho Baby Box. $50-75.

PHOTAVIT-WERK (Nuernberg, Germany) *Originally called Bolta-Werk.*
Photavit - c1937. Compact 35mm camera for 24x24mm exposures on standard 35mm film in special cartridges. $50-75.
(See photo under the Bolta heading).

Photina - c1953. 6x6cm TLR. Cassar f3.5/75mm lens in Prontor-SVS shutter. $40-75.

PHOTO DEVELOPMENTS LTD. (Birmingham, England)
Envoy Wide Angle - c1950. Wide angle camera for 6x9cm on 620 or 120 rollfilm, or cut film. f6.5/64mm Wide Angle lens. 82 degree angle of view. Agifold 1-150 shutter. $40-80 in England. Somewhat higher in U.S.A.

PHOTO HALL (Paris)
Perfect Detective - c1910. Leather covered box camera for 9x12cm plates. Extra-Rapid Rectilinear lens. $150-200.

Perfect Jumelle - c1900. Single lens jumelle-style 6.5x9cm plate camera. Magazine back. Zeiss Protar f8/110mm. $150-200.

Stereo camera - c1905. Rigid truncated pyramid "jumelle" style camera for 6x13cm plates in single metal holders. Guillotine shutter 10-50. Folding Newton finder. $75-95.

PHOTO-IT MFG. CO. (LaCrosse, WI)

The Photo-It - Round subminiature pinhole camera, 65mm dia. Stamped metal body,Cream enamel with brown lettering. Takes 8 exposures on a 12mm film strip wrapped on an octagonal drum. $1000-1500.

PHOTO MASTER - c1948. For 16 exposures 3x4cm on 127 film. Rollax 50mm lens, single speed rotary shutter. Brown or black bakelite or black thermoplastic body. $3-7.

PHOTO MASTER SUPER 16 TWIN 620 - Cast aluminum eye-level camera for 16 exposures 4x5.5cm on 620 film. Styling similar to the aluminum "Rolls" cameras. Fixed focus Rollax 62mm lens. Instanat & Time shutter. $5-10.

PHOTO MASTER TWIN 620 - Simple

cast-metal camera for 16 shots on 127 film. Identical to the Monarch 620, and probably made in the same factory in Chicago. $8-12.

PHOTO MATERIALS CO. (Rochester, NY)

Trokonet - c1893. Leather covered wooden magazine box camera. Holds 35 cutfilms or 12 glass plates, 4x5". Gundlach rectilinear lens, variable speed shutter. Inside the box, the lens is mounted on a lensboard which is focused by rack and pinion. $400-600.

PHOTO-PAC CAMERA MFG. CO., INC. (New York City & Dallas, TX)

Photo-Pac - c1950. Disposable cardboard mail-in camera. We have seen two different body variations under the Photo-Pac name. One had a Dallas address and it had the shutter release near the TOP of the right side. The other type has a N.Y.C. address and has the shutter release on the lower front corner of the right side. The two versions also have their address labels on opposite sides. $15-25.

PHOTO-PORST (Hans Porst, Nuernberg) *Makers of Hapo cameras.* *Hapo* = HAns POrst.

Hapo 5, 10, 45 - c1930's. 6x9cm folding rollfilm cameras, made by Balda for Porst. Schneider Radionar f4.5/105mm or Trioplan f3.8/105mm lens. Compur or Compur Rapid shutter. $15-25.

Hapo 35 - c1955. Folding 35mm, mad by Balda for Porst. Enna Haponar f2.9/50mm lens. Prontor-SVS 1-300 shutter. Coupled rangefinder. $15-25.

Hapo 36 - 35mm, non-coupled rangefinder. f2.8 Steinheil in Pronto shutter. $15-25.

Hapo 66, 66E - 6x6cm. Enna Haponar f3.3 or f4.5/75mm lens in Pronto sync. shutter, ½-200. Model 66E has rangefinder. $15-25.

Haponette B - c1960's. 35mm camera. Color Isconar f2.8/45mm in Prontor shutter. $5-10.

PHOTO SEE CORP. (N.Y.C.)

Photo-See - An art-deco box camera and developing tank for photos in 5 minutes. An interesting, simple camera. According to a popular but untrue rumor, the viewfinders are on backwards and instructions were never printed. Actually the finders are as

Photolet

designed and instructions exist, though not often found with the cameras. These are usually found New in the box, with developing tank, and always with traces of rust from storage in a damp area. $20-35.

PHOTOLET - c1932. French subminature for rollfilm. Meniscus f8/31mm. Single speed rotary shutter. 2x2cm. Similar to the Ulca. $60-100. *(Illustrated bottom of previous page.)*

PHOTON 120 CAMERA - Grey & black plastic camera of the "Diana" type. Matching flash for AG-1 bulbs fits in hot shoe. Made in Hong Kong. $1-5.

PHOTOPRINT A.G. (Germany)
Ernos - c1949. Small bakelite camera for 25x25mm exposures on 35mm wide rollfilm. Identical to the pre-war "Nori" from Norisan Apparatebau. $25-40.

PHOTOSCOPIC (Brussels, Belgium) - c1924. Unusually designed early 35mm camera for 50 exposures 24x24mm on 35mm film in special cassettes. Metal body with black hammertone enamel. Tubular Galilean finder. O.I.P. Gand Labor f3.5/45 lens. Pronto or Ibsor shutter. Only 100 examples were made according to the inventor, Mr. A Van Remoortel, and several variations are known, including: 1. Full focusing. Pull-tab film advance like earlier Amourette camera. 2. Knob advance. Full focusing. 3. Fixed focus, knob advance. $400-500.

PIC - c1950. Unusual English disk-shaped plastic camera. 3x4cm exposures on 127 rollfilm. Meniscus lens, rotary sector shutter. $100-125. *(Illustrated top of next page.)*

PICTURE MASTER - Stamped metal minicam for 16 exposures on 127 film. Body style identical to Scott-Atwater Photopal. $10-20.

PIERRAT (Andre Pierrat, France) *During the occupation of France, Andre Pierrat was secretly working on his copy of the Zeiss Ikonta camera, and it became one of the first quality French-made cameras after the end of WWII.*

Pic

Drepy - c1946-1950. The Drepy, named from a contraction of the designer's name, was essentially a copy of the Zeiss Ikonta. Takes 8 or 16 exp. on 120 film. The most common model has leatherette covered body with black enameled edges. Drestar Anastigmat f4.5/105mm in Drestop shutter B,1-250. $15-25.

PIGGOTT (John Piggott, London, England)
Sliding-box wet-plate camera - c1960. Mahogany body. 8x8". Petzval-type lens. $1200-1800.

PIGNONS AG, (Ballaigues, Switzerland)
Pignons S.A. is a family business, founded in 1918 for making watches and clocks. Because of continual fluctuations in that business, the decision was made in 1933 to move into the photographic market by producing a camera

which combined the advantages of reflex viewing and a rangefinder.

The first of these prototypes appeared in 1939, and bore the name "Bolca", before the name "Alpa Reflex", which first was shown in 1944 at a public fair in Basel. The company remains in the camera business today, still producing exceptionally fine cameras which are virtually hand-made.

- Editor's note: *The information in this section is primarily the work of Jim Stewart, whose particular interests revolve around Alpa, 35mm, and subminiature cameras. In addition to this section, he has made other important contributions to this guide.*

Cameras are listed chronologically by year of introduction. Serial number ranges are approximate. Some prototypes fall into the 10000 and 25000 range. Display dummies are in the 29000 range. Discontinuance dates indicate the end of series production. Special orders of later bodies often occurred as long as parts were available. Almost any custom variation could be factory ordered.

There were many notable "firsts" by Alpa including the following:
1. First and only CRF in SLR (Model 7, 1952).
2. First with mirror tele lens (f6.3 Delft Fototel, 1950).
3. First mirror lock-up (1942, and with collapsible lens only 2" thick!)
4. First full auto diaphragm (1956).
5. First patented (1947) and produced (1963) TTL SLR.
6. First built-in multifocal finder (50, 90, 135mm; 1952).
7. First macro lenses as standard equipment (1959 to 11").
8. First Apochromat lenses (normal 1952, tele 1959).
9. Widest range of lenses (1.9mm to 5000mm) in the 1970's.

Bolca I - 1942-46 (#11000-13000). Waist-level SLR, eye-level VF and split-image CRF. Cloth FP shutter 1-1000. Berthiot f2.9/50mm in collapsible mount. Last run marked "Bolsey Model A". All are rare, especially the "Bolsey A". Bolca I: $350-500. Bolsey A: $400-600.

Bolca (Standard) - 1942-50. (#11000-13000). Similar to the Bolca I, but without reflex viewing. VF/CRF only. From 1947-1950, sold as "Alpa Standard". Very rare. $250-400.

Alpa (I) - 1947-52. (#13000-25000). Non-reflex type similar to the "Bolca" but with a modified lens bayonet. Angenieux f2.9/50mm in collapsible mount. $300-500. (A few have no slow speeds (25-1000 only): $600.)

Alpa Reflex (II) - 1947-52. (#13000-25000). Features of Alpa (I) above, but SLR & CRF. Full speed range. Also sold as "Bolsey Reflex". With Angenieux f2.9/50mm collapsible: $150-250. With f1.8/50mm rigid lens: $175-350.

Alpa Prisma Reflex (III) - 1949-52. (#13000-25000). WL reflex hood and finder of the Alpa Reflex were replaced with 45 degree eye-level prism. (One of the earliest prism SLR's). Lenses as "Reflex" above, plus some late models have Xenon f2.0. $200-275.

Alpa 4 - 1952-60. (#30001-ca.39000). All new diecast magnesium alloy body. Integral magnifier hood for non-prismatic reflex viewing. Spektros f3.5/50mm collapsible lens. $250-350.

Alpa 5 - 1952-60. (#30001-ca.39000). As model 4, but integral 45 degree prism. Old Delft f2.8/50mm, rigid or collapsible mounts. $125-175.

Alpa 7 - 1952-59. (#30001-ca.39000). As model 5, but adds self-timer, superimposed image vertical base RF & multi-focal (35, 50, 135) built-in finder (first time done). Kern Switar f1.8. $150-175.

Alpa 6 - 1955-59. (#30001-ca.39000). As model 5, but adds split-wedge RF on ground glass, plus self-timer. $150-200.

Alpa 8 - 1958-59. (#37201-ca.39000). As model 7, plus prism RF of model 6. First auto lenses. Very short production run. $150-175.

Alpa 7s - 1958-59. (#37201-ca.39000). As model 7, but single frame (18x24mm) format. Rare. $350-400.

Alpa 4b - 1959-65. (#40701-48101). As model 4, but rapid return mirror and added advance lever. Normal auto lens mount redesigned and black finished. Old Delft f2.8/50mm, rigid mount only. $275-300.

Alpa 5b - 1959-65. (#39801-48101). As model 5, but rapid return mirror and added advance lever. Macro Kern Switar f1.8/50mm (focus to 8"). $125-175.

Alpa 6b - 1959-63. (#39601-48100). As model 6, but rapid return mirror and added advance lever. Macro Kern Switar f1.8/50mm (focus to 8"). $140-175.

Alpa 7b - 1959-65. (#40001-48101). As model 7, but rapid return mirror and added advance lever. Macro Kern Switar f1.8/50mm. $175-225.

Alpa 8b - 1959-65. (#40001-48101). As model 8, but rapid return mirror and added advance lever. Macro Kern Switar f1.8/50mm. $175-225.

Alpa 6c - 1960-69. (#42601-46500). Kern 45 degree prism replaced with standard pentaprism. Uncoupled selenium meter added. Macro Kern Switar f1.8/50mm. $145-175.

Alpa 9d - 1964-69. (#46501-52000). As model 6c, but top deck match-needle TTL CdS meter. Some gold or black finish with red or green covering. Macro Kern Switar f1.8/50mm. $250-350.

Alpa 9f - 1965-67. (#46201-46500). As model 9d, but without meter. Macro Kern Switar f1.8/50mm. Rare. $250-325.

Alpa 10d - 1968-72. (#58501-56400). New body with cross-coupled "zero center" match needle CdS meter. Normal lens reformulated. Kern Macro Switar f1.9/50mm. Gold or black with colored leather: $275-350. Chrome: $175-225.

Alpa 11e - 1970-72. (#57201-58300). As 10d, but lighted over-under exposure arrows, both off at correct exposure. Many all black, some gold or black with red or green covering. Kern Macro Switar f1.9/50mm. Black leather: $250-300. Colored leather: $300-375.

Alpa 10f - 1968-72. (#52501-56400). As 10d, but single frame 18x24mm format. Very low production. Rare. $300-350.

Alpa 10s - 1972. (#57101-?). As 10d, but no meter. Rare. $350-375.

Alpa 11el - 1972-74. (#58301-59500). As 11e, but both arrows lighted on correct exposure. Colored leather: $350-400. Black: $275-350.

Alpa 11si - 1976-80? (#60001-?). As 11el, but lighted arrows replaced by red, green, yellow diodes. Gold-plated: $2000. Majority of production black with black chrome top deck. $350-450.

Alpa 11fs - 1977-80? (#60001-?). As 11si, but single frame (18x24mm) format. Xenon f1.9/50mm. Rare. $375-475.

Alpa 11z - c1977-? (#61300-?). Special order single frame model. Similar to 11fs, but no meter, shutter 1/60 only, microprism screen only, no prism. Rangefinder. Very rare. $400-500.

PIONEER - Blue and black plastic camera of the "Diana" type. $1-5.

PIPON (Paris)

Magazine camera - c1900. Leather covered wood box for 9x12cm plates. Aplanoscope f9 lens. $75-100.

Self-Worker - c1895. Jumelle camera for 9x12cm plates. Goerz Double Anastigmat 120mm lens. 6-speed guillotine shutter. $175-250.

PLANOVISTA SEEING CAMERA LTD.
(London) *Imported a camera with their name on it, but it was actually made by Bentzin. See Bentzin.*

PLASMAT GmbH

Roland - 1934-37. Telescoping front camera for 4.5x6cm exposures on 120 rollfilm. Coupled rangefinder. Designed by Dr. Winkler in association with Dr. Paul Rudolph, who designed the various Plasmat lenses. It was highly regarded for its 6-element Plasmat f2.7/70mm lens and sold new for $93-143. Two basic models. First one had built-in optical exposure meter. Second model had no meter, but had automatic exposure counter. Either model was available with normal Compur 1-250 or Compur Rapid to 400. After a rapid surge of speculative buying and high prices a few years ago, the Roland has rapidly fallen to its earlier range of $475-800.

PLASTICS DEVELOPMENT CORP.
(Philadelphia, Penn.)
Snapshooter - c1970. Black plastic slip-on camera for 126 cartridges. $3-7.

PLAUBEL & CO. (Frankfurt, Germany)
Aerial Camera - c1955. Hand-held aerial camera for 6x9cm on 120 film in interchangeable magazine backs. Reports indicate that 60 were made for the Swedish Army. Grey hammertone body. Anticomar f3.5/100mm interchangeable lens. Focal plane shutter 20-1000. With universal 100-600mm viewfinder, 2 film magazines, case, and filters. Three were offered for sale a few months apart at German auctions during 1985, with reserve of 2500 DM (approx. $1000-1200 at the time). The first two sold for just over the minimum bid, while the third remained unsold at that price.

Baby Makina - 1912-35. 4.5x6cm size. Anticomar f2.8/75mm. Compur shutter. $400-650.

Folding-bed plate cameras - 6x9cm and 9x12cm sizes. Double extension bed and bellows. Anticomar or Heli-Orthar lens. Ibso or Compur shutter. $30-40.

Makina (I) - 1920-33. Compact strut-folding 6.5x9cm sheet film camera. No rangefinder. Anticomar f2.9 lens. Compur shutter. $100-150.

Makina II - 1933-39. Anticomar f2.9/ 100mm lens converts to 73mm wide angle or 21cm telephoto by changing front elements. Compur shutter to 200. Coupled rangefinder. $115-150.

Makina IIa - 1946-1948. Fixed, non-changeable Anticomar f4.2/100mm or Xenar f4.5/105mm lens. Shutter to 1/400. Self-timer. $140-170.

Makina IIS - 1936-49. Interchangeable Anticomar f2.9/50mm. All lens elements in front of the shutter, unlike the Makina II. Shutter 1-200. $150-190. *(Illustrated top of next column.)*

Makina III - 1949-53. 6x9cm strut-folding camera. Anticomar f2.9/100mm lens. Rim-

Makina IIS

Makina III

set Compur shutter 1-200. Coupled rangefinder. $150-200.

Makinette - c1931. Strut-folding camera for 3x4cm on 127 rollfilm. Anticomar f2.7 or most often with Supracomar f2/50mm. Compur 1-300. Rare. $750-1000.

Roll-Op (II) - c1935. Although the camera itself is simply labeled Roll-Op, original brochures called it Roll-Op II. Folding bed for 16 exposures 4.5x6cm on 120 film. Anticomar f2.8/75mm lens. Compur Rapid shutter 1-250. Coupled rangefinder. $110-175 in U.S.A. Somewhat higher in Germany.

Stereo Makina, 6x13cm - 1926-41. Strut-folding stereo camera. Anticomar f2.9/90mm lenses in stereo Compur shutter 1-100. Black bellows. Black metal body, partly leather covered. $575-900.

Veriwide 100

Stereo Makina, 45x107mm - 1912-27. Similar, but f6/60mm Orthar or f3.9 Anticomar lens. $500-850.

Veriwide 100 - c1960. Wide angle camera for 6x9cm on 120 film. 100 degree angle of view. Super-Angulon f8/47mm in Synchro Compur 1-500 shutter, B, MXV sync. $450-625. *(Illustrated bottom of previous column.)*

PLAUL (Carl Plaul, Dresden, Germany) Field camera, 9x12cm - c1900-10. Simple wooden tailboard style field camera. Square bellows or tapered red bellows. Carl Plaul Prima Aplanat lens in brass barrel for waterhouse stops. $100-140.

PLAVIC - c1920. Leather covered wood body. 6x9cm on rollfilm. Meniscus len, guillotine shutter. $20-30.

PLAYTIME PRODUCTS INC. (New York, NY) Cabbage Patch Kids 110 Camera - c1984. Made in China. Yellow plastic 110 pocket camera with black trim. Green "Cabbage Patch Kids" decal on front. Uses flip-flash. Retail $13.

Go Bots 110 Camera - c1984. Grey plastic 110 camera with black & red trim. Go Bots sticker on front. Same basic camera as Cabbage Patch Kids above. New price: $13.

PLUS (Paul Plus Ltd., Newcastle, England)

Plusflex 35 - c1958. 35mm SLR with Exa/Exakta bayonet mount. Made by Tokiwa Seiki Co. for Paul Plus Ltd. Similar to the pentaprism version of the Firstflex 35. Simple mirror shutter, B, 60, 125. Auto Pluscaron 45mm/f2.8 lens. $35-50.

POCK (Hans Pock, Munich, Germany) Detective camera - c1888. Mahogany detective camera, concealed in a leather satchel. Gravity-operated guillotine shutter, 1-100. Magazine holds 15 plates 6x9cm. Voigtlander Euryskop fixed-focus lens. $2500-3000.

POCKET MAGDA - c1920. Compact French all-metal folding camera in 4.5x6cm and 6.5x9cm sizes. Meniscus lens, simple shutter. 4.5x6cm size: $400-500. 6.5x9cm size: $150-200.

POCKET PLATOS - French 6.5x9cm folding plate camera. Splendor f6.2/90mm lens in Vario shutter. $75-125.

POLAROID (Cambridge,MA) *Polaroid cameras, using the patented process of Dr. Land, were the first commercially successful instant picture cameras which were easy to use, and were not in need of bottles of chemicals, etc. The idea of in-camera development is not new; there are records of ideas for instant cameras from the first year of photography. In 1857, Bolles & Smith of Cooperstown, New York patented the first instant camera which actually went into production.*

Polaroid 95

Jules Bourdin of France invented a simple system which was successfully marketed as early as 1864. Many other attempts met with mediocre success, but Polaroid caught on and became a household word. Because of the success of the company, their cameras generally are quite common, and obviously none are very old. There is more supply than demand for most models in the present market. We are listing them in order by number, rather than chronologically. We have not listed cameras introduced after 1965, so this list is by no means a complete history of Polaroid.

80 (Highlander) - 1954-1957. The first of the smaller size Polaroid cameras. Grey metal body. 100mm/f8.8 lens. Shutter 1/25-1/100 sec. Hot shoe. $5-10.

80A (Highlander) - 1957-1959. Like the 80, but with the shutter marked in the EV system. (Orig. price: $72.75) $5-10.

80B - 1959-1961. Further improvement of the 80A with new cutter bar and film release switch. $5-10.

95 - 1948-1953. The first of the Polaroid cameras, which took the market by storm. Heavy cast aluminum body, folding-bed style with brown leatherette covering. f11/135mm lens. Folding optical finder with sighting post on the shutter housing. Diehard collectors like to distinguish between the early models with the flexible spring sighting post and the later ones with a rigid post. $10-20. *(Illustrated bottom of previous column.)*

95A - 1954-57. Replaced the Model 95. Essentially the same but sighting post was replaced with a wire frame finder, X-sync added, and shutter speeds increased to 1/12-1/100. 130mm/f8 lens. $10-20. *(Illustrated top of next page.)*

Polaroid 95A

95B (Speedliner) - 1957-61. Like the 95A, but shutter is marked in the EV (Exposure Value) system, rather than the traditional speeds. (Orig. price: $94.50) $10-20.

100 (rollfilm) - 1954-1957. (Not to be confused with the 1963 "Automatic 100" for pack film.) Industrial version of the 95A. Better roller bearings and heavy duty shutter. Black covering. $10-20.

100 ("Automatic 100") - 1963-1966. An innovative, fully automatic transistorized electronic shutter made the world stand up and take notice once again that the Polaroid Corporation was a leader in photographic technology. In addition to the marvelous new shutter, Polaroid introduced a new type of film in a flat, drop-in pack which simplified loading. Furthermore, the photographs developed outside the camera so that exposures could be made in more rapid succession. Three-element f8.8/114mm lens. Continuously variable speeds from 10 seconds to 1/1200. RF/viewfinder unit hinged for compactness. $10-15.

101, 102, 103, 104, 125, 135 - c1964-1967. Various low-priced pack cameras following after the Automatic 100. $5-10.

110 (Pathfinder) - 1952-1957. Wollensak Raptar f4.5/127mm lens and coupled rangefinder. Shutter 1-1/400 sec. $50-65.

110A (Pathfinder) - c1957-60. Improved version of the 110. Rodenstock Ysarex f4.7/127mm lens in Prontor SVS 1-1/300 shutter. Special lens cap with f/90 aperture added in 1959 for the new 3000 speed film. Charcoal covering. (Originally $169.50) $40-70.
110B - 1960-64. Like the 110A, but with single-window range/viewfinder. $40-65.
These professional models can be converted to pack film. See p.659.

120 - 1961-65. Made in Japan by Yashica. Similar to the 110A, but with Yashica f4.7/127mm lens in Seikosha SLV shutter 1-500,B. Self-timer. CRF. Not as common in the U.S.A. as the other models, because it was made for foreign markets. $40-80.

150 - 1957-1960. Similar to the 95B with EV system, but also including CRF with focus knob below bed, parallax correction, and hot shoe. Charcoal grey covering. (Originally $110.) $7-15.

160 - 1962-65. Japanese-made version of the 150 for international markets. $7-15.

180 - 1965-69. Professional model pack camera made in Japan. Tominon f4.5/114mm lens in Seiko shutter 1-1/500 with self-timer. Zeiss-Ikon range/viewfinder. Has retained its value as a usable professional camera. $175-220.

415 - Variation of the Swinger Model 20. $3-7.

700 - 1955-1957. Uncoupled rangefinder version of the 95A. $15-20.

800 - 1957-1962. All the features of the 150, but with carefully selected lens, electronically tested shutter, and permanently lubricated roller bearings. (Original price: $135 with flash, bounce bracket and 10 year guarantee.) $7-12.

850 - 1961-63. Similar to the 900 below, but with dual-eyepiece rangefinder & viewfinder. $8-12.

900 - 1960-1963. The first Polaroid with fully automatic electric-eye controlled shutter. Continuously variable shutter speeds (1/12-1/600) and apertures (f/8.8-f/82). $8-12.

Big Shot - 1971-73. Unusually designed pack-film camera for close-up portraits at a fixed distance of one meter. Since the lens is fixed focus, the rangefinder functions only to position the operator and subject at the correct distance. Built-in socket and diffuser for X-cubes. $5-10.

J-33 - 1961-1963. Newly styled electric-eye camera to replace the "80" series. Still using the 30 series double-roll films for 6x8cm pictures. $5-10.

J-66 - 1961-1963. Newly styled electric-eye camera, with simple f/19 lens. Tiny swing-out flash for AG-1 bulbs. $5-10.

Swinger Model 20 - 1965-1970 - White plastic camera for B&W photos on Type 20 roll film, the first roll film to develop outside the camera. If this is not the most common camera in the world, it certainly must be near the top of the list. Current value $5 per truckload, delivered.

Swinger Sentinel M15 - 1965-1970. Variation of the Swinger Model 20. Lacks built-in flash. $3-7.

SX-70 (Deluxe Model) - 1972-77. The original SX-70 camera. Ingeniously designed folding SLR which ushered in a new era of instant photography. The miracle was watching the colored photo slowly appear in broad daylight after being automatically ejected from the camera. The technical and esthetic marvel was the compact machine which fit easily into a coat pocket. The basic folding design was not new. Perhaps one of Polaroid's engineers had seen the circa 1905 "Excentric" camera of R. Guenault, which is surprisingly similar. But Guenault would never have dreamed of an even more compact camera incorporating SLR focusing to 10½ inches, automatic exposure up to 14 seconds, and motorized print ejection, all powered by a disposable flat battery which came hidden in the film pack. This is a landmark camera, but quite common because it was so popular. $25-40.

POLYFOTO - c1933. Repeating-back camera, taking 48 ½x½" exposures on a 5x7" plate. Plate moves and exposure is made when a handle is cranked. $150-250.

PONTIAC (Paris) *Founded in 1938 by M. Laroche, whose first product was a polarising filter. The first cameras of the firm were the streamlined "Bakelite" models based on the Ebner camera from Germany. During the war, the aluminum-bodied Bloc-Metal cameras were produced in an attempt to improve the quality and durability of both the cameras and the company image. While other materials were in short supply during wartime, aluminum was produced in abundance in France. Its availability and strength led to its choice for the bodies of the Bloc-Metal and Lynx cameras.*

Bakelite - c1938-41. Folding camera for 8 exposures 6x9cm on 120 rollfilm. Bakelite body similar in style to its predessors, the Gallus and Ebner cameras. Berthiot f4.5/105mm lens. Shutter 25-150. $20-40. *(Illustrated bottom of previous column.)*

Bloc-Metal 41 - 1941-1948. Cast aluminum-alloy body with grained texture and painted finish, due to wartime shortage of leather. Original 1941 model has MFAP shutter to 100. Later versions have Pontiac or Prontor II shutter to 150. Pontiac or Berthiot f4.5 lens. $20-30.

Pontiac Bakelite

Bloc-Metal 45 - c1946. As the model number indicates, this was to have been a 1945 model, but it did not actually appear until late in 1946. It was more professional than the model 41 in features and appearance. Streamlined die-cast top housing incorporates an optical finder and a rotating depth of field scale. Usually with Flor Berthiot or Trylor Roussel f4.5/105mm in Prontor II with body release. Early examples still have cloth rather than leather bellows. $30-50.

Lynx, Lynx II - c1948. Polished aluminum body. 16 exposures 3x4cm on 127 film. Berthiot Flor f2.8/50mm coated lens in Leica-style collapsible mount. Focal plane shutter. $40-60.

Super Lynx, I, II - c1950's. Made in Paris and Morocco. 35mm body has an aluminum finish, black enamel, or is leather covered. f2.8 or f3.5 Flor lens; Super Lynx has interchangeable lenses. Rarely seen with the fast f2.0 Salem Hexar lens. FP shutter. Some dealers really stetch the point by calling this a Leica copy. $150-200.

POPPY - Rare Japanese subminiature. Price negotiable. Estimate: $500-750.

POPULAR PHOTOGRAPH CO. (NY)
Nodark Tintype Camera - c1899. All wood box camera for 2½x3½" ferrotype plates. The camera has a capacity of 36 plate. With tank: $500-700. Less $100 if missing tank.

POPULAR PRESSMAN - see Butcher.

POTENZA CAMERA - c1981. 110-cartridge camera shaped like a tire. Meniscus f11 lens, single speed shutter. New in box: $15-40.

POTTHOFF (Kamerafabrik Potthoff & Co., Solingen, Germany)
Plascaflex PS 35 - c1952. TLR for 6x6cm. Plascanar f3.5/75mm in Prontor-S shutter. $40-60.

POUVA (Karl Pouva, Freital, Germany)
Start - c1952-56. Helical telescoping

camera for 6x6cm exposures on 120 rollfilm. Bakelite body and helix. Fixed focus Duplar f8 lens. Z&M shutter. $6-12.

PRECISION CAMERA INC. (Minneapolis, MN)
Andante 100 - Large blue and gray plastic "school" camera. Twin lens reflex style. Uses bulk rolls of 35mm film. $50-70.

PREMIER INSTRUMENT CO. (NY)

Front and back views of Kardon Signal Corps model

Kardon - c1945. 35mm Leica IIIa copy. Made for the Signal Corps, and also for civilians. Ektar f2/47mm lens. Cloth focal plane shutter, 1 to 1000. Coupled rangefinder. Body: $175-225. With lens: $250-375.

PRINCE - c1960's. Rectangular green and black bakelite subminiature from Japan. Uses Mycro-size rollfilm. Fixed focus f10, B,I shutter. Scarce. $200-250.

PRINTEX PRODUCTS (Pasadena, CA)
Printex - c1946. Rigid-bodied, all-metal press camera. Telescoping lens mount

rather than the bellows found on the popular Speed Graphics of its day. Made in 2¼x3¼" and 4x5" sizes. Uncommon. $75-125.

PRO CAMERA - Factory loaded disposable camera. 28x31mm on 35mm film. $12-18.

PUTNAM (F. Putnam, N.Y.)
Marvel - c1885-1895. 5x8" horizontal folding view camera. Appears to be the same as the Scovill Waterbury View. Scovill Waterbury lens with rotating disc stops. Earlier Examples have removable washer-style waterhouse stops. $150-175.

PYNE (Manchester, England)
Stereoscopic Camera - c1860. Tailboard stereo, 8x17cm plates. Ross lenses. One sold at auction in 1979 for $4800. Sorry, but we know of no recent sales.

Q.P. - (pronounced "Kewpie"). c1950. Japanese "Hit" type novelty camera for 16mm paper-backed rolls. $15-25.

Q.R.S.-DeVRY CORP. (Chicago)

Q.R.S. Kamra - c1928. Brick-shaped brown bakelite body. 40 exposures, 24x32mm, on 35mm film in special cassettes. Graf Anastigmat f7.7/40mm. Single speed shutter trips by counter-clockwise motion on winding crank. With crank intact: $75-100. As normally found with broken crank: $40-50.

RAACO - Cardboard box camera for 4.5x6cm. Meniscus lens. Segment shutter. $75-110.

RADIX - c1897. Box camera for 3¼x4¼" glass plates in standard double holders. Hinged door on side of camera to change and store plateholders. $40-60. *(Illustrated top of next column.)*

Radix

RAJAR LTD. *A manufacturer of sensitised photographic materials, it merged with several other photographic companies in 1921 to form APM (Amalgamated Photographic Manufacturers, Ltd). It was one of the companies that split from APM in 1929 to form Apem Ltd.* See APM for more information, including the Rajar No. 6 camera.

RAKSO - c1970's. One of the up and coming collectibles. Special purpose camera for close-up work. Self-erecting, single extension, telescoping front. Built-in 10-90mm zoom. Ball-bearing shutter with body release. Automatic flash. $10-12.

RALEIGH - 4x4cm novelty of the "Diana" type. $1-5.

RANDORFLEX - Small novelty TLR for 4x4cm on 127 film. Same as Bedfordflex, Splendidflex, Stellarflex, Windsorflex, Wonderflex, etc. $1-5.

RANKOLOR LABORATORIES (U.S.A.)
Rank - c1975. Small plastic camera, factory loaded with 110-size film. This is the European name variation for the "Lure" camera. Made in U.S.A. for distribution by Rank Audio Visual of Brentford, England. Camera is returned intact for processing and a new camera is returned with processed prints. $1-5.

RAY CAMERA CO. (Rochester, N.Y.)
Originally established in 1894 as Mutschler, Robertson & Co., the company began making "Ray" cameras in 1895. In 1898 the company moved to a new building and changed its name to "Ray Camera Co." In 1899, it became part of the new "Rochester Optical & Camera Co."
Box camera - For 3½x3½" glass plates. Rear section of top hinges up to insert holders. $30-40.

Ray No. 1, No. 4, No. 6 - c1899. 4x5" wooden plate camera. Red bellows. Black leather covered. $50-70.

Ray No. 2 - c1899. 5x7" folding plate camera, similar construction to the No. 1. Dark mahogany interior, red bellows, double pneumatic shutter. $60-90.

Ray Jr. - c1897. For 2½x2½" plates. $40-60.

Telephoto Ray Model C - c1901. Folding bellows camera, 10x13cm. Wollensak Automatic shutter. $50-80.

RAYELLE - c1954. Side-loading metal box camera, 6x9cm on 120. Made in Italy. $5-10.

REAL CAMERA - Japanese novelty subminiature of the Hit type. $10-15.

RECORD CAMERA - c1890. English mahogany twin-lens reflex style box camera. 3¼x4" plates. Fixed focus lens. T,I shutter. $800-1200.

RECTAFLEX (Italy)

Rectaflex Junior - c1952. 35mm SLR. Angenieux f2.9/50mm. 25-500 shutter. $100-150.

Rectaflex Rotor - c1952. 35mm SLR with 3-lens turret. With normal lens: $400-600. Wide angle and tele lenses, each $50-75. Add $50-75 for grip or gunstock.

Rectaflex Standard - 1948-56. One of the first prism SLR's, along with VEB Pentacon Contax S of early 1949. Schneider Xenon f2.0 or f2.8/50mm or Angenieux f1.8/50mm lens. Focal plane shutter 1-1000 (up to 1300 after 1952), sync. These standard (non-rotor) Rectaflex cameras are also designated Rectaflex 1000 and 1300 after their top shutter speed. Model 1000: $175-225. Model 1300: $125-175.

RED FLAG 20 - c1971-76. Chinese copy of Leica M4. Reportedly only 182 made. First two digits of serial number indicate year of production. With Red Flag 20 f1.4/50mm (Summilux copy) lens. Although quite rare, we have seen these offered under $3000 in less than ideal condition. Complete with shade and case have reached $4800 at auction.

REDDING (H.J. Redding & Gyles, London, England)

Redding's Patent Luzo - c1896-99. (Formerly made by Robinson from 1889.) Mahogany detective box camera. Brass fittings. Several sizes, including 2¼x3¼" and 3x4" exposures on Eastman rollfilms. The first English rollfilm camera. f8 lens, sector shutter. $600-850.

Focal plane postcard camera

REFLEX 66 - c1955-65. Japanese copy of the Reflex Korelle. Anastigmat f3.5/75mm. FP shutter to 1000. $125-175.

REFLEX CAMERA CO. (Newark, NJ & Yonkers, NY) *(Originally located in Yonkers, from about 1900-09, when they moved to Newark and took over the Borsum Camera Co.)*
Focal plane postcard camera - c1912. Vertical styled folding plate postcard camera. Focal plane shutter. Cooke Anastigmat or Ilex RR lens in plain mount. $140-160. *(Illustrated previous column.)*

Patent Reflex Hand camera - c1902. Early model leather covered 4x5" SLR box camera. Internal bellows focus. Focal plane shutter. Red focusing hood. Fine finished wood interior. Without lens: $200-350.

Reflex camera, 4x5" - c1900's. Slightly later model than the above listing. Leather covered wood box with tall viewing hood. Internal bellows focus. Euryplan Anastigmat 7" lens. $125-165.

Reflex camera, 5x7" - c1900's. f16/210mm Anastigmat lens. $225-325.

Junior Reflex - c1930. Simple SLR box camera for 3¼x4¼" plates. Simple lens,

Junior Reflex

4-speed sector shutter coupled to mirror. $125-150.

REGAL FLASH MASTER - Black bakelite box camera wiht integral flash. Identical to Spartus Press Flash. $5-10.

REGAL MINIATURE - Plastic novelty camera for half-frame 828. $3-7.

REGENT - Japanese 14mm novelty camera. $10-15.

REICHENBACH, MOREY & WILL CO. (Rochester, N.Y.)
Alta Automatic - c1896. Folding camera for 4x5" plates. Self-erecting front, which is not common among cameras of this type. Leather covered mahogany body. Light tan leather bellows. Reversible back. R.M.&W. shutter, I&T. The shutter is easily removable from the front board with a simple twist of the locking plate whose milled edge surrounds the shutter. $60-90. *(Illustrated bottom of next column.)*

Alta D - c1896. 5x7" folding plate camera. $75-125.

REID & SIGRIST (Leicester, England)

Reid IA

Reid - c1953. Models I, IA, II, III. Leica copies. Collapsible Taylor Hobson f2/50mm lens. Focal plane shutter 1-1000, sync. Models with military markings have sold for about twice as much. $200-275.

RELIANCE - 4x4cm "Diana" type novelty camera. $1-5.

REMINGTON MINIATURE CAMERA - Black bakelite minicam for half-frames on 127 film. $3-7.

REPORTER MAX - c1960. Black plastic 6x6cm camera. Single-speed. $10-15.

le REVE - c1908. French folding camera for 3¼x4¼" plates or special rollfilm back. Beckers f6.3 or Roussel Anastigmat f6.8/135mm lens. Unicum shutter. Red bellows. $150-200.

REVERE
Automatic-1034 - c1969. Inexpensive plastic camera for 126 cartridges. Its only claim to fame is that the plastic body, leatherette covering, and metal trim came in several color combinations. $1-5.

Eyematic EE 127 - c1958. 127 film. Wollensak f2.8/58mm lens. $20-30. *(Illustrated on front cover.)*

Reichenbach Alta Automatic

Stereo 33 - c1953. Amaton, Wollensak, or Enna Chromar S f3.5/35mm. Shutter 2-200, MFX sync. Rangefinder. $95-140.

REWO (Delft, Netherlands)
Rewo Louise - Metal box camera with black hammertone finish. Meniscus lens, M&T shutter. $12-18.

REX
Baby Powell - Small rollfilm camera. Copy of Zeiss Baby Ikonta. Hexar f4.5/50mm lens in Konishiroku rimset shutter. $75-100.

REX KAYSON - Japanese 35mm RF camera. f3.5/45mm lens. Compur 1-300 shutter. Looks like a small Leica M. $30-45.

REX MAGAZINE CAMERA CO. (Chicago)

Rex Magazine Camera - c1899. 4x5" and 3¼x4¼" sizes. Simple lens & shutter. Holds 12 plates. Unusual plate changing mechanism. Plates are moved from rear storage slots to plane of focus by: 1) Select plate number by placing peg in hole. 2) Slide receptacle to rear until stopped by peg. 3) With receptacle in vertical position, invert camera. 4) Slide receptor to focal plane and re-invert camera to normal position. 5) After exposure, return exposed plate to storage by reversing these steps. $150-200.

Rex Magazine Camera - 2x2" format. Baby brother of the above model. $200-250.

REYGONAUD (Paris)
Stand camera - c1870. Jamin Darlot lens. Brass trim. For 8x11cm plates. $400-550.

REYNOLDS & BRANSON (Leeds, England)
Field camera - c1890. Full or half plate size. Mahogany body. Brass barrel RR lens. $75-125.

RHEINMETALL (VEB Rheinmetall, Soemmerda, East Germany)
Perfekta - c1955. Black bakelite eye-level box camera for 6x6cm on 120. Rigid rectangular front. Large folding frame finder. Achromat f7.7 lens. M,Z shutter. $8-12.

Perfekta II - Black bakelite camera with collapsible telescoping front. Optical eye-level finder built into top. Achromat f7.7/80mm. B,25,50,100 shutter. $8-12.

RICH-RAY TRADING CO.
Rich-Ray - c1951. Small bakelite camera for 24x24mm exposures on Bolta rollfilm. Nearly identical to Start-35. Marked "Made in Occupied Japan" on the bottom; "Rich-Ray" on top. Simple fixed focus f5.6 lens with lever-operated f8 waterhouse stop. B,I shutter. $15-25.

Richlet 35 - c1954. Rectangular bakelite camera with metal faceplate. Takes 24x36mm on Bolta-size rollfilm. Focusing f5.6 lens. B,25-100 shutter. Stores spare film roll inside. $20-35.

RICHARD (F.M. Richard)
Detective - c1895. Magazine box camera for 13x18cm plates. Rack and pinion focusing. $500-700.

RICHARD (Jules Richard, Paris, France)

Glyphoscope - c1905. 45x107mm stereo camera of simple construction. Black ebonite plastic or leather covered wood. Meniscus lens, guillotine shutter. $60-100.

Homeos - c1914. The first stereo for 35mm film. 25 exposures on standard 35mm cine film. Optis or Zeiss Krauss Anastigmat f4.5/28mm. Guillotine shutter. $1000-1400. (Add $500-750 for viewer and printer.)

Homeoscope - c1900. Stereo cameras in 6x13 and 9x18cm sizes. $180-240.

Verascope *The Verascope line of stereo cameras bridged from the 1890's to the 1930's, with numerous variations. They were made in 45x107mm, 6x13cm, and 7x13cm sizes, with many shutter and lens combinations. Although definitely collectible, their value is still largely related to their usability.*

Verascope, simple models - Fixed-focus lenses, single speed shutter. All metal body, made only in 45x107mm size. Basic camera: $65-85. Add $35-50 for magazine back. Add $100-150 for usable 127 or 120 film rollback, less for early 126 and 116 rollbacks.

Verascope, better models - With higher quality lenses and shutters. More common than the simple models. $75-100. Add $35-50 for magazine back. Add $100-150 for usable 120 or 127 film rollback, less for early 126 and 116 rollbacks.

Verascope F40 - c1950's. Stereo camera for 24x30mm pairs of singles. Berthiot f3.5/40mm lens. Guillotine shutter to 250. RF. Made by Richard in France but sold under the Busch name in the U.S.A. Generally considered to be one of the best stereo cameras, and not often found for sale. With printer and transposing viewer: $600. Camera and case: $300-400.

RICSOR - Rangefinder 35, similar to the Pax M2. Luna f2.8/45mm. $30-50.

RIDDELL (A. Riddell, Glasgow)
Folding plate camera - c1880's. 9x12cm. Built-in roller-blind shutter. $150-200.

RIETZSCHEL (A. Heinrich Rietzschel GmbH Optische Fabrik, Munich, Germany) *Merged with Agfa in 1925, at which time the Rietzschel name was no longer used on cameras and the first Agfa cameras were produced.*

Clack - c1910. Folding bed camera for plates. 9x12cm or 10x15cm sizes. Red bellows, black leathered wood body, aluminum standard, nickel trim. f6.3 or f8 lens. $75-125.

Heli-Clack, horizontal type - c1910. 9x12cm or 10x15cm horizontal format folding plate cameras. Double extension bellows. Double Anastigmat f6.8 lens in Compound shutter. $50-80.

Kosmo-Clack Stereo - c1914. 45x107mm format. Double Anastigmat f6.3, Rietzschel f4.5/60mm lenses in Compur 1-250 shutter. Panoramic photos also possible. $125-175. A usable rollback would add $100-150 to this price.

Miniatur-Clack 109 - c1924. Small folding bed camera for 4.5x6cm plates. The first camera produced by Rietzschel in this size. Double extension bellows. Linear Anastigmat f4.5/165mm in Compound or Compur shutter. $150-240.

Reform-Clack - c1910-1920's. 6.5x9cm folding plate camera. Dialyt f6.8/105mm in Compound or Dial-set Compur 1-250. Double extension bellows. $30-40.

Universal Heli-Clack - Folding bed camera. Similar to the regular Heli-Clack, but with wide lensboard.
- Type I - Panoramic with single lens. 13x18cm size, with Linear Anastigmat f4.8/210mm lens: $100-125. 8x14cm size: $50-80. *(Illustrated top of next column.)*
- Type II - Stereo with two lenses in stereo shutter. 13x18cm size with Doppel Apotar f6.3/120mm stereo lenses: $350-450. 8x14cm size: $200-300. *(Illustrated top of next column.)*

Universal Heli-Clack, Type I

Universal Heli-Clack, Type II

- Type III - 3 lenses in Stereo-Panorama shutter. No sales data.

RIKEN OPTICAL (Japan)
Golden Ricoh 16 - c1957. Subminiature for 25 exposures 10x14mm on 16mm film. Interchangeable Ricoh f3.5/25mm fixed

Riken Golden Steky

focus lens. Sync. shutter 50-200,B. Often found with case and presentation box for $100-125. Camera and normal lens only: $80-100.

Golden Steky - c1957. Subminiature for 10x14mm on 16mm film. Same as Golden Ricoh 16 except for name. Shutter 50-200, B. Stekinar fixed focus f3.5/25mm lens: $120-150. Add $50 for f5.6/40mm telephoto. *(Illustrated bottom of previous page.)*

Hanken - c1952. Subminiature camera nearly identical to the Steky III, but with additional waist-level viewer. Rare. $150-300.

Ricoh 16 - c1958. Subminiature for 10x14mm exposures on 16mm film. Interchangeable Ricoh f2.8/25mm focusing lens. Shutter 50-200,B. Rapid wind. Like the Golden Ricoh 16, but in chrome. Much less common. $100-125.

Ricoh 35 - c1955. 35mm RF. Ricomat f3.5/45mm lens in Riken shutter 10-200,B, or f2.8/45mm in Seikosha-Rapid 1-500,B. $15-25.

Ricoh Six - c1952. 6x6cm or 4.5x6cm on 120 rollfilm. Orinar f3.5/80mm. Riken shutter 25-100,B. $35-50.

Ricoh Super 44 - c1958. 127 TLR. Riken f3.5/60mm. Citizen-MV 1-400,B. $45-70.

Ricoh Teleca 240 - c1971. Half-frame 35mm camera built into 7x50 binoculars. Rikenon f3.5/165mm lens. Copal 60-250 shutter. Motorized film transport. Same camera/binoculars sold under the Nicnon name. $225-275.

Ricoh TLS-401 - c1970. 35mm SLR. Pentaprism converts from normal eye-level to reflex viewing by turning small knob on side of prism housing. $70-90.

Ricoflex - Models III (1950), IV (1952), VI (1953), VII (1954), VIIS (1955). (Note: There are no models I, II, or V.) 6x6cm TLR.

Ricoh Anastigmat f3.5/80mm lens. $15-25.

Ricohmatic 44 - c1956. Gray TLR, 4x4mm on 127. Built-in meter. Riken f3.5/60mm. Shutter 32-170,B. $40-60.

Ricolet - 1954. First Riken 35mm camera. No rangefinder. "RICOLET" on front of cast-metal finder housing. Ricoh f3.5/45mm. Riken 25-50-100, B shutter. $20-30.

Roico - c1940-43. Eye-level camera for 4x4cm on 127 film. Telescoping front. Automatic film stop. Roico Anastigmat f3.5/60mm. Early model c1940 has T,B, 5-200 shutter. Later, c1943, with R.K.K. T,B,1-200 shutter. $75-100.

Steky - c1947. Subminiature for 10x14mm on 16mm film. Stekinar Anastigmat f3.5/25mm fixed focus lens. Shutter 25, 50, 100. $35-50. Slightly higher in Europe.
Steky II, III, IIIa, IIIb - c1950-55. Only minor variations in the models. $30-45. Slightly higher in Europe. *(Add $25 for tele lens.)*

Super Ricohflex - c1955. TLR for 3 different film sizes: 6x6cm on 120, 4x4cm on 127, 24x36mm on 35mm. Ricoh Anastigmat f3.5/80mm. Riken shutter 10-300, B. $15-30.

RILEY RESEARCH (Santa Monica, CA)
Rilex Press - c1948. 2¼x3¼" press camera. Tessar f4.5 lens. Chrome and stainless. $100-150.

RILO - 6x9cm metal box camera, leatherette covering. $10-15.

RIVAL 35 - c1950. German folding 35mm sold by Peerless Camera Stores in U.S.A. Radionar or Ennagon f3.5/50mm. Prontor S shutter. $20-30. *(Illus. bottom of next column.)*

RIVAL 120 - c1957. 6x9cm, black and chrome folding camera. $8-12.

RO-TO (Turin, Italy)
Elvo - c1938. Brown bakelite strut-folding camera for 3x4cm on 127 film. Achromatic f8 lens. $40-55.

Nea Fotos - c1948. Bakelite camera for 4x6.5cm on 127 film. Styled like a 35mm camera. Eye-level finder. Focusing f7.7/54mm lens. Shutter: 25-100,B. $15-25.

ROBBIN PRODUCTS (Hollywood, CA)

Robbin Reflex - Simple twin-lens reflex-style box camera similar to Herco-Flex 620. Made by Herbert George Co. for Robbin. A common looking camera, but uncommon with this name. Originally with a cheap imitation leather ever-ready case. $1-5.

ROBINSON (J. Robinson & Sons)

Luzo - c1889. Mahogany detective box camera. 6x6cm on rollfilm. A model also

Rocamco

exists for glass plates. Aplanat f8/75mm.
Rotary sector shutter. $650-1000.

ROCAMCO PRODUCTS (Boonton, NJ)
*Also known as Rochester Camera Co., New York
City. Named for its president, Richmond Rochester.*
Rocamco - c1936. Small metal box for
2.5x3cm on special 35mm film. $100-200.
(Illustrated bottom of previous page.)

**Rocamco No. 3 Daylight Loading
Rollfilm Camera** - c1938. For 30x32mm
on special rollfilm. Small bakelite camera.
"A Rochester Product" molded on back.
"No. 3 Daylight Loading Rollfilm Camera"
designation is used on the original box.
$25-40.

ROCHECHOVARD (Paris)
Le Multicolore - c1912. Magazine box
camera for 9x12cm plates. Color filters
could be moved into place, one-at-a-time
behind the lens for color separation plates.
Rapid Rectilinear lens. Guillotine shutter.
$800-1200.

ROCHESTER CAMERA MFG. CO.
ROCHESTER CAMERA & SUPPLY CO.
ROCHESTER OPTICAL COMPANY
ROCHESTER OPTICAL & CAMERA CO.
*The Rochester OPTICAL Company was
established in 1883 when W.F. Carlton took
over the business of Wm. H. Walker & Co. The
Rochester CAMERA Mfg. Co. was founded in
1891 by H.B. Carlton, brother of W.F. Thus
there existed in Rochester, N.Y. two comtemporary
companies, with similar names, and owned by
brothers. Their major camera lines even had
similar names. The Rochester CAMERA Mfg. Co.
made POCO cameras, while the original Rochester
OPTICAL Company began the PREMO camera
line in 1893. To further complicate the name
game, the Rochester Camera Mfg. Co. changed
its name in 1895 to "Rochester Camera Co.",
and in 1897 to "Rochester Camera & Supply
Co.". In 1899, the two "Rochester" companies
merged with the Monroe Camera Co, the Ray
Camera Co. (formerly Mutschler & Robertson
Co.), and the Western Camera Mfg. Co. of
Chicago (mfr. of Cyclone cameras), to form the
new "Rochester Optical and Camera Company".
The new company retained the original products:
Cyclone, Poco, Premo, and Ray. In 1903, George
Eastman purchased the company and shortened*
the name again to "Rochester Optical Co.". In
1907 it became "Rochester Optical Division,
E.K.C." and finally "Rochester Optical
Department" in 1917. While the many name
changes can seem confusing at first, they do help
to date particular examples of cameras:

*Rochester Camera Mfg. Co.: 1891-1895
Rochester Camera Co.: 1895-1897
Rochester Camera & Supply Co.: 1897-1899
Rochester Optical Co.: 1883-1899,
(& 1903-1907, owned by Eastman)
Rochester Optical & Camera Co.: 1899-1903
Rochester Optical Div., EKC: 1907-1917*

ROCHESTER CAMERA MFG. CO.
Favorite - 8x10". c1890. Emile No. 5 lens
with waterhouse stops. $125-175.

Folding Rochester - c1892. The first
folding plate camera that they made. 4x5"
and 5x7" sizes. Made only briefly. Seldom
seen. $295-395.

Poco Cameras - Introduced in 1893.
Listed here by size:

- **3¼x4¼", Pocket Poco** - Red bellows,
single pneumatic shutter. $35-50.

- **4x5", Folding-bed plate cameras** -
Models 1-7, A,B,C, including Cycle Poco.
Leather covered wood body and bed.
Nicely finished wood interior. Often with
B&L RR lens, Unicum shutter. $40-60.

- **5x7", Folding-bed plate cameras** -
Models 1-5, including Cycle Pocos. Black

leather covered wood body. Polished interior. Red bellows. RR lens. Unicum shutter. $55-85.
- 8x10" Poco - Similar, but larger. Double extension bellows. B&L Symmetrical lens. $65-100.

Gem Poco - c1897. 4x5" box for plates. Focuses by sliding lever at left front. Shutter tensioned by brass knob on face. $35-50.

Gem Poco, folding - c1895. Very compact folding camera for 4x5" plates in standard holders. Red bellows. Polished wood interior. Shutter built into polished wood lensboard. $75-100.

King Poco - c1899. 5x7" folding view, advertised as "Compact, elegant in design, and equipped with every known appliance. Especially adapted for those desiring the most perfect camera made." This was the top of the line. Not seen often. $125-180.

Telephoto Poco, Telephoto Cycle Poco:
- 4x5" - c1891. Folding plate camera. Triple extension red leather bellows. B&L lens in Auto shutter. Storage in back of camera for extra plateholders. $75-100.
- 5x7", 6½x8½" - c1902. Folding plate cameras. Red leather bellows, double or triple extension. B&L RR lens, Auto shutter. $75-100.

Rochester Carlton

Tuxedo - c1892. Leather covered 4x5" folding plate camera. Black wood interior, black wood front standard. This is an all-black version of the Folding Rochester camera. Brass trim. $225-295.

ROCHESTER OPTICAL CO.
Carlton - c1893-1903. All-wood, double extension view, similar to the Universal. Double swing back. Brass trim. With lens: $150-250. *(Illustrated bottom of previous page.)*

Cyclone *(pre-1899, made by Western)*

Magazine Cyclone - No. 2, 4, or 5. c1898. For 3¼x4¼" or 4x5" plates. Black leathered wood box. Meniscus lens, sector shutter. $35-50.

Cyclone Junior - c1902. Plate box camera for 3½x3½" glass plates in standard holders. Top door hinges forward to load plateholders. A cheaper alternative to more expensive magazine cameras. $25-35.

Cyclone Senior - c1902. 4x5" plate box camera for standard plateholders. $25-35.

Cyko Reko - c1900. An export model of the Pony Premo D. Made for Army & Navy Auxiliary Supply, London. Folding bed camera for 4x5" plates. Meniscus Achromatic in Unicum shutter. $60-90.

Empire State View - c1895. Folding field camera. Polished wood. Brass fittings. 5x7" & 6½x8½": $60-100. 8x10": $75-125. 11x14": $60-90.

Folding Pocket Cyko No. 1 - For 3¼x4¼" plates. Aluminum body. Sector shutter. $200-250.

Handy - c1892. 4x5" detective box-plate camera. Internal bellows focus. A simple, less expensive version of the Premier. $100-160.

View - c1895. Made in all the common sizes from 4x5" to 8x10". $125-200.

Peerless view - c1897. Dark mahogany. $100-150.

Premier Cameras:

Detective box camera - c1891. Internal bellows focus with external control knob. Side panel opens to insert plate holders. 4x5 and 5x7" sizes. $90-140.

Ideal - c1885-1895. Folding view cameras, 4x5" to 8x10" sizes. Cherry wood, brass trim. Ranging in price, depending on size, from $100-150.

Premier folding camera - c1892. 4x5 or 5x7" size, for plates. Originally with shutter built into wooden lensboard: $300-400. Later with B&L pneumatic shutter: $175-225.

Monitor - c1886. View camera in full plate and 8x10" sizes. Wood body folds in the "English" compact style. $100-150.

Premo Cameras *See also Eastman for their continuation of the Premo line. Prices here are for cameras with normal shutter/lens combinations. (Often B&L lenses, Victor shutter.)*

New Model View, New Model Improved

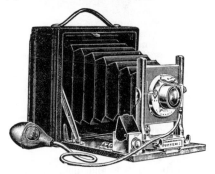

No. 2 Pony Premo

- 4x5" - c1900. Folding plate cameras, including: Pony Premo *(illus. bottom of previous page.)*, Premo Senior, Star Premo, Premo A-E, 4, and 7. Red bellows. $35-60.

- 5x7" - c1900. Folding plate cameras, including: Pony Premo, Pony Premo Sr., Premo No. 6, Premo B, and Premo Senior. Red bellows. $50-80.

Pocket Premo

Premo Folding Film Camera No. 1 - 1904-05. Folding bed camera for filmpacks. Made in 3¼x4¼", 3¼x5½", and 4x5" sizes. Double RR lens in Gem Automatic shutter. $60-80.

Long Focus Premo - 1895-1904. Triple extension red bellows. Sizes 4x5", 5x7", 6½x8½". $85-135.

Folding Premo Camera - 1893-94. This is the original folding plate model. Rapid Rectilinear lens, Star shutter. Sizes 4x5", 5x7", and 6½x8½". $100-125.

Pocket Premo - 1903-05. 3¼x4¼" folding bed camera for plates or filmpacks. Various lenses in B&L Automatic or Volute shutter. $20-30. *(Illustrated top of next column.)*

Pony Premo No. 5 - 1898-1903. Various lens/shutter combinations. For plates. 4x5", $40-60. 5x7", $60-90. 6½x8½", much less common, $75-125.

Premo Reflecting Camera - 1905-06. 4x5" single lens reflex with front bed and bellows (unlike the later Premograph). Various B&L or Goerz lenses. FP shutter. Reversible back. Tall focusing hood supported by trellis strut. This is a rare model and should not be confused with the less rare Premograph. Price negotiable. Estimate: $600-900.

Rochester Universal

Premo Sr. Stereo - 1895-1900. 5x7" or full plate. Rapid Rectilinear lens. B&L Stereo pneumatic shutter. Maroon bellows. Folding plate camera, a modification on the Premo Sr. $200-350.

Reversible Back Premo - 1897-1900. 5x7". Looks like a Long Focus Premo, but back shifts from horizontal to vertical. $85-135.

Reko - c1899. Folding camera for 4x5" plates. Leather covered mahogany body with brass trim. Red leather bellows. Special Reko Rectilinear lens in Unicum shutter. Uncommon. $50-70.

Snappa - c1902. Unusual ¼-plate folding-bed view with integral magazine back. Holds 12 plates or 24 cut films. Red bellows,

nickel & brass fittings. RR lens. Quite rare. We have only one sale on record, in early 1982, at $585.

Rochester Stereo Camera - c1891. Wooden stereo field camera with folding tailboard. 5x7" or 6½x8½" size. B&L shutter. Red bellows. $250-350.

Universal - intro. 1888. Polished wood view, 5x7" or 6½x8½". Brass trim, brass barrel lens with Waterhouse stops. $125-165. *(Illustrated top of previous column.)*

ROCKET CAMERA CO. LTD. (Japan)

General, Palmer, Rocket Camera - c1955. Simple metal box cameras, 4x5cm on 120 film. Fixed focus, B,I shutter. $3-6.

New Rocket - Early postwar Japanese novelty subminiature, 14x14mm. Some cameras are marked "Rocket Camera Co." below lens, others have "Tokyo Seiki Co. Ltd." Chrome: $140-160. Gold: $175-200.

RODEHUESER (Dr. Rodehueser, Bergkamen, Westf., Germany)
Panta - c1950. Cast metal body with telescoping front. Two sizes: 5x5.5cm on 120, or 4x6.5cm on 127 rollfilm. Ennar f4.5, or Steiner or Radionar f3.5/75mm lens. Prontor, Prontor S, or Vario shutter. $30-40.

RODENSTOCK (Optische Werke G. Rodenstock, Munich)

Citonette - c1933. Self-erecting folding bed camera for 16 exposures, 4.5x6cm. Trinar f2.9 or f3.9, Ysar f3.5 or f4.5/75mm. Pronto S or Compur S shutter. $25-35.

Clarovid, Clarovid II - c1932. Folding-bed dual-format rollfilm cameras for 6x9cm or 4.5x6cm exposures. Trinar Anastigmat f4.5 or f3.8/105mm lens. Rim-set Compur 1-250. Coupled rangefinder. $95-150.

Folding plate/sheetfilm camera - 9x12cm. f2.9, f3.8, or f4.5 Trinar. $25-35.

Folding rollfilm camera - Models for 120 rollfilm, 4.5x6 and 6x6cm, or 116 rollfilm. Rodenstock Trinar f2.9 or Eurynar f4.5 lens. Rim-set Compur 1-250. $20-30. *(Illustrated bottom of next column.)*

Perforette Super - c1950. 35mm viewfinder camera. Rodenstock Trinar Anastigmat f3.5/75mm. Prontor 1-175, B,T. $20-30.

Prontoklapp - c1932. Self-erecting folding bed camera for 6x9cm on 120 film. Trinar Anastigmat f4.5 or f5.8/105mm. Vario, Pronto, or Compur shutter. $20-30.

Robra - c1937. Folding camera, 4.5x6cm on 120. Robra Anastigmat f3.5/75mm. Compur shutter. $25-35.

Rodinett - c1932. Small rollfilm 3x4cm camera. Clamshell front doors. Body identical to the equally scarce Glunz & Bulter Ingo. $60-90.

Rofina II - c1932. Strut-folding vest pocket camera for 4x6.5cm on 127 film. Trinar f2.9/75mm in Compur-S. $30-50.

Wedar, Wedar II - c1929. Folding bed plate camera. Model II has rack and pinion focus. Made in 6.5x9cm and 9x12cm sizes. Various lenses and shutters. $25-35.

Ysella - c1932. Strut folding camera with bed. Half-frame 127. Trinar f2.8 or 4.5/50mm in Compur shutter. $60-90.

ROGERS JUNIOR - Folding 6x9cm rollfilm camera. $15-20.

Rodenstock Folding rollfilm camera

ROKUWA CO. (Japan)
Stereo Rocca - c1955. Plastic stereo camera for 23x24mm stereo pairs side-by-side on 120 rollfilm. Film travels vertically through camera. Fixed focus f8 lens, shutter 30,B. $100-135.

ROLLS CAMERA MFG. CO. (Chicago)

Beauta Miniature Candid - Bakelite minicam for half-127 film. Originally sold as a punchboard premium. $3-7.

Rolls - c1939. Bakelite novelty camera for half-frame 127. $3-7.

Rolls Twin 620 - c1939. Cast aluminum box camera for 620 film. $8-12.

Super Rolls 35mm, f3.5 - Inexpensive 35mm cast metal camera with body release. Retractable front with helical focusing. Shutter 25-200. Achromatic Rollax f3.5 lens. $10-15.
Super Rolls 35mm, f4.5 - Similar, but without body release. Anastigmat f4.5 lens. $10-15.

Super Rolls Seven Seven - Heavy cast metal camera for 4x5.5cm on 620 film. T,B,I leaf shutter with body release. Named for its f7.7 Achromatic Rollax lens. Focuses 3' to infinity by manually extending the front to proper footage mark. $10-15.
(Illustrated top of next column.)

RONDO COLORMATIC - c1962. 35mm camera with meter cell surrounding lens. $10-15.
RONDO RONDOMATIC - c1962. Identical to the Colormatic. $10-15.

Super Rolls Seven Seven

ROROX - 3x4cm on 127 film. Bottom loading. $30-45.

ROSKO - Novelty camera of the "Diana" type. Imitation meter grid on top housing. $1-5.

ROSS (Thomas Ross & Co.)

Folding Twin Lens Camera - c1895. Boxy twin lens reflex style camera. Front double doors open straight out. Goerz Double Anastigmat f7.7/5" lens. $500-700.

Kinnear's Patent Wet-Plate Landscape Camera - c1860's. Wet plate field camera. Mahogany construction, tapered bellows. Named for the patented bellows design of C.G.H. Kinnear, a Scottish photographer. His tapered bellows folded more compactly than the typical square type of the day. 6x7" or 10x12" size. Brass barrel landscape lens. $500-550.

Portable Divided Camera - c1891. Called "Portable Twin Lens Camera" beginning in 1895. Boxy twin-lens reflex. Front door is hinged at left side and

379

swings 270 degrees to lay flat against the side of the body. Wooden body is covered with hand-sewn black hide. Ross Rapid Symmetrical lens. $500-700.

Stereo camera - c1900. ½-plate. Polished mahogany, tapered leather bellows. Ross lenses. Thornton-Pickard shutter. $500-700.

Sutton Panoramic Camera - c1861. This camera, made for Thomas Sutton by Ross, takes curved glass plates in special curved holders. And wet-plates at that! Only about 30 were made. The lens is water-filled and gives an angle of 120 degrees. Three of these cameras sold at auction in 1974 for approximately $24,000 to $27,000. In June 1983 two were offered for sale at $14,000 and $17,000. Confirmed sales indicate a current value in the $12,000-14,000 range.

Wet-plate camera (sliding box style) - Recent sales: $800-1200 range.

Wet-plate camera (tailboard style) - c1865. Mahogany camera with folding tailboard and bellows. 12x12" plates. Brass fittings. Euryscop lens with waterhouse stops. $750-950.

Wet-plate Stereo (sliding-box style) - Grubb lenses. $4000-5000.

Ross Ensign Fulvueflex Synchroflash

Wet-plate Stereo (tailboard style) - c1865. Full plate size. Maroon square bellows. Ross Petzval 6" lenses, waterhouse stops. $2500-3500.

ROSS ENSIGN LTD.
Fulvueflex Synchroflash - c1950. Inexpensive plastic reflex-style box camera, 6x6cm on 120 film. Fixed focus Astaross lens, B&I shutter. Twin sockets for flash. $15-25. *(Illustrated bottom of previous column.)*

Snapper - Self-erecting camera for 6x9cm on 620 film. Cast aluminum body with integral eye-level finder. Grey crinkle-finish enamel. $15-25.

ROTH (L. Roth, Vienna)
Reflex, 4.5x6cm - c1926. SLR. Hugo Meyer Trioplan f6.3/75mm lens in FP shutter 10-1000. $300-350.

Reflex, 8x10.5cm - c1910. SLR. Hugo Meyer Trioplan f2.8/95mm lens in FP shutter 10-1000. $200-300.

ROUCH (W.W. Rouch & Co., London)
Eureka - c1888. Polished mahogany detective camera. Magazine for 12 8x8cm exposures or ¼-plate size. Brass barrel Rouch 150mm lens, rollerblind shutter. $250-400.

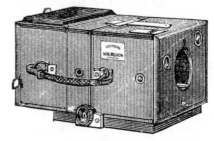

Excelsior - c1890. Mahogany detective camera, similar to the Eureka, but takes ordinary double slides as well as the Eureka magazine back. ¼-plate size. $350-500.

Patent camera - c1892. ½-plate mahogany field camera with brass fittings. Ross Rapid Symmetrical lens with Waterhouse stops. $125-200.

ROUSSEL (H. Roussel, Paris)

Stella Jumelle - c1900. 9x12cm plates. Roussel Anti-Spectroscopique f7.7/130mm in 7-speed guillotine shutter. Leather covered wood body. $175-225.

ROVER - Hong Kong "Diana" type novelty camera. $1-5.

ROYAL CAMERA CO. (Japan)
Royal 35M - c1957. 35mm camera with coupled rangefinder and built-in selenium meter. Tominor f2.8/45mm lens in Copal MXV shutter. $20-30.

ROYCE MFG. CO.
Royce Reflex - c1946. Twin lens reflex, cast aluminum body and back. Externally gear-coupled lenses. f4.5/75mm in Alphax shutter 25-150, T,B. $25-35.

ROYER (Fontenay-sous-Bois, France)
Altessa - c1952. Telescoping front camera for 6x9cm or 6x6cm on 120 film. f3.5/105 interchangeable Angenieux. $50-100.

Royer A - c1949. Self-erecting folding bed camera for 6x9cm on 120 film. Built-in optical finder. Angenieux Type VI f4.5/105mm in Sito 10-200. $15-20.

Savoyflex - c1959. 35mm SLR. Som Berthiot f2.8/50mm. Prontor Reflex interlens shutter, 1-500. $50-75.

ROYET (Paul Royet, St. Etienne, France)
Reyna Cross III - Black painted cast aluminum bodied 35mm. f3.5 Berthiot or f2.9/45mm Cross. Two blade shutter 25-200, B. This camera was essentially a continuation of the Cornu Reyna line, but

manufactured away from Paris which was under German occupation. See Cornu for similar models. $20-30.

RUBERG & RENNER

Baby Ruby - Small bakelite 3x4cm camera. Front extends to focus position via ring and helix. Fixed focus lens with 2 stops, "BIG" and "Small". T & I shutter. $40-50.

Fibituro - c1934. Metal body in red marbelized enamel. 4.5x6cm or 3x4cm on rollfilm. Rodenstock Periscop f11. M&Z shutter. $25-35.

Ruberg Futuro

Ruberg - c1953. Metal body, 4x6cm on rollfilm. Front section screws out like the Photax. $25-35.

Ruberg Futuro - Metal body, 4.5x6cm on 127 rollfilm. Helical lens mount. $25-35. *(Illustrated bottom of previous page.)*

RUTHINE - 35mm CRF. Friedrich Corygon f2.8/45mm lens. Shutter 25-100, B. $15-25.

SAINT-ETIENNE (France)
Universelle - c1908. Vertical folding plate/ rollfilm camera, along the lines of the Screen Focus Kodak, but with a removable back. Beckers Anastigmat f6.8/150mm in B&L Unicum shutter. $150-200.

SAKURA SEIKI CO. (Japan)

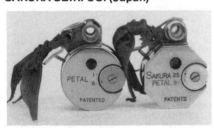

Petal, round and octagonal versions
Petal - c1948. Subminiature camera about the size of a half-dollar. (Approximately 30mm dia.) Takes 6 exposures on circular film. Original price about $10. Two models:
- **Octagonal model** - This is the later version, but not as common. Made by Sakura and identified on the front as "Sakura Petal". $200-250.
- **Round model** - More common early model, made by Petal Kogaku Co. Pre-dates the Sakura octagonal model. $100-135.

SALYUT-S - Russian Hasselblad 500C copy. Interchangeable Industar-24 f2.8/ 80mm. FP shutter 2-1500, T. $200-250.

SAN GIORGIO (Genova, Italy)
Janua - c1949. 35mm rangefinder Leica copy. Essegi f3.5/50mm. FP shutter 50-1000. Built-in meter. $500-750.

Parva - c1947. Subminiature for 16mm rollfilm. Less than 10 made. No known sales. rare. Estimate: $500+.

SANDERS & CROWHURST (Brighton, England)
Birdland - c1904. ¼-plate SLR. Extensible front. Waist-level focusing hood also allows for eye level focusing. Aldis Anastigmat f8 or Dagor f6.8. FP shutter to 1000. $200-350.

SANDERSON CAMERA WORKS (England) *Mr. Frederick H. Sanderson (1856-1929) was a cabinet maker, and a wood and stone carver. In the 1880's, he became interested in photography, particularly in architectural work, which required special camera movements not readily available on the cameras of the day. He designed his own camera, and in January of 1895 he had a patented new design. All Sanderson cameras incorporate his patented lens panel support system. The production models of the camera were built and marketed by Houghton's, with ads appearing as early as 1896.*

Sanderson Field camera - c1898. Mahogany folding cameras in ½-plate, full plate, and 10x12" sizes. Brass fittings. Double extension, tilt/swing back. Sanderson's Patent Universal lens f8. Thornton-Pickard foller-blind shutter. $150-250.

Sanderson Regular

Sanderson "Regular", "Deluxe", and "Junior" - Folding plate hand and stand cameras with finely polished wood interior. Heavy leather exterior. Fairly common. ½- plate (4¼x6½") size: $150-225. 3x4" to 4x5" sizes: $100-150 in England. Sometimes higher elsewhere.

Sanderson Tropical Hand and Stand cameras - ½-plate to 4x5" sizes. Polished teak with brass fittings. Goerz Dagor f6.8, Aldis f6.3, or Beck f7.7 lens. Compur shutter. $300-550.

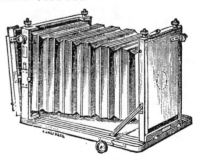

Sands Tailboard field camera

SANDS, HUNTER & CO., LTD. (London, England)
Field cameras - c1890. Tailboard or folding bed styles. Full plate to 10x12" sizes. Rectilinear lens. $175-250. *(Illustrated bottom of previous page.)*

SANEI SANGYO (Japan)
Samoca LE - c1957. 35mm rangefinder camera of conventional design. Built-in selenium meter. Ezumar f2.8/50mm. Shutter 1-300,B. $20-40.

Samoca 35 III

Samoca 35, 35II, 35III -c1950's. Simpler viewfinder models. Ezumar f3.5/50mm. Shutter 25-100 or 1-200. $16-25.

Samoca 35 Super - c1956. "Super Rangefinder" on front. 35mm camera for 36 exposures, 24x36mm on standard cartridges. Ezumar f3.5/50mm lens. Shutter 10-200. Coupled rangefinder. Versions with *(illustrated)* and without built-in selenium meter. $25-35.

Samocaflex 35 - c1955. 35mm TLR. Ezumar f2.8/50mm lenses. Seikosha 1-500,B. Not common. $75-125.

SANEIKOKI (Japan)
Starrich 35 - Small bakelite camera for 24x36mm exposures on "Bolta" size 35mm paper-backed rollfilm. Similar to the Ebony and Start, but not as common. $30-45.

SANRIO CO. LTD. (Japan)

Hello Kitty Camera - c1981. 110 film plastic camera in bright colors. Rotating kitty acts as cover for lens and viewfinder. Built-in electric autowinder and electronic flash. A cute but expensive camera for the child who already has a silver spoon. Retail price near $100.

SANWA CO. LTD., SANWA SHOKAI (Japan) *Some of the company's Mycro IIIA Cameras were also sold under the name of Mycro Camera Company Ltd.*
Mycro (original model) - 1938. The first pre-war model of the Mycro camera. There is no streamlined top housing as on the later Sanwa Mycro cameras, but rather a square optical finder attached to the top. Next to the finder is a small disc marked "T.A.Co.", but we have not yet discovered the meaning of these initials. This early model is uncommon, and diehard subminiature collectors have been known to pay $75-100.

Mycro - 1940-49. 14x14mm novelty camera. Mycro Una f4.5/20mm. 3-speed shutter. There are a number of variations of the Mycro cameras, most of which sell for $20-35.

Mycro IIIA - c1950. Similar to the normal Mycro, but shorter, streamlined viewfinder. Some versions are marked "Mycro Camera Company Ltd." and others are marked "Sanwa Co. Ltd". $50-75.

SASSEX - c1951. Simple eye-level camera for 6x6cm on 120 film. Body is shaped like the Reflex Korelle, but this camera is not a reflex. Large eye level folding frame finder. Sas-Siagor f9/80mm lens. T,B,M shutter. $15-25.

SATELLITE - "Hit" type subminiature. $10-15.

SAWYERS INC. (Portland, Ore.)
Mark IV (same as Primo Jr.) - c1958. TLR, 4x4cm on 127 film. Topcor f2.8/60mm lens. Seikosha MX shutter 1-500,B. Auto wind. $60-85.

Nomad 127

Nomad 127, Nomad 620 - c1957. Brown bakelite box cameras. 4x6.5cm on 127 and 6x6cm on 620. $4-8.

View-Master Personal Stereo - c1952. For making your own view-master slides. Film was wound twice through the camera with lenses raised/lowered for each pass. 69 stereo pairs, 12x13mm. Anastigmat f3.5/25mm lenses. 1/10-1/100 shutter. Quite common. Brown & beige model: $90-125. Black models with flash: $75-100. Mark film punch: $75-120.

Sawyers Europe: View-master Stereo Color - c1963-71. The European model, made in Germany. Some models are marked "Viewmaster Mark II". For stereo

exposures 12x13mm on 35mm film. Diagonal film path allows stereo pairs to be exposed on one pass of the film. Rodenstock Trinar f2.8/20mm lenses and single-speed shutter. $90-125.

S.C.A.T. (Societa Construzioni Articoli Technici, Rome)

Scat - c1950. Subminiature for 7x10mm exposures on 16mm film in special cassettes. f3.5 lens, single speed revolving shutter. Leather covered metal body. Uncommon. $100-150.

SCHAPP & CO. (Amsterdam)
Van Albada Stereo - c1900. 6x13cm box stereo. FP shutter with variable tension and slit width. Four-element lenses in nickel-plated lens mounts with rotary stops. $600-850.

SCHATZ & SONS (Germany)

Sola - c1938. Unusually-shaped subminiature, 13x18mm on unperforated film in cassettes. Spring drive, 12 exposures per wind. Interchangeable Schneider Kinoplan f3/25 or Xenon f2/25 lens.

Behind-the-lens shutter, 1-500, B. Waist-level or eye-level viewing. $800-1200.

SCHIANSKY
Universal Studio Camera - c1950. All metal, for 7x9¼" sheet film, with reducing back for 13x18cm (5x7"). Zeiss Apo-Tessar f9/450mm. Black bellows extend to 1 meter. Only 12 were made. One known sale in 1976 for $500.

SCHMITZ & THIENEMANN (Dresden)
Uniflex Reflex Meteor - c1931. SLR box for 6.5x9cm. Meyer Trioplan f4.5/105mm in self-cocking Pronto shutter 25-100. $150-175.

SCHUNEMAN & EVANS (St. Paul, Minnesota)
Lightning - Folding 4x5" plate camera. Black leather exterior, polished mahogany interior. Red bellows. B&L Unicum shutter. $50-70.

SCOTT-ATWATER MFG. CO. (Minneapolis, Minn.)

Photopal - Simple, stamped metal novelty camera, enameled black. 3x3.5cm or 4x6cm sizes. $25-35.

SCOVILL MANUFACTURING CO. (N.Y.)
Brief summary of name changes & dates: Scovill & Adams, 1889; Anthony & Scovill, 1902; Ansco, 1907. (See also Anthony and Ansco.) Scovill produced some excellent cameras, all of which are relatively uncommon today.

Antique Oak Detective - c1890. 4x5" box-plate camera finished in beautiful golden oak. String-set shutter, variable speeds. $400-500.

Book Camera - c1892. Camera disguised as a set of 3 books held with a leather strap. Rare. Estimate: $8000+.

Field/View cameras:
- **4x5"** - Square black box with folding beds on front and rear. Bellows extend both directions. Top and side doors permit loading the plateholders either way into the revolving back when only the front bellows are being used. Nickel plated Waterbury lens. $125-175.
- **8x10"** - ca. early 1880's. Light colored wood body. $125-175.

Irving - c1890. 11x14" compact folding view. RR lens, waterhouse stops. $250-350.

Knack Detective - c1891. The Antique Oak Detective camera with a new name. $400-500.

Mascot - c1890-1892. 4x5" format leather covered wood box camera. Similar to the Waterbury detective camera listed below, but with an Eastman Roll Holder. String-set shutter. $350-450.

Waterbury Detective, Improved model - c1892. Same as original model, except focus knob is at top front. $250-375.

Scovill Detective - c1886. Leather covered box detective camera for 4x5" plates in standard plateholders. Entire top of camera hinges open to one side to reveal the red leather bellows (and to change plates). The bottom of the camera is recessed, and the controls are located there, out of sight. A very uncommon detective camera, it was never shown close-up in original advertising to preserve its "concealed aspects". $550-650.

St. Louis - c1888. 8x10" reversible back camera No. 116. With lens: $125-175.

Stereo Solograph - c1899. A compact folding stereo for 4x6½". Stereo RR lenses in Automatic Stereo shutter. $275-375.

Waterbury Stereo - c1885. 5x8". All wood body. Scovill Waterbury lenses. $300-400.

Triad Detective - c1892. Leather covered 4x5" box detective camera for plates, rollfilm, or sheet film. Variable speed string-set shutter. $200-350.

Waterbury Detective Camera, Original model - c1888. Black painted wood box, or less common leather-covered model. Side door for loading plates. Focused by means of sliding bar extending through camera's base. Recessed bottom stores an extra plateholder. 4x5": $350-475. 5x7": $450-650

Waterbury View, 4x5" - c1886-1894. Folding-bed collapsible bellows view camera. Eurygraph 4x5 RR lens, Prosch Duplex shutter. $135-175.

Waterbury View, 5x8", 6½x8½" -

c1886-1894. Horizontal format. Light wood finish. Brass barrel Waterbury lens. $125-175.

Wet-plate camera - c1860's. 4-tube wet-plate tintype camera for 4 exposures on a 5x7" plate. $1400-1800.

SDELANO: *Identifying mark on some Russian cameras beginning in the late 1950's. It means "Manufactured in the U.S.S.R." This is not a camera model or manufacturer's name.*

SEARS (Seroco) *Seroco is an abbreviation for Sears, Roebuck & Co., whose cameras were made by other companies for sale under the Seroco name. The Conley company made many cameras for Sears after the turn of the century, and was purchased by Sears.*

Delmar - box camera for plates. Top rear door hinges up to insert plateholders. Storage space for extra plateholders. For 3¼x4¼" or 4x5" plates. $25-35.

Marvel S-16 - c1940. 116 rollfilm box cameras. Art-deco faceplate. $4-8.

Marvel S-20 - c1940. 120 rollfilm box camera made by Ansco for Sears. Art-deco faceplate. $4-8.

Marvel-flex - c1941. 6x6cm TLR. Wollensak Velostigmat f4.5/83mm. Alphax 10-200,T,B shutter. $15-20.

Perfection - 4x5" plate camera. $30-40.

Plate Camera - "Cycle-style" camera for 4x5" plates, styled somewhat like the Pony Premo E. Shutter concealed in wooden lensboard. "Sears Roebuck & Co. Chicago Ill." at base of lens standard. $75-100.

Seroco 4x5" folding plate camera - c1901. Black leathered wood body with polished interior. Red bellows. Seroco 4x5 Symmetrical lens and Wollensak shutter

Seroco 4x5" folding plate camera

are common. $40-70.

Seroco 5x7" folding plate camera - similar except for the size. $45-75.

Seroco 6½x8½" folding plate camera - Red double extension bellows. $75-105.

Seroco Magazine - c1902. 4x5" box camera. Leather covered, nickel trim. 12-plate magazine. $45-60.

Seroco Stereo - 5x7" plates. Leather covered mahogany body with polished interior. Red leather bellows. Wollensak Stereo shutter & lenses. $275-325.

Tower No. 5 - c1958. 4x4cm on 127 rollfilm. Styled like a 35mm. Blue-gray enameled with gray plastic partial covering. Made by Bilora for Sears and similar to the Bilora Bella. $8-12.

Tower 16 - c1959. Mamiya-16 Super with the Tower name on it. $35-50.

Tower 18B - c1962. 35mm camera with coupled rangefinder and built-in meter. Made by Mamiya for Sears. Mamiya-Kominar f2/48mm lens in Copal SVKB, 1-500. $15-25.

Tower 35, Model 50

Tower, 35mm - c1955. Various models of 35mm cameras, styles vary from boxy to compact. Includes "Tower 35" Models 39, 41, 50, 55. Various features. $10-25.

Tower, Type 3 - c1949. Made by Nicca Camera Co. in Occupied Japan, and sold by Sears. Copy of a Leica III. This is the same camera as the Nicca III. Nikkor f2/50mm interchangeable lens. With normal lens: $95-125. Body only: $60-75.

Tower 22, Tower 23, Tower 24 - c1954-1959. 35mm SLR cameras made by Asahi Optical Co. in Japan and sold by Sears. Export versions of the Asahiflex IIA and IIB. Takumar f3.5/50mm or f2.4/58mm. FP shutter to 500. $50-110. Higher in Europe.

Tower 26 - c1958-59. Name variation of Asahi Pentax (original model). Takumar f2.4/55mm lens. $150-200.

Tower 51 (35mm) - c1955. Rangefinder 35. Made by Iloca for Sears. $25-50.

Tower 51 (rollfilm) - c1955. Folding bed 6x9cm camera, identical to the United States Camera Corp. Rollex. $5-10.

Tower One-Twenty, One-Twenty Flash,

Flash, Flash 120 - c1950's. 6x9cm box cameras. Leatherette or enamel finish. $1-5.

Tower 127EF - Horizontally styled camera for 1-5/8x1⅝" on 127 film. Electronic flash beside lens. Capacitor and electronics in detachable handle. Early example of a camera with built-in flash. $15-25.

Tower Automatic 127 - c1960. Horizontally styled white plastic body. Flash and meter built-in. 4x4cm on 127. Looks like the United States Camera Corp. Automatic 127. $5-10.

Tower Bonita Model 14 - Metal twin-lens box camera with reptile-grained covering. Made by Bilora for Sears. "Bilora" on strap, "Bonita" on viewing hood. "Tower Model 14" on front plate. Time & Inst. shutter. Taking lens focuses via lever concealed under finder hood. $15-25.

Tower Camflash 127, Camflash II 127 - Horizontal style 4x4cm, like the United States Camera Corp. Comet 127. Built-in flash. $5-10.

Tower Companion - Plastic 6x6cm box camera, identical to Imperial Debonair. $1-5.

Tower Hide Away - c1960. Grey and green plastic box camera made by Imperial, same style as the Imperial Mark 27. Built-in flash with retractable cover. $1-5.

Tower Junior - c1953-56. Small bakelite box camera with eye-level finder. Made by Bilora for Sears and identical to the Bilora Boy. "Tower" on front, "Bilora" on back. $10-20.

Tower Pixie 127, Pixie II 127 - Gray plastic 4x4cm, 127 camera. $1-5.

Tower Reflex - c1955. 6x6cm TLR. Isco Westar Anastigmat f3.5. Pronto 25-200 shutter. Same as Photina Reflex. $20-30.

Tower Reflex Type - c1955. Various styles of 6x6cm pseudo-TLR bakelite box cameras. $5-10.

Tower Skipper - 4x4cm plastic box. Identical to the Mercury Satellite 127. $1-5.

Tower Snappy - Plastic 6x6cm 620 camera, identical to the Herbert-George Savoy. In colors. $1-5.

Tower Stereo - c1955-60. Made in Germany by Iloca for Sears. Same as Iloca Stereo II. Isco-Westar f3.5/35mm lenses. Prontor-S shutter 1-300. $85-100.

Trumpfreflex - c1940. German-made 6x6cm TLR sold in the U.S. by Sears. Looks very similar to the Balda Reflecta and Welta Reflekta. Parallax correction accomplished by the taking lens tilting up at close focusing distances. Normally found with Trioplan f3.5/75mm lens. Shutter 1-300. $20-25.

SECAM (Paris)

Stylophot cameras - c1950's "pen" style cameras, according to the name, but even if compared to the large deluxe European fountain pens, it ends up looking a bit hefty. The pocket clip is the closest resemblance to a pen. For 18 exposures 10x10mm on

16mm film in special cartridges. Shutter cocking and film advance via pull-push sliding mechanism which pushed film from cartridge to cartridge. Automatic exposure counter. Weight: 3 oz. (85 gr.) *Note: The same camera was also sold in Germany as the Foto-Fueller, listed in this guide under Knuik.*

Stylophot "Standard" or "Color" model - Cheaper of the two models, with fixed focus two-element f6.3 coated lens, single speed shutter,1/50. Also sold under the name "Private Eye". Original price: $15. Current value: $85-110. *(Illus. previous page.)*

Stylophot "Luxe" or "Deluxe" model - with f3.5/27mm Roussel Anastigmat lens. Iris diaphragm. Focus to 2½ ft. (0.8m). Single speed shutter, 1/75, synched for flash. Original price: $33. This model is very uncommon. $125-150. *(Illustrated on previous page.)*

Stereophot - An unique stereo camera consisting of two Stylophot cameras mounted side-by-side on a special mounting plate. Awkward, maybe... but rare. $450-550.

SEE - Another name variant of the "Diana" type for 120 film. $1-5.

SEEMAN (H. Seeman)
Stereo camera - Black wooden strut-folding camera, nickel-plated fittings. Goerz Dagor 120mm lenses. $300-450.

SEIKI KOGAKU CO. *(Seiki Kogaku means "Precision Optical" and this name was used on more than one occasion by unrelated companies. This company is not related to the Seiki Kogaku which made the early Canon cameras.)*

Seiki - c1950. Oval-shaped 16mm subminiature. Seek Anastigmat f3.5/25mm. B, 25, 50, 100 shutter. $500-700.

SEISCHAB (Otto Seischab, Nuernberg, Germany)
Esco - c1922. 400 exposure half-frame 35mm. Similar in style to the Leica Reporter. Steinheil Cassar f3.5/35mm. Dial-set Compur 1-300. Rare. One recorded sale at $2000. Failed to reach a reserve of about $5800 at a 1986 auction. Estimate: $4000-5000.

S.E.M. (Societe des Etablissements Modernes; Aurec, France) *In 1942-45, during the German occupation of Paris, the Reyna Cross 35mm cameras were made in St. Etienne under license from Cornu. Once the war was over, the St. Etienne firm broke the ties with Cornu and re-established itself in the neighboring town of Aurec under the S.E.M. name. The Reyna-Cross camera design, with some improvements, soon appeared as the Sem-Kim, and S.E.M. went on to design and build a number of small and medium-format cameras up through the early 1970's.*
Babysem - c1949. Grey-enameled 35mm. Some models are partially blue or red leather covered. Cross f2.9/45mm lens. Orec shutter 25-200 or 15-250. $15-25.

Challenger - c1959. Aluminum-colored plastic camera for 16 exposures 4x4cm on 620 film. $15-25. *(Illustrated top of next page.)*

S.E.M. Challenger

Colorado - Grey plastic dual-format camera. Takes 16 exposures 4x4cm or 20 exposures 24x35mm on 620 film. $20-30.

Kim - c1947. Simple cast aluminum 35mm camera. Successor of the Reyna-Cross. Cross Anastigmat f2.9/45mm. Shutter 25-200, later extended to 1-200. $20-30.

Semflex (Standard) - c1950. Twin-lens

reflex camera for 6x6cm on 120 film. Several model variations. $20-40.

Semflex Joie de Vivre 45 - Light-gray plastic covered TLR. Metal faceplate. Berthiot f4.5/80mm lens. $35-50.

Semflex Studio Standard - c1951-72. 6x6cm TLR with extended front for use with Tele-Berthiot f5.4/150mm lens. f3.9 viewing lens. Long focusing rack allows close focus to 1.5m. Two versions: Crank advance or knob advance. Single lever below lens tensions and releases shutter. Synchro Compur shutter after 1972. $200-275.

SEMMENDINGER (A. Semmendinger, Ft. Lee, NJ)
Excelsior - c1870. Wet-plate cameras in sizes 5x5" to 12x12". Large sizes have sliding backs. With lens: $500-800. Without lens: $250-350.

SENECA CAMERA CO. (Rochester, NY)
Kao - Box cameras for glass plates in standard double holders. Fixed focus. All black. Kao Jr. is for 3½x3½" plates; Kao Sr. is 4x5". $25-40.

Busy Bee - c1903. 4x5" box-plate camera. Fold-down front reveals a beautiful interior. $45-65.

Camera City View - c1907-25. 5x7" to 8x10" view cameras. Seneca Anastigmat lens. Ilex shutter. $85-135.

Chautauqua 4x5" - Folding plate camera. Wollensak lens. Seneca Uno shutter. A very plain all-black camera. $35-60.
(Illustrated top of next page.)

- 5x7" - All black "ebonized" model: $50-70. With polished wood interior: $100-150.

Chief 1A - c1918. 2½x4¼" on rollfilm. $12-18.

Seneca Chautauqua, 4x5"

Competitor View - c1907-25. 5x7" or 8x10" folding field camera. Light colored wood or medium colored cherry wood. $90-135.

Competitor View, Stereo - Same as normal 5x7 Competitor, but equipped for stereo. $200-250.

Duo - Not a camera name. This was the medium-priced shutter in the Seneca line-up with T,B,1,2,5,25,50,100.

Filmett - 1910-1916. Folding film-pack camera for 3¼x4¼" packs. Leather covered wood body. Black bellows. Wollensak Achromatic or Rapid Rectilinear lens. Uno or Duo shutter. $20-30.

Folding plate cameras:

3¼x4¼" - Wollensak f16 lens. Uno shutter. $30-45.
3¼x5½" - Black double-extension bellows and triple convertible lens. $30-45.
4x5" - Black leathered body with nickel

trim. Double extension bellows. Seneca Uno or Auto shutter. $40-60.
5x7" - Similar, black or polished wood interior, black leathered wood body. 7" Rogers or Seneca Anastigmat lens in Auto shutter. $50-80.

No. 9 Folding Plate Camera - c1907-23. 4x5". Maroon bellows. Velostigmat lens. Compur shutter. $50-75.

No. 1 Seneca Junior - c1916. 2¼x3¼" exposure folding rollfilm camera. Strut-supported lensboard and hinged front cover. Ilex shutter. $15-20.

Pocket Seneca No. 3A - c1908. Folding plate camera. Double extension bellows. Rapid convertible lens, Auto shutter 1-100. $20-30. *(Illustrated top of next page.)*

Pocket Seneca No. 29 - c1905. Simple 4x5" folding plate camera. Seneca Uno shutter. f8 lens. $25-35.

Pocket Seneca No. 3A

Box Scout cameras, No. 2, 2A, 3, 3A - c1913-25. For rollfilm. $6-12.

Folding Scout cameras:
No. 2A - c1915-25. Wollensak lens, Ultro shutter. $12-18.
No. 2C - c1917-25. $12-18.
No. 3 - c1915-25. Ultro shutter. $12-18.
No. 3A - c1915-25. Seneca Trio shutter. 122 film. $12-18.

Stereo View - c1910. 5x7" folding-bed

collapsible bellows view camera with wide front lensboard. Leather covered wood body. Wollensak lenses. Stereo Uno or Automatic Double Valve Stereo shutter. $275-375.

Trio - Trio is a shutter name, not a camera name.

Uno - Not the name of a camera, but rather the low-priced shutter on Seneca cameras. Provides I,T,B speeds.

Vest Pocket - c1916-25. Compact folding camera for 127 film. Seneca Anastigmat f7.7 lens. Shutter 25-100. $25-45.

View Cameras:
5x7" - c1903. Seneca Rapid convertible or Goerz Syntor f6.8 lens. Ilex shutter 1-100. Black double extension bellows. Polished wood body. $85-125.

5x7" Improved - c1905-25. Wollensak Planatic Series III lens. Auto shutter. Black leather bellows. Fine wood body. $85-125.

6½x8½" Improved - c1905-24. Goerz Double Anastigmat f6.8/7" lens in Volute shutter. $80-120.

8x10", including the Improved model - c1902-25. With Wollensak Velostigmat Ser. 2, f4.5/12" lens or double anastigmat lens in Optimo or Wollensak Regular shutter. $90-145.

SEVILLE SUPER SW 500 - c1985. Novelty 35mm from Taiwan styled with small pseudo-prism. $1-5.

SEYMORE PRODUCTS CO. (Chicago, IL) *See alternate spelling "Seymour".*

Brenda Starr Cub Reporter - Bakelite minicam for 16 exposures on 127 film. Enameled 4-color illustrated faceplate. Probably the rarest and most desirable of the "Minicam" type cameras. $25-35.

Dick Tracy - Like the Seymour Sales Dick Tracy, but black faceplate. $12-20.

SEYMOUR SALES CO. (Chicago) *See also alternate spelling "Seymore".*
Dick Tracy - Black bakelite minicam for 3x4cm on 127 film. Picture of Dick Tracy and camera name are printed in red on the metal faceplate. $12-20. *See second variation above under "Seymore Products".*

Flash-Master - Inexpensive 3x4cm 127 rollfilm minicam with sync. $3-7.

S.F.O.M. (Societe Francaise d'Optique Mechanique)
Sfomax - c1949. Cast aluminum subminiature, black or grey leatherette covering. Split image rangefinder. Takes 20 exposures 14x23mm on unperforated 16mm film in special cartridges. S'fomar f3.5/30mm lens. Shutter 30-400 (early models 25-400). $400-600. *(Illustrated top of next column.)*

SGDG: *Brevete S.G.D.G. (Sans garantie du gouvernement) indicates French manufacture. According to French patent law, if an article is marked "brevete" (patented) it must also be marked "sans garantie du gouvernement" or S.G.D.G.*

S.F.O.M. Sfomax

SHACKMAN (D. Shackman and Sons, London, England)
Auto Camera, Mark 3 - c1953. 24x24mm on 35mm film in 250 exposures cassettes. Recording camera designed for scientific work. Motorized advance. Dallmeyer fixed focus lens. Gray painted body. $50-100.

SHAJA - 9x12cm double extension plate camera. Tessar f4.5/135mm in Compur shutter. $25-35.

SHAKEY'S - Plastic novelty 4x4cm camera of the "Diana" type. Made in Hong Kong. $1-5.

SHALCO - 14x14mm Japanese novelty camera. $10-15.

SHANGHAI - c1950's. Chinese copy of Leica IIIf. Collapsible f3.5/50mm lens. $300-500.

SHANSHUI B - Chinese plastic 120 camera. $25-30.

SHAW (H.E. Shaw & Co.)

Oxford Minicam - Black plastic half-127, made by Utility Mfg. Co. for Shaw Co. $3-7.

SHAW-HARRISON
Sabre 620 - c1962. Plastic 6x6cm box camera. Various colors. $4-8.

Valiant 620 - Colored plastic 6x6cm box camera. Identical to the Sabre 620. $4-8.

SHAYO - Japanese novelty subminiature of the Hit type. $10-15.

SHEW (J. F. Shew & Co., London) Day-Xit - c1910 variation of the Xit. Meniscus lens, synchro shutter. Black leathered wood body. $125-175.

Eclipse - c1890. Mahogany with dark brown bellows. Darlot RR lens in inter-lens shutter named "Shew's Eclipse Central Shutter". 3¼x4¼", 4¼x6½": $150-225.

Guinea Xit - c1906. Mahogany gate-strut folding camera. Red bellows. 8x10.5cm on plates or cut film. Achromatic 5½" lens. Central rotary shutter. $125-175.

Stereo Field Camera - c1900. 5x7". Mahogany body with brass trim. Front bed supported by wooden wing brace at side. Tapered wine-red bellows. Double extension rack and pinion focus. Tessar f6.3/120mm lenses in double pneumatic shutter. Unusual style and rare. $800-1100.

Xit, Aluminum Xit - c1900. ¼ and ½-plate sizes. Similar to the Eclipse with aluminum and mahogany construction. $150-225.

Xit Stereoscopic - Folding gate-strut stereo camera. $600-700.

SHIMURA KOKI (Japan) Mascot - c1950. Vertical subminiature for 14x14mm on paper-backed "Midget" rollfilm. Mascot f4.5/25mm. Shutter 25-100, B. $250-350.

SHINANO CAMERA CO. LTD., SHINANO OPTICAL WORKS (Japan)

Pigeon - c1952. Viewfinder 35mm. Tomioka Tri-Lausar f3.5/45mm. Synchro shutter 1-200. Advance knob. $25-35.

Pigeon III - c1952. Viewfinder 35mm. Tomioka Tri-Lausar f3.5/45mm. NKS or TSK shutter 1-200. Lever wind. $25-35.

SHINCHO SEIKI CO. LTD. (Japan)

Albert - A name variation of the Darling-16. " Albert Fifth Avenue New York" on metal faceplate. $250-325.

Darling-16 - c1957. Vertically styled subminiature accepts 16mm cassettes for 10x12mm exposures. Bakelite body with metal front and back. $250-325.

SHINSEI OPTICAL WORKS (Japan)
Monte 35 - c1953. Inexpensive Japanese 35mm. Monte Anastigmat f3.5/50mm in Heilemann or SKK shutter. $15-20.

SHOEI MFG. CO. (Japan)
Ruvinal II, III - c1951. 6x6cm folding cameras taking 120 or 620 rollfilm. Pentagon f3.5/80mm or Seriter f3.5/75mm lens. Shutter 1-200. $15-25.

SHOWA KOGAKU (Japan)

Gemflex - c1949. Subminiature TLR for 14x14mm on standard "Midget" paper-backed rollfilm. Gem f3.5/25mm, shutter 25-100. Early models: Back plate has serial number and "Made in Occupied Japan"; finder hood opens for eye level viewing. Later models: No serial number; not marked Occupied Japan; no eye-level viewing provision. $265-300.

Leotax Cameras *Prices include normal lens.*
Leotax Model I - 1940 Leica copy. Uncoupled rangefinder, no accessory shoe. $500-600.

Leotax Special, Special A - Wartime camera. Viewfinder window to left of RF windows. No slow speeds, coupled RF. $300-500.

Leotax Special B - Wartime camera. Viewfinder window to left of RF windows. Slow speeds. $275-400.

Leotax Special DII - 1947. Viewfinder window between RF windows. No slow speeds. $250-400.

Leotax DII MIOJ - $125-175.

Leotax Special DIII - 1947. Viewfinder window between RF windows. Slow speeds. $250-400.

Leotax DIII MIOJ - $125-175.

Leotax DIV - 1950. Rangefinder magnification 1.5X, no sync. $125-175.

Leotax S - 1952. RF magnification 1.5X, sync. $100-175.

Leotax F - 1954. Fast speed dial now 25-1000. Slow speed dial, self-timer. $90-150.

Leotax T - 1955. Top speed 1/500. Slow speed dial, self-timer. $90-150.

Leotax K - 1955. Top speed 1/500, self-timer. No slow speeds. $110-160.

Leotax TV - 1957. Slow speeds, self timer. $125-200.

Leotax FV - 1958. Lever wind, self timer, slow speeds to 1000. $160-225.

Leotax T2 - 1958. Slowest speed on fast speed dial now 1/30. Slow speed dial, no self-timer. $125-200.

Leotax K3 - 1958. Slow speeds limited to ⅛ & 1/15. No self timer. $125-200.

Leotax TV2 (Merit) - 1958. Lever wind, self timer, slow speeds to 500. $160-225.

Leotax T2L (Elite) - 1959. Lever wind, no self timer. Slow speeds to 500. $160-225.

Leotax G - 1961. Shutter 1-1000. Small dial. $200-250.

Semi-Leotax - c1940's. Folding camera for 4.5x6cm exposures on 120 film. f3.5/75mm lens. 1-200 shutter. $35-50.

S.I.A.F. Amiga

SIAF (Chile)
Amiga - Black plastic eye-level camera. Streamlined design like many Kaftanski cameras. Dual format, 6x9cm or 4.5x6cm with metal insert, on 120 film. f7.5/135mm lens. Instant & Pose speeds. $20-30. *(Illustrated bottom of previous page.)*

SIDA GmbH (Berlin-Charlottenburg)

Sida - c1930. Small eye-level camera, 24x24mm exp. Variations include early black cast metal body, later version made in France with black plastic body, and Italian version in red marbelized plastic. $20-40.

Sida Extra - c1935. Small eye-level camera making 24x24mm exposures. Dark brown/black plastic body. Similar to the Sida, but the name "Extra" is molded into the body above the lens. $30-50.

Sida Standard - c1935. Black cast-metal miniature for 25x25mm exposures. Several variations include shutter release on bottom. $25-40.

Sidax - c1948. Small black bakelite camera similar to the Sida and Extra. Made in Paris by Kafta. Fritz Kaftanski, the designer of Sida in Berlin, had moved to Lyon France during the war and then to Paris, where he reincarnated the Sida.

Uses Lumiere #1 rollfilm for 25x25mm exposures. $40-60.

SIGRISTE (J.G. Sigriste, Paris)
Sigriste - c1900. Jumelle-style camera 6.5x9cm or 9x12cm sizes. Zeiss Tessar f4.5. Special Focal Plane shutter 40-2500. (This shutter had speeds to 1/10,000 on some cameras.) Rare. $3000-4000.

Sigriste Stereo - Rare stereo version of the above. One was offered for sale in late 1984 at $5000, which seems like a realistic figure.

SIL-BEAR - "Hit" type camera. $10-15.

SIMCO BOX - 6x6cm reflex style box camera made in Germany. Stamped metal with black crinkle-enamel. $5-10.

SIMDA (Le Perreux, France)

Panorascope - c1955. Wide angle stereo camera for 16mm film. Fixed focus Roussel or Angenieux f3.5/25mm lenses. Stereo shutter 1-250, sync. Black or grey covered metal body. Less than 2500 were made. $400-500.

SIMMON BROTHERS, INC. (N.Y.)
Omega 120 - c1954. A professional rollfilm press camera for 9 exposures 2¼x2¾" on 120 film. Omicron f3.5/90mm lens. Sync shutter 1-400. Coupled rangefinder. $125-195. *(Illustrated top of next page.)*

Simmon Omega 120

Signal Corps Combat Camera - Cast magnesium camera with olive drab finish for 2¼x3¼" filmpacks only. Wollensak Velostigmat f4.5/101mm in Rapax shutter. $125-175.

SIMONS (Wolfgang Simons & Co., Bern, Switzerland)

Sico - c1923. Dark brown wooden body with brass trim. For 25 exposures 30x40mm on unperforated 35mm paper-backed rollfilm. Rudersdorf Anastigmat f3.5/60mm lens in focusing mount. Iris diaphragm to f22. Dial Compur shutter 1-300. $1000-1200.

SIMPRO CORP. of AMERICA
Simpro-X - Novelty camera front for 126 cartridges. Film cartridge forms the back of the camera. $1-5.

SIMPRO INTERNATIONAL LTD.
Slip-on - 126 film cartridge forms the back of the camera body. $1-3.

SINCLAIR (James A. Sinclair & Co., Ltd., London)
Traveller Roll-Film Camera - c1910. Horizontally styled box camera for 3¼x4¼" on #118 rollfilm. Goerz Dagor f6.8 lens in B&L Automat shutter, concealed behind the hinged front panel with sliding lens cover. Unusual. $175-200.

Traveller Una - c1927. Similar to the Una, but made of Duralumin, a special metal, almost as light as aluminum, but stronger. 6x9cm. Xenar f4.5/105mm. Compur shutter. $2500-3500.

Tropical Una - 1910's-1920's. Similar to the Una, but polished mahogany with brass fittings. 6x9cm to ½-plate sizes. $800-1200.

Una, Una Cameo - c1895. Folding plate camera, 6x9cm to 4x5" sizes. Heavy wood construction. Goerz f6.8 Double Anastigmat lens. Revolving back. $200-250.

Una Deluxe - c1908. Same as the Una, but hand-stitched brown leather exterior. $650-850.

SING 88, 388 - 14x14mm novelty subminiatures, later rectangular versions of the "Hit" types. Made in Hong Kong. $10-20.

SIRATON - Japanese novelty subminiature of the "Hit" type. $10-15.

SIRCHIE FINGER PRINT LABORATORIES INC. (Raleigh, NC)
Finger Print Camera - All-metal close-up camera with built-in lights. Various models for 2¼x3¼" filmholders, filmpacks, or for 3¼x4¼" Polaroid pack film. Raptar f6.3 lens. Alphax 25-150 shutter. $45-85.

SIRIO (Florence, Italy)
Elettra I - c1950. Viewfinder 35mm. Fixed Semitelar f8/50mm. Shutter 25-200. $100-150.

Elettra II - c1950. Viewfinder 35mm. Scupltor f5.6/40mm. Shutter 25-200. $125-175.

SITACON CO. LTD. (Taiwan)

Sitacon ST-3 - c1982. Inexpensive 35mm novelty camera. Identical to the Windsor WX-3. Original price: $8-12. Collectible value: $1-5.

SKAIFE (Thomes Skaife, London, England)
Pistolgraph - c1858. Brass miniature camera for 28mm dia. exposures on wet-plates. Dallmeyer Petzval-type f2.2/40mm, waterhouse stops. Double-flap shutter. One known sale at auction in August 1977 for $15,000.

SKYFLEX - c1955. Japanese twin lens reflex for 6x6cm on 120 film. Tri Lausar f3.5/80mm in B,1-300 shutter. Manufacturer unknown, but body style is very similar to Toyocaflex IB. $50-75.

SKYVIEW CAMERA CO. (Cleveland, OH)
Skyview Aerial Camera Model K - c1939. Small hand-held aerial camera for 2¼x3¼" filmpacks. One-piece cast aluminum body with integral finder. Hinged aluminum back. Wollensak Aerialstigmat f4.5/5" lens. $75-125.

SMITH (Gosport, England)
Detective camera - Polished mahogany magazine box camera for 12 plates 3¼x4¼" distributed by Smith. Built-in leather changing bag. Brass trim. Two waist level viewfinders with brass covers. Guillotine shutter. $400-600.

SMITH (James H. Smith, Chicago, IL)
Known mainly for the manufacture of professional equipment.
Multiplying Camera - c1870's. 4¾x6½" plate can be moved hoizontally and vertically to take 2 to 32 exposures on it. Polished mahogany body; sliding back. Brass trim. Bellows focus. Portrait lens, pneumatic flap shutter. $500-750.

SNAP 16 - Black and gold cardboard half-127 box camera. $15-25.

SOENNECKEN & CO. (Munich)
Field Camera - 5x7". Mahogany body. Univ. Aplanat Extra Rapid lens with iris diaphragm. $75-100.

Folding camera - 6x9cm. Double extension. Steinheil Unofocal f5.4/105mm lens. $20-30.

SOHO LTD. (London) *Soho was the result of the split of APM in 1928 and consisted of the equipment manufacturers of APM. Kershaw of Leeds took the dominant role. Eventually Soho became absorbed by Kershaw into Kershaw-Soho (Sales) Ltd. During the 1930's the firm produced a number of plastic-bodied cameras of good quality which are very collectable.*

Soho Altrex - c1932. 6x9cm folding bed

rollfilm camera. Leather covered body. Kershaw Anastigmat lens, 7-speed shutter. $15-25.

Soho Pilot

Soho Cadet - c1930. Brown bakelite 6x9cm folding bed rollfilm camera. Meniscus lens. 2-speed shutter. $40-50.

Soho Precision - c1933. Well-made self-casing triple extension camera with full range of movements. Takes 2½x3½" plates. A fine professional view camera, still usable today, which helps supports its value. A nice example, complete and original, can sell for $600-700.

Soho Model B - Reddish-brown folding bakelite camera for 6x9cm on 120 film. Cross-swinging metal struts support bakelite front. Wine-red bellows. Fixed focus lens, T & I shutter. An attractive camera. $35-50.

Soho Myna Model SK12 - Metal folding-bed rollfilm camera with self-erecting front. 6x9cm on 120. $15-25.

Soho Pilot - c1933. Black bakelite folding rollfilm camera for 6x9cm on 120 film. Octagonal bakelite shutter face. Intricate basket-weave pattern molded into front & back. Angular art-deco body styling. Fixed focus lens, T & I shutter. $25-35. *(Illustrated top of next column.)*

Soho Vest Pocket - c1930. Strut-folding camera for 4x6.5cm on 127 film. Leather covered. Single Achromatic lens, 3-speed shutter. $15-25.

SOKOL AUTOMAT - c1970's. Russian 35mm with Industar 70 f2.8/50mm lens in 30-500 shutter. Rapid wind lever. $15-25.

SOLAR MATES
Sunpet 826 - c1986. Simple plastic camera for 126 cartridges. Nothing exciting about it except that it comes with a matching pair of sunglasses. This must have been designed with Chicago Bears quarterback Jim McMahon in mind. Available in red, blue, or yellow. Retail about $4. *(Illustrated top of next page.)*

Solar Mates Sunpet 826

SOLIGOR *Soligor was a trade name used by Allied Impex Corp. for cameras imported from various manufacturers.*

Soligor 35 - c1955. 35mm SLR made by Tokiwa Seiki. Same camera as the earlier Firstflex 35, but sold originally with a different lens. Interchangeable Soligor f3.5/50 lens. Leaf shutter 1-200, B. Waist-level finder. Built-in meter. $60-90.

Soligor 45 - c1955. Viewfinder 35mm made by Nihon Seiki Co. Nearly identical to the Nescon 35. Soligor f4.5/40mm. Shutter 25-100. $20-35.

Soligor 66 - c1957. 6x6cm SLR. FP shutter 25-500, T,B. Interchangeable Soligor f3.5/80mm. $60-100.

Soligor Reflex, Reflex II, Semi-Auto - c1952. 6x6cm TLR for 120 film. Made in Japan. Soligor f3.5/80mm, Rektor rim-set shutter. $25-35.

SONORA INDUSTRIAL S.A. (Manaus, Brasil)

Love - c1975-present. A disposable camera which comes pre-loaded with 16mm wide film for 20 exposures. After exposure, the entire camera is returned for processing, and a new camera is returned with the finished prints. Two-element f11/28mm lens. Film advanced by rotating magicube socket. Over 5 million had been sold in Brazil by 1984. Similar to "Lure" from USA. New price about $5.00

SOUTHERN (E.J. Southern Ind., New York City)

Mykro-Fine - Japanese subminiature of the Hit type. This one actually has the U.S. distributor's name on the shutter faceplate. $15-20.

SPARTUS CORP. (Chicago, Ill.) *Began as Utility Mfg. Co. in New York about 1934, which sold out to the Spartus Corp. of Chicago in the 1940's. During the 1940's, several names were used including Falcon Camera Co., Spencer Co., and Spartus Corp., all of which were probably the same company. In 1951, the firm was purchased by its Sales Manager, Harold Rubin, who changed the name to Herold Mfg. Co.*

Meanwhile, the former President of Spartus, Jack Galter started a new company called "Galter Products" about 1950. See also "HEROLD" for later model Spartus cameras.

Spartus Cinex

Spartus box camera

Spartus folding camera

Cinex - Reflex-style novelty camera for 3x4cm on 127. Bakelite body. Identical to Spartus Reflex. $5-10. *(Illustrated in previous column.)*

Spartus box cameras - including Spartus 116, 116/616, 120, 620, Rocket. $1-5. *(Illustrated in previous column.)*

Spartus folding cameras - including Spartus 4, Spartus Vest Pocket. $8-12. *(Illustrated in previous column.)*

Spartus 35, 35F - c1947-54. Bakelite 35mm. Simple lens and shutter. $10-15.

Spartus Full-Vue - c1948-60. Reflex-style 120 box camera. $5-10.

Spartus Junior Model - Bakelite folding vest-pocket camera for 4x6.5cm on 127 film. Like the earlier Utility Falcon Junior Model, but different back latches. $5-10.

Spartus Press Flash - 1939-50. Bakelite box camera with built-in flash reflector. This camera was advertised in April 1939

Special Camera

under both the Spartus Press Flash (Utility Mfg. Co.) and Falcon Press Flash names. As far as we know, it is the first camera to have a built-in flash reflector. It also exists under other names, such as Galter Press Flash and Regal Flash Master. Historically significant and interesting from a design standpoint, yet common. $5-10.

Spartus Super R-I - TLR-style camera, non-focusing finder. $5-10.

Spartus Vanguard - c1962. 4x4cm plastic box camera. $1-3.

Spartacord - Brown plastic TLR. $10-15.

Spartaflex - c1950. Plastic TLR. $5-10.

SPECIAL CAMERA - c1930's. Japanese novelty folding "Yen" camera for sheet film in paper holders. Ground glass back. $15-25. *(Illustrated top of next column.)*

SPECTRA SUPER II - c1985. Novelty 35mm from Taiwan styled with small pseudo-prism. $1-5.

SPEED-O-MATIC CORP. (Boston, MA) Speed-O-Matic - An early instant-picture camera with meniscus lens, single speed shutter. $20-30. (Clear plastic salesman's "demo" model - $35-50.)

SPEEDEX - 14x14mm "Hit" type Japanese novelty subminiature. $10-15.

SPENCER CO. (Chicago, IL) *The Spencer Co. name is one of many names used by the manufacturers at 711-715 W. Lake Street in Chicago. Among the other names emanating from this building were: Falcon, Galter, Herold, Monarch, Monarck, and Spartus. The Spencer name often appears on the instruction books for cameras which bear one of the other brand names. Some cameras do carry the Spencer brand name, but usually the same camera is also available with one or more of the other brand names.*

Flex-Master - Reflex style minicam for 16

exposures on 127 film. Synchronized and non-sync versions. $5-10.

Majestic - This black plastic "minicam" would be hard to identify as a Spencer model without the original instructions. The camera faceplate has no company name, and the box says simply "Candid Type Camera". However, the original instructions bear the imprint of the Spencer Co. Takes 16 exposures on 127 film. $3-7.

SPIEGEL
Elf - Metal box camera, 6x9cm on 120. $8-12.

SPIROTECHNIQUE (Levallois-Perret, France)
Calypso - c1960. The first commercially produced camera which was specifically designed for underwater use without any external housing. It takes standard 24x36mm frames on 35mm film, and the overall size is about the same as a normal 35mm camera. Features interchangeable lenses (Angenieux f2.8/45mm, Flor f3.5/35mm, or Berthiot Angulor f3.3/28mm.) Guillotine shutter 30-100. Body covering is a grey plastic imitation sealskin. Nikon bought the design and the Calypso evolved into the successful line of Nikonos cameras. Uncommon. $125-175.

SPITZER (Otto Spitzer, Berlin)
Espi, 4.5x6cm - Compact lazy-tong strut camera for 4.5x6cm plates. Isconar f6.8/90mm lens in Pronto shutter. $100-140.

Espi, 13x18cm - c1910. Folding bed camera for 13x18cm plates. Wood body with leather covering. Wine red double extension bellows. Nickel trim. Dagor f6.8/180mm in Compound ½-250. $40-60.

SPLENDIDFLEX - 4x4cm reflex-style plastic novelty camera. $1-5.

S.P.O. (Societe de Photographie et d'Optique, Carpentras, France)
Folding camera - 6x9cm folding rollfilm camera, self-erecting. Anastigmat Sphinx Paris f6.3/105mm. $10-15.

SPUTNIK - Japanese novelty subminiature of the "hit" type. A rather uncommon name. The few examples we have seen have come from Germany. Normally this type of camera sells for $10-15, but we have several confirmed sales for "Sputnik" in 1986 at $40-50. In at least one case though, the buyer thought he was bidding on the more valuable Sputnik Stereo camera. (See next listing.)

SPUTNIK (CNYTHNK) (U.S.S.R.)
Sputnik Stereo - c1960. Black bakelite three-lens reflex for 6x13cm stereo pairs on 120 film. f4.5/75mm lenses. Shutter 15-125. Ground glass focus. $225-275.

SPY CAMERA - Plastic 127 camera, made in Hong Kong. $1-5.

STANDARD CAMERA (Hong Kong) - Small black plastic camera for 3x4cm on rollfilm. Meniscus f11/50mm lens. Simple shutter B,1/50. $1-5.

STANDARD CAMERAS LTD. (Birmingham)

Conway Camera - Box camera for 6x9cm on 120 rollfilm. Several models, including Standard model, Colour Filter Model, Conway Deluxe. $5-15.

Standard Camera No. 2 - Inexpensive cardboard box camera with blue leatherette covering. "No.2 Standard Camera - Made in England" on metal faceplate. We assume that this is made by Standard Cameras, Ltd., but we have no confirming references. Takes 6x9cm on 120 film. I & T shutter. $15-20. *(Illustrated top of next page.)*

No. 2 Standard Camera

STAR LITE - c1962. Inexpensive reflex-style camera. $5-10.

STAR-LITE - Japanese "Hit" type novelty camera. $10-15.

STARLITE - 1960's. Inexpensive 35mm, 24x36mm. Made by Yamato. Luminar f3.5/45mm. Shutter 25-300,B. $10-15.

STEGEMANN (A. Stegemann, Berlin)
Field camera - 13x18cm. Mahogany body. Single extension square cloth bellows. Normally with Meyer or Goerz lens. $150-175.

Hand-Camera, 6.5x9cm - c1905-18. Folding strut camera. Black wooden body. Metal knee-struts. Focal plane shutter. Tessar f4.5/120mm lnes. $300-500.

Hand-Camera, 13x18cm - c1895-1905. Strut-folding camera for 13x18cm plates. Unusual design with hinged struts made of wood rather than metal. Fine wood body with nickel trim. Tapered black single pleat bellows. Folding Newton finder. Carl Zeiss

Anastigmat f7.7/195mm with iris diaphragm. $750-825.

Stereo Hand-Camera - c1905. Strut-type folding camera for 9x18cm plates. Polished black wooden body. Focal plane shutter. Sliding lens panel has provision for two separate square lensboards, allowing use as a non-stereo camera with two different lenses mounted. $400-600.

STEINECK KAMERAWERK (Tutzing)

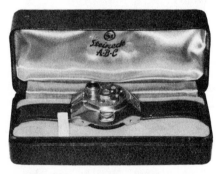

Steineck ABC Wristwatch camera - c1949. For 8 exp. on circular film in special magazine. Steinheil f2.5/12.5mm fixed focus lens. Single speed shutter. $400-450.

STEINER OPTIK (Bayreuth, Germany)
Hunter 35 - c1950. 35mm viewfinder camera. Steiner f3.5/45mm lens, shutter 1/25-1/100. $10-20.

STEINHEIL (Optische Werke C. A. Steinheil Soehne, Munich)
Casca I - c1949. Viewfinder 35. Culminar f2.8/50mm lens in special mount. Focal plane shutter 25-1000. $100-150.

Casca II - c1948. Similar to Casca I, but with coupled rangefinder. $150-200.

Detective camera - c1895. Magazine camera for 12 plates, 9x12cm. Wood body with nickel trim. Steinheil or Periskop lens. Rotary or guillotine shutter. $550-750.

Kleinfilm Kamera - c1930. Small bedless strut-folding camera for 3x4cm on 127 film. Style similar to Welta Gucki. Cassar f2.9/50mm lens in Compur 1-300. $40-60.

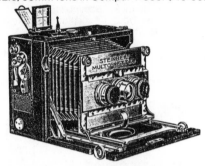

Multo Nettel - c1910-12. Folding-bed stereo camera for 3½x5½" (9x14cm) plates. Three convertible lenses on one lensboard allow for stereo or single exposures with a choice of several focal lengths. FP shutter. $375-450.

Tropical camera - 9x12cm plates. Double extension brown tapered bellows. Fine wood with nickel trim. $400-600.

STELLAR - Japanese novelty subminiature of the Hit type. $10-15.

STELLAR FLASH CAMERA - 4x4cm "Diana" type novelty camera with sync. $1-5.

STELLARFLEX - Twin lens reflex style novelty camera for 4x4cm on 127 film. Identical to the Bedfordflex and a few other names. $1-5.

STEREO CORPORATION (Milwaukee, Wisc.)
Contura - ca. mid-1950's. Stereo camera designed by Seton Rochewhite, who also designed the Stereo Realist for the David White Co. It was styled by reknowned product stylist Brooks Stevens, who was also responsible for the Excalibur automobile. It was engineered to be the finest stereo camera ever made. The f2.7/ 35mm Volar lenses focus to 24 inches with a coupled single-window rangefinder. Probably the first camera to incorporate "Auto Flash" which adjusted the diaphragm automatically based on the focus distance. The camera reached the production stage too late, just as stereo camera sales were plummeting, and a corporate decision was made to abandon the project. Ultimately, 130 cameras were assembled and sold to stockholders for $100 each. The rarity and quality of this camera keep it in demand among collectors. There are usually more offers to buy than to sell in the range of $500-600.

STEREOCRAFTERS (Milwaukee, Wisc.)
Videon - c1950's. Stereo camera for standard 35mm cassettes. Black metal and plastic construction. Iles Stereon Anastigmat f3.5/35mm lenses. Sync shutter. $75-100.

Videon II - c1953. Similar to the Videon, but top and faceplate are bright metal. $85-125.

STERLING - Hit type novelty camera. $10-15.

STERLING MINIATURE - Black plastic "minicam" for 28x40mm exposures. $3-7.

STIRN (C. P. Stirn, Stirn & Lyon, N.Y., Rudolph Stirn, Berlin)

Concealed Vest Camera, No. 1 - c1886-1892. Round camera, six inches in diameter, for 6 photos 1¾" diameter on 5" diameter glass plates. Original price, $10.00, and early ads proclaimed, "Over 15,000 sold in first 3 years." Needless to say, many are lost. $600-750. The original wooden box, which also allows the camera to be used on a tripod, doubles the value of the camera.

Concealed Vest Camera, No. 2 - c1888-1890. Similar to the above, but for 4 exposures, 2½" (6.5cm) dia. Camera measures 7" in diameter. $1000-1400.

Magazine camera - c1891. Mahogany box camera for 12 plates 6x8cm. Leather changing bag. Aplanetic lens. Rotating shutter. $500-800.

STOCK (John Stock & Co., New York, NY)
Stereo Wet-plate cameras, 5x8" - Very early models of heavier construction: $2000-3000. Later models, more common, lighter construction: $1000-1300.

STOECKIG - (Hugo Stoeckig, Dresden)
Union camera - Early folding plate cameras with leather covered wood body and finely polished interior. 9x12cm and 13x18cm sizes. With Meyer Anastigmat f7.2 or Union Aplanat f6.8 lens in Union shutter. Double extension bellows. $70-100.

SUGAYA KOKI, SUGAYA OPTICAL CO., LTD. (Japan)
Myracle, Model II - c1950. Subminiature for 14x14mm on 17.5mm rollfilm. Similar to the Hit-type cameras, but with a better lens and shutter. Hope Anastigmat f4.5. Shutter 25-100. Red, blue, or black leather. Some examples marked "Made for Mycro Camera Co. Inc. N.Y." on bottom. $35-50.

Rubix 16 - c1950's. Subminiature for 50 exposures 10x14mm on 16mm cassette film. Several variations. Hope f3.5 or 2.8/25mm. Shutter 25-100 or 25-150. $75-100.

SUMIDA OPTICAL WORKS (Japan)
Proud Chrome Six III - c1951. Japanese Super Ikonta B copy. 6x6cm or 4.5x6 cm on 120. Coupled rangefinder. Congo f3.5/75mm in Proud Synchront 1-200 shutter. B. $75-100.

SUMNER (J. Chase Sumner, Foxcroft, Maine)
Stereo rollfilm box camera - similar to the No. 2 Stereo Kodak box camera. $350-400.

SUNART PHOTO CO. (Rochester, N.Y.)
Sunart folding view - c1898. Various Vici and Vidi models. Black leather covered wood body, polished cherry interior. Double extension bellows. B&L RR lens. Unicum shutter. 5x7": $75-135. 4x5": $65-100.

Sunart Jr. - c1896. 3½x3½" and 4x5" plate box cameras, similar in style to the Cyclone Sr. $35-50.

SUNBEAM CAMERA CO.
Sunbeam Minicam - Black bakelite minicam for 16 exposures 3x4cm on 127 film. $4-8.

Sunny

SUNBEAM SIX TWENTY - Gray plastic twin-lens 6x6cm box camera. Spartus name concealed beneath Sunbeam label. $4-8.

SUNNY - Small Japanese bakelite camera for 24x24mm exposures on 35mm film. Cartridge-to-cartridge film advance with standard 35mm cartridges elimates the need to rewind. Combination eye-level direct or reflex finder with semi-silvered mirror. $30-40. *(Illus. bottom of previous page.)*

SUPEDEX VP 35 S - Inexpensive 35mm camera from Hong Kong. Simple focusing Supedex f3.5/40mm lens. Three-speed shutter. $3-7.

SUPER CAMERA - c1950. Japanese paper covered wooden "Yen" cameras for sheet film in paper holders. Folding style: $15-20. Box Style: $10-15.

SUPERIOR FLASH CAMERA 120 - 6x9cm metal box camera. Sync. $1-5.

SURUGA SEIKI CO.
Mihama Six IIIA - c1953. Horizontally styled folding camera for 6x6cm or 4.5x6cm on 120 film. Separate eye-level finders for each size. Mihama or Kepler Anastigmat f3.5 in NKS shutter. $40-60.

SUTER (E. Suter, Basel, Switzerland)
Detective magazine cameras:

Early model - c1890. For 12 plates, 9x12cm. Periskop lens, guillotine shutter. Polished wood with nickel trim. $500-600.

Later model - c1893. For 20 plates, 9x12cm. Suter f8 lens with iris diaphragm, rotating shutter. Leather covered mahogany box with brass trim. $500-650.

Stereo Detective - c1895. Polished wood stereo box camera for 9x18cm plates. Not a magazine camera. $800-1100.

Stereo Detective, Magazine - c1893. Leather covered stereo magazine camera, for 6 plates 9x18cm. The built-in magazine changing-box sits below the camera body and is operated by pulling on a knob. f10/90mm Rectilinear lenses. Coupled rotary sector shutters. $800-1000.

Stereo Muro - c1890's. Press-type body, side struts, 9x18cm plates. f5/85mm Suter lenses. FP shutter 30-1000. $300-400.

SUZUKI OPTICAL CO. (Japan)

Camera-Lite - c1950. Cigarette-lighter spy

camera which looks like a Zippo lighter. Very similar to the Echo 8. A supply of Camera-Lites was discovered at a flea market about 1966-67, but released slowly into the collector market. This helped to maintain the same market value for several years. $175-225.

Camera-Lite Seastar - Normal Camera-Lite, but with Seastar logo on narrow back edge of body. We don't know the origin or meaning, but one sold at auction in late 1985 for $350.

Tachibana Beby Pilot

TAISEI KOKI (Japan)

Echo 8 - 1951-56. Cigarette-lighter camera. Designed to look like a Zippo lighter, it also takes 5x8mm photos with its Echor f3.5/15mm lens on film in special cassettes. There are at least two sizes, the larger measuring 17x47x58mm and the earlier but more common smaller size measuring 15x42x56mm. There were also different film cassettes, either "square" or "rapid" shaped. Also sold under the name Europco-8. $175-225. With presentation box and film slitter add $100.

Press Van - c1953. Japanese 6x6cm strut-folding rangefinder camera Two variations: One takes an alternate image size of 4.5x6cm on 120, the other 24x36mm on 35mm film. Takumar f3.5/75mm in Seikosha Rapid shutter 1-500,B. $250-350.

SWALLOW - Hit type novelty subminiature. $10-15.

TACHIBANA TRADING CO. (Japan)
Beby Pilot - c1940. Bakelite-bodied folding camera for 3x4cm on 127 film. Pirot (sic) Anastigmat f4.5/50mm in "Pilot,O" shutter. $60-75. *(Illustrated top of next column.)*

TAHBES (Holland)
Populair - c1955. All metal camera with telescoping front. Nickel-plated body with chrome front: $50-60. Leatherette-covered model with black faceplate: $20-40.

Welmy Six - c1951. Folding camera for 6x6cm on 120 film. Terionar f4.5/75mm or f3.5/75mm lens. Shutter 1-200 or 1-300. Eye-level and waist-level finders. $25-35.

Welmy 35 - c1954. Non-rangefinder folding 35mm. Terionar f3.5 or f2.8/50mm lens. Welmy shutter 25-150,B. $20-25.

Welmy M-3 - c1956. Rangefinder model with Terionar f3.5/45mm in 5-300 shutter. $20-25.

Welmy Wide - c1958. 35mm viewfinder camera with Taikor f3.5/35mm lens. Shutter 25-200,B. $20-25.

TAIYODO KOKI (T.K.K., Japan)
Beauty - c1949, occupied Japan subminiature. Eye-level and deceptive angle finders. f4.5/20mm fixed focus lens. B,25-100 shutter. $50-75. *(Illustrated top of next page.)*

Taiyodo Beauty

Beauty Canter - c1957. Coupled rangefinder 35mm. Canter f2.8/45mm lens. Copal-MXV 1-500,B. $20-30.

Beauty 35 Super II - c1958. 35mm CRF. Canter f2/45mm in Copal SV 1-500,B shutter. Lever advance. $20-30.

Beauty Super L - c1958. Similar to Super II, but with built-in meter with booster. Canter-S f1.9/45mm. $25-35.

Beautycord - c1955. 6x6cm TLR for 120 film. Beauty f3.5/80mm in 10-200 shutter. $25-35.

Beautyflex - c1950-55. 6x6cm TLR. Several slight variations, but usually with f3.5/80mm Doimer Anastigmat lens. 1-200 shutter. $25-35.

Epochs - c1948. Heavy cast metal subminiature for 14x14mm on "Midget" size rollfilm. Identical to the Vestkam and Meteor cameras. "Epochs" on top only, not on face of shutter. This name is not common. Talent f3.5/20mm. TKK shutter 25,50,B. $125-175.

Meteor - c1949. Same as Epochs, except for name. "Meteor" name on top and shutter face. This name is not common. Vestkam f4.5/25mm lens. TKK shutter 25,50,B. $125-175.

Reflex Beauty II

410

Reflex Beauty - c1954-56. Japanese copy of the Kochmann Reflex Korelle for 6x6cm on 120 film. This was the first 6x6cm SLR from Japan. Canter f3.5/75mm lens. Focal plane shutter to 500. Model I has chrome nameplate with script lettering. Model II has embossed nameplate and bayonet-mounted lens. $75-125. *(Model II illustrated bottom of previous page.)*

Vestkam - c1949. Same as Epochs and Meteor, except for name. Marked "Made in Occupied Japan". This is the most common name. Vestkam f3.5/20mm. TKK shutter 25,50,B. $80-125.

TAIYOKOKI CO., LTD. (Japan)
Viscawide-16 - c1961. Panoramic camera for 10 exposures 10x46mm on specially loaded 16mm film. Lausar f3.5/25mm lens. Shutter 60-300. 120 degree angle of view. $150-200.

TAKAHASHI OPTICAL WORKS
Arsen - c1938-1942. Similar to the more common Gelto, but for 12 exp. 4x4cm on 127 film rather than 16 exp. Collapsible front. f3.5 or f4.5/50mm lens in 5-250 shutter. $45-60.

TALBOT (Romain Talbot, Berlin) *Makers of the Errtee cameras. In German, the letters R.T. (for R. Talbot) are pronounced "Err-Tee".*

Errtee button tintype camera - c1912. A cylindrical "cannon" for 100 button tintypes 25mm diameter. Processing tank hangs below camera and exposed plates drop through chute. Laack f4.5/60mm lens. Single speed shutter. $700-1000.

Errtee folding plate camera - c1930. 9x12cm. Double extension bellows. Dialytar or Laack Pololyt f4.5/135mm lens. Compur shutter 1-200. $25-35.

Errtee folding rollfilm camera, 6x9cm - For 120 rollfilm. Anastigmat Talbotar f4.5/105mm in Vario shutter 25-100. Brown bellows, brown leather covering: $30-45.

Black leathered: $20-30.
-5x8cm size - Poloyt Anastigmat f6.3/90mm in Vero shutter. Black leather and bellows. $20-35.

TALBOT (Walter Talbot, Berlin)

Invisible Camera - c1915-1930. Unusual camera shaped like a 7cm wide belt, 34cm long, with a film chamber at each end. The camera is made to be concealed under a vest with the lens protruding from a buttonhole. The versions advertised around 1930 are made for 35mm daylight-loading cartridges, but these ads usually mention that the camera had been in use for "over 15 years", (before there were standard 35mm cartridges.) We suspect that they were not commercially available in the early years. This suspicion is based on the lack of advertising until the late 1920's, and also because of their rarity in the current collector market. Rare. Price negotiable.

TALBOT & EAMER CO. (London, England)

Talmer - c1890. Magazine box camera with changing bag. 8x10.5cm plates. $300-350.

TANAKA OPTICAL CO., LTD. (Japan)

Tanack, Type IV-S - c1955. Copy of Leica IIIb. Tanar f2/50mm lens. Shutter 1-500. $75-125.

TARGET (Paris)

New Folding Stereo - Folding bed stereo camera for 9x18cm plates. Leathered wood body, polished wood interior, nickel trim. Stereo shutter built into wooden lensboard. Focusing knob on front of bed. $250-300.

TARON CO. (Japan)
Chic - c1961. Vertically styled camera for 18x24mm half-frames on 35mm film. Taronar f2.8/30mm. Taron-LX shutter controlled by selenium meter. $20-30.

TAUBER - c1920's. German 9x12cm folding plate camera. Rapid Aplanat f8/135mm lens. $25-35.

TAYLOR (A & G Taylor, England)
View camera - Tailboard style ½-plate mahogany view. Clement & Gilmer brass barrel lens, iris diaphragm. $175-225.

TECHNICOLOR CORP.
Techni-Pak 1 - c1960. Plastic 126 factory loaded cartridge camera. Camera must be returned for processing and reloading. $1-5.

TEDDY CAMERA CO. (Newark, NJ)
Teddy Model A - c1924. Stamped metal camera in bright red and gold finish. Takes

direct positive prints 2x3½" which develop in tank below camera. Original price just $2.00 in 1924. Current value with tank: $300-400.

TEEMEE - Japanese novelty subminiature of the Hit type. $10-15.

TELLA CAMERA CO. LTD. (London, England)
No. 3 Magazine Camera - c1899. Leather covered box camera for 50 films in a filmpack. Taylor Hobson f6.5, pneumatic shutter. Detachable rise/cross front. $350-500.

Tennar Junior

TENNAR, TENNAR JUNIOR - c1954. Folding cameras for 6x9cm, 620 film. Made in Italy. $12-18.

TEX - c1949. German miniature for 3x4cm on unperforated 35mm film. Collapsing Vidar or Helur f4.5/50mm lens, Singlo or Compur shutter. Most common with Helur in Singlo. Body identical to the Nova camera. $75-100.

THOMAS (W. Thomas, London)
Wet-plate camera - c1870. Folding-bed bellows camera for ½-plates. Brass trim. f11 lens. $800-1200.

THOMPSON (W. J. Thompson Co., NY) Direct positive street camera - Box-style street tintype camera. Plates, devloping tank, etc. all packed inside the camera's body. $75-125.

THORNTON-PICKARD MFG. CO.
(Altrincham, England) *The company was formed in 1888 when Mr. Edgar Pickard joined the Thornton Manufacturing Co. Its first major product was the T-P roller blind shutter and it soon claimed "the largest sale in the world". T-P undertook a short-lived and relatively unsuccessful scheme to break into the American market in 1894. Camera production concentrated on the Ruby field camera which really took off after 1896 with the introduction of the cheaper version, the Amber. It also produced a range of folding and pocket type cameras in an attempt to break into Kodak's market.*
The firm prospered until 1914 when the war upset production and marketing. Immediately post-war the firm's position seemed hopeful but to consolidate its position T-P was involved with APM in 1921 and Soho Ltd in the 1930's. This did nothing, however, to halt its decline which resulted from a lack of investment. T-P ceased to exist in 1940 although the name was kept alive until at least 1963.

Aerial Camera, Type C - c1915. Brass reinforced mahogany camera for 4x5" plates in special magazines. Long body accomodates Ross Xpres f4.5/10¼" lens. Focal plane shutter. Detachable cylindrical brass finder. Only one recorded sale, in 1986 for $2600 with original wooden case.

Amber - c1899-1905. Compact "English style" folding view camera. Sizes from ¼ to full plate. Front door/bed often has turntable for tripod legs. Round opening in bed allows lens and shutter to protrude when camera is folded. $75-125.

Automan (Nimrod Automan, Oxford Automan) - c1904. Hand and stand folding plate camera made in 3¼x4¼" and 4x5" sizes. Polished mahogany interior. Leather covered exterior. Red bellows. Aldis Anastigmat f6 lens. B&L Automat or T-P Panoptic shutter. $75-120.

College - c1912-26. Compact folding double extension field camera. Five sizes from 9x12cm to 18x24cm. Mahogany and brass. Thornton-Pickard Rectoplant lens in rollerblind shutter. $75-125.

Duplex Ruby Reflex - c1920-30. SLR. Aldis Anastigmat f4.5. FP shutter. $75-100.

Duplex Ruby Reflex, Tropical - SLR. 6.5x9cm and ¼-plate sizes. Teak and brass. Double extension orange bellows. Focal plane shutter to 1000. Cooke Anastigmat f6.3 lens. $1800-2200. *(Illustrated top of next column.)*

Thornton-Pickard Duplex Ruby Reflex, Tropical

Folding plate camera, 5x7" - c1890. Zeiss Unar f5/210mm lens. Focal plane shutter 15-80. $150-180.

Folding Ruby - c1920's. 3¼x4¼" folding plate camera. Revolving back, fine wood interior, leathered exterior, various correctional movements. Cooke Anastigmat f6.5 lens. $125-175.

Imperial Pocket - c1916. Folding-bed plate cameras. Lower priced models have wood body, single extension metal bed. Better models have all metal body, rack focusing. $25-35.

Imperial Stereo - c1910. Folding bed camera, 9x18cm. Accomodates single or stereo lensboards. $250-350.

Imperial Triple Extension - c1904-26. ½-plate size. One of the more advanced field cameras with triple extension tapered leather bellows. Mahogany with brass trim. Rollerblind shutter. Beck Symmetrical or T-P Rectoplanat lens. Common in England. $90-140. Somewhat higher elsewhere.

Junior Special Ruby Reflex - c1928.

Mark III Hythe Camera

Press-type SLR, 6x9cm on plates or 120 rollfilm back. Black leather covering. Dallmeyer Anastigmat f4.5/130mm. FP shutter 10-1000, T. $75-90.

Limit - c1912. Small rigid body camera for 4.5x6cm plates or rollfilm. Cooke f6.3/55mm in telescoping mount. FP shutter 15-100, T. $800-1000.

Mark III Hythe Camera - c1915-25. Used in WWI to train British R.A.F. machine gunners to hit a moving target from a moving plane. Has the look and feel of a machine gun. Records images of the target as the trigger is pulled. The first two models were hastily prepared to fill the immediate needs while the Mark III was perfected. 4.5x6cm on 120 rollfilm. f8/300mm. Central shutter. $300-600. *(Illustrated top of this page.)*

Puck Special - 4x5" plate box camera. Focus and shutter adjustable. $50-60.

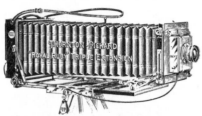

Royal Ruby - c1904-30. Folding plate camera, same as the Ruby, but triple extension model. $175-250.

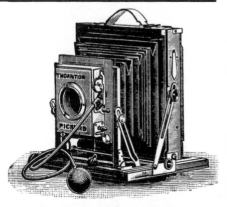

Ruby - c1899-1905. Compact folding field camera. Front door becomes baseboard, with tripod legs fastening to built-in turntable. Ruby R.R. lens. T-P rollerblind shutter. $100-160.

Ruby Deluxe - c1912. Mahogany ¼-plate SLR with brass binding. Goerz Dogmar or Ross Xpres f4.5 lens. Focal plane shutter 10-1000. $125-225.

Ruby Reflex - c1928. 4x5" SLR. Ross Homocentric f6.3/6". FP shutter. $150-250. *(Illustrated top of next page.)*

Ruby Reflex

Ruby Speed Camera - c1925. Small focal plane camera with f2 lens. Inspired by the 1924 Ermanox. Even the folding optical finder is the same. Taylor-Hobson Cooke Anastigmat f2/3" lens in helical focusing mount. Machined cast aluminum body with leather covering. Focal plane shutter T, 1/10-1000. Only one recorded sale, at auction in 1985 for about $2700.

Rubyette No. 1, No. 2 - c1934. SLR. 6.5x9cm for plates or rollfilm. Dallmeyer Anastigmat f8, f4.5 or f2.9 lens. FP shutter 10-1000. $150-250.

Special Ruby Reflex - c1923-38. 2¼x3¼" or 3¼x4¼" sizes. Cooke Anastigmat f4.5 lens. Focal plane shutter. $125-175.

Stereo Puck - c1925. Cheap black covered wood box camera. 6x8.5cm on 120 film. Meniscus lenses, simple shutter. $50-80.

Victory Reflex - c1925. 2¼x3¼" SLR. Dallmeyer or Cooke lens. $75-100.

THORPE (J. Thorpe, NY)
Four-tube camera - c1862-64. Wet-plate camera. 4 lenses for up to 4 exposures on a 5x7" plate. One on record in 1980 with wet-plate holder and dipping tank: $1250.

THOWE CAMERAWERK (Freital & Berlin)
9x12cm folding plate camera - c1910. Leather covered wood body. Doxanar f6/135mm. Shutter 25-100. $25-35.

Field camera, 9x12cm - Horizontal format. Rear bellows extension. Blue square bellows with black corners. Meyer Primotar f3.5/115mm. $100-150.

Tropical plate camera, 9x12cm - Folding bed camera. Reptile leather covering. Brown double extension bellows. Brown lacquered metal parts. Brass trim. $250-300.

TIME - Minimum-quality 35mm camera from Taiwan. All black plastic with red & white "TIME" on front of top housing. Given free with $20 subscription to TIME magazine in mid-l985. $1-5.

TIME FC-100 - Similar to the above, but with model number and slight variation in body style. Given free during the same promotion, this version of the camera showed up in Australia. $1-5. *(Illustrated above with Time camera.)*

TIME-FIELD CO. (Newark, Delaware)
Pin-Zip 126 - c1984. Cardboard camera with drilled brass pinhole. Uses 126 cartridge film. An interesting modern pinhole camera, named for the sound made by the light as it enters the pinhole. $5-10.

TIRANTY (Paris)
Stereo Pocket - Jumelle type stereo camera for 45x107mm plates. Transpar f4.5/54mm lenses in Jack shutter 25-100, B,T. With magazine back: $125-175.

TISDELL & WHITTELSEY (pre-1893)
TISDELL CAMERA & MFG. CO. (post-1893) (New York)

T & W Detective Camera - c1888.

Detective box camera for 3¼x4¼" plates. All wood box. Truncated pyramid rather than bellows for focusing. Achromatic meniscus lens. Rare. One sold a few years ago for $1200, and another for $2800.

Tisdell Hand Camera - c1893. In 1893, the name of the T & W Detective Camera was changed to "Tisdell Hand Camera". Leather covered. Internal bellows focus. $400-650.

TIVOLI - c1895. English ½-plate camera. Mahogany body. Rectilinear lens. $175-225.

TIZER CO. LTD.
Can Camera 110 TX Coca-Cola - 1978. Camera the size and color of a Japanese 250ml Coke can. 110 cartridge film. Synched and non-synched versions. Fixed focus. Single speed shutter. $35-65. *See Eiko Co. Ltd. for later can cameras from Hong Kong.*

TOAKOKI SEISAKUSHO (Japan)

Gelto D III - c1938 and 1950. ½-frame 127 film cameras. Pre-war model has black body and Grimmel f4.5/50mm lens in collapsible mount. Post-war model has chrome body and f3.5 lens. Common

features include: eye-level optical finder, shutter T,B,5-250. $45-75.

TOGODO OPTICAL CO. (Japan)
Established in 1930 by Masanori Nagatsuka and named for Admiral Tougo of the Japanese Navy. ("Togodo" and "Tougodo" are roman spelling variations of the same name.) See Tougodo.

TOHOKOKEN CAMERA CO.
Camel Model II - c1953. Inexpensive 35mm camera with styling similar to Canon, but with front shutter and no rangefinder. Even the type style for the name "Camel" is similar to the style used by Canon. Camel f3.5/50mm. Nippol 1-200 shutter. $30-45.

TOKIWA SEIKI CO. (Japan)
Bioflex - c1951. TLR for 6x6cm on 120 film. First Anastigmat f3.5/8cm lens, externally gear-coupled to the viewing lens. B,10-200 shutter. Not to be confused with the cheap plastic Bioflex novelty camera. $20-30.

First Six I, III, V - c1952-54. Horizontal folding cameras for 6x6cm or 4.5x6cm on 120 rollfilm. Separate viewfinder for each image size on Models I, III. Model V has uncoupled rangefinder. Neogonor Tri-Lauser Anastigmat f3.5/80mm. (See First Camera Works for an earlier camera with the same name.) $40-60.

Firstflex - c1951-55. A series of 6x6cm TLR cameras. f3.5/80mm. Some models have shutters to 1/200, others have MSK 1-400 shutter, B. Cheaply made. $15-25.

Firstflex 35 (1955 type) - 35mm SLR with waist-level finder. Removable bayonet-mount f3.5/50mm lens. Behind-the-lens leaf shutter 25-150,B. $75-100.

Firstflex 35 (1958 type) - 35mm SLR with built-in prism. Mirror acts as shutter. Exa/Exakta bayonet mounted Auto Tokinon f2.8/45mm. Also sold under the Plusflex name in England and GM 35 SLR in the USA. $35-50.

Lafayette 35 - c1955. Export version of the Firstflex 35. Waist level finder. Interchangeable Soligor Anastigmat f3.5/50mm lens. behind-the-lens leaf shutter B,25-100. $75-100.

TOKYO KOGAKU (Japan)
Cyclops - c1950's. 16mm Japanese binocular camera, identical to the Teleca. f4.5/35mm lens. Shutter 250-100. $300-450. *(Illustrated top of next page.)*

Laurelflex - c1951. 6x6cm TLR. Toko or Similar f3.5/75mm. Konan Rapid-S or Seikosha Rapid 1-500, B. $30-40.

Tokyo Kogaku Cyclops

Minion - c1939. Folding bed camera for 4x5cm on 127 film. Toko f3.5/60mm. Seikosha Licht 25-100, B,T. $50-75.

Minion 35 - c1948. Viewfinder 35. Toko f3.5/40mm. Seikosha Rapid 1-500, B. $50-75.

Primo Jr. - c1958. 4x4cm TLR for 127 film. Sold in the U.S.A. by Sawyers. Topcor f2.8/60mm. Seikosha 1-500,B. $80-110.

Tokyo Koken Dolca 35

Komeil f3.5/50mm lens in Nipol shutter B,1-200. ASA sync post. $25-45.

TOKYO KOKI CO. (Japan)

Teleca - c1950. 10x14mm subminiature 16mm telephoto camera built into binoculars. Non-prismatic field glasses have camera mounted on top center. $300-450.

Topcon RE Super - Introduced 1963. The first fully 35mm SLR with fully coupled through the lens metering system. (Note that the Mec-16 SB subminiature already had a coupled behind the lens metering system in 1960.)Removable prism. FP shutter 1-1000. With f1.4/58mm lens: $100-150.

TOKYO KOKEN CO. (Tokyo)
Dolca 35 (Model I) - c1953. Leaf-shutter 35mm camera without rangefinder. Extensible front with helical housing.

Rubina Sixteen Model II - c1951. Subminiature for unperforated 16mm film in special cassettes. Made in Occupied Japan. Ruby f3.5/25mm lens. Shutter 25-100,B. $100-125.

TOKYO SEIKI CO. LTD. *see Rocket Camera Co.*

Doris - c1952. Folding camera for 4.5x6 cm on 120. "Occupied Japan". Perfa Anastigmat f3.5/75mm lens, NKS shutter B,10-200. $15-20.

TOP CAMERA WORKS

Top - c1948. Cast metal subminiature from Occupied Japan. Eye-level frame finder. Fixed focus lens. B,I shutter. Same as the pre-war "Guzzi" camera. Not to be confused with the boxy rectangular "Top" subminiatures from Maruso Trading Co. $75-125.

TOPPER - Cheap plastic box camera for 127 film. Long shutter release plunger on left side. This is the same camera which is built into the Secret Sam Attache Camera and Dictionary. $3-7.

TOSEI OPTICAL (Japan)

Frank Six - c1951. Folding camera for 6x6cm or 4.5x6 cm on 120. f3.5/75mm Anastigmat lens. T.K.S. shutter B,1-200. Optical eye-level viewfinder. $30-40.

TOUGODO OPTICAL (Japan)

Baby-Max - c1951. Novelty subminiature, similar in construction to "Hit" types, but different shape. f11/30mm fixed focus lens. Single-speed shutter. $15-25.

Buena 35-S - c1957. Export version of the Toyoca 35S. Buena f3.5/45mm lens. Shutter B,25-300. $25-35.

Click - c1951. Subminiature camera of "Hit" type. $10-15.

Colly - c1951. "Hit" type subminiature for 14x14mm exposures. Meniscus f11 lens. $10-15.

Hit - c1950's. Japanese novelty camera for 14x14mm exposures on 16mm paper backed rollfilm. Similar cameras are available under a number of other names, but usually called "Hit type" cameras by collectors. Many of these were probably made by Tougodo, but some have come from other manufacturers. Gold models: $40-60. "Occupied Japan" model ("Made in Occupied Japan" below lens): $35-50.

Normal chrome models: $10-15.

Hobiflex, Model III - c1952. 6x6cm TLR. Externally gear-coupled lenses. Hobi Anastigmat or Tri-Lausar f3.5/80. Shutter 1-200,B. $20-25.

Hobix - c1951. Compact camera for 28x28mm on Bolta-size film. All-metal. Meniscus f8/40mm. Complete shutter, B,25,50,100. $20-30.

Hobix Junior - c1955. Inexpensive camera for 28x28mm on Bolta-size rollfilm. Fixed focus lens; B,I shutter with PC sync. $15-20.

Kino-44 - c1959. Baby Rollei-style TLR for 4x4cm on 127. Kinokkor f3.5/60mm in Citizen MXV 1-500 shutter. $35-50.

Leader - c1955. Japanese 35mm stereo. Looks like the Windsor Stereo. Black bakelite with aluminum trim. Leader Anastigmat f4.5/45mm lenses, 3 speed shutter 1/25-1/100. Takes single or stereo exposures. $75-125.

Meikai - c1937. Twin lens reflex for 35mm film. In addition to the normal viewfinder for eye-level framing, this uniquely Japanese design incorporates a waist-level reflex finder with true twin-lens focusing. The lenses are located side-by-side, which allowed the overall size to be only barely larger than a standard 35mm rangefinder camera. The first two models used "No Need Darkroom" sheet film in paper holders for daylight developing. (See "Yen-Kame" for description of this process.) The first rollfilm versions c1939 used 16-exposure spools of paper-backed 35mm wide rollfilm for 3x4cm exposures. Meikai f3.5 or f4.5/50mm Anastigmat. Later models had f3.8/50mm Meikai Anastigmat. $300-450.

Meikai EL - c1963. Cheap 35mm viewfinder novelty camera. Imitation exposure meter on front. Fixed focus lens, simple shutter. $8-12.

Meisupi, Meisupi II, Meisupi IV - c1937. Side-by-side twin lens camera for 3x4cm on sheet film. Uncommon. $300-500.

Meisupii Half - c1959. Simple inexpensive 35mm half-frame camera. $8-12.

Metraflex II - TLR for 6x6cm on 120 film. Metar Anastigmat f3.5/80mm. $50-75.

Stereo Hit - c1955. Plastic stereo camera for 127 film. S-Owla f4.5/90mm lens. B,I synch shutter. $100-150.

Tougo Camera - 1930. Tougo Camera was the first of the popular "Yen" cameras from Japan, produced by Tougo-do in the Kanda district of Tokyo. The camera itself is of simple construction, with a wood body

with a paper covering, ground glass back, and simple shutter. The most historically significant feature was the novel film system, which incorporated a 3x4cm sheet of film in a paper holder. The disposable film holder also carried the film through the developing process without the need of a darkroom. The process used a red-colored developer, which effectively filtered daylight into red light. Its simplicity made it very popular, and soon there were many other simple "Yen" cameras on the market. An early example (clearly identified "Tougo Camera" on the shutter face) would easily fetch $50+ from a knowledgeable collector, while the later versions usually sell for $10-15.

Toyoca 16 - c1955. 14x14mm subminiature, styled like a miniature 35mm. "Toyoca 16" on top. Two models; essentially identical except that the "improved" model has exposure counting numbers on the winding knob. $80-95. *Not to be confused with at least two other styles of "Toyoca" which are cheaper novelty cameras of the "Hit" type.*

Toyoca 35 - c1957. 35mm RF camera. Lausar f2.8 or Owla f3.5/45mm. $30-35.

Toyocaflex - c1954. 6x6cm Rolleicord copy. Triotar or Tri-Lausar f3.5/80mm. Synchro NKS 25-300 or 1-200. $25-40.

Toyocaflex 35 - c1955. Side-by-side 35mm TLR. Direct and reflex finders. Owla

Anastigmat f3.5/45mm viewing and taking lenses. NSK shutter 1-300, B. $150-250.

TOWN - Unusual marriage of two Japanese specialties of the postwar period. This camera is styled just like the Hit types, but is considerably larger, taking 24x24mm exp. on "Bolta-size" film. "Made in Occupied Japan" on front. Unusual and uncommon. Only one known sale, in 1984 for $100.

TOY'S CLAN

Donald Duck Camera - Plastic camera shaped like Donald Duck's head. The lens is in one eye and the viewfinder in the other. The tongue serves as a shutter release lever. Takes 3x4cm photos on 127 film. Made in Hong Kong. We saw one at a German auction in the 1970's, but never again until 1984 when a small number, new in boxes, came into circulation and rapidly began selling to avid duck fans for $60-90.

TOYO KOGAKU (TOKO, Japan)
Mighty - c1947. Made in Occupied Japan. Subminiature for 13x13mm exposures on "Midget" size rollfilm. Meniscus lens, single speed. With auxiliary telephoto attachment in case: $75-125. Camera only: $50-75. *(Illustrated in next column.)*

Trambouze Plate camera

Toyo Kogaku Mighty

Tone - c1948. Subminiature for 14x14mm on "Midget" size rollfilm. Made in Occupied Japan. Eye-level and waist-level finders. f3.5/25mm lens in 3 speed shutter. $75-100.

TOYOCA - Lightweight Japanese novelty camera of the Hit type. $10-15. *Not to be confused with the heavy "Toyoca 16" made by Tougodo.*

TRAID CORPORATION (Encino, CA)

Fotron & Fotron III - Grey and black plastic cameras of the 1960's, originally sold by door-to-door salesmen for prices ranging from $150 to $300 and up. The cameras were made to take 10 exposures 1x1" on special cartridges containing 828 film. They featured many high-class advancements such as built-in electronic flash with rechargeable batteries, electric film advance, etc. At the time these cameras were made, these were expensive features. Still, the Fotron camera campaign is considered by some to be the greatest photographic "rip-off" of the century. $25-35.

TRAMBOUZE (Paris)
Plate camera - 13x18cm. Tailboard style. Brass barreled f8 lens. $175-225.
(Illustrated top of previous page.)

TRAVELER - 14x14mm "Hit" type Japanese novelty subminiature. $10-15.

TRAVELLER - Simple plastic Hong Kong 6x6cm TLR-style novelty camera. Shutter 25, 50. $10-15.

TRIOFLEX - Post-war Japanese TLR. Tri-Lausar f3.5/80mm lens. $50-75.

TRU-VIEW - 4x4cm "Diana" type novelty camera. $1-5.

TRUSITE CAMERA CO.

Girl Scout Official Camera - Like the Trusite Minicam, but with Girl Scout faceplate. $25-35.

Trusite Minicam - c1947. Cast metal

Trusite Minicam

minicam for 3x4cm on 127 film. $5-10.

T.S.C. TACKER - 14x14mm subminiature from Occupied Japan. f4.5 lens, rotary disc stops. Shutter 25, 50, 100, B. $150-175.

TURILLON (Louis Turillon, Paris)

Photo-Ticket No. 2 - c1905. Aluminum jumelle-style rollfilm camera; No. 2 for 4x5cm, No. 3 for 4.5x6cm. Petzval-type f4.5/95mm. FP shutter. $800-1200.

TURRET CAMERA CO. (Brooklyn, N.Y.)

Panoramic camera - c1905. For 4x10" panoramic views. $700-900.

TYLAR (William T. Tylar, Birmingham, England)

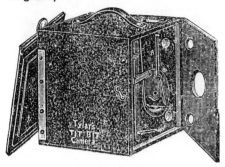

Uca Ucaflex

Tit-bit - c1895. Makes 2 exposures on a 6x9cm plate. Lens is mounted on circular plate which is rotated to position it over one half of the plate to make the first exposure, then rotated again over the other side to make the second exposure. $250-350.

TYNAR CORP. (Los Angeles, CA)

Tynar - c1950. Shaped like a small movie camera (similar to Universal Minute 16). For 14 exposures, 10x14mm on specially loaded 16mm cassettes. f6.3/45mm lens. Single speed guillotine shutter. $20-30.

UCA (Uca Werkstatten fuer Feinmechanik & Optik, Flensburg, Germany) *Associated with the Elop Kamerawerk of Flensburg.*
Ucaflex - c1950. 35mm SLR. Elolux f1.9/50mm lens. Focal plane shutter, 1-1000. Also sold under the name Elcaflex. $275-375. *(Illustrated top of next column.)*

Ucanett - c1952. 35mm camera for 24x24mm. Ucapan f2.5/40mm in Prontor-S. Successor of Elop Elca II. $80-110.

UCET - Box camera for 6.5x11cm. $5-10.

ULCA CAMERA CORP. (Pittsburgh, PA)

Ulca - c1935. 20x20mm on rollfilm. Meniscus lens, simple shutter. Cast steel body. $30-50. *Note: Ulca cameras were also made in England and Germany. The shutter settings are the best indication of country of origin. TMS & STM are German. STI- English. TSL- American.*

UNDERWOOD (E. & T. Underwood; Birmingham, England)

Field camera - 8x11cm. Rear extension, square leather bellows. Brass-barrel

Underwood f11 lens with iris diaphragm. Thornton-Pickard shutter. Swing-out ground glass. $150-200.

Instanto - c1896. Mahogany quarter plate tailboard camera. Underwood landscape lens. $75-125.

Stereograph - c1896. Tailboard style stereo camera. Almost identical to the Instanto, but with stereo lenses. $300-425.

UNGER & HOFFMAN (Dresden)
Verax - Precision folding plate cameras, 4.5x6cm and 6.5x9cm sizes. Ground glass back. Single extension bellows. f3.5 or 4.5 lens. Compound shutter 1-300. $50-75.

Verax Gloria - c1924. Deluxe version of 4.5x6cm Verax. Brown morocco leather covering with light brown bellows. Dogmar f4.5/75mm in Compur 1-300. $250-350.

UNITED OPTICAL INSTRUMENTS (England)

Merlin - c1936. Cast-metal 20x20mm subminiature. Black, blue, or green crackle-finish enamel. No identification on the camera except small name decal on some examples. $50-100. *(Illustrated on back cover.)*

UNITED STATES CAM-O CORP.
Cam-O - Oddly shaped wooden TLR "School camera". 250 exposures 4x6.5cm on 70mm film. Wollensak Raptar f4.5/117mm. Alphax shutter. $35-50.

UNITED STATES CAMERA CORP. (Chicago)
Box and TLR cameras - c1960's. Cheap cameras such as Reflex, Reflex II, Vagabond, etc. $1-5. *(Vagabond illustrated top of next column.)*

Auto Fifty - TLR for 6x6cm on 120. Biokor f3.5/80mm. Synchro MX 1-300, B.

Made in Japan. $25-40.

United States Camera Vagabond

Auto Forty - Good quality TLR, made in Japan. Rack and pinion focus. Tritar Anast. f3.5/8cm. Synchronized shutter, B, 25-300. Automatic film stop and exposure counter. $20-30.

Automatic - c1960. Cast aluminum TLR with black plastic hood and front. Selenium meter cell above viewing lens for automatic exposure. 6x6cm on 620 film. Fixed focus lens. $30-40.

Rollex 20 - c1950. Folding 6x9cm rollfilm camera with self-erecting front. Cheap construction. $4-8.

USC 35 - Viewfinder 35mm. Made in Germany. Built-in extinction meter. Steinheil Cassar f2.8/45mm. Vario 25-200 shutter. $15-25.

UNIVERSAL CAMERA CORP. (NYC) *The Universal Camera Corporation was founded on January 26, 1933 in New York by Otto Wolff Githens and Jacob J. Shapiro. Githens, a former New York loan company executive and Shapiro, ex-vice president of an Indianapolis insurance firm formed the company on the assumption that what America needed most was a photographic line that would be affordable to everyone. The company boasted of manufacturing "more cameras per year than any other company in the world". That claim may very well have been true. Their first venture, Univex Model A, at a cost of $.39, sold over 3 million in 3 years. Universal's early success was not solely attributed to the sale of inexpensive cameras; but more so to the sale of the low-cost six exposure rollfilm that was necessary to utilize these cameras. The #00 rollfilm, which was packaged in Belgium on a special patented V-spool, sold for only $.10 in the United States. Twenty-two million rolls were sold by 1938. The special Univex films proved to be one of the major factors responsible for the company's collapse twenty years later.*

Universal became involved with home movies in 1936, when it introduced the model A-8 camera for just under $10 and its companion P-8 projector for less than $15. They used a special Univex Single-8 film, manufactured by Ansco. In the next two years, 250,000 cameras and 175,000 projectors were sold.

During Universal's brief existence, it manufactured almost forty different still and movie cameras and a complete line of photographic accessories. The 1939 New York World's Fair provided Universal with an opportunity to exhibit the newly introduced non-standard 35mm Mercury and the new B-8 and C-8 movie cameras.

Universal verged on bankruptcy in 1940, when all film shipments from Belgium were temporarily suspended because of the war in Europe. Two years later there was still a film shortage, even though Universal was now packaging its film in the United States. The U.S. entry in the war brought Universal a government contract to manufacture binoculars, gunsights, and other optics, and by 1943 Universal had acquired $6,000,000 in sales from the United States government.

After the war, Universal returned to its pre-war line of cameras, some of which were given different names. Having gained experience in optics during the war years, Universal was now able to manufacture most of their own lenses. Universal again met with financial difficulties during the 1948-49 recession. At that time, Universal's prized post-war Mercury II was, for the most part, rejected by the public, mainly because the price had been set at more than triple that of the pre-war Mercury! Two other reasons for the eventual failure of Universal presumably were the $2,000,000 investment into the poorly designed Minute-16 and another investment into a complicated automatic phonograph. Neither of these items proved profitable. Consequently, · Universal declared bankruptcy on April 15, 1952.

Universal never gained much respect from the photographic industry, because its business practices were generally believed to be somewhat unethical. Nevertheless, the one thing that Universal will always be remembered for is the originality and ingenuity it displayed in designing some of the most unusual cameras in America.

Our thanks to Cynthia Repinski for her help with the Universal Camera Company in this section and in the movie camera section at the end of the book. Cindy is an active collector of all products of the Universal Camera Co. If you have questions on rare Universal items, you may contact Cindy at N80 W13004 Fond du Lac Ave. Apt. 24, Menomonee Falls, WI 53051.

Universal Corsair

Buccaneer - c1945. Bakelite 35mm

camera. CRF. f3.5/50mm Tricor lens. Chronomatic shutter 10-300. Built-in extinction meter, flash sync. $20-25.

Corsair I - c1938. For 24x36mm exposures on Special Univex #200 perforated 35mm film. Univex f4.5/50mm lens in rimset shutter 25-200. $20-25. *(Illustrated on previous page.)*

Corsair II - c1939. Similar to Corsair I model, but accepts standard 35mm film cartridge. $20-25.

Duovex - c1934. Two Univex A's mounted in a special attachment for stereo work. Manufactured by Pacific Coast Merchandise Co. of Los Angeles and sold as a package with a simple metal viewer and 12 mounting cards. Scarce. With viewer and original box $250-300. Camera only $130-140.

Iris - c1938. Heavy cast-metal camera for 6 exposures 1⅛x1½" on No. 00 Universal film. Vitar f7.9/50mm lens. Ilex shutter. Common. $10-15.

Iris Deluxe - c1938. Similar to the standard Iris, but with leatherette covering and chromium finish. Late Deluxe models had an adjustable focus lens, focusing to 4'. Flash models were factory mounted with a hot shoe. There is currently no price difference with or without the flash. Not common. $20-28.

Mercury (Model CC) - 1938-42. The first Mercury model. Takes 18x24mm vertical exposures on Universal No. 200 film, a special 35mm wide film. 35mm Wollensak f3.5 Tricor, f2.7 Tricor, and f2.0 Hezar lenses. Rotating focal plane shutter, 1/20-1/1000. Common. $20-35.

Mercury (Model CC-1500) - 1939-40. Similar to the standard model CC but with 1/1500 shutter speed. Same lenses as Model CC. Scarce. $120-140. *Note: This price is for the combination of the rare body and the rare Hexar lens. One without the other would only bring half as much.*

Mercury II (Model CX) - c1945. Similar to Mercury CC, but for 65 exposures on standard 35mm film. 35mm Universal Tricor f3.5, f2.7 or Hexar f2.0 lenses. Rotary shutter 20-1000. Common. $20-35.

Meteor - c1949. For 6x6cm on 620 rollfilm. Telescoping front. Extinction meter. $8-12. *(Illustrated top of next page.)*

Minute 16 - c1949. 16mm subminiature which resembles a miniature movie camera. Meniscus f6.3 lens. Guillotine shutter. Very common. With flash and original box: $35-40. Camera only: $10-15. *(Illustrated on next page.)*

Universal Meteor

Roamer I - c1948. Folding camera for 8 exposures 2¼x3¼" on 620 film. Coated f11 lens, single speed shutter, flash sync. $8-12.

Roamer II - c1948. Similar to the Roamer I. f4.5 lens. $8-12.

Stere-All - c1954. For pairs of 24x24mm exposures on 35mm film. Tricor f3.5/35mm lenses, single speed shutter. $40-55.

Universal Minute 16

Norton-Univex - c1935. Cheap black plastic camera taking 6 exposures on Univex #00 film. Because of the overwhelming success in 1933 of the Univex Model A, the Norton camera made by Norton Labs never gained public interest when introduced in 1934. The Norton-Univex appeared in 1935, after Norton Labs sold the remains of their line to Universal. Not common. $15-25.

Roamer 63 - c1948. Folding camera for 120 or 620 film. Universal Anastigmat Synchromatic f6.3/100mm lens. $8-12.

Twinflex - c1939. Plastic TLR for 1⅛x1½" (29x38mm) on No. 00 rollfilm. Meniscus lens, simple shutter. $20-25.

Uniflash - c1940. Cheap plastic camera for No. 00 rollfilm. Vitar f16/60mm lens. With original flash & box: $8-12. Camera only: $1-5. *(Illustrated on next page.)*

Uniflex, Models I & II - c1948. TLR for 120 or 620 rollfilm. Universal lens, f5.6 or 4.5/75mm. Shutter to 200. $10-20. *(Illustrated on next page.)*

Univex, Model A, Century of Progress - c1933. Special commemorative model of the simple Model A camera made for the Chicago World's Fair. $50-75.

Univex Model AF-5

Univex AF, AF-2, AF-3, AF-4, AF-5 - c1935-39. A series of compact collapsing cameras for No. 00 rollfilm. Cast metal body. Various color combinations. $10-18.

Universal Uniflash

Universal Uniflex II

Univex, Model A - c1933. The original small black plastic gem for No. 00 rollfilm. Similar to the Norton, which was originally designed for Universal Camera Corp. Wire frame sportsfinder attached to front of camera, and molded plastic rear sight. Cost $0.39 when new. Several minor variations. $8-15.

Univex AF, Special models - c1936-38. Special faceplates and colors transformed the normal Univex AF into a promotional or premium camera. These include such models as the Official Girl Scout model, G.E. Toppers Club Convention, or the Hollywood. $25-45.

Vitar - c1951. Viewfinder 35mm. Extinction meter. Telescoping Anastigmat f3.5/50mm lens. This camera was a promotional item and supposedly never advertised to the public. Not common. $20-25.

Zenith - c1939. Lightweight aluminum body, leatherette covering, chrome finish. Six exposures on Univex #00 film. Univex f4.5/50mm, shutter 25-200. Lens focuses to 3½'. Flash models were factory mounted with a hot shoe. Rare. $75-150.

UNIVERSAL RADIO MFG. CO.
Cameradio - ca. late 1940's. 3x4cm TLR box camera built into a portable tube radio. Like the Tom Thumb listed under Automatic Radio Mfg. Co. $100-125.

UTILITY MFG. CO. (New York & Chicago)
Carlton Reflex - TLR style box camera for 6x6cm. $4-8.

Falcon - 4x6.5cm folding 127 camera. Cast metal body with black or colored enamel. $10-15.

Utility Falcon Miniature

Falcon Junior - Bakelite folding vest-pocket camera for 4x6.5cm on 127 film. At least two different faceplate styles with different art-deco patterns. Colored models: $10-20. Black: $5-10.

Falcon Miniature - c1938. Minicam for 3x4cm on 127 film. Several different body styles. $3-7. *(Illustrated bottom of previous column.)*

Falcon Minicam Senior - c1939. Half-frame (3x4cm) camera for 16 exposures on 127 film. Cast aluminum body with leatherette covering. Minivar 50mm lens. Optical finder is in an elongated top housing, as though styled to look like a rangefinder. Has a body release, which is unusual for this type of camera. The same camera was also sold under the Falcon Camera Co. name in Chicago. $10-15.

Falcon Model Four - c1939-42. 6x9cm self-erecting folding camera. Pre-1940 model has black art-deco shutter face. $10-15.

Falcon Model F - c1938. This was one of the better models from Utility in 1938, selling for $17.50 with its Wollensak Velostigmat f4.5 lens in Deltax shutter. Eye-level optical finder. Body made of black "Neilite" plastic. Metal helical focusing mount. Takes 16 exposures on 127 film. $12-18.

Falcon Model FE - c1938. Same as Model F, but with extinciton meter in top housing next to viewfinder. $15-20.

Falcon Model G - c1938. Half-frame 127. Wollensak f3.5/50mm. Alphax 25-200 shutter. Telescoping lens mount, helical focusing. $15-20.

Falcon Model GE - c1938. Same as Model G, but with extinction meter. $15-20.

Falcon Model V-16 - Bakelite folding vest-pocket camera identical to the Falcon Junior, but for 16 exposures 3x4cm (½-frame) on 127 film. Colored models: $10-20. Black: $5-10.

Utility Falcon-Flex, 6x6cm

Falcon Press Flash - c1939-41. Bakelite 6x9cm box camera, with built-in flash for Edison-base bulbs. Forerunner of Spartus Press Flash. The first camera with built-in flash, introduced in April 1939 under the Falcon Press Flash and Spartus Press Flash name. $5-10.

Girl Scout Falcon - Half-frame 127. Green front plate with Girl Scout logo. $10-15.

"Minicam" types, 3x4cm - c1939, including Carlton, Falcon Midget, Falcon Minette, Falcon Miniature, Falcon Minicam Junior, Falcon Special, Rex Miniature, Spartus Miniature, etc. Plastic-bodied cameras for 3x4cm on 127 film. Various body styles and names, but no proctical difference. Usually with Graf or Minivar 50mm lens. $3-7.

UYEDA CAMERA (Japan)
Vero Four - c1938. Eye-level camera for 4x4cm on 127 film. Verona Anastigmat f3.5/60mm. Rapid Vero shutter T,B,1-500. $40-60.

Falcon Special - c1939. Black bakelite camera for 16 exposures on 127 film. Cast metal back. Extinction meter on top next to viewfinder. Wollensak Velostigmat f4.5 in Alphax Jr. T,B,25-200 shutter. Helical focusing mount. "The Falcon Special" on focusing ring. $15-20.

VAN DYKE BITTERS CAMERA - Box camera for 9x9cm dry plates in double holders. An early example of a camera used as a premium. $60-80.

VANGUARD - Cast metal camera styled like a 35mm, but for 4x4cm on 127. Telescoping front. $8-12.

Falcon-Abbey Electricamera - c1940. Black bakelite box camera, nearly identical to the original Falcon Press Flash, but with additional shutter button on front. Normal shutter lever at side for manual shutter release. Front button is electric release for solenoid which trips shutter and fires flash in synchronization. $10-20.

Falcon-Flex, 3x4cm - TLR-style novelty camera for 127 film. Cast aluminum body. Similar in style to the Clix-O-Flex. $10-15.

Falcon-Flex, 6x6cm - c1939. Pseudo-TLR box camera. Cast aluminum body. $8-12. *(Illustrated top of next column.)*

Vanity Fair The Incredible Hulk

VANITY FAIR
Character 126 cartridge cameras -
"Recent" collectibles. Prices are for NEW condition.
Barbie Cameramatic, Holly Hobbie, Sunny-Bunch, Super Star - $4-8.

Incredible Hulk, Spider-Man - $9-15.
(Illustrated bottom of previous page.)

VARIMEX (Poland)

Alfa 2 - c1963. Vertical format 35mm. Aqua or red body, cream colored trim. Emitar f4.5/45mm. Shutter 30-125. Unusual style. $75-125.

VARSITY CAMERA CORP.

Varsity Model V - Streamlined oval bakelite camera for 1⅝x1⅝" exposures on rollfilm. Also called the "Streamline Model V". $5-15.

VAUXHALL - Folding camera for 12 or 16 exposures on 120 film. Styled like Zeiss Super Ikonta. f2.9 lens. Coupled rangefinder. $30-40.

VEGA S.A. (Geneva, Switzerland)
Telephot Vega - c1902. A compact camera for long focus lenses. The top section of the camera has the lens in front and an internal mirror at the rear. The light path is reflected to the front of the lower section, where it is again reflected to the plate at the rear of the lower section. For compactness, the top section drops into the bottom half, effectively reducing the size of the camera to just over ⅓ of the focal length of the lens. Several variations in size and in method of folding. $2000-3000.

Vega - c1900. Folding book-style camera for plates. The camera opens like a book, the lens being in the "binding" position, and the bellows fanning out like pages. Plate changing mechanism operated by opening and closing the camera. $500-700.

VENA (Amsterdam, Netherlands)
Venaret - Telescoping camera for 6x6cm exposures on 120 film. f7.7/75mm doublet lens. Simple shutter 25, 50. Leather covered metal body. Nickel trim. $15-20.

VICAM PHOTO APPLIANCE CORP.
(Philadelphia, PA)

I.D. Camera - A compact "school camera"

for bulk rolls of 35mm unperforated film. Fixed focus lens. Small compartment on front conceals the string used to measure subject-to-lens distance. $50-75.

VICTORY MFG. CO.
Lone Ranger - Photo-ette novelty camera for 28x40mm on 828 with drawing of Lone Ranger on his horse. $15-20.

VIDMAR CAMERA CO. (New York, NY)

Vidax - c1948. Rollfilm press-type camera for 3 formats on 620 or 120 film: 6x9cm, 6x6cm, 4.5x6cm. Also accepts cut film or filmpacks. Ektar f4.5. Built-in RF. Designed and manufactured by the late Vic Yager, who also designed the Meridian. Only 100 body castings were made. About 50 units were assembled before the announcement of the first Polaroid camera rocked the industry and dried up investment funds. Total production was 75-85 units. $250-350.

VIENNAPLEX (Austria)
Pack 126 - c1980. Dispoable camera for 126 cassette. $5-10.

VIFLEX - c1905. Unusual SLR box camera for 4x5" plates, or sheetfilm. Viewing hood becomes carry case when folded. $175-225.

VINTEN (W. Vinten, Ltd., London)
Aerial reconnaissance camera - For

500 exposures 55mm square on 70mm film. Black laquered body. Anastigmat f2/4" lens. $100-150.

VISTA COLOUR - Black plastic box camera styled like oversized "Bilora Boy" for 6x6cm on 120 film. Made in England. Fixed focus lens; single speed sector shutter. $15-20.

VIVE CAMERA CO. (Chicago)
Folding B.B. - Folding "cycle" style camera for 4x5" plates. $40-60.

M.P.C. (Mechanical Plate Changing) - c1900. Magazine plate box cameras. Side crank advances plates. Two sizes: 4¼x4¼" or 4x5" plates. Focusing model was called "Vive Focusing Portrait and View Camera". $45-60.

Souvenir Camera - c1895. Small cardboard box camera for single plates, 6x6.5cm. "Vive Souvenir Camera" in gold letters on front. $75-125.

Twin Lens Vive - c1899. For stereo pairs on 3½x6" plates. Similar to the No. 1, but stereo. $400-500.

Vive No. 1 - c1897. The first commercially successful U.S. camera to use the dark-sleeve to change plates in a camera. Actually, the Blair Tourograph had a sleeve (mitt) in 1879, but there was very limited production. For 12 plates 4¼x4¼". Simple lens and shutter. $60-90.

Vive No. 2 - c1897. An improved model of the Vive No. 1, with a self-capping shutter, and with the viewfinder at the center front. $55-85.

Vive No. 4 - c1897. Like the Vive No.1, but for 4x5" plates. Focusing model. $55-85.

VOIGT JUNIOR MODEL 1 - Horizontally styled bakelite folding camera for 6x6cm on 120 film. Identical to the Vokar, Model B. Not made by Voigtlander, but "Voigt" is written on the camera in script deceptively similar to Voigtlander. Similar cameras also sold under the Wirgin Deluxe and Vokar names. $15-25.

VOIGTLANDER & SON (Braunschweig)
Please note that the Voigtlander name has never had the letter "h" in it until collectors started spelling it incorrectly.
Alpin - 1907-28. Folding plate camera for horizontal format 9x12cm plates. Light metal body, painted black. Black tapered triple extension bellows. Voigtlander Collinear f6.8/120mm or Heliar f4.5/135mm lens. Koilos, Compound, or Compur shutter. $125-200. *(Illustrated top of next column.)*

Alpin Stereo-Panoram - c1914-26. Three-lens stereo version of the Alpin

Voigtlander Alpin

camera in the 10x15cm size. Triple Compound or Compur shutter. $350-500.

Avus, folding plate cameras:
6.5x9cm - c1927-36. Skopar f4.5/105mm. Compur 1-250. $40-50.

9x12cm - c1919-34. Skopar f4.5/135mm. Compur or Ibsor shutter. $40-50.

Avus, rollfilm models: *Although the plate models are much more common, rollfilm versions also exist.*
6x9cm - c1927. Folding bed style camera. Metal body with leather covering. Voigtar f6.3/105mm in Embezet or Skopar f4.5 in Compur. $20-30.
6.5x11cm - c1927. Folding bed camera in 1A size, 2½x4¼". Voigtar f6.3/105mm in Embezet or Skopar f4.5 in Compur. $20-30.

Bergheil folding plate cameras - c1914-1920's. These cameras were also called "Tourist" in English language advertising. *Note: Models in colors other than black are listed below under Bergheil Deluxe.*

Actually, the 4.5x6cm and 6.5x9cm sizes are less common in the standard black color that in the deluxe versions, but lack the appeal of the colored leather models.

- 4.5x6cm - Folding plate camera with double extension bellows. Heliar f4.5/80mm lens, Compur 1-300 shutter. Rare in this size. $150-200.

6.5x9cm - c1930. Bayonet system for interchanging of lens/shutter units. Heliar f4.5/105 lens. Compur 1-250. $90-130.

9x12cm - c1925. Double extension. Heliar f3.5 or f4.5/135mm lens. Compound or Compur shutter. $85-145.

10x15cm - c1924. 165mm Skopar f4.5 or Collinear f6.3 lens. Compur shutter. $75-100.

Bergheil Deluxe - *There are two distinct styles of the Bergheil Deluxe. The most deluxe and desirable is the small 4.5x6cm model with BROWN leather and bellows and GOLD metal parts. The larger versions with green Russian*

Bergheil Deluxe, 4.5x6cm

leather covering and green bellows are a step up from the normal black models, but are not truly "Luxus" models.

4.5x6cm, Deluxe - c1923-27. Brown leather, brown bellows, gold colored metal parts. Heliar f4.5/75mm lens; Compur 1-300 shutter. $400-600. *(Illustrated bottom of previous column.)*

6.5x9cm, Deluxe - c1933. Green leathered body and green bellows. f3.5 or f4.5/105mm Heliar lens. Compur 1-200 shutter. Nickel trim. $150-225.

9x12cm Deluxe - c1933. Green leather and bellows. $100-140.

Bessa cameras:

Folding rollfilm models - c1931-49. Most have waist-level and eye-level viewfinders. Various shutter/lens combinations, including Voigtar, Vaskar, and Skopar lenses f3.5 to f7.7. Single, Prontor, or Compur shutters. Better models with f3.5 or f4.5 tend to fall in the range of $25-40. Models with f6.3 or f7.7 usually sell for $15-30.

Bessa RF - c1936. CRF. Compur Rapid 1-400 shutter. With Heliar f3.5/105mm: $120-130. With Helomar or Skopar f3.5/105mm: $80-115.

Bessa I - With Skopar or Helomar f3.5/105mm: $50-60. With Vaskar f4.5: $30-45.

Bessa II - c1950. Coupled rangefinder. With Apo-Lanthar f4.5 (rare): $800-1200. With Heliar f3.5: $225-325. With Skopar f3.5/105mm: $125-175.

Bessa 46 "Baby Bessa" - c1939. Self-erecting folding camera for 16 exposures 4.5x6cm on 120 film. Optical finder incorporated in top housing. Trigger release for shutter protrudes from side of front door. Voigtar or Skopar f3.5/75mm lens in Compur shutter, or Heliar f3.5/75mm in Compur Rapid. $25-35.

Bessa 66 "Baby Bessa" - c1930. Several viewfinder variations: folding frame finder, folding optical finder, optical finder incorporated in top housing. With Skopar f3.5: $30-40. With Voigtar f3.5/75mm or Vaskar f4.5: $20-30. *(Illus. next column.)*

Bessa 66 with folding direct finder (top), and with folding optical finder (below)

Bessamatic - c1959. 35mm SLR with built-in meter. Synchro-Compur shutter. Interchangeable lenses. With Zoomar f2.8/36-82mm (world's first SLR Zoom lens): $300-400. With Skopar f2.8/50mm: $50-75.

Bessamatic Deluxe - c1963. Similar, but diaphragm and shutter speed visible in finder. Externally recognizable by the small T-shaped window above the meter cell. With Septon f2 lens: $75-125. With Skopar f2.8: $50-75.

Dynamatic

Bijou - c1908. The first miniature SLR, 4.5x6cm plates. All-metal box body, tapers toward the front. Helical focusing lens, Ross WA Xpress f4/4". $500-550.

Box - c1950. Metal box camera for 6x9cm on 120. Meniscus f11 lens, 3-speed shutter. $25-35.

Heliar Reflex - c1902. Boxy SLR for 9x12cm plates. Heliar f4.5/180mm. FP shutter 20-1000. $150-250.

Inos (I) - c1931-32. Dual-format folding bed camera for 6x9cm and 4.5x6cm exposures on 120 film. Wire frame finder indicates both formats. Compur to 250, or Embezet shutter to 100. With Heliar f4.5: $50-80. With Skopar f4.5/105mm: $45-65.

Brillant - c1933. Cheap TLR camera. 75mm f6.3 or 7.7 Voigtar, f4.5 Skopar, or f3.5 Heliar lens. Quite common. $20-30.

Daguerreotype "cannon" replica - Reproduction of the original 1841 Voigtlander brass Daguerreotype camera. 31cm long, 35cm high. Makes 80mm diameter image. $1000-1250.

Dynamatic, Dynamatic II - c1961. 35mm with automatic electronic meter. Lanthar or Color-Skopar f2.8/50mm in Prontor-Matic-V or Prontormat-SV shutter. $30-50. *(Illustrated top of next column.)*

Folding plate cameras (misc. models) - $25-35.
Folding rollfilm cameras (misc. models) - 5x8cm, 6x9cm, and 6.5x11cm sizes. $15-45.

Inos II, 6x9cm - c1933-34. Like Inos, but front standard automatically slides forward when bed is dropped. Focusing knob on body can be preset before opening camera. For 6x9cm or 4.5x6cm with reducing masks. Small folding frame finder with hinged mask for half-frames. Skopar f4.5/105mm lens. Compur 1-250 shutter. $50-75.

Inos II, 6.5x11cm - c1933-34. Like the more common 6x9cm size but for 6.5x11cm and 5.5x6.5cm images on 116 film. Uncommon in this size. With Heliar f4.5/118mm lens: $75-125.

Jubilar - c1931. Folding camera for 6x9cm on 120 rollfilm. Voigtar f9 lens. $20-30.

Perkeo, 3x4cm - c1938. Folding camera with self-erecting front. For 16 exposures 3x4cm on 127 film. Camera can be focused before opening, via external knob. With Skopar f3.5 or 4.5/55mm lens: $125-175. With Heliar f3.5: $160-200.

Perkeo I - 1952. Folding camera for 6x6cm exposures on 120 film. Prontor shutter. f4.5 Vaskar lens. $25-40.

Perkeo II - c1952. Similar, but f3.5 Color Skopar in Synchro-Compur shutter. $45-60.

Perkeo E - c1954. Like the Perkeo II, but with rangefinder. Color-Skopar lens in Prontor SVS shutter. $125-150.

Prominent - c1932. Folding camera for

6x9cm on 120 film, or 4.5x6cm with reducing masks. Self-erecting front. Coupled split-image rangefinder. Extinction meter. Heliar f4.5/105mm lens in Compur 1-250 shutter. $400-700.

Prominent - c1952. 35mm rangefinder. With f2 Ultron or f1.5 Nokton: $100-150.

Prominent II - c1958. Similar but with bright frame finder. $125-175.

Stereflektoskop - c1913-1930's. Stereo cameras with plate changing magazine. 45x107mm and 6x13cm sizes. Three Heliar f4.5 lenses in Stereo Compur shutter. (Early version had only two Heliar lenses with a small triplet finder lens above and between the taking lenses.) This is a three-lens reflex, the center lens used for 1:1 reflex viewing. This style was later used in the Heidoscop and Rolleidoscop cameras: **45x107mm size** - $200-400. **6x13cm size** - $200-400.

Stereophotoskop - c1907-24. Rigid-body 45x107mm stereo camera. Magazine back for 12 plates. Simple reflex bright finder and side Newton finder. Heliars f4.5; sector shutter. $200-275.

Virtus

6x9cm and 9x12cm sizes. Voigtar f6.3 or Skopar f4.5 lens in Ibsor or Embezet shutter. $30-45.

Virtus - c1935. Similar to the Prominent, but smaller and more common. For 16 exposures on 120 film. Automatically focuses to infinity upon opening. Compur shutter 1-250. With Heliar f3.5/75mm: $175-250. With Skopar f4.5/75mm: $125-200. *(Illustrated top of previous column.)*

Vitessa Cameras: *A series of smartly-styled folding 35mm cameras introduced in 1950. 'Barn-doors" on front. Several variations: Originally had smooth top without shoe. Manual parallax correction. Pressure plate hinged to body, not back. Ultron f2 lens only. Second variation, still 1950, had the pressure plate on the back door. Third model, 1951, has sync contact on door, accessory shoe top, and automatic parallax correction. f2.0 or f2.8 lens.*

Superb - c1933. TLR for 120 film, later version has sportsfinder hood. A prism reflects the settings for easy visibility. With Heliar: $175-225. With f3.5/75mm Skopar: $125-175.

Vitessa - c1950. 35mm camera. f2.8 Color Skopar or f2 Ultron lens. Synchro Compur 1-500 shutter. Coupled rangefinder. $65-85.

Vitessa L - c1954. Like Vitessa (1951 type) but with selenium meter. Ultron f2/50mm lens. Coupled rangefinder. $85-110.

Vitessa N - c1951. Same as Vitessa, 1951 type, but f3.5 Color Skopar only. $55-80.

Vag - c1920's. Folding plate cameras,

Vito III - c1950. Folding style with coupled rangefinder. f2 Ultron. Synchro Compur 1-500 shutter. $100-150.

Vitessa T - c1957. Rigid front without clamshell doors. Color Skopar f2.8/50mm lens. Compur 1-500 shutter, sync. Coupled rangefinder. Common. $60-80.

Vito - c1950. Folding style 35mm. Skopar f3.5/50mm. Compur 1-300 shutter. $20-30.

Vito Automatic - c1962. f2.8/50mm Lanthar. Prontor Lux shutter. $20-30.

Vito II - c1950. 35mm. Color Skopar f3.5 or Ultron f2 lens. Prontor or Compur shutter. $30-40.

Vito B - c1954. Normally with f3.5 Color Skopar in Pronto or Prontor SVS shutter. Less common with f2.8 Color Skopar in Prontor SVS. $20-25. (Add $10-20 for Ultron f2 lens.)

Vito IIa - c1955. Less common that the Vito and Vito II. $40-55.

Vito BL - c1957-59. Color-Skopar f2.8/50mm. Built-in exposure meter. $20-30.

Vito C - c1961. f2.8/50 Lanthar lens. Prontor shutter. $15-25.

Vitomatic (I), II, IIa, Ia, Ib, IIb, IIIb - c1958-68. f2.8 Skopar lens in Prontor. $25-40. (Add $10-20 for Ultron f2 lens.)

Vitrona - c1964. 35mm. Built-in electronic flash. Prontor 1-250, f2.8/50mm Lanthar. Never made in any large quantity, because they were novel and expensive. $35-45.

Vokar I

VOJTA (Josef Vojta, Praque)
Magazine Camera - Wooden box camera. 6.5x9cm plates manually changed through leather sleeve at top rear of camera. Two reflex finders. M&Z shutter. $150-200.

VOKAR CORPORATION (Dexter, Michigan) *Formerly "Electronic Products Mfg. Corp." of Ann Arbor, Michigan.*

Vokar, Models A, B - c1940. Bakelite folding camera for 6x6cm on 120. Also sold under the Voigt Junior and Wirgin Deluxe names. $15-25.

Vokar I, II - c1946. 35mm RF cameras. f2.8/50mm Vokar Anastigmat lens in helical mount. Leaf shutter 1-300. $55-85. *(Illustrated bottom of previous column.)*

VORMBRUCK CAMERABAU (W. & P. Fertsch, Germany)
Feca - Folding plate camera, made in 6x9cm and 9x12cm sizes. Tessar or Xenar f4.5 lenses. Double extension bellows, GG back. $25-35.

VOSS (W. Voss, Ulm, Germany)

Diax (I), Ia, Ib, II, IIa, IIb - c1948-1950's.

35mm RF cameras. Xenon f2/45mm lens in Synchro-Compur 1-500 shutter. Coupled rangefinder on models II, IIa, IIb. Models Ia, IIa, and IIb have interchangeable lenses. $25-50.

Diaxette - c1953. Low-priced viewfinder 35mm based on the early Diax I body. Non-interchangeable Steinheil Cassar f2.8/45mm. Prontor 25-200. $15-30.

VREDEBORCH (Germany)
Alka Box - c1953. Metal box camera, 6x9cm on 120. $8-12.

Felica, Felita - c1954. Metal eye-level box cameras for 6x6cm on 120 film. Meniscus lens, zone focus, simple shutter 25,50,B. Light gray or black colored. $5-10.

Haaga Syncrona Box - c1955. Basic rectangular box camera, similar to normal Sychrona Box. Meniscus lens, M,B,T shutter. Uncommon name. $15-25.

Junior - c1954. Same as the Felica, but with the "Junior" name. $5-10.

Nordetta 3-D - c1951. Strut-folding stereo, taking two 42x55mm exposures on 127 film. f4.5/75mm lenses. Guillotine shutter. Cheap construction, but not very common. $85-125.

Optomax Syncrona - c1952. Basic metal box camera for 6x9cm, but covered in light grey leather. Meniscus lens. Synchronized M,T shutter. $10-15.

Reporter Junior II - c1950's. Eye-level 6x6 camera like Felica and Felita. Grey or black leather covering. $5-10.

Slomexa - c1950's. Basic metal box camera like Vrede Box. Meniscus f11 lens. $15-25.

Texar Box - Metal box camera for 6x9cm on 120 rollfilm. $5-10.

Union-Box - c1950's. Box camera for 6x6cm. M & Z shutter. Union-Box nameplate below lens. $15-25.

Vrede Box - c1953. Metal box camera with paper covering in various colors. Models include Paloma, Paloma S, Synchrona, etc. With and without PC flash sync. $10-15.

WABASH PHOTO SUPPLY
(Terre Haute, IN)
Direct positive camera - c1935. Wood body. Ilex Universal f3.5/3" portrait lens. Dimensions 5x8x20". With enlarger and dryer: $150-180.

WALDES & CO. (Dresden)
Foto-Fips - c1925. Unusual, low cost folding camera made of light cardboard and paper. Uses single 4x4cm plates. Actually, the camera is built into the bottom half of a small box which also stores the plates, bromo paper, developer and fixer. Boxtop and supplies are all labeled in Czech. Very rare. Only known sale was at German auction in 3/85 where a complete outfit sold for $350.

WALDORF CAMERA CO.

Waldorf Minicam - Black bakelite half-127 camera. Made by Utility Mfg. Co. for Waldorf. $3-7.

WALES-BABY - Plastic half-127 novelty camera. $1-5.

WALKER MANUFACTURING CO. (Palmyra, N.Y.)

TakIV - c1892. Cardboard and leatherette construction. Multiple exposures for 4 pictures, each 2½x2½" on dry plates. Rotating shutter and lens assembly. Septums for 4 exp. at rear. $800-1200.

WALKLENZ - Japanese novelty subminiature of the Hit type. $10-15.

WALLACE HEATON LTD. (London)

Zodel - c1926. Folding 6.5x9cm plate camera. Zodellax f4.5/120mm lens in Compur shutter. $25-35.

WALZ CO. (Japan)

Walz Automat - c1959. 4x4cm TLR. Zunow f2.8/60mm. Copal shutter 1-500, B. $100-150.

Walz Envoy 35 - c1959. Rangefinder 35. Kominar f1.9/48mm. Copal SLV shutter, 1-500,B, MFX sync. ST. Single stroke advance. $15-25.

Walz-wide - c1958. 35mm. Walzer f2.8/35mm lens. Copal shutter 1-300,B. $30-40.

Walzflex - c1955. 6x6cm TLR for 120 film. f3.5/75mm Kominar lens in Copal shutter. $20-30.

Warwick No. 2 Camera

Watson Acme

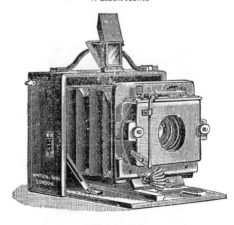

Watson Alpha

WANAUS (Josef Wanaus & Co., Vienna)
Full-plate view camera - c1900. Field camera for 13x18cm plates. Light colored polished wood, nickel trim. Gustav-Rapp Universal Aplanat lens, waterhouse stops. Geared focus, front and rear. $175-200.

WARWICK (Birmingham, England)
Warwick No. 2 Camera - Basic box camera for 6x9cm on 120 film. Dark brown leatherette covering. $10-15. *(Illustrated on previous page.)*

WATSON (W. Watson & Sons, London)
Acme - c1890. 8x10" folding bellows field camera. $150-200. *(Illustrated on previous page.)*

Alpha - c1892. Tropical hand camera with extreme rising front. 9x12cm or 4x5" sizes. Mahogany body with brass reinforcements, maroon bellows. B&L lens, Unicum shutter. $400-475. *(Illustrated on previous page.)*

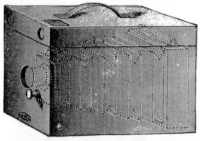

Detective Camera - intro. 1886. Black leather covered box contains a ¼-plate bellows camera. Box also holds three double plateholders behind the camera, or Eastman's roll-holder also could be used. External controls in bottom of box. Two waistlevel viewfinders in the lid. Rapid Rectilinear lens, adjustable guillotine shutter. Focus by means of a lever in the bottom of the box, from 15' to infinity. $500-800.

Field camera - c1885-1887. Tailboard style in sizes from ½-plate to 8x10". Fine wood body, brass trim. Thornton-Pickard roller blind shutter. Watson f8 brass barrel lens. $125-250.

Magazine box camera - c1900. Falling-plate magazine box cameras, including, "Tornado", "Repeater", etc. Most common in ¼-plate size for 12 plates. $30-50.

Stereoscopic Binocular Camera - c1900. English imported version of the Bloch Stereo Physiographe. Krauss Tessar lenses. 45x107mm. $1000-1500.

Twin Lens Camera - c1899. An early twin lens style camera for quarter plates. Black leather covered mahogany body. Rapid Rectilinear lens, iris diaphragm. Thornton-Pickard T,I shutter. Reflex viewing. $300-400.

Vanneck - intro. 1890. Plate-changing compartment holds 12 3¼x4¼" plates. Rapid Rectilinear lens. First SLR with instant return spring mirror. Leather covered body. $350-450.

WAUCKOSIN (Frankfurt, Germany)
Waranette - c1930. Folding rollfilm camera for 5x8cm. f6.3/85mm Polluxar lens in Vero shutter 25-100. $25-35.

WEBSTER INDUSTRIES INC. (Webster, NY) *Founded c1947. In 1953 the company name was changed to "Monroe Research", then within a few months to "Zenith Film Corp." Cameras and printed materials are also found using the name "Winpro Camera Co." and sometimes the city is listed as Rochester, of which Webster is a suburb.*

Winpro 35 - 1947-55. Regular or "Synchro Flash" models. Gray or black "Tenite" plastic body 35mm. Non-interchangeable

Crystar f8/40mm. Rotary shutter, 50, B. $15-20.

WEIMET PHOTO PRODUCTS CO.

Rocket - c1947. Inexpensive plastic 3x4cm camera. $3-7.

WELTA KAMERAWERKE (Waurich & Weber, Freital, Germany)
Diana - c1926. 9x12cm folding bed plate camera. Poloyt f4.5/135mm lens in Ibsor shutter. $25-35.

Dubla, 9x12cm - c1930. Two-shuttered triple extension plate camera. Eurynar, Tessar, or Xenar f4.5 lens; Compur and FP 1/10-1000 shutters. $120-140.

Dubla, 10x15cm - c1930. Two-shuttered folding plate camera. Goerz Dogmar f4.5/165mm. Compur front shutter to 200. Rear focal plane shutter to 1000. $120-140.

Gucki - c1932. Strut-folding 127 rollfilm camera. 3x4cm and 4x6.5cm sizes. Some models have a folding bed in addition to the struts. Schneider Xenar f2.9 or Radionar f3.5. Compur shutter. $40-50.

Peerflekta (I), II, V - c1956. 6x6cm TLR for 120 film. Pololyt f3.5/75mm lens in Prontor shutter 1-300. $25-30.

Perfekta - c1934. Folding TLR of unusual

design for 6x6cm exposures on 120 film. Meyer f3.5 or Tessar f3.8/75mm lens. Compur shutter 1-300. $125-185.

Perle, 4.5x6cm - c1934-39. Self-erecting camera with front lens or helical focusing. Folding Newton finder. Trioplan, Xenar, or Tessar 75mm lens. Compur shutter. $35-50.

Perle, 5x8cm - c1932. Self-erecting camera with radial focusing lever at front of bed. Lever automatically resets to infinity when camera is closed. Brown leather bellows and exterior. Reversible brilliant finder on lens standard, plus folding frame finder on body. Weltar f6.3, or Trinar or Xenar f4.5/90mm. Pronto, Prontor, Ibsor or Compur shutter. $75-100.

Perle, 6x6cm - c1934-38. Similar to the 4.5x6cm except for image size. $35-50.

Perle, 6x9cm - c1932-36. Similar to 5x8cm size, but black leather and bellows.

Same lens choices but 10.5cm focal length. $20-35.

Perle, 6.5x11cm - c1932-36. Also similar to the 5x8cm size, but black leather. 12cm lens. $30-40.

Reflecta, Reflekta - c1930's-1950's. 6x6cm TLR for 120 film. Various lenses and shutters. $20-30. *Pre-war models c1930-38 seem to spell the name with "c" and postwar models with "k". After the war until about 1952, Kamerawerk Tharandt in Freital was the manufacturer. We also have references to C. Richter, Tharandt as manufactruer. We would appreciate hearing from any reader who can help us with a brief history of the Reflecta and Reflekta cameras.*

Reflekta II - c1950's. Various f3.5/75mm lenses including: Meritar, Trioplan, Triotar. Junior or Vebur shutter. $30-40.

Reflekta III - c1955. Similar to II. Row Poloyt f3.5/70. Prontor SV 1-300. $30-40.

Solida - c1933. Folding 6x9cm rollfilm

camera. Coupled rangefinder. Schneider Radionar or Xenar f4.5/105mm. Compur 1-250, T,B. $60-90.

Superfekta - c1932. Folding 6x9cm TLR for 120 film. An unusual design, similar to the Perfekta. Pivoting back for taking horizontal pictures. Tessar or Trioplan f3.8/105mm lens. Compur shutter. $170-300.

Symbol - c1937-39. Self-erecting folding rollfilm camera for 6x9cm on 120 film. Beginning in about 1938, a mask was provided to allow half-frame (4.5x6cm) negatives also. This was the budget priced model, with Weltar f6.3/105mm lens in Vario, Prontor, or Prontor II shutter. $15-25.

Trio - c1936. 6x9cm on 120 film. Also allowed 4.5x6cm beginning about 1938. f4.5/105mm lens in rimset Compur shutter. $20-30. *(Illustrated top of next page.)*

Welta, 6x6cm - 120 film. f4.5 Weltar, or f2.8/75mm Tessar. Compur shutter. $20-40.

Welta, 6x9cm - Folding plate camera. Orion Rionar, Meyer Trioplan, Tessar, or Xenar f4.5/105mm lens. Ibsor shutter 1-125. $30-50.

Welta Trio

Vebur, Cludor, or Compur shutter. $20-30.

Welta, 9x12cm - c1933. Folding plate camera. f3.5 Rodenstock Eurynar or f4.5 Doppel Anastigmat 135mm lens. Compur shutter. $25-35.

Welta 35 - c1936. Folding 35mm optical viewfinder. Similar to Retina cameras of the same time period. Trioplan f2.9/50mm. Ring Compur or Vebur shutter. $20-35.

Weltaflex - c1955. TLR for 6x6cm on 120 film. Ludwig Meritar f3.5/75mm lens in Prontor 1-300 shutter or Trioplan f3.5 in Vebur 1-250. $25-30.

Weltini - c1937. Folding 35mm with coupled rangefinder. With Elmar f3.5/50mm in Compur Rapid: $150-250. With Xenon f2 or Tessar f2.8 lens in Compur: $35-70.

Weltax - c1939. Dual format folding bed camera, 4.5x6cm or 6x6cm images on 120 film. Xenar or Tessar f2.8; Meritar, Tessar, or Trioplan f3.5/75mm lens in Tempor, Junior, Compur, or Prontor shutter. $20-35.

Welti (I), Ic, II - c1935-1950's. Folding 35mm. Tessar f2.8 or Xenar f3.5/50mm in

Welta Weltur

Weltix - c1939. Folding 35mm. Steinheil Cassar f2.9/50mm lens in Compur. $20-30.

Weltur - c1936-40. For 16 exposures 4.5x6cm on 120 film. Similar to the Super Ikonta. Coupled rangefinder. With 75mm Tessar f2.8, f3.5, f3.8: $85-115. With 75mm Xenar f2.8, Trioplan f2.9: $60-80. *(Illustrated bottom of previous page.)*

WEMBLEY SPORTS - c1950-56. Black bakelite camera for 6x9cm on 120 film. Helical front with four click-stops for focusing positions. Sportar f11/85mm lens in Rondex Rapid shutter 25,50,100. Made in England, but reminiscent of Kaftanski body designs such as Photax and Fex models. $10-15.

WENK (Gebr. Wenk, Nuernberg, Germany)

Wenka - Post-war 35mm camera with interchangeable Leica-thread Xenar f2.8/50mm lens. Behind the lens shutter. $90-150.

WESTERN CAMERA MFG. CO. (Chicago) *The Cyclone cameras listed here were made in 1898, before Western became a part of Rochester Optical & Camera Co. in 1899. See Rochester for later models.*
Cyclone Jr. - 3½x3½" plate box camera. $25-35.

Cyclone Sr. - 4x5" plate box camera. Not a magazine camera. Top rear door to insert plateholders. $25-30.

Magazine Cyclone No. 2 - $30-45.
Magazine Cyclone No. 3 - 4x5". $30-45.

Magazine Cyclone No. 4 - 3¼x4¼". $30-45.
Magazine Cyclone No. 5 - 4x5". $30-45.

Pocket Zar - c1897. Cardboard box camera for 2x2" glass plates. $50-75.

WESTFAELISCHER KAMERA & APPARATEBAU *This small company existed only a few years.*
Navax - c1953. Viewfinder 35mm. Roeschlein Pointar interchangeable f2.8/45mm. FP shutter 5-1000, sync. Very low

production. One sold on auction in March 1983 for $190.

WESTON WX-7 - c1985. Novelty 35mm from Taiwan. This is only one of many cheap cameras disguised to resemble a 35mm SLR, but of all that we have seen, this one takes the prize as the most convincing look-alike. The size, color, and weight of the camera are frighteningly realistic. Only the small viewfinder window and the lack of serious control knobs expose it for what it is. X-rays of the body reveal carefully designed and placed weights which make the plastic body feel as solid as your favorite $300 SLR! As a photographic instrument, it rates poorly. As a deceptive work of art, it is fantastic. $5-10.

WHITE (David White Co., Milwaukee, Wisc.)

Realist 35 - c1955. (not stereo) 35mm camera made for David White by Iloca. Identical to Iloca Rapid A. Cassar f3.5 or 2.8 lens. $25-35.

Realist 45 (Model 1045) - 1953-57. Stereo 35 made for White by Iloca. f3.5 Cassar lenses. $80-110.

Stereo Realist - c1950's. 35mm stereo camera. Movable film plane controlled by focus knob. Model 1042 with f2.8 lenses, case, flash: $200-250. Model 1041 with f3.5 lenses, case, flash: $95-125.

Stereo Realist Custom (Model 1050) - c1960. With matched color corrected, coated "rare earth" f2.8 lenses. Shutter 1-200,T,B. Black coarse-grained kangaroo leather covering. $450-550.

Stereo Realist Macro (Model 1060) - c1971. Probably less than 1000 were produced. Matched f3.5 lenses, focused at 4-5". Sync shutter to 125. $800-1000.

Stereo Realist Viewers:
Model 2061 - Black with red buttons and knobs. Doublet lenses. $50-60.
Model 2062 - Black with green buttons and knobs. AC/DC fittings. Doublet lenses. $90-110.
Model 2063 - Pale green with black front. $25-45.
Model 2064 - Dark brown with white knobs and buttons. Single lens. Uncommon. $50-60.
Model 2065 - Black with green buttons and knobs. DC only. $80-95.
Model 2066 - Black with gold buttons and knobs. For use with views from Macro camera Model 1060. Pairs of doublet lenses. Rare. $150-200.

WHITEHOUSE PRODUCTS (Brooklyn, N.Y.)
Beacon, Beacon II - c1947-55. Plastic rollfilm camera for 3x4cm on 127 film. Plastic lens, simple spring shutter. Colored models: $8-12. Black: $4-8.

Beacon 225 - c1950-58. Similar to the

other Beacons, but 6x6cm on 620. Colored: $8-12. Black: $4-8.

Charlie Tuna - 126 cartridge camera, shaped and colored like Starkist's Charlie Tuna. Truly a novelty camera in "good taste". Sorry, Charlie. $60-85. *There is a companion radio, somewhat smaller, but also shaped like Charlie Tuna. Beware if your collecting takes such a turn, because you'll also need a Coke can radio to match your Coke can camera... then a Rolls Royce automobile to go with your "Rolls" camera...*

WHITTAKER (Wm.R. Whittaker Co. Ltd, Los Angeles, Calif.)

Micro 16 - c1950's. Subminiature for 16mm film in special cassettes. Cartridge to cartridge feed. Meniscus lens, single

Widmar Cowi

speed shutter. Black, blue, or green: $25-40. Chrome: $20-30.

Pixie - c1950. Black plastic 16mm subminiature wriststrap camera. $20-40. With flash, wrist strap, etc.: $35-60.

Pixie Custom - Marbelized brown plastic body. Gold-plated metal parts. $150-175.

WIDMAR (Robert Widmar, Germany) Cowi - Plastic camera for 3x4cm on rollfilm. $15-25. *(Illustrated bottom of previous column.)*

WILCA KAMERABAU (West Germany)

Wilca Automatic - c1963. Subminiature for 24 exposures 10x19mm on 16mm film in special cassettes. Wilcalux Filtra f2/16mm lens. Prontor shutter, sync. Coupled selenium meter. Rare, reportedly less than 100 made. $350-500.

WILKIN WELSH CO. (Syracuse, NY) Folding plate camera - c1900. Folding bed camera for 4x5" plateholders. Leather covered body with polished wood interior. Red bellows. Rauber & Wollensak brass shutter. Rare. $75-125.

WILLIAMSON MANUFACTURING CO. LTD. (London, England)

Pistol Aircraft camera - c1930. 6x9cm plate or filmpack camera, with a pistol grip. Dallmeyer Ross Xpress f4.5/5" lens. Behind the lens louvre shutter 50-200. $300-500.

WINDSOR - 4x4cm "Diana" type novelty camera. $1-5.

WINDSOR WX-3 - Inexpensive plastic 35mm from Taiwan. Like new: $8-12.

WINDSOR CAMERA CO. (Japan)
Cameras were probably made by Tougodo or Toyo Kogaku for marketing under the Windsor name.
Windsor 35 - c1953. 35mm RF, made in Japan. Color Sygmar f3.5/50mm lens. Shutter 1-200 or 1-300,B. $15-20.

Windsor Stereo - c1954-60. Black bakelite 35mm stereo camera. Windsor f4.5/35 lenses. Windsor 1/25-1/50. $75-100.

WINDSORFLEX - Plastic 4x4cm novelty TLR. Made in Hong Kong. Same as the Bedfordflex, Wonderflex, Randorflex, Splendidflex, etc. $1-5.

WING (Simon Wing, Charlestown, Mass.)

Multiplying View Camera - c1862. Multiple images on single 5x7" collodion plate. Mahogany body, vertical and lateral back movements, shadow box front. About $5000.

New Gem - c1901. For 15 exposures on 5x7" plates. Sliding front lens panel. $700-1000.

WIRECRAFT CO.
Jewel Sixteen - Small 3x4cm plastic novelty camera, similar to the Cardinal. $3-7.

WIRGIN (Gebr. Wirgin, Wiesbaden, Germany)

SHUTTER RELEASE—

Baky - c1936. Bakelite folding bed camera for 16 exposures 4.5x6cm on 120 film. Black or brown bakelite body. Schneider Radionar or Cassar f2.9 lens in Compur, Compur-Rapid, or Prontor II shutter. Body release, folding optical finder. Also sold in England as the Westminster Victoria and Norfolk Miniature. There is no identification on the camera itself. $40-60.

Edina - c1954. Viewfinder 35mm. Edinar f2.8 or f3.5/45mm. Vario 25-200 or Velio 10-200 shutter. $15-25.

Edinex - c1930's-1950's. Compact 35mm camera, almost identical to the Adox Adrette. Also sold in the USA under the name "Midget Marvel" although not marked as such. Telescoping front. Film loads from bottom. Late models such as IIIS with coupled rangefinder. $30-45. Early models, without rangefinder, with f4.5, 3.5, 2.8, or f2 lens. $20-35.

Edinex 120 - c1953. Folding rollfilm camera for 2 formats: 6x9cm, 4.5x6cm. $15-25.

Klein-Edinex (127 film) - c1938. Marketed in the U.S.A. under the name "Gewirette". We can find no original advertising with the "Klein Edinex" name, but it has appeared in some collector publications. See Gewirette below.

Edixa - c1955. Viewfinder 35mm. Commonly found with Isconar f2.8/43mm in Prontor SVS shutter. $20-25.

Edixa 16, 16M, 16MB, 16S - c1960's. Subminiature cameras for 12x17mm exposures on 16mm film. Schneider Xenar f2.8/25mm lens. $25-40.

Edixa Electronica - c1962. 35mm SLR. Fully automatic with selenium meter. Culminar or Xenar f2.8/50mm lens. Compur sync shutter 1-500. $150-175.

Edixa Reflex, Edixaflex - c1960. 35mm SLR. f2.8/42mm screw-mount Isconar or Westanar lens. Focal plane shutter 1-1000. $30-50.

Edixa Stereo - c1955. 35mm stereo. Steinheil Cassar f3.5/35mm lenses. Vario shutter. $70-90.

Edixa Stereo II, IIa - c1957. Rangefinder

35mm stereo. No meter. Steinheil f3.5. Pronto or Prontor SVS to 200, ST. $70-95.

Edixa Stereo III, IIIa - c1957. 35mm stereo rangefinder camera. Built-in light meter. Prontor SVS shutter. $100-145.

Gewir - c1936. 6.5x9cm folding bed plate camera. Double extension with rack and pinion focusing. Rise and cross front with micrometer movement. Gewironar f2.9, f3.5; Wirgin Zeranar f3.8; Meyer Trioplan f2.9/105mm lens. Compur shutter. $35-50.

Gewirette - c1937. Eye-level camera for 3x4cm exposures on 127 film. Telescoping front. Film loads from the top. Similar in appearance to the 35mm Edinex, but for 3x4cm exposures on 127 film. Gewironar f4.5, Steinheil Cassar, or Schneider Xenar f2.9/50mm lens. $75-125.

Midget Marvel - see Edinex.

Reporter - Similar to Gewirette. Fixanar f2.9/50mm in Compur 1-300. $80-100.

Twin Lens Reflex - c1940. Similar to Welta

Reflekta, but with Wirgin nameplate. The same camera was also sold as the "Peerflekta" by Peerless Camera Stores, and nearly identical cameras sport the names "Trumpfreflex" and "Vitaflex". Anastigmat Triolar f4.5/75mm in Stelo T,B, 100,50,25 shutter.$20-30.

Wirgin Deluxe - Bakelite bodied folding camera for 6x6cm on 120 film. Similar to Vokar Model B and Voigt Jr. Art-deco metal plates on top, bottom, and front door. $15-25.

Wirgin folding rollfilm camera - 6x9cm on 120 film. Schneider Radionar f4.5, or Gewironar f8.8 or 6.3 lens. $13-23.

Wirgin Stereo - For 22x24mm stereo pairs on 35mm film. Steinheil Cassar f3.5/35mm lenses with coupled focusing. Vario B,25, 75,200 stereo shutter. Ratcheted lever film advance. $80-110.

Wirgin 6x6cm TLR - c1950. Rodenstock Trinar f2.9/75mm. Built-in extinction meter. $30-50.

WITT (Iloca Werk, Wilhelm Witt, Hamburg, Germany)
Iloca I, Ia, II, IIa - c1950's. Basic 35mm cameras. f2.9 or f3.5/45mm Ilitar lens in Prontor shutter. Models II and IIa with coupled rangefinder. $20-30.

Iloca Quick A - c1954. Viewfinder 35. Ilitar f3.5/45mm. Vario 25-200 shutter, B. $13-17.

Iloca Quick B - c1954. Coupled rangefinder. Ilitar f2.9/45mm in Prontor SV 1-300. $15-20.

Iloca Rapid, Rapid B, Rapid IIL - c1950. Coupled rangefinder, 35mm. Rapid wind. Cassar f2.8/50mm. $15-25.

Iloca Reporter - c1951. Basic viewfinder 35mm. Black covering with horizontal white stripes. Reporter Anastigmat f3.5/45mm. Prontor-S shutter. $20-30.

Iloca Stereo, Original Model - c1950. Individually focusing lenses. Apertures and shutters coupled through tube at bottom. Unusual. $100-125.

Iloca Stereo, Models I & II - c1950's. 35mm stereo camera for 23x24mm pairs. Ilitar f3.5 lenses, 35mm or 45mm. Prontor-S shutter to 300. $75-125.

Iloca Stereo Rapid - c1955. Coupled rangefinder 35mm stereo, 23x24mm pairs. Rapid wind. Cassarit f2.8 or Cassar f3.5 lenses. Prontor SVS 1-300 or Vero 25-200. Rangefinder version of Realist 45. $200-325

Photrix Quick B - 35mm. Cassar f2.8/ 50mm, Prontor-SVS to 300. $12-18.

WITTIE MFG. & SALES CO.

Wit-eez - Black bakelite minicam, styled like the Rolls. $3-7.

WITTMAN (R. Wittman, Dresden, Germany)
Tailboard camera - c1880. 13x18cm plates. Square bellows. Wittman Universal

Aplanat lens, waterhouse stops. $250-350.

WITTNAUER

35mm cameras - c1959. Misc. models including Adventurer, Automaton, Festival, Challenger, Continental, Legionaire, Scout. RF. Chronex f2.8/45mm lens. $15-20.

WOEHLER (Dr. Woehler, St Ingbert, Saarland)

Favor - c1949. Basic 35mm camera. Docar f2.8 or Citar f3.5/45mm lens. Prontor-S or Prontor-SVS shutter. $100-140.

WOLLENSAK OPTICAL CO.

Wollensak Stereo, Model 10 - c1955. 35mm stereo camera. f2.7 lenses; shutter to 300. Similar to the Revere Stereo 33, but faster lenses and shutter, and in black leather, not brown. $175-225.

WONDER CAMERA - Falling-plate magazine box camera for 2½x3½" glass plates. $35-45.

WONDERFLEX - c1965. Hong Kong

4x4cm plastic novelty TLR-style camera. Same camera sold as Bedfordflex, Splendidflex, etc. $1-5.

WOOD (E.G. Wood, London)
Wet plate camera, sliding box - Half-plate mahogany sliding-box camera. Petzval lens with rack focusing and waterhouse stops. $800-1000.

WRATTEN & WAINWRIGHT (London, England)

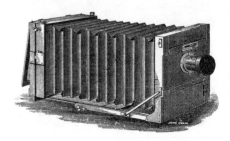

Tailboard camera - c1890. Mahogany 5x8" view. Maroon square bellows. A&N Auxiliary 6½x8½" lens. $200-250.

WRAY OPTICAL WORKS (London)
Peckham Wray - 1955. 4x5" SLR. Looks like an overgrowm 35mm SLR. Wray Lustvar interchangeable f4.8/135mm. FP shutter 5-800 and Comnpur shutter 1-500. $140-190.

Stereo Graphic - Made under license to Graflex. Same as the Graflex version, but with Wray lenses. $50-100.

Wrayflex - c1950. The only commercially successful English-made 35mm SLR. Originally for 24x32mm, later for standard 24x36mm. Wray f2/50mm interchangeable lens. FP shutter ½-1000. $100-125.

WUENSCHE (Emil Wuensche, Reick b/ Dresden)
Afpi - c1904-08. *Folding bed plate cameras for 9x12cm plates. Many variations were made, and we are listing only a few.*
Afpi (vertical) - $30-40.

Afpi, square - Called "Quadratisch" in original catalogs. Allows horizontal or vertical format. Double extension. Fine wood bed. Black bellows and leather covering. $70-100.

Alpi (with "metal shutter, Model III") - Polished wood lensboard with interesting shutter. Brown leather bellows. $100-150.

Field cameras - c1900. Wood body. For 5x7" or 10x15" plates. Wuensche Rectilinear Extra Rapid f8 brass barrel lens. $125-150.

Juwel - c1895-1900. 9x12cm falling-plate magazine box camera. f12 lens. Single speed shutter. $50-75.

Knox - c1906. Polished wood folding bed camera for 9x12cm plates. Rotary shutter built on front of wooden lens standard. Tapered single extension blue-green bellows with red corners. $275-325.

Lola - c1905. Strut-folding, 9x12cm plates. Leather covered body. Shutter built into leather covered front. Design of knee-struts is nearly identical to the earliest Folding Pocket Kodak Camera. $150-200.

Lola Stereo - c1905. Strut-folding stereo for 9x18cm plates. Leather-covered wood body, nickel trim. Anastigmat f7.7/90mm lenses. $250-350.

Mars 99 - c1895. Leather covered box camera for 9x12cm plates. Aplanat f12/ 150mm lens. Rotating shutter. $250-300.

Mars Detective - c1893. Polished mahogany 12-plate magazine camera. ¼ or ½-plate sizes. Aplanat f8/130mm. Rotary shutter. Plates are moved to and from the plane of focus by sliding a moving sheath above the desired plate, then inverting the camera to drop the plate into the sheath. The sheath is then moved to the plane of focus. When the camera is righted, the plate slides into position for use. $350-400.

Mars Detectiv-Stereoskop - c1897. Wooden magazine plate camera, 8.5x17cm plates. Takes single or stereo exposures. Aplanat lenses. See Mars, above, for description of plate changing mechanism. The stereo model has the film sheath at the side rather than at the top. Holds 12 plates. Rare. $800-950.

Postage stamp camera - c1907. 12 lens camera, makes twelve 24x30mm exp. on a ½-plate. Wood body with wooden door (flap shutter) covering the lenses. $1500-2000.

Reicka - c1912. Folding plate camera for 9x12cm. Leather covered wood body. Double extension bellows. Rodenstock Heligonal f5.4/120mm lens in Koilos 1-300 shutter. $50-80.

Sport - c1895. Stereo box camera for 8.5x17cm plates. Polished wood body. Two brass barrel lenses. Stereo sector shutter. Unusual hinged lenscaps. $350-400.

YALE CAMERA CO.
Yale Camera - c1910. Small paper box camera for 5x5cm glass plates. Single plates must be darkroom loaded. Similar to the Zar, but with exposed brass shutter pivot. $60-90.

YAMATO KOKI KOGYO CO. LTD.
YAMATO CAMERA INDUSTRY CO. LTD (Tokyo)
Bonny Six - Zeiss Ikonta B copy. Bonny Anast. f4.5/75mm. $25-35.

Konair Ruby - c1955. Rangefinder 35. Konair f3.5/45mm lens in Sunchro 10-300 shutter. $20-30.

Pax - c1950's. Models I, M2, M3, M4, Ruby. Small rangefinder 35mm styled after the Leica. Most have Luminor or Color Luna f2.8 or f3.5/45mm lens and Synchro shutter 10-300. $25-45.

Yashica 44

Pax Golden View - Deluxe version of the Pax. All metal parts are gold-colored. Green leather covering. $75-100. *(Illustrated on front cover.)*

Pax Jr. - c1960's. Luminor Anastigmat f3.5/45mm lens. Shutter 1/25-300. $25-45.

YASHICA (Japan)
Yashica 44 - c1958. TLR for 4x4cm on 127 rollfilm. Yashikor f3.5/60mm lens. Copal-SV 1-500,B shutter. Available in black, grey, or brown. $30-50. *(Illustrated bottom of previous page.)*

Yashica 44A - c1960. TLR for 4x4cm on 127 rollfilm. Yashikor f3.5/60mm lens. Copal shutter 25-300,B. Available in arious colors, including blue, grey, or black enamel with grey leatherette. $30-45.

Yashica 44LM - c1959. Built-in uncoupled meter. Yashinon f3.5/60mm lens. Copal-SV shutter 1-500,B. Available in black, grey, and brown. $40-60.

Yashica 72E - c1962. Half-frame 35mm camera, 18x24mm. Selenium meter surrounds Yashinon f2.8/28mm lens. $20-30.

Yashica A - c1959. Inexpensive TLR for 6x6cm on 120 rollfilm. Yashikor f3.5/80mm lens. Copal 25-300 shutter. $25-35.

Yashica Atoron - c1965. Subminiature for 8x11mm on 9.5mm film (Minox cassettes). Selenium meter. Yashinon f2.8/18mm fixed focus lens. Shutter 45-250,B. With case, flash, filters in presentation box: $30-40. Camera only: $20-30.

Yashica Atoron Electro - c1970. Black 8x11mm subminiature. CdS meter. Yashinon DX f2.8/18mm focusing lens. Automatic shutter 8-350. Outfit with case, flash, filters, presentation box: $40-55. Camera only: $20-40.

Yashica C - c1958. TLR, 6x6cm on 120. Yashikor f3.5/80mm lens. Copal MX 1-300 shutter. $25-35. *(Illustrated top of next page.)*

Yashica C

Yashica Rapide - c1961. Half-frame 35mm. Unusual style: stands vertically like a pocket-sized transistor radio. Built-in meter. Interchangeable Yashinon f2.8/28mm lens in Copal 1-500 shutter. $40-60.

Yashica D - c1958-74. 6x6cm TLR. Yashikor f3.5/80mm in Copal MXV 500 shutter. $30-50.

Yashica EE - c1962. Viewfinder 35mm. Yashinon f1.9/45mm. Copal SVA 1-500, MX sync. Meter cell around lens. $25-35.

Yashica Mimy - c1964. Half-frame 35mm with automatic exposure controlled by selenium meter which encircles lens. $20-30.

Yashica Sequelle - c1962. 35mm half-frame for 18x24mm. Styled like a movie camera. Yashinon f2.8/28mm lens in Seikosha-L shutter 30-250,B. Built-in meter. Battery-powered motor drive. $60-80.

Yashica Y16 - c1959. Subminiature for 10x14mm on 16mm cassette film. f2.8 or 3.5/25mm Yashinon lens. Various color combinations include: aqua & grey, royal blue & grey, maroon & grey, two-tone grey, tangerine & cream. $15-20. *(Illustrated bottom of previous column.)*

Yashica YE - c1959. Rangefinder 35mm, made by the newly acquired Nicca factory. Has similarities to the Leica IIIg and M3 cameras. Interchangeable Yashikor f2.8/50mm. FP shutter 1-500, B,T. Rapid wind lever. $125-175.

Yashica Y16

Zeh Goldi

Yashica YF - c1959. Leica M3 copy. (Actually a continuation of the Nicca camera line. Yashica had purchased Nicca in 1958.) Interchangeable Yashinor f1.8/50mm lens. FP shutter 1-1000,B. $125-175.

Yashica YK - c1959. Rangefinder 35mm. Yashinon f2.8/45mm lens. Between-the-lens 25-300 shutter. Single-stroke advance lever. $20-35.

YASHINA SEIKI CO. LTD. (Japan)
Pigeonflex - c1953. 6x6cm TLR. Tri-Lausar f3.5/80mm. NKS shutter 1-200, B. $35-45.

YEN-KAME (Yen cameras): *A unique and inexpensive camera type which flourished during the 1930's in Japan, and continued to be popular after WWII. They are occasionally found with "Made in Occupied Japan" markings.) The cameras are simple ground-glass backed box or folding cameras which take single sheets of film in paper holders. The negative could be processed in daylight by dipping the entire paper holder into a red-colored developer and then a green-colored fixer. The red coloring in the developer eliminated the need for a darkroom, and the slogan "No Need DarkRoom" is often printed on the camera faces. This slogan is also used to identify the film type. There are many names on the low-priced cameras, and several are listed alphabetically in this guide. We do not have space to give each "brand" a separate listing, but some of the names you might encounter are: Amco, Asahi, Asahigo, Baby, Baby Reflex, Baby Special, Baby Sports, Camera, Camerette, Collegiate, Highking, Hitgo, Kamerette, Kamerette Junior Nos. 1-4, Kamerette Senior No. 1, Katei, King, King Super, Koseido, Light, Lion, Maruso, Milbro, Million, Nichibei, Nymco Folding Camera, Pocket, Special Camera, Special King, Super Camera, Tokyo, Tougo Camera, Victory Camera, and Yuuhigo. There are even generic versions with no name at all. To the street vendors and the public, the name was not as important as the low-cost magic of the*

camera. Generally, the box versions sell for $10-15. Folding models: $15-20.

YUNON YN 500 - c1984. One of the many inexpensive "Taiwan-35" types. Hot shoe, single speed shutter, 4 stops with weather symbols. The "Yunon" name was used in a promotion by Prestige Travel Club, which had about 5000 surplus cameras in late 1985. $1-5.

ZEH (Zeh-Camera-Fabrik, Paul Zeh, Dresden)
Bettax - c1936. Folding 6x6cm rollfilm camera. Radionar f4.5/100mm. Compur shutter. $15-30.

Goldi - c1930. Folding-bed camera for 16 exposures 3x4cm on 127 film. f2.9 or 4.5 Zecanar lens. Vario, Prontor, or Compur shutter. $45-60. *(Illus. top of previous column.)*

Zeca, 6x9cm - c1940. Folding sheet-film camera. Steinheil f6.8 or Periskop f11 lens. Vario shutter, 25-100. $20-35.

Zeca, 9x12cm - c1937. Folding sheet-film camera. 135mm lenses:f6.3 Schneider Radionar, f6.8 Jena, f2.9 Zecanar or Xenar. Leather covered wood body. $20-30.

Zeca-Flex - c1937. Folding 6x6cm TLR

for 120 film. f3.5/75mm Schneider Xenar lens. f2.9 viewing lens. The folding style 6x6cm reflex never became popular, so this model, along with Perfekta and Superfekta from the neighboring suburb of Freital, was not made in large quantities. $400-600.

ZEISS, ZEISS IKON A.G. *(Before 1926, the Carl Zeiss Optical Co. was located in Jena. In late 1926, the largest camera manufacturers in Germany, Contessa-Nettel, Ernemann, Goerz, Ica, and Carl Zeiss merged to form Zeiss-Ikon, and the headquarters became Dresden. In 1946, after WWII, Zeiss-Ikon A.G. located in Stuttgart, West Germany. Some camera models were still being made in the Jena and Dresden factories, but they were not really "Zeiss Ikon" cameras, even though some bore the Zeiss Ikon trademark. (We have listed these models under the manufacturer Pentacon.) Camera production ceased in 1971 with assembly continuing into 1972.*

In a single year Zeiss Ikon offered in their catalog 104 different model names with an average of 3 separate formats and more than 3 lens and shutter combinations per format- 936 choices or "stock" models in that one catalog. The most variations that year were offered in the Deckrullo (later called "Nettel") press camera. One could order it in 4.5x6, 6.5x9, 9x12, 10x15, and 13x18cm formats plus all except the smallest in tropical style with varnished teak and brown leather bellows. With an actual count of 30 different lenses for the 9 types, one had 39 possible choices for this single model! This was in the 1927 catalog before any of the really famous Zeiss Ikon cameras like the Contax, Contarex, Contaflex, Kolibri, and Super Ikontas had been introduced.

From the above you can get some idea of the complexity of identifying and pricing all Zeiss Ikon cameras so please regard this list as covering only the more usual types and/or those of exceptional value. Where the Zeiss Ikon model number is available this number is included in the description to help in identification. Often, these numbers appear on the camera body. Sometimes, especially on U.S.A. models, they are not on the camera itself, but only in the catalog. The number is usually expressed as a fraction such as 250/7 for a 9x12cm Ideal and 250/3 for a 6.5x9cm Ideal. Basically, the first number designates the camera model; the second number indicates negative size and is standard from one model to another. The following chart (listed in "Zeiss Historica" Journal Vol. 3 No. 1) gives the size numbers used on Zeiss Ikon still cameras from 1927 to 1960, after which decimal numbers for models were used. (The focal length of the most usual lens for the format is also shown.) A new or improved model usually changes only the last digit of the first number, generally increasing it by one. Hopefully this information will help the user of this guide to locate his Zeiss camera by name, number, illustration, or a combination of the three.

Number	Metric size	F.L.
---	4.5x6cm	75mm
---	22x31mm	45, 50mm
1	45x107mm	twin 65mm
2	6x9cm	105mm
3	6.5x9cm	105mm
4	6x13cm	twin 75mm
5	8.5x11.5cm	135mm
6	8x14cm	150mm
7	9x12cm	135mm
8	9x14cm *(Ica)*	---
9	10x15cm	165mm
10	9x18cm *(Ica)*	---
11	13x18cm	210mm
12	4x6.5cm	75mm
13	13x18cm *(Ica)*	---
14	5x7.5cm	90mm
15	6.5x11cm	120mm
16	6x6cm	80mm
17	8x10.5cm	120mm
18	3x4cm	50mm
20	18x24cm	---
21	24x30cm	---
24	24x36mm	50mm
27	24x24mm	40mm

Zeiss Ikon cameras have attracted a following whose buying habits resemble those of Leica collectors in some respects. This has led to a wider range of prices based on condition. Since most items are not rare, their condition is a very important consideration in establishing prices. The prices here are from our database, showing cameras in condition range 4 to 5. Items in condition range 2-3 would bring a bit more. Range 6 to 9 would not only bring less money, but also be harder to sell. It should also be noted that cameras bearing the Zeiss-Ikon logo are generally worth from 10% to 50% more than their counterparts from the earlier companies, which accounts for the somewhat higher prices here than in the Contessa, Ernemann, Goerz, and Ica sections of this guide.

Editor's note: We are deeply indebted to Mr. Mead Kibbey for the excellent job of researching and assembling this section of the book. Mr. Kibbey is widely respected as one of the world's foremost authorities on Zeiss-Ikon. In addition to his Zeiss collecting, Mead also serves as an officer of the Zeiss Historica Society. It should also be noted that cameras bearing the Zeiss-Ikon logo are generally worth from 10% to 50% more than their counterparts from the earlier companies, which accounts for the somewhat higher prices here than in the Contessa, Ernemann, Goerz, and Ica sections of this guide.

Adoro - see Tropen Adoro

Aerial Camera, 13x18cm - c1930. Cast metal aerial camera for hand use. Two hand grips. Folding frame finder. Tessar f3.5/ 250mm, focal plane shutter. $250-300.

Baby Box Tengor - Baseball sized box camera with name on front or back. 3x4cm on 127 film. Note: Shutter won't work unless wire front sight is lifted.

54/18 - 1931. Frontar f11 lens. Plain leather front. $40-60.

54/18 - 1934-38. Metal front plate with "Baby Box" under lens. $30-60.
54/18(E) - 1931-34. Focusing Novar f6.3 lens. Black metal front plate. $40-75. *(Illustrated top of next column.)*

Baby Deckrullo (12, 870) - 1926-29. 4.5x6cm plate camera. Strut-folding, with bed. Focal plane shutter to 1200. Zeiss Tessar f4.5 or f2.7/80mm lens. Camera focus knob on top. $250-375.

Baby Ikonta (520/18) - 3x4cm rollfilm. Novar f3.5/50mm (1936): $45-85. Tessar f3.5/50mm (1936): $80-110. Novar f6.3, f4.5 or Tessar f4.5 (1932): $40-80.

Baldur Box (51) - 1934-36. Inexpensive black box camera for 16 exposures 4.5x6cm on 120. Frontar f11/90mm. Shutter

Baby Box Tengor, 54/18(E)

Baldur Box, 51

1/30, T. Rare, but usually selling for around $20-35.

Baldur Box 51/2 - 1934-36. For 8 exposures 6x9cm on 120 film. Goerz Frontar f11/115mm lens. Shutter 1/30, T. Very rare. Estimate: $25-50.

Bebe (342) - 4.5x6cm strut camera with unpleated bellows. Front cell focus. Tessar f4.5 or Triotar f3.5/75mm in dial set Compur (1928): $100-200. Tessar f3.5 in rimset Compur (1930): $150-275.

Bebe (342/3) - 6.5x9cm folding camera. Tessar f4.5/105mm or rimset Compur with Tessar f3.5. $100-200.

Bob (510, 510/2) - 1934-41. Inexpensive black folding cameras, 4.5x6 and 6x9cm sizes. Nettar lens. Gauthier shutter 25-75, B, T. $20-30.

Bob IV, V - 1927. (Cameras left over from Ernemann.) Sizes: 4x6.5, 6x6, 6x9, 6.5x11, 7.25x12.5cm. 33 different lens/shutter combinations. 7.25x12.5cm size: $50-90. Other sizes: $25-50.

Bobette I (549) - 1929. Strut folding camera for 22x31mm on rollfilm. With Ernoplast f4.5/50 or Erid f8/40: $150-175. With Frontar f9/50mm: $55-75.

Bobette II (548) - 1929. Folding camera for 22x31mm on rollfilm. Leather covered body. Black bellows. Ernostar f2/42mmor Ernon f3.5/50mm lens. Shutter ½-100. The first miniature rollfilm camera with f2 lens. $250-500.

Box Tengor 54 - 1934-39. 4.5x6cm (½-frame) on 120 film. Goerz Frontar f11 lens, rotating waterhouse stops, 1 close up lens controlled from the front of the camera. Single speed shutter. Flash synch. Diamond shaped winding knob. 2 ruby windows. $15-25.

Box Tengor 54/14 - 5x7.5cm on 127 film. Frontar f11. Plain leather front. Winding knob on bottom right side, as viewed by operator. First model (1926-28) has two finder lenses vertical at upper front corner. Quite rare. $60-100. Second model (1928-34) has two finder lenses horizontal across the top of the front. $50-90.

Box Tengor 54/2 - 6x9cm on 120 film. Frontar f11 lens.
- 1926-28. Plain leatherette front. Viewfinder objectives vertical in upper front corner. Winding knob at bottom. $10-25.

- 1928-34. Plain leatherette front. Viewfinder objectives horizontal across front. Winding knob at top. Stops and closeups. $10-25.

- 1934-38. Extended hexagon front plate around lens with stops and closeup settings around it. Black enamel trim around front edge of camera. Diamond shaped winding knob at top of operator's right side. $10-25.
- 1938. Same as the previous listing, but release button moved to the top of camera on operator's right. $15-25.

Box Tengor 55/2 - 1939. Same as the 54/2 of 1938, but serrated round winding knob with leatherette center, black front trim, and double exposure interlock on winding knob. $15-25.

Box Tengor 56/2 - 1948-56. Chrome trim. Lever shutter release on lower right side, flash contact on lower left (from operator's viewpoint). Frontar f9 lens, internal sync. $15-35.

Box Tengor 54/15 - 6.5x11cm (2½x4¼") on 116 rollfilm. Fairly rare, since this size was not offered after 1938-39. Goerz Frontar lens.
- 1926-28. Ground glass viewfinder windows. Viewfinder objective lenses vertical in upper corner. Winding knob at bottom. $20-40. *(Illustrated top of next page.)*
- 1928-33. Viewfinder objectives horizontal across top of front. Winding knob at top. Shutter has mirror on front.

Box Tengor 54/15, 1926-28

Close up lenses and diaphragm control on metal strips pulled up on top of camera. $20-40.
- 1933-38. Similar to the 1928-33 model, but metal plate like elongated hexagon on front around lens. Brilliant viewfinders with square lenses. Close up and diaphragm settings on front metal plate around lens. $25-50.

Citoskop (671/1) - A top quality stereo for 45x107mm cut film or plates. Sucher Triplett f4.5/65mm viewing/focusing lens located between Tessar f4.5/65mm taking lenses. All metal pop-up viewing hood with newton finder lens at front. "Citoskop" on front of camera. Fairly rare. $235-275.

Cocarette, 514/14

Cocarette - 1928-29. Rollfilm is loaded by removing the winder and film track from the side of the camera, somewhat like a Leica (the back does not open). (Also made in a plate back model.) Single extension.

Derval, Klio, and Compur dial set shutters. Frontar, Periskop, Novar, Dominar, and Tessar lenses. 64 different lens/shutter combinations. Made in black models. #514 in 5 sizes. #517, #518: lever focus, vertical lens adjustment, each in 2 sizes. #519: lever focus, no vertical lens adjustment, in 3 sizes. $30-50. *(In 1930, #517, #518, #519 were made with rimset Compur. Add $5-10 for these rimset models.)*

Cocarette Luxus (521/2, 521/15, 522/17) - 1928. 6x9 and 8x10.5cm sizes. Brown leather covering, polished metal parts. Double extension. Dial set Compur. Dominar f4.5/105mm: $85-130. Tessar f4.5/105: $150-300.

Colora (10.0641) - 1963-65. An inexpensive 35mm camera. "Colora" on top. Novica f2.8/50mm (a fairly unusual lens). Prontor 125 shutter, X sync. $20-30.

Colora F (10.0641) - 1964-65. Similar to the Colora, but AG-1 flash bulb socket under the accessory shoe. Shoe tips back to become the flash reflector and to uncover the socket. Rewind knob has flash calculator in top. $15-25.

Contaflex (860/24) - TLR 35mm. 80mm viewing lens. 8 interchangeable 35mm to 135mm taking lenses. First camera with built-in exposure meter. $800-1200 if EXC to Mint. (Worth much less if meter is broken, shutter jammed, or Albada finder discolored.) In average condition, these regularly sell at auction in the $400-700 range.

Contaflex TLR lenses:
- 35mm Orthometer or Biotar: $450-600.
- 50mm Sonnar f2 or f1.5: $100-200.
- 50mm Tessar f2.8: $100-200.
- 85mm Sonnar f2: $200-400.
- 85mm Triotar f4: $200-400.
- 135mm Sonnar f4: $225-450.
- 35mm viewfinder: $200.

Contaflex I (861/24) - 1953-58. 35mm SLR. Tessar f2.8/45mm. Synchro-Compur. No exposure meter. Common. $40-65.

Contaflex II (862/24) - 1954-58. Like the I, but with built-in exposure meter. Common. $50-70.

Contaflex III (863/24) - 1957-59. 35mm SLR. Tessar f2.8/50mm, interchangeable front element. Knob for film advance and shutter tensioning. No meter. Not as common as Contaflex II. $50-70.

Contaflex IV (864/24) - 1957-59. Like the III, but with built-in exposure meter. Door covers the meter. LVS settings. Common. $50-75.

Contaflex Alpha (10.1241) - 1958-59. Same as the Contaflex III, but with the less expensive Pantar f2.8/45mm lens. Interchangeable front element for Pantar series lenses. $40-60.

Contaflex Beta (10.1251) - Like the Alpha, but with exposure meter. $45-65.

Contaflex Rapid, Prima, Supers, S Automatic: *all have rapid film advance, accessory shoe on prism housing, and interchangeable magazine backs.*

Contaflex Rapid (10.1261) - 1959-61. Tessar f2.8/50mm, interchangeable front element. Rarely offered for sale. $60-85.

Contaflex Prima (10.1291) - 1959-65. Like the Rapid, but with Pantar f2.8/45mm. Uncovered match needle exposure meter on operator's right side. Quite rare. $60-90.

Contaflex Super (10.1262) - 1959-62. Same as the Rapid, but with coupled exposure meter. Uncovered meter window in front of prism housing. Meter adjustment wheel on front of camera, operator's left. No other Contaflex has this external wheel. Common. $45-75.

Contaflex Super (New Style- 10.1271) - 1962-67. "Zeiss-Ikon" printed on front of larger exposure meter window. No external setting wheel as above. Tessar f2.8/50mm. Shutter says "Synchro-Compur X" under lens. Exposure meter window on top has two red arrows and no numbers. Inside viewfinder tiny "2x" visible at top of exposure meter slot. No automatic exposure control. Common. $45-85.

Contaflex Super B (10.1272) - 1963-68. Looks like the new style Super, except has numbers in exposure meter indicator on top and in viewfinder. Shutter says "Synchro-Compur" under lens. Automatic exposure control. $65-90.

Contaflex Super BC (10.1273) - 1967-1970. Similar to above except no external exposure meter window. Has internal through-the-lens CdS meter. Black rectangle over the lens, with "Zeiss-Ikon". Battery compartment with square door at 9 o'clock from lens. Chrome: $100-150. Add $50-75 for black model.

Contaflex S Automatic (10.1273-BL) - 1970-72. "Contaflex S" on front of prism housing. "Automatic" above lens on shutter. $150-200.

Contaflex 126 (10.1102) - 1970-73. For 28x28mm on 126 cartridge film. Fully automatic exposure control. "Contaflex 126" on front. Interchangeable f2.8/45mm Tessar or Color Pantar. Not unusual to find an outfit with camera and four lenses; f2.8/45, f2.8/32, f28./85, and f4/135 for $150-250. With f2.8/45mm lens only, very common: $70-125.

Contaflex lenses for full frame SLRs
- 35mm f4 Pro-Tessar (11.1201, and 1003). 49mm external filters. $30-40.
- 35mm f3.2 Pro-Tessar (11.1201). 60mm external filters. $45-85.
- 85mm f4 Pro-Tessar (11.1202, and 1004). 60mm external filters. $50-80.
- 85mm f3.2 Pro-Tessar (11.1202). 60mm external filters. $50-85.
- 115mm f4 Pro-Tessar (11.1205). 67mm external filters. $60-100.
- Pro-Tessar M-1:1 (11.1204). High resolution close copy lens. $90-125.

ZEISS (cont.)

- Monocular 8x30B: *see Contarex lenses below.*
- Teleskop 1.7x (fits models I and II only) (11.1203) With bracket: $50-80.
- Steritar A (Stereo prism for above) (20.2004, and 812). $125-175.

For Alpha, Beta, Prima, and Contina III
- 30mm f4 Pantar (11.0601). $25-40.
- 75mm f4 Pantar (11.0601 or 1002). $60-80.
- Steritar D (20.2006 or 814). $100-130.
- Steritar B (20.2005 or 813) (for Contaflex III through S). $125-175.

Contaflex 126 lenses
- Distagon f4/25mm (11.1113). Very rare. No sales records. Estimate: $150.
- 32mm f2.8 Distagon (11.1101). Mint: $18-30.
- 45mm f2.8 Color Pantar (11.1102). $12.
- 45mm f2.8 Tessar (11.1103). $18.
- 85mm f2.8 Sonnar (11.1104). $45-75.
- 135mm f4 Tele Tessar (11.1105). $25-40.
- 200mm f4 Tele Tessar (11.1112). $100-200.

Contarex Cameras: *All models of this superbly made 35mm camera except the microscope version have the word "Contarex" on front. KEH Camera Brokers, Atlanta assisted in pricing this series.*

Contarex "Bullseye" (10.2401) - 1960-1967. Large round coupled exposure meter window over lens. Interchangeable Planar f2/50mm. Early models had no data strip slot at rear. $175-275.

Contarex Special (10.2500 body) - 1960-66. No meter. Interchangeable reflex or prism view hood. "Contarex" in script-like letters. $275-400.

Contarex Professional (10.2700 body) - 1967-68. No meter. Only prism viewer. "Professional" on front. Very rare. Less than 1000 made, and almost no mint examples remaining. Absolutely like new: $700-825. Excellent: $325-450.

Contarex Super (10.2600 body) - 1968-1972. "Super" on front. First model has through-the-lens meter switch on front at 2 o'clock from the lens (opposite from focus wheel). Second model has switch on top under the winding lever. Front switch: $300-500. Top switch: $450-600.

Contarex Electronic (Super Electronic) (10.2800 body) - 1970-72. "Electronic" on front. Chrome or (rarer) black body. Mint: $650-850. Excellent: $400-600.

Contarex Hologon (10.0659 outfit) - 1970-72. "Hologon" on front. Fixed focus lens f8/15mm, linear type (not a fisheye). With camera, grip, cable release, special neutral density graduated filter, and case for all: $900-1200. Camera only: $500-700.

Contarex Microscope Camera - "Zeiss Ikon" in block letters on top. No lens, viewfinder, or exposure meter. Interchangeable backs. Quite rare. $300-400.

Contarex Lenses: *These lenses, made between 1959 and 1973 by Carl Zeiss, Oberkochen are seldom equalled and never surpassed even with today's technology. Up to 1965, 135mm and shorter lenses have chrome finish, and 180mm and longer have black finish. After 1965, all were black finished.*
- 16mm f2.8 fisheye Distagon (11.2442) 1973. Rare. $400-700.
- 18mm Distagon f4 (11.2418) 1967-73. With adapter ring for B96 filters. $300-425.
- 21mm Biogon f4.5 (11.2402) 1960-63. (for Bullseye only.) $140-195. *Add $100 for finder.*
- 25mm Distagon f2.8 (11.2408) 1963-73. Black: $350-425. Chrome: $225-325.
- 35mm Distagon f4 Chrome (11.2403) 1960-73. $75-115.
- 35mm Blitz Distagon f4 Black (11.2413) 1966-73. Built-in flash automation. $80-130.
- 35mm f4 PA Curtagon (11.2430) 1973. Made by Schneider, but mounted and sold by Zeiss Ikon, Stuttgart. Automatic stop down. Perspective control by up to 7mm lateral movement in any of 4 directions. Rare. $350-500 with B56 filter ring.
- 35mm f2 Distagon (11.2414) 1965-73. $225-325.
- 50mm f4 S-Planar (11.2415) 1963-68. For critical close ups to 3". $300-500.
- 50mm f2.8 Tessar (11.2501). Black: $125-175. Chrome: $85-110.
- 50mm f2 Planar Chrome (11.2401) 1960-73. $45-75.
- 50mm f2 Blitz Planar Black (11.2412) 1966-73. $75-110.
- 55mm f1.4 Planar (11.2407) 1965-73. Black: $200-245. Chrome: $130-165.
- 85mm f2 Sonnar (11.2404) 1960-73. Black: $190-235. Chrome: $160-195.
- 85mm f1.4 Planar 1974. Very rare. Estimate: $600-750.

- 115mm f3.5 Tessar (11.2417) 1960-73. For use with bellows. Estimate: $350-400. Bellows: $100. Bellows with cable socket: $125.
- 135mm f4 Sonnar (11.2405) 1960-73. Black: $90-130. Chrome: $80-120.
- 135mm f2.8 Olympia-Sonnar (11.2409) 1965-73. $250-300.
- 180mm f2.8 Olympia-Sonnar (11.2425) 1967-73. Fairly rare. $400-700.
- 250mm f4 Sonnar (11.2406) 1960-63. Manual preset focus. $125-180.
- 250mm f4 Olympia-Sonnar (11.2421) 1963-73. Knob focus auto stop-down. $300-380.
- 400mm f5.6 Tele Tessar (11.2434) 1970-73. Very rare. Estimate: $700-1200.
- 500mm f4.5 Mirotar (11.2420) 1963-73. Catadioptric. Very rare. $1500-2000.
- 1000mm f5.6 Mirotar (11.2422) 1964-70. Catadioptric. Super rare. $2500-3500.
- 40/120mm f2.8 Vario-Sonnar (11.2423) 1970-73. Rare. $1000-1400.
- 85/250 f4 Vario-Sonnar (11.2424) 1970-73. Very rare. $1500-2500.

- Monocular 8x30B with 27mm threaded eyepiece to fit Contaflex SLR or Contarex by use of an adapter. First model (1960) (20.1629) with eyepiece focus and line for 140 feet. $80-120. Second model (1963) with front end focussing and a distance scale. (This second model is the most common type seen.) $120-160. Third model (1969) (11.1206) has porro prism with front end focus. This model is straight and looks like a small refracting telescope. $175-225.
- Adapter to use monocular with 50mm f2 Planar: $40-50.
- Adapter to use monocular with 50mm f1.4 Planar: $70-90.

Contax Series: *Introduced in 1932 as a top quality rangefinder 35mm system camera, it was manufactured until 1961 with the exception of the 1944-52 period. Dr. Stanley Bishop assisted in the preparation of this section.*

Contax I (540/24) - 1932-36. *Identifying features: black enamel finish, square appearance, "Contax" in white on upper front and winding knob on front to operator's right of lens.*

Contax I(a) - Serial numbers starting with "AU" or "AV". No low (below 1/25) shutter speeds, no "foot" on tripod socket and often had one or more raised "dimples" over ends of shafts on front of camera. Viewfinder window closer to center of camera than rangefinder window. With contemporary lens: $475-650.

Contax I(b) - Same as the I(a) in appearance except front bezel extends across front to viewing and rangefinder window. $450-600.

Contax I(c) - "Foot" on tripod socket, slow speeds added, guard attached to lens bezel surrounds slow speed setting ring. Like the above models, it has no button to unlock infinity stop when external bayonet lenses are in use. $300-450.

Contax I(d) - Same as the I(c), but button to release infinity lock present at 1 o'clock from lens, and distance scale around base of lens mount now finished in chrome with black numbers rather than in black with white numbers as on earlier models. $300-400.

Contax I(e) - Same as I(d), except viewfinder window moved to outside of rangefinder window, and a shallow vertical groove in front bezel between lens mount containing word "Contax" and focus wheel. $250-450.

Contax I(f) - Same as I(e), but has 4 screws in accessory shoe, and the marker for setting shutter speeds changed from an apparent slotted screw head to a small pointer. $250-450.

Contax II (543/24) - 1936-42. Identified by satin chrome finish on top and trim. Winding and speed setting on top right (viewed from behind), shutter speeds to 1/1250, and rangefinder and viewfinder windows combined. A superb rugged camera with no external variations during its production life. It can be differentiated from the postwar Contax II(a) by its larger size, a narrow frame around the small rangefinder window, and the absence of sync connection on upper back. With Sonnar f2/50mm: $80-175.

ZEISS (cont.)

Jena Contax (II) - c1947. Very similar to pre-war Contax II. Says "Carl Zeiss Jena" in shoe. Back is made of brass, not aluminum. Black bezel around self-timer. Lettering style is slightly different. Rare. $500-700.

Contax III (544/24) - 1936-42. Same as the Contax II, except had built in, uncoupled exposure meter on top and rewind knob was much higher. $100-200.

"No Name" Contax, Contax D, and Contax F - Using captured parts and personnel, other variations of the Contax II and Pentaprism versions were produced after WWII in East Germany. They tended to be of inferior quality and sell in the range of $50-150. These cameras are covered in more detail under the manufacturer "Pentacon" on pages 295-297.

Contax II(a) (563/24) - 1950-61. An excellent quality camera produced at Stuttgart and identified by satin chrome top, "Contax" on front, wide frame around right rangefinder window, sync fitting on back near top, and film speed and type indicator on rewind knob.
- First model: all numbers on speed setting dial are black. Sync attachment looks like flat plunger in socket. Requires special attachment to convert mechanical motion to electric contact. (#1361 for bulbs, #1366 for electronic flash.) $125-175.
- Second model: Same, but numbers on speed dial in color (1-1/25 black, 1/50 yellow, 100-1250 red) and regular p.c. flash connector at rear. Many of these are still in use. $200-275.

Contax IIIa - Same as the IIa, except uncoupled exposure meter on top. First model (black dial): $200-300. Second model (colored dial): $200-300. (Mint condition brings 25-35% more.)

Prewar Contax Lenses: *Earliest were black enamel and heavy chrome trim. These are worth from a little to a lot more than the later satin chrome versions. All these lenses plus innumerable*

Contax accessories are described in a book published by David Gorski. Even the viewfinders in the Contax series are collected and vary from $20 up to several hundred dollars in value. Serial numbers range from about 1,350,000 to 2,700,000.
- 28mm f8 non-coupled wide angle Tessar: $75-110.
- 35mm f4.5 Orthometer. $300-500.
- 35mm f2.8 Biogon (fits only pre-war Contaxes): $50-85.
- 40mm and 42.5mm f2 Biotar. Black: $500-800. Chrome: $400-700.
- 50mm f3.5 Tessar: $40-60. *Add $10-20 if black front ring (for Contax I).*
- 50mm f2.8 Tessar: $40-60. *Add $10-20 if black front ring (for Contax I).*
- 50mm f2 Sonnar: Rigid mount: $35-60. Collapsible mount: $20-25.
- 50mm f1.5 Sonnar: $25-55. *Add $10 for black.*
- 85mm f4 Triotar: Black: $90-125. Chrome: $40-80.
- 85mm f2 Sonnar: Prewar black: $140-160. Prewar chrome: $50-100.
- 135mm f4 Sonnar: Black: $125-175. Chrome: $60-90.
- 180mm f6.3 Tele Tessar K (direct mount): Black: $400-600. Chrome: $300-500.
- 180mm f2.8 Sonnar (direct mount): $1200-1600.
- 180mm f2.8 Sonnar in flektoskop (inverted image), with case: $600-1000.
- 300mm f8 Teletessar K (direct or Flektoskop mount): $1300-1800.
- 500mm f8 Fern (distance) lens. Rare. Direct mount: $2500-3500. With Flektoskop and case: $2000-2500.

Postwar Contax lenses: *Chrome finish on all. Fern 500mm, Sonnar f2.8/180mm, and Tessar f3.5/115mm offered in black also.*
- 21mm f4 Biogon (563/013): $100-150. (Add $90 for finder.)
- 25mm f4 Topogon). Very rare, no recent ones for sale. Estimate: $400-800.
- 35mm f3.5 Planar (563/014): $100-160.
- 35mm f2.8 Biometar: $110-175.
- 35mm f2.8 Biogon (563/09): $90-150.
- 50mm f3.5 Tessar (543/00): $95-145.
- 50mm f2 Sonnar (543/59): $20-40.
- 50mm f1.5 Sonnar (543/60): $25-50.
- 75mm f1.5 Biotar. Super rare. $600-1000.
- 85mm f4 Triotar (543/02): $60-90.
- 85mm f2 Sonnar (563/05): $75-125.
- 115mm f3.5 Panflex Tessar (5522/01), for bellows. Rare. $500-700.
- 135mm f4 Sonnar (543/64): $60-90.
- 180mm f2.8 Sonnar, direct or Flektoskop mount. Rare. Estimate: $1200.
- 300mm f4 Sonnar, direct or Flektoskop. Rare. Estimate: $2300.
- 500mm f8 Tele-Lens. Flektoskop or Panflex mount and case. (In October 1952, this lens cost $835.) Infrequently offered for sale. Estimate: $2000.

- Stereotar C outfit (810/01, 20.2000). Twin lens assembly, separating prism, special viewfinder, close up lenses, and leather case: $1000-1600.

Contessa Series: *Post-war full frame 35mm.*

Contessa-35 (533/24), 1950-55 - A fine quality folding 35 with center door somewhat like a Retina. Built-in dual-range, uncoupled exposure meter. "Contessa" in gold on leather door covering, and round rangefinder window directly above lens. Shutter will not fire unless camera has film and it is advanced. Tessar f2.8/45mm. First version (1950-53), Compur Rapid, X sync. Second version (1953-55), Synchro Compur, MX sync. $80-150.

Contessa-35 (533/24), 1960-61 - Very different from the first 2 versions. Rigid lens mount. Built-in exposure meter. "Contessa" on top. Tessar f2.8/50mm. Pronto 30-250. $20-35.

Contessa LK (10.0637) - 1963-65. "Contessa LK" on top. Coupled match needle exposure meter. No rangefinder. Tessar f2.8/50mm, Prontor 500 LK shutter. $25-35.

Contessa LKE (10.0638) - 1963-65. "Contessa LKE" on top. Like the LK, but with coupled rangefinder. $25-40.

Contessa LBE (10.0639) - 1965-67. "Contessa LBE" on top. Like the LKE, but automatic flash control by linkage between distance and aperature setting. $25-40.

Contessa S-310 (10.0351) - 1971. Small very well made rigid mount automatic 35, with manual overide. "S-310" on front. Tessar f2.8/40mm. Pronto S500 Electronic shutter, exposures to 8 seconds. $30-50.

Contessa S-312 (10.0354) - "S-312" on front. Like the S-310, but with coupled rangefinder. $75-125.

Contessamatic E - (10.0645) - 1960-63. "Contessa" on top-front of lens mount. No name on top. Tessar f2.8/50mm. Prontor SLK "Special" shutter, 1-500, MX sync. Coupled rangefinder. Exposure meter. $20-35.

Contessamatic - 1960-61. Same as the "E", but no rangefinder, and Prontor SLK shutter. $25-40.

Contessamat - 1964-65. "Contessamat" on top. Fully automatic. Color Pantar f2.8/45mm. Prontormatic 30-125 shutter. Coupled exposure meter. No rangefinder. $15-30.

Contessamat SE (10.0654) - 1963-65. "Contessamat SE" on top. Like the Contessamat, but with coupled rangefinder, Prontormatic 500 shutter, 30-500. $30-45.

Contessamat STE - 1965. "Contessamat STE" on top. Like the SE, but Tessar f2.8/50mm in Prontormatic 500 SL shutter, 1-500. $30-60.

Contessamat SBE (10.0652) - 1963-67. "Contessamat SBE" on top in black. "Flashmatic" in red letters. Like the STE, but covered flash contacts on top. Automatic flash control by linking distance and diaphragm settings. $30-50.

Contina I (522/24) - 1952-55. 35mm folding camera with center door. "Contina" in gold letters on door. Model number on leather of back by back latch. Novar f3.5/45mm in Prontor SV or Tessar f2.8/45mm in Synchro Compur. X sync. $15-35.

Contina II (524/24) - 1952-53. 35mm folding camera with center door. "Contina" on door. Model number in leather of back near catch. Uncoupled built-in rangefinder. Opton-Tessar f2.8/45mm in Synchro Compur 1-500, MX or Novar f3.5/45mm in Prontor SV. $30-40.

Contina Ia (526/24) - 1956-58. Rigid mount lens. "Contina" under the lens and on bezel at 1 o'clock from lens. Model number in leather of back next to catch. Novicar f2.8/45mm (1956-57) or Pantar f2.8/45mm (1958). $15-35.

Contina IIa (527/24) - 1956-58. Rigid mount lens. "Contina" on front under lens. Model number on back. Rapid wind lever. Built in uncoupled exposure meter, match needle on top. 45mm Novar f3.5 or Novicar f2.8. Prontor SVS 1-300, MX sync. $20-40.

Contina III (529/24) - 1955-58. A system camera, with the same specifications as Contina IIa, except Pantar f2.8/45mm convertible lens. "Contina" on front bezel. Model number on back. Uses all lenses of the Contaflex Alpha series. $30-55.

Contina III Lenses
- 30mm f4 Pantar (1001): $25-45.
- 75mm f4 Pantar (1002): $60-80.
- Steritar D (814): For stereo exposures. $75-125.
- 30mm wide angle finder (422): $25-35.
- Telephoto finder (423): $25-35.
- Telephoto rangefinder (correct field of view for 75mm Pantar) (425): $50-100.
- Universal finder for all items above (426): $50-70.

Contina III Microscope Camera - Body of Contina III, but modified for use with standard Zeiss Microscope Connecting funnel. No lens. Ibsor B self-cocking shutter, 1-125, X sync. No exposure meter, rangefinder, viewfinder or name, except "Zeiss-Ikon" in middle of back. Usual shutter release button does not release shutter, but must be depressed to advance shutter. Rare. $40-70.

Contina (10.0626) - 1962-1965. Rigid mount 35mm camera. "Contina" on top. Color Pantar f2.8/45mm lens. Pronto shutter to 250, X sync, self-timer. $15-25.

Contina L (10.0605) - 1964-65. Like the Contina, but with built-in uncoupled exposure meter. "Contina L" on top. Prontor 250 shutter, 30-250. $15-25.

Contina LK (10.0637) - 1963-65. Like the "L", but coupled exposure meter. "Contina LK" on top. $25-45.

Continette (10.0625) - 1960-1961. Rigid mount 35mm camera, without rangefinder or exposure meter. "Continette" on front beside viewfinder. Pronto shutter 30-250, self-timer. Lucinar f2.8/45mm lens. (This lens was not used on any other Zeiss Ikon camera.) $20-40.

Deckrullo, Deckrullo Nettel - 1926-28. Strut-folding cameras. Focal plane shutter to 2800. Formerly made by Contessa-Nettel Camerawerk, then by Contessa-Nettel Division of Zeiss-Ikon, and continuing after 1929 as the "Nettel" camera (870 series). (See also Zeiss Nettel.) (See also Baby Deckrullo for the 4.5x6cm version.)
6.5x9cm (36), 9x12cm (90) - Zeiss Tessar f4.5 or f2.7, or Triotar f3.5. $60-150.
10x15cm (120), 13x18 (165) - Zeiss Tessar f4.5 or Triotar f3.5. $60-150.

Deckrullo Tropical, Deckrullo Nettel Tropical - Same lens/shutter combinations as the Deckrullo. Made of teak wood. $400-600.

Donata (227/3, 227/7) - 1927-31. Inexpensive folding plate camera, 6.5x9 and 9x12cm sizes. Name usually on or under handle. Dominar or Tessar f4.5 lens in Compur shutter. $25-55.

Duroll, 9x12cm - c1926-27. Folding bed camera, continued from the Contessa model. Takes 8.2x10.7cm on rollfilm or 9x12cm plates. Dominar or Tessar lens. $50-75.

Elegante (816) - 1927-34. Field camera with rigid front. Square bellows. Wood with brass. $300-400.

Erabox - 1934-38. Inexpensive version of the Box Tengor. "Erabox" around lens. 4.5x6cm or 6x9cm on 120. $15-25.

Ergo (301) - 1927-31. Detective camera made to look like a monocular. Shoots at right angles to direction of viewing. "Ergo" in eyepiece area. 4.5x6cm plates. Tessar f4.5/55mm. Self-cocking shutter. Very rare. $800-1000.

Ermanox (858) - 1927-31. 4.5x6cm plate camera. Ernostar f1.8/85mm or rare f2 lens. FP shutter 20-1200. Rigid helical focusing. $800-1200.

Ermanox (858/3, 858/7, 858/11) - 1927. Strut-folding, bellows camera. Ernostar f1.8 lens, FP shutter to 1000. 6.5x9cm (858/3) is fairly rare: $500-1000. 9x12cm (858/7) is super rare: $3000-5000. 10x15 and 13x18cm sizes are listed in original catalogs, but are so rare that they are impossible to price.

Ermanox Reflex - 1927-29. Reflex 4.5x6cm plate camera. Ernostar f1.8/ 105mm lens in rigid helical focus mount. FP shutter 20-1200. $1500-2500.

Erni (27, 27/3) - 1927-30. Box plate camera. Celluloid "ground glass". Very rare. Estimate: $150-250.

Favorit (265, 265/7, 265/9, 265/11) - 1927-35. Black bodied plate camera of excellent quality. Name or number usually on handle, number on outside of door near hinge. Interchangeable lenses on all but

the 4.5x6cm size. Tessar or Dominar f4.5 lens. 13x18cm size: Very rare. Estimate: $150-300. Other sizes: $100-180.

Favorit Tropical (266/1, 266/7, 266/9) - 1927-31. Excellent quality teakwood plate camera. Brown leather handle with name and model number. Tessar or Dominar f4.5 in Compur shutter. Price varies, depending on size and condition. $400-600.

Hochtourist - c1927-31. Double extension wood view camera. Brass trim. Square bellows. Vertical and horizontal front movements. Sizes 5x7", 8x10", and 10x12". Usually without model name on camera, but with "Zeiss-Ikon" round metal plate. Very rare. No active trading exists. Infrequent sales records indicate prices in $100-300 range. *See D.B. Tubbs "Zeiss Ikon Cameras 1926-39" for pictures.*

Hologon: *see Zeiss Contarex Hologon.*

Icarette - 1927-36. In formats 4x6.5, 6x6, 6x9, 6.5x11, and 8x10.5cm, plus one model which used 6x9cm rollfilm or 6.5x9cm plates. Most say "Icarette" on handle or in leather on body. There were over 60 different lens/shutter combinations offered and 4 qualities of bodies, #509, #500, #512, and the fanciest #551/2. There are simply more kinds of Icarettes than most people want to hear about. Interest is still light in this series and the price range is $20-60.

Icarex - 1967-73. *An intermediate priced 35mm system camera. All had cloth focal plane shutter, 1/2-1000, B, X sync.*

Icarex 35 (10.2200) - Bayonet mount. Interchangeable lenses, viewing screens, and viewfinders. With Color Pantar f2.8/ 50: $85-110. With Tessar f2.8/50mm: $90-120. Add $20-40 for black body.

Icarex 35 "TM" - Threaded 42mm lens mount, marked "TM" at 1 o'clock from the lens. With Tessar f2.8/50mm: $125-175. With Ultron f1.8/50mm: $135-185.

Icarex 35 CS - Either of the Icarex 35 models becomes an Icarex 35 CS by the addition of a pentaprism viewfinder containing a through-the-lens CdS meter. The finder says "Icarex 35 CS" on its front, and looks like a part of the camera. $65-125.

Icarex 35S - intro. 1970. Available in TM (10.3600) and BM (10.3300) models. This camera differs from the Icarex 35 in that the viewfinders and view screens are not interchangeable. The CdS meter is built in and coupled with stop-down metering. Five Zeiss lenses were available for the TM model, 9 for the BM model. Chrome or black versions. Some of the early black models are marked "Pro". With Pantar: $75-110. Tessar f2.8: $80-125. Ultron f1.8: $110-180. For black models, add $20-40.

Icarex Lenses: *All take 50mm bayonet or 56mm screw-over filters and shades.*
Bayonet mount:
- 35mm f3.4 Skoparex (11.2003): $60-90.
- 50mm f2.8 Color Pantar (11.2001): $20-40.
- 50mm f2.8 Tessar (11.2002): $30-50.
- 50mm f1.8 Ultron (11.2014): $75-110
- 90mm f3.4 Dynarex (11.2004): $70-120.
- 135mm f4 Super Dynarex (11.2005): $65-100.
- 200mm f4 Super Dynarex (11.2008): $140-215.
- 400mm f5 Telomar (11.2010). Rare: $275-475.
- 36-82mm f2.8 Zoomar (11.2012): $180-300.
Thread mount:
- 25mm f2.8 Distagon (11.3503). Rare: $110-170.
- 35mm f3.4 Skoparex (11.3510): $65-95.
- 50mm f2.8 Tessar (11.35??): $40-60.
- 50mm f1.8 Ultron (11.3502): $80-100.
- 135mm f4 Super Dynarex (11.3511): $70-110.

Ideal 9x12cm (250/7)

Ideal - 1927-38. A fine quality double extension folding plate camera usually having the name and model number stamped on the leather body covering under the handle. 9x12cm size was the most common, followed by 6.5x9cm. They were offered with Compur shutters, and Dominar, Tessar, or Double Protar lenses, the Tessars being by far the most common. Interchangeable lens/shutter on all but the 6.5x9cm size. Special "pop-off" backs. 6.5x9cm (250/3): $30-60. 9x12cm (250/7): $30-50. 10x15cm (250/9), rare: $50-100. 13x18cm (250/11), very rare: $75-125.

Ikoflex Series - 1934-60. *Twin lens reflex for 6x6cm format. "Ikoflex" on front.*

Ikoflex (850/16) - 1934-37. Original "coffee can" model. All black enamel finish on body. Novar f4.5 or 6.3/80mm lens. Derval, Klio, or Compur-Rapid shutter. 2 film counters (for 120 and 620 films); lever focus under lens; "Ikoflex" on shutter above lens. Early version has art-deco finder hood, but later hoods are leather covered like other models. $100-200.

Ikoflex I (850/16) - 1939-1951. This is basically the same camera that was earlier called the Ikoflex II (1937-39). Slight changes were made to the body design when production was resumed under the Ikoflex I name. Nameplate is black, with a small chromed area surrounding the name "Ikoflex". Chrome trim. Tessar or Novar f3.5/75mm. Compur, Klio or Prontor-S shutter to 250. Knob focus. $30-50.

Ikoflex Ia (854/16) - 1952-56. "Ikoflex" in chrome against a black background on front of viewfinder. Novar or Tessar f3.5/75mm. Prontor SV to 300. Does not have a folding shutter release. $60-100.

Ikoflex Ib (856/16) - 1956-58. Improved version of Ia. Tessar or Novar f3.5/75mm in 1956-57; Novar only in 1957-58. Prontor SVS shutter, folding shutter release. Focusing hood opens and closes with single action, magnifies over diaphragm and shutter speed dials. No exposure meter. $45-70.

Ikoflex Ic (886/16) - 1956-60. Similar to the Ib, but with built-in exposure meter. Needle visible on ground glass inside hood. $60-100.

Ikoflex II (851/16) - 1936-39. "Ikoflex" nameplate on front is all chrome. Zeiss Tessar f3.5/75mm in Compur Rapid 1-500, or Zeiss Triotar f3.8/75mm in Compur 1-300. Auto film counter. Viewing lens in chromed tube appears to stick out further than on other models. Focus lever in 1937, knob in 1938-39. (This basic model was continued as the Ikoflex I.) $60-85.

Ikoflex II/III (852/16) - 1938-1940's. Entire area of taking and viewing lenses is surrounded by a front housing, with 2 peep windows above the viewing lens. Lens aperture and shutter speed show in the peep windows. Aperture and shutter speed are set by levers under shutter housing. Double exposure prevention. This model was introduced in 1938 as Ikoflex III, but was renamed "New Style Ikoflex II" in 1939 (when the original Ikoflex II (851/16) was discontinued). Zeiss Tessar f3.5/75mm lens in Compur Rapid 1-1/500, or Zeiss Triotar f3.5/75mm in Compur 1-1/300. $60-140.

Ikoflex IIa (855/16, early) - 1950-52. Similar to Ikoflex II, but the front housing surrounds only the taking lens, with the peep windows located on both sides of the viewing lens. Flash sync. Tessar f3.5/75mm, Compur Rapid shutter. $75-100.

Ikoflex IIa (855/16, re-styled) - 1953-56. Features similar to earlier IIa, but the peep windows are combined into one window above the viewing lens. Shutter and aperature set by wheels. Body design like the Favorite, but no meter. Tessar f3.5/75mm, Synchro-Compur shutter. $75-100.

Ikoflex III (853/16) - 1939-40. Only Ikoflex with huge Albada finder on front of viewing hood (like Contaflex TLR). Crank advances film and winds shutter. Tessar f2.8/80mm. Compur Rapid 1-400 or 500. $125-225.

Ikoflex Favorit (887/16) - 1957-60. Last of the Ikoflex line. Tessar f3.5/75mm. Synchro Compur MXV to 1/500. Built in LVS exposure meter. Cross-coupled shutter and aperature set by wheels. $125-200. *(Illustrated top of next page.)*

Ikomatic A (10.0552) - 1964-65. Inexpensive square-looking, for 126 cartridge film. Color Citar f6.3/45mm lens. Shutter 1/90 for daylight, 1/30 for flash. Built in electric eye exposure control. Hot shoe. "Ikomatic A" on lower front. $5-15.

Ikoflex Favorit

Ikomatic F (10.0551) - 1964-65. Same general appearance as the "A", but has Frontar fixed focus lens. No exposure control. Built-in pop-up reflector for AG-1 bulbs on top of camera. "Ikomatic-F" on lower front. $5-15.

Ikonette (504/12) - 1929-31. Small 127 rollfilm camera. Frontar f9/80mm. Self-cocking shutter. The whole back comes off to load film. There were at least 2 variations in the body catch mechanism. $30-50.

Ikonette 35 (500/24) - A unique 35mm camera (for Zeiss) made entirely of grey high impact plastic. Body is curved into a kidney shape and a single lever on the front winds the film, advances the counter, and cocks the shutter on a long stroke. The same lever then releases shutter on a short stroke. Red flag appears in the viewfinder when the shutter is cocked. Two-tone grey and blue plastic case with name on front available (1256/24). $15-35.

Ikonta cameras - 1929-56. *Early models also known as Ikomats in the U.S.A. All had front cell focus lenses. see also Baby Ikonta.*
Ikonta (520/14) - 1931. 5x7.5cm. With Tessar f4.5/80mm in Compur: $30-45. With Novar f6.3/80mm in Derval shutter. $25-35.

Ikonta A (520) - 1933-40. 4.5x6cm on 120 film. Compur shutter. With Tessar f3.5/80: $35-50. With Novar f4.5/80mm: $25-35.

Ikonta A (521) - c1940's. 4.5x6cm size. With Tessar f3.5/75mm in Compur Rapid or Synchro Compur: $60-90. With Novar f3.5 or 4.5/75 in Prontor or Compur. $40-60.

Ikonta B (520/16) - 1937-39. For 12 exposures 6x6cm on 120. With Tessar f3.5/75mm in Compur Rapid: $30-55. With Novar f3.5 or f4.5/75mm in Compur or Klio shutter: $25-35.

Ikonta B (521/16) - 1948-53. Similar to the 520/16, but with chrome lens mount and more chrome trim. $30-55.

Ikonta B (523/16) - 1954-56. Also similar, but with chrome top plate. Prontor SV or Synchro Compur shutter. $45-65.

Ikonta B (524/16) - 1954-56. Built in uncoupled rangefinder. With Tessar f3.5/105mm in Synchro Compur: $60-100. With Novar f3.5 or f4.5/105mm in Prontor SV shutter: $50-70.

Ikonta C (520/2) - 1930-40. 6x9cm on 120. With 105mm lenses: Tessar f4.5: $30-50. Tessar f3.8 (1936-37 only): $35-45. Novar f6.3: $20-35.

Ikonta C (521/2) - Postwar. With Tessar f3.5/105: $40-60. With Novar f3.5 or f4.5: $30-45.

Ikonta C (523/2) - 1950-56. 6x9cm. Heavy chrome trim at top. With Tessar or Novar f3.5: $60-90. With Novar f4.5/105mm: $35-75.

Ikonta C (524/2) - 1954-56. Like the 523/2 but with built in uncoupled rangefinder. With Tessar: $125-150. With Novar: $60-100.

Ikonta D (520/15) - 1931-39. Ikomats seem to be more common in this size than Ikontas. Early versions for 116 film, later for 616 film. With Tessar f4.5/120mm in Compur: $35-50. With Novar f6.3/120mm in Derval shutter: $30-40.

Ikonta 35 (522/24) - 1949-53. Folding 35mm with central door and very rigid front standard. Novar f3.5/45mm, Tessar f2.8/45mm, or Xenar f2.8/45mm (1949-51 only). "Ikonta" in leather on back. Later models had accessory shoe. $25-45.

Magnar-Kamera

Juwel (275/7) - 1927-38. 9x12cm plate camera. Superb quality, all metal, leather covered with rotating back. Rising/falling, shifting/tilting front. Pop-off backs. Triple extension by means of two rack-and-pinion knobs on folding bed; one moves back and front, one moves lens standard. Interchangeable bayonet lenses. "Juwel" or "Universal Juwel" on or under the handle. Price depends on condition and lens. $300-400.

Juwel (275/11) - 1927-39. 13x18cm. As above except lens interchanges with aluminum "board". This camera used extensively by Ansel Adams. With a Triple convertable Protar, this was Zeiss's most expensive camera throughout the prewar years. Quite rare, still usable. With Tessar f4.5/210mm: $300-500. With Protar: $450-700.

Kolibri (523/18) - 1930-35. A compact rollfilm camera giving 16 exposures 3x4cm on 127 film. "Kolibri" below lens in leather. Lens extends for picture taking on brightly polished chromed tube. Came with unique shaped case in brown or black. Looking at hinge on right side of open case is a screw in "foot" which is inserted in lens mount for vertical still pictures. With Telma shutter, Novar f4.5/50mm: $75-120; Novar f3.5/50mm, rare: $100-175. With Rimset Compur shutter, Tessar f3.5/50, most common: $150-225; Tessar f2.8/50, rare: $200-325; Biotar f2/45mm, super rare (also called "Night Kolibri"): $450-550. Microscope version with no lens or shutter, very rare: $200-300.

Kosmopolit - 1927-34. Wood double extension field camera with brass trim. Reversing back, vertical and horizontal front movements (no swing). Tapered bellows. 5x7" (818, 818/11) or 7x9½" (819, 818/20) size. Very seldom offered. $200-300.

Liliput - 1927-28. Tiny strut folding plate camera. Celluloid "ground glass". Struts are inside the bellows. f12.5 lens. 4.5x6cm (361) or 6.5x9cm (370). $100-150.

Lloyd (510/17) - 1928-31. Black leather covered folding rollfilm camera, can also take 9x12cm cut film. Ground glass focusing by sliding out a back cover plate. "Lloyd" in leather on front. Tessar f4.5/120 in Compur. $30-45.

Magnar-Kamera - c1906. (Carl Zeiss, Jena.) Elongated focal plane box camera with telescoping tube in front. Designed for Magnar f10/800mm telephoto lens. Newton finder or monocular finder. A very rare camera. Only one known sale, at auction in Germany for DM 3000 (about $1500 at the time). *(Illustrated top of previous page.)*

Maximar A (207/3) - 1927-39. 6.5x9cm folding plate camera. Slide in holders. "Maximar" on or below handle in leather. Tessar f4.5/105mm in Compur. $40-65.

Maximar B (207/7) - 1927-39. Similar to the "A", but for 9x12cm. Tessar f4.5/135mm in Compur. $40-70.

Maximar (207/9) - 1927-37. Similar, but 10x15cm. Tessar f4.5/165mm in Compur. Rare. $60-90.

Minimum Palmos, 9x12cm - c1905 (Carl Zeiss, Jena). Strut-type focal plane camera for 9x12cm plates. Tessar f6.3/145mm. FP shutter 1/15-1000. $80-120.

Minimum Palmos Stereo - c1908 (Carl Zeiss, Jena). Strut-camera for stereo or panoramic exposures on 9x18cm plates. Focal plane shutter 10-1000. With single f6.3/112mm lens for panoramic use: $200-250.

Miroflex A (859/3) - 1927-36. Folding 6.5x9cm SLR plate camera. Focal plane shutter 3-2000. "Miroflex" in leather on front. Can be used as a press camera by leaving the mirror up, focusing hood folded, and using the wire finder. With Tessar f3.5/135mm or Bio Tessar f2.8/135mm: $240-350. With Tessar f4.5/120mm: $200-300.

Miroflex B (859/7) - Similar to the "A", but 9x12cm. More common. With Tessar f3.5 or Bio Tessar f2.8/165mm: $150-250. With Tessar f4.5/165mm: $120-200.

Nettar - Bob (510) was known as the Nettar (510) in England. "Nettar" on leather. Inexpensive folding rollfilm cameras. 1937-41: 4.5x6cm (515), 6x6cm (515/16), and 6x9cm (515/2). 1949-57 (Fancier style with body release and chrome top): 6x6cm (518/16) and 6x9cm (517/2). With Tessar: $30-50. With Novar or Nettar lens: $20-40.

Nettax (538/24) - 1936-38. 35mm. Looks somewhat like a Contax II, but has rotating rangefinder window attached to interchangeable lens. Focal plane shutter to 1000. With Tessar f2.8/50mm, quite rare: $450-650. With Tessar f3.5/50mm, rarest: $500-800. For additional Triotar f5.6/105mm lens, add $375-500.

Nettax (513/16) - 1955-57. Folding 6x6cm rollfilm camera. Chrome top. Built in uncoupled exposure meter. Novar f4.5/75mm, Pronto shutter. $40-65.

Nettel - 1929-37 (some sizes discontinued before 1937). "Nettel" below the focal plane shutter winding/setting knob. Black leather covered press camera. 4.5x6cm (870), 6.5x9cm (870/3), 9x12cm (870/7) (most common), 10x15cm (870/9), 5x7" (870/11) sizes. $50-150.

Nettel, Tropen (Tropical) - Focal plane press camera made of polished teak with brown leather bellows. 6.5x9cm (871/3), 9x12cm (871/7), 10x15cm (871/9), 5x7" (871/11) sizes. $200-600.

Nixe - 1927-34. High quality double extension folding cameras. "Nixe" on handle or in body leather. Dominar, Tessar, or Double Protar. 551/17 (8x10.5cm rollfilm or 9x12cm cut film): $45-70. 551/6 (8x14cm rollfilm or 9x14cm cut film): $50-80.

Onito - 1927-29. Inexpensive single

extension folding plate cameras. Novar f6.3 lens, lever focus. 6.5x9cm (126/3) or 9x12cm (126/7). $25-35.

Orix (308) - 1928-34. Quality double extension folding press camera, 10x15cm plates. (Special spring back model also made.) Rack-and-pinion focus. Usually seen with Tessar f4.5/150mm lens. $60-120.

Palmos-O - 1927-28. 4.5x6cm plate camera with struts and folding door. Sold in Europe in 1927 only as the "Minimum Palmos". High-speed Tessar f2.7/80mm lens. Focal plane shutter 50-1000. Rare. $350-500.

Perfekt - c1927-31. Double extension, polished mahogany view camera. Tapered bellows. Vertical and horizontal front movements. Sizes 5x7" (834, 834/11, 835, 835/11) and 18x24cm (836, 837, 834/20, 835/20). Usually without model name on camera, but with "Zeiss-Ikon" round metal plate. Very rare. No active trading exists. Infrequent sales records indicate prices in $100-300 range.

Piccolette (545/12) - 1927-30 in Germany, 1927-32 in the U.S.A. "Piccolette" below lens, "Zeiss-Ikon" above. Inexpensive all metal strut camera for 4x6.5cm on 127 film. Metal front pulls out for use. Achromat f11, Novar f6.3, or Tessar f4.5/75mm lens. $40-60.

Piccolette-Luxus (546/12) - 1927-30. Deluxe model with folding bed and lazy tong struts. Brown leather covering and bellows. Dominar or Tessar f4.5/75mm lens, dial-set Compur shutter. $150-200.

Plaskop - 1927-30. Stereo box cameras.
602/1 - 45x107mm. "Plaskop" under left lens (viewed from front). f12 lenses. No brilliant finder. $75-125.
603/1 - 45x107mm. "Plaskop" in oval on left (viewed from front). Better model than the 602/1, with Novar f6.8/60mm lenses. No brilliant finder. $130-200.
603/4 - 6x13cm. Like the 603/1, but a larger size. Brilliant finder in top center. $150-250.

Polyskop - 1927-30. Precision stereo box cameras. Black leather covering. Septum magazine for 12 plates. Brilliant finder in top center. Tessar f4.5 lenses in Compur dial set stereo shutter. 45x107mm (609/1), or 6x13cm (609/4). $150-300.

Simplex (112/7) - 1928-30. Inexpensive folding camera for 9x12cm plates. "Simplex" in leather under handle. "Zeiss Ikon" under lens on front of front standard. Frontar f9/140 or Novar f6.3/135mm. $20-50.

Simplex (511/2) - 6x9cm brown plastic rollfilm camera. "Simplex" on body. Several variations of struts and hardware exist. Nettar f6.3/150mm in Telma or Derval shutter. $40-60.

Simplex-Ernoflex - SLR. "Ernemann" on side in 1927-29 version, "Simplex Ernoflex" over lens from 1930-on. Ernoplast f4.5 or f3.5, Ernon f3.5, or Tessar f4.5 lens. Helical focusing. Focal plane shutter 20-1000. 4.5x6cm (853), 6.5x9cm (853/3), or 9x12cm (853/7). Rare. 4.5x6cm size: $400-550. 6.5x9cm or 9x12cm size: $200-275.

Sirene - Inexpensive folding plate camera. "Sirene" under handle. 1927: 6.5x9cm (135/3), 9x12cm (135/7: *this number was later used on Volta*). $25-35. 1930-31: 8x10.5cm (135/5) made for the American market. Dominar f4.5/135 in Compur. Rare. $45-55.

SL-706 (10.3700) - 1972-73. An improved type of Icarex, with "SL-706" on body at 11 o'clock direction from the lens. Zeiss lenses. Open aperture metering. These cameras were remaindered out by Cambridge Camera at $257, with case, and most are seen in mint condition. With Ultron f1.8: $85-125.

Sonnet - 1927-30. Teakwood folding plate camera. Brown leather covering on door and brown bellows. "Sonnet" inside door at front. Radial lever focusing. Dominar or Tessar f4.5, or Novar f6.3. Originally came with 3 German silver film holders. 4.5x6cm (303) or 6.5x9cm (303/3): $300-600.

Stereax, 6x13cm - c1926-28. Strut-folding focal plane stereo camera, a continuation of the Contessa-Nettel Stereax. Left lensboard may be reversed for use as panoramic camera. Tessar f4.5/90mm lenses. Focal plane shutter 1/10-1200. Rare with the Zeiss name. One sold at auction in Germany in 3/86 for $750 in nearly mint condition with original box.

Stereo-Ernoflex (621/1) - 1927-29. Top quality folding stereo. Door on hood extends across entire top of camera. Ernotar f4.5, Ernon or Tessar f3.5/75mm lenses. Focal plane shutter 20-1000. $1000-1500. *(illustrated on p. 183 under Ernemann)*

Stereo-Simplex-Ernoflex (615/1) - 1927-30. Medium quality non-folding stereo box camera. "Ernemann" on front between lenses. Viewing hood cover is on half of the camera's top, the other half has a pop-up frame finder. Ernon f3.5/75 or Tessar f4.5/75mm or 80mm lenses. Focal plane shutter. $400-600. *(illustrated on p.184 under Ernemann)*

Stereo Ideal (651) - 6x13cm folding plate stereo camera, black leather covering. Identified on the handle. 1927 version with Dial-set Compur shutters, 1928 version with Compound shutters. Tessar f4.5/90mm. $200-300.

Stereo Ideal (650) - Similar to 651, but larger 9x18cm size for films. Tessar f4.5/120mm lenses. Compur shutter. $250-400.

Stereo Nettel - 1927-30. Scissors strut stereo cameras. Black leather covering. Knob focus. Tessar f4.5 lenses. Focal plane shutter. Wire finder. Removable roller blind inside separates the two images, or allows for full frame use. 6x13cm (613/4): $250-350. 10x15cm (613/9): $200-300.

Stereo Palmos

Stereo Nettel, Tropical - Same as the Stereo Nettel, but in teakwood with brown bellows. 6x13cm (614/4) or 10x15cm (614/9). $350-600.

Stereo Palmos - c1905-11 (Carl Zeiss Optical Co.) Folding-bed stereo camera for 9x12cm plates. FP shutter 25-1000. Zeiss Tessar f6.3/84mm lenses. Rack focusing. $300-500. *(Illustrated bottom of previous page.)*

Stereolette-Cupido (611) - 1927-28. 45x107mm folding plate stereo camera. Black leather covering. "Stereolette-Cupido" on handle, "Stereolette" on outside of door. $150-250.

Steroco (612/1) - 1927-30. 45x107mm plate stereo box camera. Tapered shape. Leather covered. "Steroco" on upper front, "Zeiss-Ikon" below. Tessar f6.3/55mm lenses. Derval or Dial-set Compur shutter. Rare. $150-250.

Suevia - c1926-27. Folding-bed camera for 6.5x9cm plates. Nostar f6.8 or Contessa-Nettel Periskop f11 lens in Derval 25-100 shutter. Uncommon. $50-65.

Super Ikonta Series: *Top quality black leather covered folding rollfilm cameras, with coupled rangefinder of the rotating wedge type gear coupled to front cell focussing lens. The early cheaper lens models were sometimes called "Super Ikomat" before WWII in the U.S.A. Introduced in 1934, they were continued in gradually improving forms until 1959 or 1960. The most recent models with MX sync have increased in value because they have been rediscovered as usable cameras... a lower cost nostalgic alternative to such modern cameras as the new folding Plaubel Makinas.*

Super Ikonta A (530) - 1934-37. 16 exposures 4.5x6cm on 120 film. Usually seen with Tessar f3.5/70mm uncoated lens. No sync. Body release 1935-37. Direct finder (not Albada). $100-180.

Super Ikonta A (531) - 1937-50. Same as the above, but with body release, Albada finder, and double exposure prevention. Usually with Tessar f3.5/75mm lens. Novar f3.5 lens is rare. Schneider Xenar in 1948. No sync. $100-150.

Super Ikonta A (531) - 1950-56. Chrome top. Normal lens is Tessar f3.5/75mm. Compur Rapid, X sync, until 1952; later MX sync; and finally Synchro Compur. $250-400. *The latest model with Synchro Compur is increasing in demand as a usable camera, and in Excellent to Mint condition will bring at least $100 more the the prices indicated.*

Super Ikonta B (530/16) - 1935-37. 11 exposures 6x6cm on 120. Separate rangefinder/viewfinder windows. f2.8/80mm or (rarely) f3.5/80mm Tessar. Compur Rapid to 400. No sync. Lens/shutter housing black enameled. Some of the earliest say "Super Ikomat" on the door. $85-125. *In 1936 a model was produced in meters with European tripod socket and "Super Six 530/16" on the back of the camera and front of the ER case. These are rare, but only a modest premium seems obtainable.*

Super Ikonta B (532/16) - 1937-56. Single window range/viewfinder. Lens/shutter housing in black enamel through 1948, chrome after 1948. "Super Ikonta 532/16" in back leather. Tessar f2.8/80mm. Compur Rapid shutter, no sync to 1951. Synchro Compur shutter, MX sync 1951-on. (Some Compur Rapid models c1951 have X sync.) Compur Rapid: $100-160. Synchro Compur: $250-300.

Super Ikonta BX (532/16)

Super Ikonta BX (533/16)

Super Ikonta BX (532/16) - 1937-52. 12 exposures 6x6cm on 120. Double exposure and blank exposure prevention. Uncoupled exposure meter. "Super Ikonta- 532/16" in leather on back. Tessar f2.8/80 in Compur Rapid to 400. Exposure meter in DIN or Scheiner before 1948, ASA after 1948. $90-165. *(Illustrated in previous column.)*

Super Ikonta BX (533/16) - 1952-57. Uncoupled exposure meter in chrome and lower profile than the 1937-52 type. "Super Ikonta 533/16" on back. Synchro Compur MX shutter to 500. Coated Tessar or Opton Tessar lens. $165-250.
(Illustrated bottom of previous column.)

Super Ikonta III (531/16) - 1954-58. A redesigned "B" with no exposure meter. Smaller than the "B". No "front window" at lens for rangefinder. Synchro Compur MX shutter to 500. Novar or Tessar (until 1956) f3.5/75mm. $100-140.

Super Ikonta IV (534/16) - 1956-60. Like the III, but with built in exposure meter using the LVS system (where you lock in a guide number on shutter, after which shutter and diaphragm settings move together). "534/16" in leather on back by latch. Tessar f3.5/75mm only. (During 1983, KEH Camera sold off NEW Super Ikonta IV's for $395.) $150-300.

Super Ikomat C (530/2)

Super Ikonta C (530/2) - 1934-36. "Super Ikonta" or "Super Ikomat" in leather on front. "530/2" in back leather by hinge. Black enamel finish, nickel plated fittings. No body release. Triotar f4.5/120 in Klio shutter, or Tessar f4.5 or f3.8/105mm in Compur to 250 or Compur-Rapid to 400. $100-150.

Super Ikonta C (531/2) - 1936-50. Front of rangefinder is chrome. "531/2" in leather by back hinge. Body release, double exposure prevention. Albada finder. Tessar f3.8/105mm until 1938, Tessar f4.5 or f3.5/105mm after 1938. Compur to 250, or Compur-Rapid to 400 shutter. $130-170.

Super Ikonta C (531/2) - 1950-55. "531/2" in leather by back latch. Double exposure and blank exposure prevention. Tessar f3.5. Compur Rapid, X sync, or Synchro Compur, MX sync. This model is both a usable and collectable and many are sold in Japan. VG to EXC: $200-300. *Add $100 if mint.*

Super Ikonta D (530/15) - 1934-36. "Super Ikomat" or "Super Ikonta" in front leather. "530/16" in leather by back hinge. Black enamel on rangefinder. 6.5x11cm on 616 film, mask for ½-frame (5.5x6.5cm). Flip-up mask in viewfinder for ½-frame. No body release. Tessar f4.5/120mm in Compur to 250, or Triotar (rare) f4.5/120mm in Klio shutter 5-100. $135-220.

Super Ikonta D (530/15) - 1936-39. "530/15" by back latch. Bright chrome on front of viewfinder. Albada viewfinder with ½-frame marks. Body release. No double exposure prevention. Compur to 250 or Compur Rapid to 400. No sync. $150-200.

Super Nettel (536/24) - 1934-37. 35mm folding bellows camera. Black enamel and leather. "Super Nettel" in leather on door. Focal plane shutter 5-1000. 1934-36, Tessar f3.5 or f2.8/50mm lens; 1935-37, Triotar f3.5/50mm. $230-350.

Super Nettel II (537/24) - 1936-38. Similar to the first model, but with polished chrome door and matte chrome top. Tessar f2.8/50mm. $400-750.

Symbolica (10.6035) - 1959-62. 35mm viewfinder camera. Coupled match needle exposure meter. "Symbolica" on top. Tessar f2.8/50mm, front cell focus. $25-45.

Taxo - Inexpensive folding plate camera, single extension. "Taxo" on body under handle. Periskop f11/105, Novar f6.3/105 or f6.3/135, Frontar, or Dominar lens. Derval shutter. Two variations:
1927-31 - Focus by sliding front standard on track, 6.5x9cm (122/3) or 9x12cm (122/7). $20-35.
1927-30 - Focus by radial lever, 6.5x9cm (126/3) or 9x12cm (126/7). $25-35.

Taxona: *see PENTACON VEB.*

Tenax (plate version) - 1927. Popular strut-folding plate cameras. "Tenax" or "Taschen Tenax" on front or top. These appear to be clean-up items which were never actually manufactured by or marked "Zeiss Ikon". 4.5x6cm, 6.5x9cm, and 45x107mm (stereo) sizes. Various lenses. $80-150.

Tenax I (570/27) - 1930-41. 35mm camera for 50 exposures 24x24mm on a 36 exposure roll. "Tenax" under lens. No rangefinder. Novar f3.5/35mm lens. Compur shutter, cocked and film advanced by left-hand lever. $35-60.

Tenax I - 1948. Like the 570/27, but with coated Tessar f3.5/37.5mm lens. Flash sync contact on top of shutter. "Zeiss Ikon" above lens, "Tenax" below. This model was made by the East German "VEB Zeiss Ikon" which later became VEB Pentacon" after settlement of the trademark disputes. Earlier data indicated higher prices, but recent sales are in the same range as the pre-war models $35-60.

Tenax II (580/27) - 1937-41. More expensive and earlier version with coupled rangefinder, interchangeable lenses, and shoe for viewfinders and contameter (1339). Most often found with Tessar f2.8/40mm: $180-275. With Sonnar f2/40mm: $200-325. For the Orthometar f4.5/27 (wide angle) or Sonnar f4/75 (telephoto) with viewfinder, add $300-500.

Tenax Automatic (10.0651) - 1960-63. Full frame 35mm. "Tenax" at 11 o'clock from lens on exposure meter window. Automatic exposure control by selenium cell. No rangefinder. Front cell focus. Tessar f2.8/50mm in Prontormat shutter. $25-45.

Tengoflex (85/16) - 1941-42. Box camera for 6x6cm exposures on 120 film. "Tengoflex" on front. Large brilliant finder on top, giving the appearance of a twin lens reflex. Extremely rare. Several sales 1974-81 in the range of $275-325. One sale at 9/86 auction for $675.

Tessco (761) - 1927. Double extension 9x12cm folding plate camera. "Tessco" in leather of handle. Seen with one of five different lenses, from Periskop f11 to Tessar f4.5. Rare. $50-75.

Trona (210 series) - 1927-30. Quality folding plate camera, double extension, screw controlled rise and shift. "Trona" and model number under handle. Dominar or Tessar f4.5 lens. 9x12cm (210/7): $40-60. 6.5x9cm (210/3) or 8.5x11cm (210/5): $50-100. *The 8.5x11cm (210/5) was apparently made for the English and American market for use with 3¼x4¼" film. This size is rare.*

Trona (212/7) - c1928-36. 9x12cm, similar to the 210/7. Tessar lens, Compur shutter. $50-70. *(Illustrated top of next column.)*

Trona (214 series) - 1929-38. A fancier version, with aluminum ground glass back (frequently exchanged for a regular back). Tessar f3.5 or f4.5 lens in Compur shutter (rimset after 1930). "Trona" and model number on body under handle. 6.5x9cm (214/3): $70-125. 9x12cm (214/7): $60-100. (Slightly less for f4.5 models.)

Trona (212/7)

Tropen Adoro - 1927-36. Polished teak, folding plate camera. Brown leather covering on door and back, brown double extension bellows. "Tropen Adoro" and model number on leather of door. Tessar f4.5 lens, Compur shutter. 6.5x9cm (230/3), 105 or 120mm lens. 9x12cm (230/7), 135 or 150mm lens. 10x15cm (230/9), 165 or 180mm lens. $300-550.

Tropica - 1927-31 (to 1935 in foreign catalogs). A heavy polished teak folding plate camera, the second most expensive camera in 1930 Zeiss line. Strongly reinforced with German silver corners and battens. No leather anywhere on the outside, even the door on the ground glass back is teak. Black bellows. Back rotates ¼ turn. "Zeiss-Ikon" between pull knobs on front stand. 14 different lenses available, all in Compur shutter. Sizes 9x12cm (285/7) and 10x15cm (285/9) are both rare. The 5x7" (285/11) is VERY rare. Sales records are hard to find. Estimate: $600-1100.

Unette (550) - 1927-30. Wood box camera, with leatherette covering. For paper-backed rollfilm, 22x31mm. "Unette" on front in leatherette over lens, "Zeiss-Ikon" over lens, "Ernemann" on side. Metal frame finder at top rear. f12.5/40mm lens. Very rare. Only one known sale in 1980 at $225.

Victrix (101) - 1927-31. Small folding plate camera for 4.5x6cm. "Victrix 101" in leather on camera top. "Zeiss Ikon" on lens, between pulls, and on door. Novar f6.3/75, Dominar f4.5/75, or Tessar. Compur shutter. $85-150.

Volta - 1927-31. Inexpensive folding plate cameras. Single extension. "Volta" on body under handle, "Zeiss Ikon" on door. Dominar or Tessar lens, Klio or Compur shutter. Radial arm focusing in 6.5x9cm (146/3) or 9x12cm (146/7). Focusing by slide front standard in 6.5x9cm (135/3) or 9x12cm (135/7). (10x15cm and 13x18cm sizes were sold in 1926/27 as clean up of old stock on hand at the time of the union.) Although Voltas are not common, there is little interest in them. $25-45.

ZENIT (Russia)
Photo Sniper - c1968. Zenit E camera

with a special Tair-3 f4.5/300mm lens attached to a pistol-type grip. $140-180.

Zenit, Zenit 3, Zenit 3M, Zenit B - 1960's-1970's. 35mm SLR cameras. Fixed pentaprism. FP shutter 30-500, B. Including one of the various "normal" lenses. $15-25.

Zenit 80 - c1971. Copy of Hasselblad. Industar f2.8/80mm lens. FP ½-1000 shutter. With magazine: $150-250.

ZENITH CAMERA CORP.

Comet - c1947. Plastic camera for 4x6cm on 127 film. Vertical style. Telescoping front. $8-12.

Comet Flash - c1948. Plastic camera with aluminum top and bottom. 4x6cm on 127. $8-12.

Sharpshooter - c1948. Black & silver metal box camera. Identical to the J.E. Mergott Co. JEM Jr. $4-8.

Vu-Flash "120" - Hammertone finished 6x9cm box camera. $5-10.

ZENITH EDELWEISS - Folding rollfilm camera for 6x6cm on 620 film. $12-18.

ZENITH FILM CORP.
Winpro 35, Synchro Flash - c1948. Gray plastic 35mm. f7/40mm. $15-25.

ZION (Ed. Zion, Paris)

Pocket Z - c1920's. Folding strut-type camera for 6.5x9cm plates. Rex Luxia or Boyer Sapphir lens. Dial Compur shutter. Leather bellows. Metal body. $75-125.

Pocket Z, stereo - c1928. Strut-folding camera for 6x13cm plates. Zion Anastigmat f6.3/75mm lenses. Gitzo stereo shutter. $125-175.

Simili Jumelle, 6.5x9cm - c1893. Rigid-bodied camera for 6.5x9cm plates in magazine back. Zion Anastigmat lens. Guillotine shutter. Folding Newton finder. $125-175.

ZODIAC - Novelty 4x4cm "Diana" style camera. $1-5.

ZORKI (USSR) *Manufacturers of 35mm cameras, copies of various Leicas. Zorki cameras, as well as many other Russian cameras, are seen with the name written in Roman letters or in Cyrillic letters.*

Zorki - c1952. Leica II copy. f3.5/50mm Industar or f2/50mm Jupiter lens. $40-90.

Zorki 2 - Leica copy. $60-90.

Zorki C - Leica thread lenses. $40-60.

Zorki 2C - $50-80.

Zorki 3 - c1955. f2.8 lens. Coupled rangefinder. $40-60.

Zorki 4 - c1955. Jupitar f2/50mm lens. Focal plane shutter 1-1000. Coupled rangefinder. The most common model. $30-50. *(Two versions illustrated top of next column.)*

Zorki 4 cameras with Cyrillic lettering (top) and Roman lettering (bottom)

Zorki 5 - c1961. Industar f3.5/50. FP shutter 25-500. Coupled Rangefinder. Rapid advance lever. $40-60.

Zorki 6 - c1962. Industar-50 f3.5/50mm. FP 30-500. CRF. Rapid advance lever. $35-50.

ZUIHO OPTICAL CO. (Japan)
Honor - c1956-59. Rangefinder 35, Leica copy. Konishiroku Hexar f3.5/50mm, FP shutter 1-500; or Honor f1.9/50mm, FP 1-1000. $150-200.

ZULAUF (G. Zulauf, Zurich)
Bebe - Compact camera for 4.5x6cm plates. Before 1912 it was distributed by Carl Zeiss and Krauss. Became part of the Ica line in 1911. Logo on camera is G.Z.C. in oval. $150-175.

MOVIE CAMERAS

COLLECTING MOTION PICTURE CAMERAS

Many photographic and persistence of vision developments, over a long period of time, led to the advent of motion pictures. True motion picture cameras, as we know them, did not come into being until the 1890's, and few such cameras were made during that very early period. Some were one-of-a-kind. The very few surviving pre-1900 cameras are in museums and private collections with perhaps a very few in attics, basements or warehouses throughout the world.

From about 1900 on, a variety of motion picture cameras appeared. Some were manufactured for sale to the growing number of motion picture studios; others were made by the studios themselves. A small number were made for amateurs.

The collecting of motion picture cameras from this period on can be a fascinating hobby. The limited number of early cameras available makes collecting challenging. In addition, some of the early cameras do not carry identification because some manufacturers borrowed freely from the designs of others and there were many patent infringment problems. This lack of identification calls for research by the collector to identify some of the cameras.

In the early motion picture days there were many film widths. The 35mm width pioneered by Edison (U.S.A.) and Lumiere (France) became the standard for professional motion pictures. Most of the cameras available to collectors are of the 35mm variety and they are found in a wide array of sizes, shapes, and configurations.

It is interesting to note, however, that even before 1900 there were 17½mm cameras and projectors for use by amateurs. Several amateur cameras using different 17½ film perforation configurations were made over the years. Cameras using 10, 11, 15, 20, 32, 40, 60, and 70mm film widths were also made. Motion picture cameras were made that used glass plates and circular discs of film for sequential exposures.

In 1912, Pathe of France introduced a 28mm projector and a large library of 28mm feature films for home use. A limited number of 28mm cameras followed. Also in 1912, Edison introduced a 22mm projector (3 rows of pictures per width) and a library of their films, but no 22mm cameras were offered to the public.

Movie cameras did not become available in appreciable numbers until after the introduction of the amateur film formats of 16mm in the U.S.A. and 9½mm in Europe in 1923. Amateur motion pictures then became very popular because the new 16 and 9½mm cameras were easy to use and the new reversal films were economical and had a safety film base.

With the subsequent introduction of 8mm cameras and film in 1932 and Super 8 in 1965 the motion picture camera collector can specialize in many ways, for example: particular format, country of origin, chronological period, manufacturer, or first models, etc. To those just entering the fascinating hobby of motion picture camera collecting: Happy Collecting.

Much of the information in the movie section is due to the efforts of several collectors who specialize in movie equipment. Wes Lambert is a long time collector who specializes in the very early motion picture cameras. He lectures and displays his cameras in museums, cinema schools and camera clubs. He provided most of the information and photographs for the early 35mm cameras and a few of the smaller ones, as well as price estimates for these rare early cameras. He will correspond with other movie camera collectors. Contact him at: 1568 Dapple Ave., Camarillo, CA 93010. Tel 805-482-5331.

Cynthia Repinski provided the information on the cameras of the Universal Camera Corp. of New York City. Cindy specializes in both movie and still cameras from Universal. She is an active collector and trader. You may contact her at N80 W13004 Fond du Lac Ave. Apt. 24, Menomonee Falls, WI 53051.

Much of the 8 and 16mm camera information was prepared by Joan McKeown for the 5th edition of this guide. This has been greatly expanded in this edition through the courtesy of Mr. Alan Kattelle. He not only expanded the number of cameras and the historical information concerning them, but also initiated an entirely new section on movie projectors. Cine collectors may write to him at 50 Old County Road; Hudson, MA 01749.

AGFA (Berlin)

Agfa Movex 16-12B

Movex 8 - c1937. 8mm movie camera taking a 10m length of single-8 film in Agfa-Kassettes. Black lacquered metal

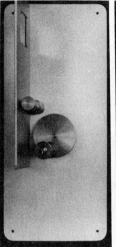

The six most basic motion picture camera movements are illustrated here in chronological order. Almost all motion picture movements are derived from these six. These models were made by Eric Berndt and are now in the Smithsonian Institution.

Top, left to right:
Demeny Beater movement, patented 1893;
Lumiere-Pathe movement, patented 1895;
Geneva Star movement, patented 1896;
Prestwich movement, patented 1899.

Bottom left to right:
Williamson movement, patented 1908;
Chronik movement, patented 1913.

body; rectangular shape. Interchangeable Agfa Kine Anastigmat f2.8/12mm focusing lens. Optical eye-level finder. Spring motor drive, 16 fps. $25-30.

Movex 8L - c1939. 8mm movie camera taking a 10m single-8 Agfa-Kassette. Black lacquered metal body; rectangular shape. Optical eye-level finder. Spring motor drive, 16 fps. Agfa Kine Anastigmat f2.8/12mm fixed focus lens. Coupled meter. $20-30.

Movex 16-12B - c1928. 16mm movie camera taking a 12m Agfa-Kassette. Black leather covered metal body; rectangular shape. Waist-level brilliant finder and eye-level Newton finder. Spring motor drive,

16 fps. Agfa Kine Anastigmat f3.5/20mm focusing lens. $30-50. *(Illustrated bottom of previous page.)*

Movex 16-12L - c1931. Identical to the 16-12B except with Agfa Symmetar f1.5/20mm lens. $30-50.

Movex 30B, 30L - c1932. 16mm movie camera taking 100' spools. Blue leather covered metal body, oval in shape. Optical eye-level finder. Spring drive. Model 30L has 8-12-16 fps; Model 30B also has 32 fps. Interchangeable Kine Anastigmat f2.8/20mm focusing lens. $85-100.

Movex 88 - c1957. 8mm movie camera,

483

using double 8 film on 25' spools. Gray crinkle-finished metal body. Optical eye-level finder. Spring motor, 16 fps. Agfa Kine Anastigmat f2.5/11mm lens. Made in focusing and fixed focus versions. $10-15.

Movex 88L - c1958. Similar to the Movex 88, but with built-in coupled meter. Agfa Movexar f1.9/13mm focusing lens. $20-30.

Movex Automatic I - c1958. Double-8 movie camera using 25' spools. Gray leather covered metal body. Optical eye-level finder. Spring motor, 16 fps. Agfa Movestar f1.9/12.5mm focusing lens. Automatic light meter. $10-15.

Movex Reflex - 1963. 8mm movie camera using spools. Spring motor. Reflex viewing, electric eye visible in viewfinder. Schneider Varigon zoom f1.8/7.5-37.5mm. $25-35.

Movexoom - 1963. Battery-driven 8mm movie camera using spool film. Gray and black enamel body. Reflex viewing. Coupled electric eye. Variogon f1.8/9-30mm manual zoom lens. $25-35.

AKELEY CAMERA, INC. (New York)
Carl Akeley, a famous naturalist, scientist, and inventor, found fault with the best available motion picture cameras for use in photographing wild animals in Africa. He then designed this camera system.

Akeley 35mm Motion Picture Camera - 1914. The Akeley camera features interchangeable taking and viewing lens pairs, and can use very long telephoto lenses. The viewfinder eyepiece optics are articulated. A unique dual gyroscope mechanism built into the tripod head provides a very smooth one hand pan and tilt. The 200 foot film magazines are the displacement type and include the supply/takeup sprocket for fast reload. The Akeley was affectionately known as the "pancake" and was a favorite of newsreel and sports cameramen for decades. Range: $500-1500. *Camera shown is Serial No. 2.*

ANSCO
Cine Ansco - c1930. The first 16mm amateur movie camera from Ansco. Includes Models A & B. Black or brown leather covered metal body; rectangular in shape. Optical eye-level finder. Spring motor, 8-64 fps. Interchangeable fixed focus Agfa Anastigmat f3.5 lens. $25-40.

Ansco Risdon Model A - c1931. 16mm movie camera manufactured by Risdon Mfg. Co., Naugatuck, Connecticut. Takes 50' spools. Black crinkle-finish lacquered metal body. Optical eye-level finder. Spring motor, 16 fps. B&L Ilex f3.5/1" fixed focus. $20-25.

ARGUS
Automatic 8 - 8mm movie camera. Two-tone green lacquered metal body. Battery-operated motor. Cinepar f1.8/13mm lens. Coupled meter. $10-15.

ARNOLD & RICHTER (Munich, Germany)
Kinarri 35 - c1925. This is the first Arri camera. The name was derived from KINe & ARnold & RIchter. The Arri name which became synonymous with professional cinematography actually was used first on a camera designed for amateur use. Drum-shaped aluminum body. Hand-cranked movement for 35mm film on 15m spools. Arrinar f2.7/40mm lens. $1200-1600.

ARROW WORKS FOTO NEWS SHA (Japan)
Arrow Cine Camera, Model 50 - c1934. Well-made 16mm spool camera. Spring motor, 3 speeds. Focusing Dallmeyer f1.8. Closely resembles the Victor 16's. $75-125.

ASSOCIATED PHOTO PRODUCTS (New York)
Magazine Pocket - c1951. There is no identification whatsoever on this camera, but it is otherwise a clone of IPC Simplex Pockette 16mm magazine camera. B&L f3/35mm lens. Telescoping finder. Footage indicator. Gray crinkle finish. $15-30.

BARKER BROS. (LOS ANGELES, CA)

King Barker 35mm Motion Picture

Camera - 1917. This camera, known as "The Educator" was manufactured by the Angeles Camera Co. for Barker Bros., a pioneer California furniture Co. It is almost identical to an early English Williamson type camera but "The Educator" can also be used as a projector and a printer. The camera was often used to photograph local events in small towns for projection in the local theater. This camera was also sold under the Omnio Mfg. Co. name. Range: $350-1000.

BAUER
Bauer 88B - c1954. 8mm spool film camera. Hammertone lacquered light blue finish. f1.9 lens. Electric eye/match needle exposure control. Four speeds. $20-30.

BELL AND HOWELL (Chicago, IL, USA)
Bell & Howell Cine Camera #2709 -This excellent studio camera was considered a revolutionary design when introduced in 1912. It features all metal construction with an external dual magazine. A four lens turret is incorporated and preview viewing and focusing can be accomplished through the taking lens. The most sophisticated feature is the fixed registration pins that engage two film perforations during exposure. This feature and the overall precision of this camera led to its use in studios throughout the world. Although initially a hand crank camera, electric motor drive was soon used. Bell and Howell 2709 cameras are plentiful but are quite expensive for the collector as they are still in use as animation and special effects cameras. Range: $1000-3500.

Eyemo 35mm Motion Picture Camera - 1926. The Eyemo camera is the 35mm version of the very successful Filmo 16mm camera introduced 3 years earlier. The Eyemo is a rugged camera that found great use in newsreel photography. Many Eyemo cameras were used by the U.S. Military during World War II. Range: $40-80.

Filmo 70 - *A series of 16mm motion picture cameras introduced in 1923 and lasting until 1979 when Bell & Howell sold the business. The first Filmo camera was introduced shortly after the Cine Kodak and Victor 16mm cameras. The Filmo is an excellent design that had previously appeared briefly as a 17½mm camera. A compact die cast metal body encloses 100' film spools and a heavy spring drive motor. It has a rugged version of the very successful Lumiere/Pathe film transport movement.*

Filmo 70A - 1923. Black crackel finish. Eye-level finder. Interchangeable Taylor Hobson f3.5/1" fixed focus lens. Spring motor wound by large key on the side. 8-16 fps. $30-60.

Filmo 70AC - 1932. Same as the 70A, except with "Morgana System", an early additive color system. Very rare. Price not established.

Filmo 70AD - c1926. Called "Golf Model". Equipped with 110 degree shutter, supposedly to permit better analysis of a golfer's swing. $75-100.

Filmo 70C - 1927. First Filmo with 3-lens turret. $35-55.

Filmo 70DR, 70HR - 1955. Last of the Filmo 70 cameras. Many professional features such as critical focuser, frame counter. Adapted for external magazines and motor drive. Still in use professionally. $100-200.

Filmo 70J - 1948. Called the "Specialist". A special professional turret model with shift-over slide base. Very rare. Price not established.

Filmo 75 - c1928. 16mm movie camera taking 100' spools. Black, brown, or grey leather covered metal body. Leather is tooled with intricate patterns. Oval shape.

Eye-level finder. Spring motor, 16 fps. Interchangeable Taylor Hobson f3.5/20mm fixed focus lens. $50-65.

Filmo 75 A-5 - 1931. Parallax viewfinder. Black pebbled leather. $75-125.

Filmo 121-A - 1934. Bell & Howell's first 16mm magazine movie camera using "Pockette" or "old style" magazines. Brown leatherette and brown lacquered aluminum body. Interchangeable Cooke Anastigmat f2.7/1" fixed focus lens. Optical eye-level and waist-level finders. Spring motor 16-24 fps. $18-24.

Filmo 127-A - 1935. First U.S. made single 8mm movie camera. Called "Filmo Straight Eight". Interchangeable Mytal Anastigmat f2.5/12.5mm lens. Spring motor 8-32 fps. Uncommon. $50-75.

Filmo 141-A, 141-B - 1937. 16mm magazine movie cameras for new Eastman Kodak magazines. Art-deco black enamel metal body. Optical eye-level finder. Spring motor. 141-A has 8-32 fps; 141-B has 16-64 fps. Interchangeable Taylor Hobson f3.5/1" lens. $25-35.

Filmo Aristocrat Turret 8 - c1940. Same as Filmo Sportster, but 3-lens turret. $5-10.

Filmo Companion

Later models also say "Sportster". Grey body. Similar to the Filmo Companion, but 16-64 fps. $5-10.

Magazine Camera-172 - c1947. 8mm magazine movie camera. Brown leatherette covered metal body. Eye-level finder. Spring motor, 16-64 fps. Interchangeable focusing Comat f1.9, f2.5, f3.5/½" lenses. Available in single lens or 2-lens turret models. $4-8.

Filmo Auto Load - c1940. 16mm magazine movie camera. Brown plastic covered aluminum body. Eye-level finder. Spring motor, 8-32 fps. Interchangeable Lumax f1.9/1" lens. $13-17.

Filmo Companion - c1941. Double-8 spool load movie camera. Brown leatherette and painted metal body. Eye-level finder. Spring motor, 8-32 fps. Interchangeable Anastigmat f3.5/12.5mm fixed focus lens. $5-10. *(Illustrated top of next column.)*

Filmo Sportster (Double Run Eight) - c1940. Double-8 movie camera. Early models only say "Filmo Double Run Eight".

Magazine Camera-200 - c1952. 16mm magazine movie camera. Chromed metal body with tan leather. Optical eye-level finder. Spring motor, 16-64 fps. Interchangeable Taylor Hobson Cooke f1.9/1" lens. Available in single lens, 2-lens turret, and 3-lens turret models. $15-25.

200EE - c1956. 16mm automatic iris control (battery operated) movie camera, advertised as the first and most famous 16mm EE camera. Also called the world's only 16mm EE movie camera in 1959. Magazine or spool-loading models. Brushed chrome aluminum body with black leatherette. Optical eye-level finder. Spring motor drive, 16-64 fps. Super Comat f1.9/20mm focusing lens. WA and Tele auxiliary lenses available. $20-35.

220 - c1954. 8mm movie camera referred to in ads as the Wilshire. Gray die-cast aluminum body. Optical eye-level finder. Spring motor. Super Comat f2.5/10mm lens. "Sun Dial" as on the 252 (see below). $5-10. *(Illustrated on back cover.)*

240 Electric Eye - 1957. Accepts single or double 16mm perforated films on 100' spools. Spring motor, 5 speeds. Automatic film threading. Remaining power dial and footage counter. Automatic exposure control. Super Comat f1.9/20mm. $50-75.

252 - intro. 1954. 8mm movie camera, referred to in ads as the Monterey. Two-tone brown die-cast aluminum body. Optical eye-level finder, marked for telephoto attachment. Spring motor, 16 fps. Super Comat f2.3/10mm fixed focus lens. "Sun Dial" diaphragm setting allows the user to set the dial for the lighting conditions and the diaphragm is set accordingly. Available in single lens or 3-lens turret models. $5-10.

319 - Double-8mm movie camera. Two-tone brown body. Spring motor, 10-40 fps. Super Comat f1.9/10mm lens. $4-7.

Bell & Howell Projectors
Design 57-A - 1923. First 16mm projector by B&H. 400' capacity; 200w lamp; belt drive to take up and rewind. First model of Design 57 series is distinguished by round base, single condenser slot, fixed resistance. $25-40.

Later models, 57-B, -C, etc. - Have oval base, auxiliary slot for Kodacolor filter, and variable resistor for motor. $10-20.

Design 122-A - 1933. "Filmosound". First B&H 16mm sound-on-film projector. 1600' capacity; 500w lamp; power rewind; built-in amplifier. Estimate: $50-75.

Design 122-A Filmo 8 Projector - 1934. First B&H 8mm projector. 200' capacity;

400w lamp; geared takeup and power rewind. Estimate: $20-30.

BELL MANUFACTURING CO. (Des Plaines, IL)
Bell Motion Picture Camera, Model 10 - c1936. 16mm movie camera taking 50' spools. Black crinkle painted metal body. Oval shape. Small sportsfinder. Spring motor. Fixed focus lens. $40-60.

BOLSEY: *See the still camera section for a description of the Bolsey 8 (page 60).*

BRISKIN MFG. CO. (Santa Monica, CA)
Briskin 8 - c1947. Regular 8mm magazine camera. 4-speed spring motor. Telescoping finder. Available in black pebble or brown alligator finish. $20-30.

BRUMBERGER
8mm-E3L, T3L - 8mm movie camera with 3-lens turret. Grey and black body. Brumberger f1.8/13mm normal lens. With normal, tele, and wide angle lenses: $10-20.

BUTCHER AND SONS LTD. (London, England)

Empire 35mm Motion Picture Camera - c1912. This wood body, hand crank amateur camera is simple and basic in design. It has 100' internal magazines and a fixed focus f6.3/50mm lens. The price was modest and the operation elementary. The English Ensign and Jury cameras are almost identical. Range: $350-1000.

CAMERA PROJECTOR LTD. (London)
Midas 9½mm Motion Picture Camera/ Projector - 1933. The Midas 9½mm camera is unusual in that it is both a camera and a projector. An internal battery pack provided power to drive the camera. As a projector it was hand cranked and

Camera Projector Ltd. Midas

illuminiation power was provided by the battery pack. Range: $30-60.

CAMERAS LTD. (Slough, England)

Dekko - c1934. 9.5mm movie camera using 10m Pathe-size cartridge. Black bakelite art deco body. Interchangeable fixed focus Taylor Hobson f2.5/23mm lens. Optical eye-level body. Spring motor, 16-64 fps. $20-30.

CAMPBELL (A.S. Campbell Co., Boston, MA)
Cello - c1918. 35mm hand-cranked movie camera. Leather covered wood body. Combination chain and belt drive. Internal wood magazine holds approx. 75' of film. B&L Tessar f3.5 lens. $200-400.
(Illustrated top of next column.)

CAMPRO LTD. (Home Cine Cameras, Ltd., London)
Campro - c1927. 35mm movie camera that could also be used as a projector by attaching two special lamp housings. Black

Campbell Cello closed (above) and with back open showing the large internal film magazine (below)

metal and wood body is partly leather covered and partly painted. Folding Newton finder. Hand crank, 1 rotation per 8 frames. Uses 100' spool. Dallmeyer focusing f3.5 lens. $250-280.

Campro Cine Camera-Projector - c1935. 9.5mm movie camera, taking 10m Pathe cartridges (later model also used Campro-cassettes). Black crinkle finish metal body. Sportsfinder on top. Spring motor, 16 fps. f3.5 fixed focus lens. Camera could also be used as a projector with an accessory attachment. $35-40.

CANDID CAMERA CORP. OF AMERICA (Chicago)
Cine Perfex Double Eight - 1947. 8mm magazine camera using 25' Kodak magazines. Spring motor drive, 8-32 fps. 3-lens turret. Through-the-body viewfinder. Footage counter. Uncommon. $15-20.

CANON (Japan)
Canon Eight-T - 1957. 8mm spool film camera with 2-lens turret. Viewfinder for 6.5mm, 13mm, 25mm, and 38mm lenses. Automatic parallax adjustment via cam surface on lens barrel. Ground glass focusing finder. Spring motor. $30-40.

CARENA S.A. (Geneva, Switzerland)
Carena Zoomex - 1962. 8mm spool camera. Electric eye, manual or automatic exposure control. Spring motor wound by turning grip. Angenieux f1.8/7.5-35mm zoom lens. Reflex viewing. $20-30.

CHRONIK BROS. MFG. (New York) *The Chronik Brothers were tool and die makers.*

Chronik Bros. 35mm Motion Picture Camera - 1908. This camera is a typical example of the Chronik Brothers' excellent workmanship and design. The unique film transport is a Chronik patent. The camera features through the lens viewing and convenient control on the lens diaphragm and focusing. Range: $700-1500.

CINCINNATI CLOCK AND INSTRUMENT CO. (Ohio)
Cinklox, Model 3-S - c1937. 16mm spool camera. Spring motor with slow motion, normal and high speed settings. Fixed focus Wollensak f2.5/1" lens. (See Paragon for similar camera.) $15-30.

CORONET (Birmingham, England)
Coronet, Models A, B - c1932. 9.5mm movie cameras taking 10m Pathe cassettes. Black leather covered metal body. Optical eye-level finder. Spring motor, 16 fps. Coronar Anastigmat f3.9 lens with four stops. $20-30.

DARLING (Alfred Darling, Brighton, England)
Bioscope - c1916. 35mm hand-crank. Rectangular wooden body, wooden 50m spools. Rotary shutter. $500-600.

DEBRIE (Etablissements Andre Debrie, Paris)

Parvo Interview 35mm Motion Picture Camera - 1908. This wood body, hand crank studio camera has co-axial 400' internal film magazines. It features critical focusing on the film, variable shutter, frame rate indicator, lever control for focus and lens aperture setting, and a precise footage counter. The design and workmanship on this camera are of excellent quality. A metal body model was also made that could use an electric motor drive. Range: $450-1200.

Sept 35mm Motion Picture Camera System - 1922. This precision, compact, short film length 35mm movie camera is extremely versatile. It is a spring motor driven, 250 exposure, pin registered camera system for a: motion picture camera, sequential camera, still camera, and with the addition of a lamphouse, motion picture projector, film strip projector, still enlarger and negative film to positve film cine printer. From these seven functions comes the name "Sept". The Sept design is based on an earlier Italian camera. The camera shown is a 1925 model Sept with a larger spring motor. Range: $100-150.

DEJUR-AMSCO CORP. (New York)
DeJur Electra Power Pan - 1962. 8mm spool camera with spring motor, zoom lens, and 120 degree panning in either direction. Viewfinder adjusts to zoom lens. Automatic or manual exposure control, backlight control. Uncommon. $20-30.

DEVRY CORPORATION (Chicago, IL)
The DeVry Corporation was founded in 1913 by Herman A. DeVry, a former arcade worker and motion picture operator, to manufacture portable projectors "...practical for use by traveling salesmen and by schools." In 1929, the company merged with Q.R.S. Corp., the famed music roll company. The marriage lasted less than three years, but during that time, a number of motion picture and still picture products were produced, variously labeled "QRS" "DeVry" or "QRS-DeVry". In late 1931 or early 1932, the company was re-organized, the music roll business left under new ownership, and H.A. DeVry continued in the motion picture business under the name Herman A DeVry, Inc. Mr. DeVry died in 1941. His sons carried on the business until 1954, when the company was purchased by Bell & Howell.
DeVry, 16mm - c1930. Various models were made with only slight variations. Black or grey cast metal body; large rectangular shape. 100' spools. Folding Newton finder. Spring motor; some models also have a hand crank. Interchangeable Graf f3.5/20mm fixed focus lens. $25-35.

DeVry 16mm Deluxe - 1930. Same shape as the DeVry Home Movie Camera, but with molded bakelite body and 3-lens turret. $100-150.

DeVry Standard - 1926. 35mm all-metal newsreel-type cine camera, using 100' film

spools. Spring motor. Of rugged design, it was nicknamed "The Lunch Box" because of its rectangular shape. Some DeVry cameras were actually launched in captured German V2 rockets at the White Sands Missile Range after World War II. The DeVry also found use as a rapid sequential still camera in sports work. Range: $60-150.

DeVry Home Movie Camera - 1930. 16mm camera using 100' spools. Die-cast aluminum body. Spring motor. Model 57 has fixed focus f3.5 lens. Models 67 to 97 have focusing f3.5, f2.5, and f1.8 lenses. $30-45.

QRS-DeVry Home Movie Camera - 1929. Bulky all-metal 16mm camera using 100' spools. Spring motor. The first model was a camera only; later models doubled as a projector when mounted on an accessory stand and 3-blade projector shutter was substituted for the camera shutter. Camera only: $15-20. With projector: $25-35.

DeVry Projectors:

Cinetone - c1928. 16mm silent projector; 300w; 400' capacity. Motor drive also drives a 12", 78 rpm turntable mounted on a common base. Record and film had starting marks which were supposed to permit synchronization. Films were supplied by DeVry; records were made by Victor Talking Machine Co. This was one of the early attempts to provide sound with 16mm film. $250.

DeVry Portable Motion Picture Projector - 1928. Suitcase-type 35mm silent projector. Entire mechanism is built into one case. 1000' reels mounted co-axially below lamp and lens head. Motor drive. $35-55.

DeVry Type ESF Projector - 1931. 35mm Sound-on-film portable projector. 500w projector in one case; 4-tube amplifier and speaker in separate case. $100.

DITMAR (Vienna, Austria)
Ditmar, 9.5mm - c1938. 9.5mm movie camera taking 10m Ditmar cassettes. Black leatherette covered metal body. Eye-level

Ditmar, 9.5mm

finder. Spring wind motor, 16-32 fps. Steinheil Cassar f2.9/20mm fixed focus lens. Built-in light meter. $30-40.

DRALOWID-WERK (Berlin)
Dralowid Reporter 8 - c1953. 8mm spool load movie camera. Green leather covered metal body. Eye-level finder. Spring motor is wound by pulling a cord. Minox Wetzlar Dralonar f2.5/12.5mm fixed focus lens. $45-65.

EASTMAN KODAK CO. (Rochester, NY)

Brownie Movie Cameras - c1951-63. Double-8 spool load movie cameras. Various models with single lens or 3-lens turret. Brown leatherette or brown lacquered bodies. Folding frame or Newton finders. Spring wind motor, 16 fps. Interchangeable fixed focus f1.9 or f2.7 lenses. Turret models also have wide angle and tele lenses. See below for a few individual listings. Generally, turret models: $5-10. Single lens models: $1-5.

Brownie Movie Camera, first model - 1951. 8mm spool camera with spring motor, open finder, and f2.7/13mm lens. Originaly sold for $47.50. $5-7.

Brownie Fun Saver - 1963-68. This was the last Brownie movie camera. Plain black body, no frills. $3-6.

Brownie Turret, Exposure Meter Model - 1958. With Scopesight and 3-lens turret with f1.9 lenses. The most expensive Brownie, selling for $99.50. $20-25.

Cine-Kodak - 1923. (Called Model A beginning in 1925 when the Model B was introduced.) This is the first Kodak movie camera. It introduced the new Eastman 16mm safety film for the amatuer. A substantial cost savings was brought about by the small 16mm format and the fact that the original film was processed by Eastman to a positive rather than a negative, thereby eliminating the extra step to make a positive print. Hand crank, one rotation per 8 frames. All metal black painted body, large boxy square shape. Eye-level finder. Kodak Anastigmat f3.5/25mm focusing lens. Camera only: $175-230. Variations:

Cine-Kodak with electric motor drive

-- **Electric Motor Drive** - Introduced Jan. 1924, for $25. Battery operated drive with built-in waist-level finder. Battery charging kit was available as an extra. Camera with motor drive: $200-250. Add $100 for the charging kit.

-- Waist Level Finder - April 1924. A waist-level finder was added to the camera. Thereafter, the electric motor drive was available without a waist level finder. The camera shown is a 1925 version with the waist-level finder.

-- f1.9/25mm lens - Feb. 1926. Original price of $200.

-- Slow Motion Attachment - July 1926. List price was $20.

-- Single Frame Attachment - Feb. 1927. List price of $20.

Cine-Kodak Model B - 1925-31. 16mm movie camera using 100' spools. Leather covered metal body. Rectangular and not as boxy looking as Model A. Newton finder and waist level brilliant finder. Kodak Anastigmat 25mm fixed focus lens. Spring motor, 16 fps. First model with f6.5 lens, black leather: $20-30. Later models, 1928-on, f3.5 lens, brown, or grey leather: $30-40.

Cine Kodak Model BB, Model BB Junior - 1929. 16mm movie cameras using 50' spools. Leather covered metal body. Newton finder. Interchangeable fixed focus f3.5 or focusing f1.9/25mm Kodak Anastigmat lens. Spring motor, 8,16 fps. Blue, brown, or grey: $25-35. Black: $15-25.

Cine Kodak Model E - c1937-46. 16mm movie camera taking 100' spools. Black crinkle finish metal body. Advertising for this peculiar shaped model said it "...safely clears hat brims." Optical eye-level finder. Spring motor, 16-64 fps. Interchangeable Kodak Anastigmat lens: fixed focus f3.5/20mm or focusing f1.9/25mm. $25-40.

Cine Kodak Model K - 1930-46, making this the longest-lived 16mm model. Takes 100' spools. Leather covered metal body. Folding Newton finder and waist level brilliant finder. Spring motor, 8,16 fps. Interchangeable Kodak Anastigmat f1.9/25mm focusing lens. Blue, brown, or grey: $30-40. Black: $20-30. *(Illustrated top of next column.)*

Cine Kodak Model K

Cine Kodak Model M - 1930 (shortest-lived model). Economy version of Model K (above). Fixed focus f3.5/20mm lens. No waist level finder. 16 fps only. $30-40.

Cine Kodak 8, Models 20, 25, 60 - c1932-47. Model 20 was the first 8mm spool load movie camera using 25' double-8 film. Leather covered metal body in gray, brown, or black. Newton finder in the handle. Spring motor, 16 fps. Kodak Anastigmat 13mm lens. Model 20 with fixed focus f3.5: $10-15. Model 25 with fixed focus f2.7: $5-10. Model 60 with inter-changeable f1.9 focusing lens and machine-turned interior:$15-20.

Cine-Kodak Royal - 1950. 16mm magazine camera with spring motor, interchangeable lens. $25-35.

Cine-Kodak Special (1933-47); Cine-Kodak Special II (1948-61) - 16mm magazine movie cameras. Left side of body is the magazine containing the film spools. The magazine can be removed at any time and replaced by another. 100' and 200' magazines were available. 2-lens

turret with interchangeable focusing Kodak Anastigmat f1.9/25mm and f2.7/ 15mm lenses. Spring motor 8-64 fps. $170-300.

Magazine Cine Kodak (1936-45); Cine Kodak Magazine 16 (1945-50) - Body style and features similar to their 8mm counterparts, but for 16mm movies using 50' magazines. $15-25.

Magazine Cine-Kodak Eight Model 90 (1940-46); Cine-Kodak Magazine 8 (1946-55) - Eastman Kodak's first magazine 8. Similar to the Model 60 (above), but takes a 25' reversing magazine. Optical eye-level finder. 16-64 fps. $5-10.

Kodak Cine Automatic Cameras - 1959-61. Six versions, all with coupled EE, 8mm spool load, spring motor. Single lens, 3-lens turret, or zoom lenses. Values vary according to lens: $15-45.

Kodak Cine Scopemeter - c1959. Double-8 spool load movie camera. Built-in meter. Optical eye-level finder in housing with meter. Spring motor, 16 fps. 3-lens turret with Ektanar f1.9 normal, tele, and wide angle lenses. $5-10.

Kodak Electric 8 Automatic - 1962. First 8mm Kodak camera with battery drive and casette loading. Kodak Duex 8 cassette was user-loaded with 25' spool which was flipped over for a second 25' run. One single lens model and two zoom lens models were produced, including the Kodak Electric 8 Zoom Reflex camera which was Kodak's most expensive movie camera, listing at $295. Reflex model, rare: $50-65. Others: $10-15.

Kodak Escort 8 - 1964. Eastman Kodak's last regular 8mm camera. Spool load, spring motor, coupled EE. Fixed focus and zoom f1.6 models. Type A (swing out) filter. $10-25.

Kodak Zoom 8 Reflex - 1960. Two models, with reflex viewing. $20-40.

Eastman Kodak Projectors:

Kodascope - 1923. First 16mm projector. Motor drive; 14v, 56w lamp; 400' reel. Earliest model distinguished by small lamp house, enclosed reels, no carrying handle, no oil tubes. 200w lamp furnished after 1924. $100-150.

Kodascope Model A, Series K - 1926. Similar to above, but with condensers and lens for use with Kodacolor film. $75-100.

Kodascope Model B - 1927. Advanced 16mm projector of unusual design. Folding reel arms at rear of projector with self-threading guides. Forward, reverse and still prijection. Power rewind. 400' reels; 200w, 56v lamp; 1" or 2" lens. Black or bronze finish with chrome plated fittings, threading light. Original price, with 2" lens, carrying case, extra lamp, oil can, and splicing kit: $275. Common. $10-20.

Library Kodascope - 1929. This is a Model B projector, in bronze, with a walnut case, folding translucent screen for rear projection with 1" lens, or direct projection with 2" lens. The octagonal shaped case has an ebony inlay and solid bronze octagonal handles, and looks something like a casket. A matching walnut cabinet, 33" high, was available, which had a folding shelf for splicing, turntable top, storage space for the projector, a floor screen and stand, 26 reels of film, splicer, etc. EKC records show that approximately 1500 Library Kodascopes were produced, and less than 500 cabinets. A few Kodascopes with the cabinet were recently sold at $750. Projector and case: $125-175.

Kodascope Model C - 1926. Compact 16mm projector. 400' reels; folding reel arms; 100w lamp. In 1928, the same projector was offered in a carrying case with 5½x7" translucent screen, and 1" lens for rear projection or 2" lens for direct projection. This outfit was called the Business Kodascope. $10-20.

Kodascope Eight Model 20 - 1932. First 8mm projector. 200' reels, belt drive to take-up and rewind. First model furnished with 6v auto headlight bulb, later that year furnished with 100w, 110v lamp. $10-15.

Sound Kodascope Special - 1937-42. Kodak's first 16mm sound-on-film projector. f16/2" lens; 750w lamp; 1600' reels; takeup reel runs at right angle to upper reel. Separate amplifier and speaker case. Very high quality design, priced at $800. Rarest of EKC's projectors; less than 500 made. $300-400.

EDISON (Thomas A. Edison, Inc., Orange, NJ)
Edison Projecting Kinetoscope - c1899. Hand-cranked or motor-driven 35mm projector. Mechanism mounted in 2-piece oak case. Bolt-on 1000' supply reel chamber. No takeup reel; film was caught in cloth bag. Four-slot Geneva intermittent; 2-blade no-fire shutter. Framing by rack & pinion raising entire mechanism. Separate light source. $300-400.

Edison Home Kinetoscope - 1912. Special 22mm hand-cranked projector designed by Edison to make home projection safe for amateurs. The film was Eastman cellulose acetate based "safety" film, carrying three rows of images across the width, each row projected in succession. Cast iron mechanism housing mounted on wood base with sheet metal lamp house, usually with small carbon-arc lamp, although acetylene lamphouse was available. Projector available with three lens systems, and also could be used to project special Edison glass slides. $475-575. *(Illustrated top of next column.)*

Edison Home Kinetoscope

ELMO CAMERA CO. LTD (Japan)
Distributed by Honeywell Photographic Products in the U.S.A.
Honeywell Elmo Dual-Filmatic and Tri-Filmatic 8mm Zoom cameras - 1966. These battery-powered 8mm cameras were the first to accept all three 8mm formats by means of interchangeable backs. The Dual-Filmatic accepted Super 8 and Single 8; the Tri-Filmatic accepted Super 8, Single 8, and Regular 8. Both cameras featured automatic/manual exposure control and remote control jack. Elmo f1.8/9-36mm lens with power or manual zoom; auxiliary telephoto lens available. Single frame or 18,24 fps, plus reverse (for Single 8 and Regular 8 only). Tri-Filmatic, very few made: $125-150. Dual-Filmatic: $75-125.

EMEL (Etablissement Emel, Paris)
Emel Model C83 - c1937. Advanced 8mm spool camera featuring 3-lens turret, multi-focal finder with parallax correction, frame counter and film-remaining meter. Spring motor, 5 speeds plus single frame and continuous run. Backwind shaft. $75-100.

ERCSAM (Paris)
Auto Camex - c1960. 8mm spool load movie camera. Reflex viewing. Spring motor, 8-64 fps. Focusing Pan-Cinor zoom lens. $30-50.

Camex Reflex 8 - c1956. First 8mm movie camera with continuous reflex viewing. Double-8 film on 25' spools. Spring motor, 8-32 fps. Interchangeable Som Berthiot f1.9/12.5mm focusing lens. $50-75.

ERNEMANN AG (Dresden, Germany)
Kino I - 1902. Ernemann entered the amateur motion picture field with this very early, center perforation, 17½mm motion

picture camera. It has a leather covered wood body. The Kino I is a well built movie camera using a Williamson type film transport with a quality Ernemann lens and a variable shutter. Range: $1000-2000.

Kino Model A 35mm motion picture camera is a wood-bodied hand cranked field camera. The film magazines are internal, one above the other. Some Kino cameras have Lumiere/Pathe type film transports and some have Williamson type transports. The Model A has a 200' film capacity; the B, 400'; and the C, 100'. $400-700.

Ernemann Projectors:

Kino II - 1904. This versatile 17½mm, center perforation, amateur camera/printer/ projector has features unusual even for professional motion picture cameras of its time. A fast lens was used. The intermittent film transport utilized an eight arm Geneva cross movement. A reciprocating glass platen at the aperture applies pressure during exposure. The Kino II shown has a large co-axial film magazine and a studio type viewfinder that has straight and reflex viewing. Range: $800-1500.

Kino Model E - 1917. 35mm motion picture camera. This wood body, hand crank studio camera has co-axial 400' internal film magazines. Its appearance and operation are very similar to the 1908 Debrie Parvo camera. Range: $700-1500.

Normal Kino Model A - 1908-18. Normal

Kinopticon - c1919. Hand-cranked 35mm projector, using Demeny "beater" film advance. Two-blade shutter, chain drive. Incandescent lamp house on common wood base. Lamp house slides over for use as magic lantern for 48mm slides. Film supply reel standard; no takeup reel. $200-250.

ERTEL WERKE (Munich, Germany)

Ertel - 1920. The Ertel 35mm motion picture camera is a well made, wood body, hand cranked field camera. Several models with minor differences were made. Lens focus and aperture control is accomplished by conveniently placed levers. Range: $350-1000.

EUMIG (Vienna, Austria)

Eumig C-3 - c1955. Double-8 movie camera taking 25' spools. Grey or black patterned metal body. Optical eye-level finder. Spring motor, 8-32 fps. f1.9/12.5mm lens. $5-10.

Eumig C-39 - c1938. 9.5mm camera, similar in style to the black C-3. Steinheil Cassar f2.8/18mm lens. $5-10.

Eumig C5 Zoom-Reflex - 1961. 8mm battery-driven spool camera. Eumig f1.8/10-40mm manual zoom, recessed into body of camera. Automatic exposure control, footage counter, outlet for synchronous sound recording with tape recorder. Die cast aluminum body with grey crinkle finish. $20-30.

Eumig C16 - c1956. 16mm movie camera for 100' spools. Lacquered metal body with green leather. Spring motor, 16-64 fps. Semi-automatic coupled meter. Eumigar f1.9/25mm focusing lens. $150-180.

Eumig Electric - c1955. Double-8 movie camera taking 25' spools. Green crinkle finish metal body. Eye-level finder. Battery driven motor, 16 fps. Eugon f2.7/12.5mm lens. $5-10.

EXCEL PROJECTOR CORP. (Chicago)

Excel 16mm No. 40 - c1938. 16mm camera, 50' spools. Spring motor. Noteworthy for cylindirical shutter, single-claw pull down with register pin amd no feed sprocket. Excel f3.5/28mm lens in non-standard mount. Diecast body, brown crinkle finish. Uncommon. $25-35.

Excel 8mm, No. 38 - Nearly identical to 16mm No. 40, above. Uncommon. $25-35.

FAIRCHILD CAMERA AND INSTRUMENT CORP.

Fairchild Cinephonic Eight - 1960. First 8mm sound-on-film camera, using pre-striped double-8 film with magnetic recording track for direct recording of sound while filming. Built-in transistorized recording amplifier. Camera driven by special nicad rechargeable battery. 3-lens turret. Exposure meter screws onto lens turret for reading. Standard, WA, and Tele lenses available. $75-125.

Fairchild Cinephonic Eight Sound Zoom - 1963. Like the listing above, but with Fairchild f1.8/10-30mm zoom lens and coupled Sekonic Photo-Meter. $75-125.

Fairchild Projectors:

Cinephonic - 1960. 8mm sound-on-film projector, companion to the Fairchild Cinephonic cameras. Magnetic striped film; 400' reels. Projector will play back, overlay, or record. f16/¾" lens. Sound level indicator. Separate unit houses speaker, extension cable, microphone, reel. $35-45.

FRANKLIN PHOTOGRAPHIC INDUSTRIES INC. (Chicago)

Franklin Magazine 8 - 1948. Compact 8mm camera using 25' magazines. Manufactured under EKC's patents. Spring motor, 16-64 fps. Wollensak f2.5/½" lens. A 2-lens turret model was also made. $20-30.

FUJI PHOTO FILM CO., LTD (Japan)

Fujica Single-8 P1 - c1965. Single-8 battery operated camera using special Fuji Single-8 drop-in cartridge. Electric eye, needle visible in finder. $10-20. Later models offered zoom lens, backwinding capability, reflex viewing. $15-25.

GERMAN-AMERICAN CINEMATOGRAPH AND FILM CO.

Everhard Schneider 35mm movie cameras:
Top photo c1898, bottom photo c1910

(New York and Berlin) *Everhard Schneider, the founder of the German-American Cinematograph and Film Co. designed and made a series of cine cameras as well as motion picture projectors, printers and film perforators. Edison filed suit against Schneider in 1898 for patent violation. This German-American Co. did not survive World War I.*

Everhard Schneider 35mm Motion Picture Camera - c1898. This very early motion picture camera was the first of a series of fine equipment. It has an external film supply magazine and an internal take-up magazine. Although some mechanical parts of the camera are castings, several are hand made. Range: $2000-3500. *(Illustrated on previous page.)*

Everhard Schneider 35mm Motion Picture Camera - c1910. This camera is an example of Schneider's less elaborate, wood body, hand crank, field type motion picture camera. 200' co-axial internal magazines are used. Range: $500-1000. *(Illustrated on previous page.)*

GUSTAV AMIGO (Berlin, Germany)

Amigo 35mm Motion Picture Camera - 1920. Though basic in design, the Amigo is a well constructed field camera and is capable of fine work. A Williamson type film transport is used. Range: $350-850.

HOUGHTON
Ensign Autokinecam - c1930. 16mm movie camera with 100' spool. Spring motor or hand cranked. Single lens. 3 speeds. $30-40.

Ensign Auto-Kinecam 16 Type B - c1935. 16mm movie camera taking 100' spools. Crinkle-finish black metal body. Eye-level finder near the top, Newton finder mounted on the side. Spring motor, 8-32 fps and hand wind. Interchangeable Dallmeyer Anastigmat f2.9/1" focusing lens. $25-50. *(Illustrated top of next column.)*

Ensign Auto-Kinecam 16 Type B

Ensign Super-Kinecam - 1931. 16mm movie camera takint 100' spools. Hand crank or spring motor 8-64 fps. 3-lens turret. Quadri-focal finder with auxillary parallax correction. $60-75.

ICA A.G. (Dresden, Germany)

Kinamo 35mm Motion Picture Camera - 1924. This compact, hand cranked, amateur camera uses 50' magazines. It has a leather covered metal body. An accessory spring motor drive was also available. It is of quality design and construction. In 1926, the ICA company joined with Contessa-Nettel-Werke, Zeiss, Goerz, and Ernemann to form the Zeiss Ikon Co. Production of the Kinamo continued and more versatile models were produced. Range: $80-150.

IKONOGRAPH CO. OF AMERICA (New York) *Founded about 1905 by Enoch J. Rector, a somewhat notorious film impressario. This company was one of the first to offer a line of* *projectors designed for the amateur. The films were 17.5mm nitrate stock, center perforated at the frame line, reduction printed from standard 35mm commercial films, and were supplied by the Ikonograph Co. in 40' cans, with titles such as "The Tramp's Bath".*

Ikonograph Model B - c1905. Hand-cranked 17.5mm projector. Due to its extremely simple mechanism, the projector could be run backward as well as forward, thus bringing a popular Hollywood trick to the home projectionist. Several models were produced, all hand cranked, with illumination by incandescent or acetylene lamp. $75-200.

INDUSTRIAL SYNDICATE OF CINOSCOPE (Italy and Paris, France)

Cinoscope 35mm Motion Picture Camera - 1924. This leather covered metal hand crank camera was made in Italy and sold in France. The camera has a Kador f3.5/50mm lens. It uses 100' magazines and has Geneva Cross film transport. With the addition of a lamphouse and reel arms, the camera can be used as a projector. Range: $500-1000.

INTERNATIONAL PROJECTOR CORP. (NY)
Simplex Pockette - 1931. First U.S.-made 16mm magazine camera, used "old style" EKC/IPC magazine. Waist-level finder, sportsfinder on side; optional top-mounted telescope viewfinder with parallax. Spring motor, 12-16 fps. Footage counter. Black or grey aluminum body with embossed art-deco pattern. Non-interchangeable fixed focus f3.5 lens. Later models, c1933, had interchangeable Kodak Anastigmat f3.5/1" focusing lens. $20-35.

IRWIN CORP. (NY)
Irwin Magazine Model 16 - c1930. Among the first U.S.-made 16mm magazine cameras. Takes Irwin 50' magazines. Rectangular metal body. Spring motor, 16 fps. f4.5/1" lens. Hexagonal tube or open top-mounted finder. $15-30.

Irwin Magazine Model 21 - Like the Model 16, but with f4.5 lens, 4 speeds, and through-body finder. $15-25.

Irwin Magazine Model 24 - Like the Model 21, but with f3.5 lens. $15-25.

KBARU (Quartz) 2M - c1960's. Russian double-eight movie camera. Spring wind, 8-32 fps. f1.9/12.5mm lens. Coupled meter. With hand grip: $12-18.

KEYSTONE MFG. CO. (Boston) *Founded in 1919 to manufacture toy movie projectors, formerly supplied by European manufacturers.*
Capri Models - c1950's. Models K-25, K-27, K-30. 8mm spool load movie cameras. Grey or brown leather covered body. Single lens and 3-lens turret models. Elgeet f1.9 lens. $4-10.

Keystone A Models - c1930's-1940's. A series of 16mm spool load cameras (models A, A-3, A-7, A-9, A-12). Oval metal bodies are either leather covered or lacquered. In black, brown, or grey. Eye-level finder. Spring motor, 12-64 fps on most models. Some models have an interchangeable lens. $25-50.

Keystone Movie Camera, Model C -
c1931. 16mm spool load movie camera. Black crinkle finish metal body. Eye level finder. Hand crank. Oval body like the later "A" models. Ilex f3.5/1" lens. $35-45.

Keystone K-8, K-22 - 1930's-1940's. Like the "A" models, but for 8mm film. $4-9.

Keystone Projectors: *Early projector models were mostly 35mm, hand-cranked, and cheaply made. Only a few representative or unusual models of projectors will be listed.*

Moviegraph - c1919. 35mm hand-cranked projector, early model, marked "Patent Applied For". Toy-like quality. $25-50.

Moviegraph - c1920. Hand-cranked simple projector. One of very few U.S.-made projectors for Pathe's 28mm film

which has three perforations on one side and one perforation on the other. No shutter; no film takeup. $25-35.

Supreme - c1930. Hand-cranked 9.5mm projector for 400' reels or 30' and 60' cassettes. Double sprocket drive; 3-color filter. Only known U.S.-made 9.5mm projector. $40-60.

KLIX MANUFACTURING CO. (Chicago)

Klix 35mm Motion Picture Camera - 1918. This compact amateur hand crank cine camera has an unusual reciprocating shutter. A Geneva Cross film transport movement is used. A heavy flywheel helps for smooth cranking. This model has 25' film magazines. A larger Model 2 has 100' magazines. Both cameras can be used as projectors with the addition of an adapter kit that includes a lamphouse, reel arms, special shutter, etc. Range: $250-500.

KODEL ELEC. & MFG. CO. (Cincinnati, Ohio)
Kemco Homovie - c1930. Unusual system for 16mm safety film. Unique design takes four frames in each 16mm frame. Film transport moves in boustrophedonic pattern (2 exposures left to right across film, down ½ frame, then right to left, etc.) 100' of film gave the equivalent of 400' in number of exposures. Individual exposures measure 3.65x4.8mm. The spring-motor driven camera was housed in a bakelite case and used an f3.5/15mm lens. The projector was motor-driven, and could project either the Kemco system or conventional full-frame by selecting the proper condenser lens. 250w, 50v lamp. Very rare. No known sales. Estimate: $400-500.

KURIBAYASHI CAMERA WORKS *A little known fact, Kuribayashi Camera produced three different cine models from 1962 through 1966. Apparently few were ever produced, making these models very rare.*

Petri Eight - 1962. Fixed focus Petri f1.8/ 13mm lens with aperture set by electric eye. Battery powered film transport and shutter (16 fps). Rare. $50.

Petri Power Eight - 1964. Petri Eight with Petri f1.8/9-25mm lens with power zoom control. Rare. Price unknown.

Petri Super Eight - 1966. CdS photometer controlled Petri f1.8/8.5-34mm lens with power zoom feature. Battery powered film transport with 18 or 32 fps setting. Drop-in super eight film loads. Rare. Price unknown.

L.A. MOTION PICTURE CO.
(Los Angeles, CA) *Also known as Angeles Camera Co. Produced original Cine camera designs and also made close copies of the designs of others. During WWI they were able to meet requirements of domestic studios for European type cameras that were not available. They also made cameras that were sold under the brand names of others.*

35mm Motion Picture Camera - c1914-1923. There is no model name on this well made, metal bodied, hand crank camera. It has several features, including 400' internal co-axial magazines. Range: $500-1000.

LEITZ
Leicina 8S - 1960. 8mm spool camera, battery operated. Reflex viewing. Built-in f2/9mm lens with snap-in auxillary f2/9mm wide angle supplementary lens. Automatic exposure control with reading in viewfinder. Film exposed gauge also visible in finder. $80-100.

LUBIN (Sigmund Lubin, Philadelphia, PA)
Sigmund "Pop" Lubin, a European imigrant, was quite knowledgeable in optics, chemistry, and mechanics. He was a very early motion picture entrepreneur. He manufactured motion picture equipment for his own studio use. At one time, however, he did offer a camera, a projector, and a phonograph for use by those

starting in the motion picture business, for a modest $150. The buyers later found that the camera and projector used only film supplied and printed by Lubin. Much of his equipment was very similar to that of other manufacturers but his versions were always an improvement. He did hold motion picture equipment patents and was involved with Edison in the Motion Picture Patent Company, a trust formed to control the motion picture industry.

Lubin 35mm Studio Motion Picture Camera - 1908. This was the workhorse of the Lubin studios. It is very similar to the Pathe studio camera but has heavier gearing, a metal body, and a speed governor. Range: $1500-3500.

MAGGARD-BRADLEY INC. (Morehead, KY)
Cosmograph Model 16-R - c1925. 35mm "suitcase" projector of unusual design. Cast aluminum projector mechanism is seated on top of wood carrying case; film is threaded from supply and take-up reels in staggered array below. Lamp house and condenser swing back for lantern slide projection with auxiliary lens. Electric motor drive. $40-60.

MARLO - c1930. No maker's name on this 16mm 100' spool camera, but it is identical in almost every detail to the DeVry 16mm cameras, and has a DeVry patent number inside. Spring motor. Graf f5.6/29mm lens. Black crinkle finish. Brass nameplate says "Marlo". $65-75.

MEOPTA
Admira A8G - c1964. Slim, tapered 8mm camera with spring wind motor, 16 fps. Mirar f2.8/12.5mm fixed focus lens. Light and dark grey lacquered metal body. $5-10.

MILLER CINE CO. (England)
Miller Cine Model CA - c1953. 8mm spool load movie camera. Brown leather

covered metal body. Eye-level finder. Spring motor, 8-64 fps. Interchangeable fixed focus Anastigmat f2.5/12.5 lens. $5-10.

MITCHELL CAMERA CORPORATION (Glendale, CA)
Mitchell - 1920. The Mitchell studio camera was a major milestone in motion picture camera design when introduced in 1920. It is somewhat similar in appearance to the earlier Bell and Howell 2709 studio camera, but has a simpler through-the-taking-lens previewing system. The Mitchell registration pins are reciprocal and hold the film perforations precisely during exposure. A wide range of accessories are available. The low operational noise level of the Mitchell compared to the Bell and Howell, soon had it replacing the Bell and Howell after the advent of sound movies. The Mitchell soon became the most popular studio camera. It is still in use to this day and its current high price is based on its status as a usable camera. Range: $2000-5000.

MOVETTE CAMERA CORP. (Rochester, NY.) *Reorganized as Movette, Inc. after 1918.*

Movette 17½mm Motion Picture Camera - 1917. Hand cranked camera using 17½mm film that has two round perforations on each side of the picture frame. The shutter has a fixed opening and the lens has a fixed aperture and focus. The camera used a simple type film magazine. The processed positive print on safety film was returned from Eastman on a similar magazine for use in the companion projector. A library of feature films was offered. This home motion picture system featured simplicity. Range:$350-700.

MOVIEMATIC CAMERA CORP. (New York)
Moviematic - 1935. Inexpensively made all-metal rectangular 16mm magazine cameras. Spring motor. Side mounted open finder. Moviematic furnished films in special magazines holding approximately 11' of film: M40 for snapshots; M50 for movie (flip) books; M60 for projection. "Mercury" model with rounded ends: $20-30. Models with bright nickel, copper-plated, or cross-hatched pattern faceplates: $5-15.

MOY (Ernest F.) LTD. (London)

Moy and Bastie's 35mm Motion Picture Camera - 1909. This wood body camera used internal 400' magazines, one above the other. The Moy uses a variable shutter and a unique film transport movement called a drunken screw. Critical focusing is accomplished by viewing the image through the film. A variant of this model has the lens mounted on what would normally be the side and has dual shutters so it can be used as a projector head. Range: $450-1200.

NEWMAN & SINCLAIR (London)
Auto Kine Camera, Model E - c1946. 35mm spring driven movie camera, 10-32 fps. Holds spools up to 200'. Polished, patterned Duralumin body. Eye-level finder. Ross Xpres f3.5 lens. $175-220.

NIPPON KOGAKU (Japan)
Nikkorex 8, 8F - c1962. Slim 8mm spool load movie cameras. Battery operated motor, 16 fps. Chrome with brown leatherette covering. Nikkor f1.8/10mm fixed focus lens. Electric eye CdS exposure meter. The model 8 has a folding optical eye-level finder. Model 8F has a thru-the-lens reflex finder. $15-25. *(Illustrated top of next page.)*

Nikkorex Zoom-8 - 1963. Battery operated 8mm spool camera. Manual zoom Nikkor f1.8/8-32mm lens. Automatic/ manual exposure control with visible needle. Split-image rangefinder focusing, reflex viewing. Film counter. Battery test. $15-20.

Nikkorex 8

NIZO (Niezoldi & Kramer GmbH, Nizo-Braun AG, Munich)

Cine Nizo 8E Models A, B, C - c1930's. 8mm spool load movie cameras. Black leather covered rectangular metal bodies. Spring motor, 6-64 fps. Interchangeable Voigtlander Skopar f2.7/12.5mm focusing lens. In addition to the optical eye-level finder found on the Model A, Models B and C have a waist level finder. $40-80.

Cine Nizo 9.5 Model A - c1925. Boxy 9.5mm movie camera for Pathe cassettes. Black leather covered metal body. Eye-level finder. Spring motor, 16 fps, and hand crank. Meyer Trioplan f3.5/77mm fixed focus lens. "N.K.M" manufacturers plate on front. $30-50.

Cine Nizo 9.5, Model F - c1925. Boxy 9.5mm movie camera for Pathe cassettes. Black leather covered metal body. Folding Newton finder. Spring motor, 16-32 fps. Steinheil Cassar f2.8/20mm fixed focus lens. $30-60.

Cine Nizo 16B - c1927. Similar to Cine Nizo 9.5 Model A, but 16mm film. $30-50.

Cine Nizo 16L - c1930's. 16mm movie cameras taking 50' spools. Black crackle finish metal body. Optical eye-level finder. Spring motor, early version 8-24 fps, later one for 8-64 fps. Interchangeable Meyer f1.5/20mm focusing lens. $30-50.

Exposomat 8R - c1955. 8mm movie camera taking a 25' Rapid cassette. Grey crinkle finish metal body. Eye-level finder. Built-in meter. Spring motor, 16-24 fps. Fixed focus Ronar f1.9/12.5mm. $15-25.

Heliomatic 8 S2R - c1951. 8mm spool load movie camra. Grey crinkle finish metal body. Spring motor, 8-64 fps.

Coupled meter. Focusing Rodenstock Heligon f1.5/12.5mm and Euron f2.8/ 37.5mm lenses. $45-65.

PAILLARD A.G. (Geneva, Switzerland)

Bolex C8

B8, C8, L8, L8V - A series of double 8mm cameras, with only minor differences in body design or features. Spring motor. Black leather covered metal body. f1.9 to f2.8 lenses available. $15-25.
L8 (1942) - single interchangeable lens; 16 fps.
L8V (1946) - single interchangeable lens; 12,16,32 fps.
B8 (1953) - 2-lens turret; 8-64 fps.
C8 (1954) - single interchangeable lens; 8-64 fps.

Bolex D8-L

B8L, C8SL, D8L - c1958. Like the B8, and C8 models above, but with built-in light meter. B8L and D8L are 2-lens and 3-lens turret models, 12-64 fps. C8SL has a single lens and 18 fps. D8L: $50-75. B8L: $50-65. C8SL: $20-30.

H8 - intro. 1936. Same body style as the H16, but 8mm. Heavier construction than the later L8, B8, and C8 models. Black

502

leather covered metal body. Optical eye-level finder. Spring motor, 8-64 fps. Interchangeable focusing lenses on a 3-lens turret. Meyer Kino Plasmat f1.5/12.5mm, Meyer Trioplan f2.8/36mm and f2.8/20mm. With 3 lenses: $95-120.

H-16 - intro. 1935. 16mm movie camera for 100' spools. Automatic film threading. Black leather covered metal body. Optical eye-level finder. Spring motor, 8-64 fps. Interchangeable lenses mounted on a 3-lens turret. Meyer Trioplan f2.8/75mm, Meyer Plasmat f1.5/6mm and f1.5/25mm. $150-200.

H-16 Leader - c1950. Similar to the Standard F-16 (above), but with thru-the-lens waist level reflex viewing. Achromatic eyepiece. $100-135.

H-16 Reflex - c1950. Similar to the Standard H-16 (above), but with an eye-level reflex thru-the-lens viewfinder. $200-250.

Bolex Projectors:
Bolex Cinema G816 - c1939. Electric-drive 16mm projector which can convert to either 8mm or 9.5mm with accessory kits of suitable spindles, sprockets, and guide rollers. 50mm/f1.6 lens; 750w lamp. Uncommon. $100-150.

PARAGON CAMERA CO. (Fond du Lac, WISCONSIN)
Paragon Model 33 - 1933. 16mm spool load, with through-body finder. Wollensak f3.5 lens. Spring motor, single speed (3-speed model made in 1938). Footage counter. Almost identical to Cinklox, possibly a predessor to it. $40-50.

PATHE FRERES, PATHE S.A., (Paris, France) *A major European motion picture company, they introduced the 28mm movie format, and reduced a large 35mm feature movie library to 28mm safety film to increase their home movie business. The 28mm format provided a modest savings in film size, cost, and*

more importantly, the use of fire resistant film in the home. 28mm projectors were made by Pathe of France and subsequently by Hall Projector and Victor Animatograph of the USA. A few 28mm cameras were made so the amateur could make his own 28mm movies for the home use.

Motocamera - c1928. 9.5mm movie camera taking 10m Pathe cassettes. Spring motor, 16 fps. Leather covered metal body. Eye-level finder built into the camera body instead of the folding frame finder found on the earlier Pathe Baby. Krauss Trinar f3.5/20mm fixed focus lens. $15-25.

Motocamera Luxe - c1932. Similar, but with 3 speeds and Zeiss or Krauss f2.9 or f2.7 lens. $15-25.

Motocamera 16 - c1933. 16mm movie camera using cassettes. Black leather covered metal body. Spring motor, 16 fps. Krauss Trinar f3/25mm lens. This 16mm model is not nearly as common as the 9.5mm model listed above. $80-120.

Pathe, 35mm - 1905. Motion picture studio camera. This leather covered wood body hand crank camera uses external 400' magazines mounted on top. The film transport mechanism is based on the movement used in the pioneer Lumiere Cinematograph camera and is still used in the modern Bell & Howell Filmo and Eyemo cameras. In the years just before WWI the Pathe was used on more movies through-out the world that any other camera. It is difficult to find a pristine Pathe as they were heavily used and generally modified to update them. Lubin, Angeles and Wilart made similar cameras in the USA. Range: $500-1200.

Pathe, 28mm - 1912. This is a scaled down version of their successful 35mm field camera. An economical 28mm version of the English Williamson/Butcher type camera was also offered later by

Pathe, 28mm

Pathescope of America. Range: $500-1000.

Pathe Baby - 1923-25. 9.5mm hand cranked movie camera, taking 9m Pathe cassettes. One rotation per 8 frames. Extremely compact leather covered metal body. Folding sportsfinder. Roussel Kynor f3.5/20mm fixed focus lens. The 9½mm width amatuer film format was introduced in Europe at about the same time 16mm film was introduced in the USA. The 9½mm film perforations are in the center of the film, between frames. The picture format extends to almost the width of the film thereby providing efficient film use. The film has a safety, reversal type base that could be processed by the user. 9½mm movie cameras were popular in Europe and the British empire. $15-25.

Pathe Baby, with motor - c1926-27. Similar to the original model, but body is about twice the width to accomodate the spring motor. 16 fps. Hermagis f3.5/20mm fixed focus lens. $20-25.

Pathe Baby, with Camo motor - Larger motor than the listing above. Marked "Camo" and "Swiss movement Suisse". Kynor f3.5/20mm lens. $30-40.

Pathe Mondial B - c1932. Similar to the Motocamera (above), but slightly smaller body, and black painted instead of leather covered. Trioplan f2.8/20mm lens. $25-35.

Pathe National I - c1930. 9.5mm movie camera taking 9m Type H Pathe cassette. Black painted metal body. Eye-level finder. Spring motor, 16 fps. Krauss Trinar f3.5/20mm fixed focus lens. $20-40.

Pathe National II - c1940's. Improved version of the National I. Grey crinkle finish body. 8-32 fps. Interchangeable Som Berthiot focusing f1.9/20mm lens. $20-45.

Pathe Projectors:

Pathe Kok Home Cinematograph - 1912. Hand-cranked projector for Pathe's new safety film on cellulose acetate base. Illumination by low voltage lamp, fed from small generator which was driven by the same mechanism that operated the film advance. Films, up to 400', were reduction prints from commercial negatives, supplied by Pathe. The large polychrome rendition of a rooster (Pathe's trademark) on the case cover is one of the attractions of this historic projector. With excellent decal: $125-175.

New Premier Pathescope - c1920. Electric drive 28mm projector of rugged construction, manufactured and marketed in the U.S. by Pathescope Co. of America, Inc. Geneva intermittent, large 3-blade shutter in front of lens. $40-60. *(Illustrated top of next page.)*

Pathe-Baby - 1922. 9.5mm projector. First model hand-cranked; later, motor drive was

Pathe New Premier Pathescope

No. 4, c1905, was the first all-metal model. No. 6, c1906, featured the first automatic fire shutter built in the U.S.A. and was the last of the "open mechanism" design. Projector head only: $75-150. Complete with lamphouse, lamp, auxiliary lantern slide lens: $350 and up.

PRESTWICH MANUFACTURING CO. (London, England)

Prestwich 35mm Motion Picture Camera - 1908. This wood body camera uses internal 400' magazines, one above the other. The patented Prestwich film transport movement is used. The lens is focused by rack and pinion. The lensboard swings out for access to the variable shutter. Critical focusing is accomplished by viewing the image through the film. 200' models were also made. The Pitman and DeFranne cameras, made in the U.S.A. are almost identical to the Prestwich. Range: $600-1200.

Q.R.S. CO. (Chicago)

available. Cassette loaded with 8.5m of film, caught in glass-front chamber, from which it is rewound by hand. Fixed resistor for low-voltage lamp. Unique film-notch system gave automatic delay at title frames for substantial economy in film. Films supplied by Pathe were reduction prints of commercial films. A library of over 100 titles was available. Die-cast shutter/flywheel is usually deformed and inoperable; as such: $20-30. Working: $30-50.

Pathe Kid - 1930. Hand-cranked 9.5mm projector, scaled-down version of Pathe Baby. No glass on lower film receptacle. Separate "cage" resistor. Sold by Pathex, Inc. NY. $25-30.

POLAROID CORP. (Boston, MA)
Polavision Land Camera - 1977. Battery-driven Super 8 instant movie camera. Special Super 8 film rated ASA 40, in Polaroid cartridge holding approximately 42' (2 minutes, 40 seconds of filming). Polaroid f1.8/12.5-24mm manual zoom lens. Two focus positions: 6'-15', 15'-infinity. Single speed, 18 fps. Reflex viewing. Flag in viewfinder for low light. Warning light for beginning and end or usable film. Battery check light. Film is developed to positive in special developer/player. Plug-in is 110v, 170 watt light available. Camera with player, lights, cords, etc.: $100-125. Camera only: $20-30.

POWER (Nicholas Power Co., NY) *This manufacturer of 35mm theatre projectors appears to have begun operation prior to 1899. The Company was merged with International Projector Corp. about 1920.*
Cameragraph - First models, such as No. 3 were built on a wooden frame, much like a 1899 Edison Projecting Kinetoscope.

Q.R.S. Projector - c1929. 16mm camera/

projector combination consisting of base motor and lamphouse, into which the appropriate Q.R.S. or Q.R.S.-DeVry 16mm camera is fitted. The correct camera is identiifed by: "window" lens on left side where lamp house fits; 3-bladed projector shutter which replaces camera shutter; projection position for aperture blade. Camera and projector base: $30-40.

Q.R.S. Model B - c1930. 16mm inexpensive projector, some models hand-cranked, some with motor drive. $15-25.

RCA VICTOR CO. INC. (Camden, NJ)
RCA Sound Camera - 1935. World's first 16mm sound-on-film camera. Sound recorded by built-in microphone placed close to operator's mouth when camera was in normal operating position. Sound track was variable area type, recorded by light beam from battery-powered 4-volt auto-headlight type bulb. Eastman 16mm Sound Recording Panchromatic Safety film. Spring motor driven. 3-lens turret with Universal focus f3.5 normally supplied. Rare. $400+.

REVERE CAMERA CO. (Chicago)
Revere, 8mm - 1940's-1950's. Turret models, including 44, 60, 63, 67, 84, 99: $5-10. Various single lens magazine models, including 40, 61, 70, 77, 88, and Ranger and spool load model 55: $5-10.

Revere 101, 103 - 1956. 16mm spring motor cameras taking 100' spools. The 101 came with Wollensak f2.5 lens; the 103 with 3-lens turret and one lens. Each lens had objective finders like the Kodak K-100. Listed at roughly half the K-100 price, these cameras typified the aggressive competition Revere offered the "big guys" at this time. $30-50.

Revere Eye-Matic CA-1 to CA-7 - 1958. 8mm automatic exposure control cameras. Spring motor. Spool and magazine load. Various combinations of single-lens and turret styles. CA-7 with Zoom lens: $10-20. Others: $5-10.

Revere Magazine 16 - c1948. 16mm magazine movie camera. Brushed chrome and grey or brown leather covered metal body. Optical eye-level finder. Spring wind, 12-48 fps. Interchangeable Wollensak Raptar focusing lens. Single-lens models have f1.9/1" lens. Turret models also have f2.7/17mm and f4/3" lenses. $15-35. *(Illustrated top of next column.)*

Revere Super 8mm - 1939. Despite its name, its not a Super-8 camera at all, but Revere's entry in the brief "craze" for single-8, started in 1936 by Univex, and almost over when this otherwise

Revere Magazine 16

undistinguished camera came on the market. Single-8 Panchromatic film in 30' spools, made for Revere by Agfa-Ansco. Spring motor. Fixed focus f3.5/½" lens. Rare. $40-60.

RISDON MFG. CO. (Naugatuck, Connecticut)
Risdon Model A - 1931. 16mm spring motor camera using 50' spools. Stamped steel body with black crinkle finish. Simple f3.5 lens, waterhouse stops. Top-mounted telescoping finder. Cameras were later distributed by Agfa-Ansco and the name-plate changed to "Ansco-Risdon". Risdon models: $30-35. Ansco-Risdon models: $20-25.

SANKYO
Sankyo 8-CM - 1963. Compact 8mm spool camera. Pronon f1.8/8.5-26mm zoom lens. Battery drive, 12-24 fps. Folding grip/battery holder. Reflex viewing. Coupled EE for film speeds ASA 10-200. Footage counter. $10-20.

SCHALIE COLLEE (Switzerland)
S.C. Kamera - c1932. Spring wind camera, 16 fps. 16mm on 15m spools. Vertical duraluminum body with rounded ends, polished hammertone finish. Trioplan f2.8/25mm lens. $150-200.

SEKONIC TRADING CO. LTD. (Toyko)
Sekonic Dual Run Simplomat 100 - 1962. 8mm spool load spring motor camera with unique "flip over" film chamber permitting full 50' run without rethreading. Auto exposure control. Reflex viewing. Zoom f1.8/11.5-32mm lens. Footage counter. $25-35.

Sekonic Dualmatic 50 Model 130 - c1963. Economy version of the above. Fixed f1.8/13mm lens. Non-reflex viewing. $20-25.

SIEMENS & HALSKE AG (Berlin)
Siemens B - c1933. 16mm movie camera taking special 50' Siemens magazines. Black leather covered body. Optical eye-level and waist level finders. Spring motor, 8, 16, 64 fps. Busch Glaukar f2.8/20mm focusing lens. $50-70.

Siemens C - c1934. Similar in style and features to the Siemens B, but with 8, 16, 24, 64 fps and a better lens. Meyer Siemar f1.5/20mm focusing lens. $40-55.

Siemens C II - c1938. Similar to Siemens C, but lens is coupled to the meter. Meyer Optimat f1.5/20 focusing lens. $50-60.

Siemens F - c1936. Similar to Siemens C, but interchangeable Dallmeyer f1.5/1" lens. $60-100.

SINEMAT MOTION PICTURE CO. (USA)

Sinemat Duplex 17½mm Motion Picture Camera - c1915. This amateur, hand-cranked, metal body motion picture camera used standard 35mm film that was split lengthwise, providing perforations only on one side. A fixed focus, fixed opening lens is used. The camera can be opened in such a manner that it can be used as a projector. The single opening shutter is disengaged and a dual opening shutter engaged when used as a projector. Range:$250-700.

SOCIETY OF CINEMA PLATES (Paris, France)
Olikos - 1912. The Olikos uses 18 glass plates, 9.5x9cm, to produce a 90 second movie. The camera, with the addition of a lamphouse is used as a projector. A conventional lens, shutter, and hand crank is used. A unique mechanism takes each plate through a sequence of positions at the focal plane of the camera. Each plate, in turn, is automatically positioned so a series of seven pictures is taken from right to left on the top of the plate. The plate is then immediately moved up and another sequence of seven photographs is taken from left to right and so on for a series of 12 rows of seven or 84 photographs on each plate. Each following plate is automatically positioned and sequenced for a total of a 1512 frame movie. The plate positioning mechanism is precise enough so that the time interval between photographs is acceptably consistent. Few Olikos camera were made. Range: $1500-2500.

SPORT-2 - c1960. Double-8 movie camera. Battery operated motor. T-40 f2.8/10mm lens. $15-20.

STEWART-WARNER (Chicago)
Buddy 8 Model 532-A - 8mm spool camera. Through-body viewfinder, folding sportsfinder on side. $10-15.

Companion 8, Model 532B - intro. 1933. 8mm spool load movie camera. Smaller version of the Hollywood camera listed below. Black lacquered metal body, oval shaped. Spring motor, 12, 16, 48 fps. Interchangeable Wollensak Velostigmat f3.5/12.5mm lens. $5-10.

Deluxe Hollywood Model - 1932. 16mm camera similar to the 531-B, but with new lens mount for standard C-mount 16mm lenses. Side-mounted telescopic finder. $20-30.

Hollywood, Model 531-B - c1931. 16mm spool load movie camera. Black lacquered metal body, oval shape. Eye-level finder. Spring motor, 8-64 fps. Stewart Warner f3.5/25mm lens. $5-15.

TECHNICOLOR CORP. (Hollywood, CA)
Technicolor Automatic 8 - c1960. Battery driven 8mm spool camera. Coupled EE. Type A swing-out filter. Footage counter. Technor f1.8/13mm lens. $5-10.

U.S.CINEMATOGRAPH CO. (Chicago)

35mm Motion Picture Camera - c1916. This wood body, leather covered field camera has 200' co-axial internal magazines. Its film transport movement is somewhat unique. It has a variable shutter and through the film critical focusing. This camera was also sold under the name "Davsco". Range: $350-700.

UNIVERSAL CAMERA CO. (Chicago)
Not to be confused with the later "Universal Camera Corporation" of New York City.

Universal 35mm Motion Picture Camera - 1914. This camera, in the classic early English design, has internal 200' film magazines, one above the other. (400' cameras were made for the US Army during World War I.) The film transport mechanism is similar to the early French Lumiere/Pathe movement. The wood body is painted black or khaki and the front and side doors are aluminum with a distinctive engine turned finish. While primarily a field camera, the Universal with added features became a studio camera. Range: $350-700.

UNIVERSAL CAMERA CORPORATION
(New York City) *Not to be confused with the earlier "Universal Camera Co." of Chicago.*
CINE 8 CAMERAS:
A-8 - c1936. Die-cast metal, black finish. Interchangeable f5.6 Ilex Univar lens. Collapsible viewfinder. Used Univex 30' patented spools of Single-8 film. Common. $10-15.

B-8 - c1939. "True View" model. Die-cast metal, antique bronze finish. Interchangeable f5.6 Ilex Univar or f3.5 Wollensak lenses. Built-on telescopic viewfinder above the body. Used Univex Single-8 film. $20-25.

C-8 - c1939. "Exposition" or "World's Fair" models. Die-cast metal, antique bronze finish. Interchangeable Ilex Univar f4.5 or f5.6 lenses. Built-in viewfinder. Used Univex Single-8 film. $20-25.

C-8 Turret model - c1939. Same features as the standard C-8, but with 3-lens turret. Sold with f4.5 Ilex Univar or f3.5 Wollensak Univar lens. Optional Wollensak Univar lenses were: f2.7/½", f1.9/½", f3.5/1" Telephoto, f3.5/1½" Telephoto. Scarce with f3.5, f1.9 and a Telephoto: $150-175. Also uncommon with f4.5 or f3.5 only: $45-65.

D-8 - c1941. Dual 8mm "Cinemaster" model, taking Univex Single-8 or standard Double-8 film. Die-cast metal with green finish. Interchangeable f4.5 or f6.3 Ilex Univar. Built-in viewfinder. Single speed. Scarce. $65-85.

E-8 - c1941. Dual 8mm "Cinemaster" model, taking Univex Single-8 or standard Double-8 film. Die-cast metal, antique bronze finish. Interchangeable Wollensak Univar f3.5/½". Built-in combination extinction meter and viewfinder. Three speeds. Scarce. $60-80.

F-8 - c1941. Dual 8mm "Cinemaster" model. Similar to E-8, but grey satin finish and front and rear chrome plates. $20-25.

G-8 - c1946. Dual 8mm "Cinemaster II"

model. Similar to F-8, except for minor improvements in the film transport system. Sold with f3.5 or f2.5 Universal Univar lens. Common. $15-25.

H-8 - c. late 1940's. "Cinemaster II" model. Identical to G-8, except only standard Double-8 film could be used. This was the last cine camera made by Universal. Scarce. $60-80.

Universal Projectors:
Univex P-8 - c1937. 8mm electric drive projector. For an "economy" projector, this machine boasted some surprising refinements: automatic fire shutter, gear-driven upper and lower sprockets, power rewind, all in a substantial die-cast frame. 100w lamp. First companion projector to the Univex A-8 movie camera of 1936. $15-25.

URIU SEIKI (Tokyo)
Cinemax 85E - c1960's. Double-8 movie camera. Spring motor, 12-48 fps. Cinemax Auto Zoom 8.5-42.5mm f1.6 lens. Automatic meter. $3-7.

VICAM PHOTO APPLIANCE CORP. (Philadelphia, PA)

Baby Standard - 1923. 35mm motion picture camera. This wood body, hand cranked camera featured simple design and construction, rather than small film size, to provide economical use for the amateur. A fixed focus lens is used with a two opening waterhouse stop bar. Internal 25' film magazines are used. A removable port in the rear allows the use as a projector. A die cast aluminum body model was also offered. Range: $100-200.

VICTOR ANIMATOGRAPH CO.
(Davenport, IA) *Alexander F. Victor's first "motion picture machine" was a spiral disk projector resembling the Urban Spirograph. Patented Nov. 29, 1910; how many of these projectors were actually produced is unknown.*

Victor - 1923. This basic hand crank 16mm camera was produced shortly after the introduction of the Cine Kodak 16mm system. It uses a double push claw for a film transport. The fixed focus lens is fitted with wheel stops. Range: $80-150.

Victor, Models 3, 4, 5 - late 1920's- early 1940's. 16mm movie cameras taking 100' spools. Black or brown crinkle lacquered finish on metal body. Newton finder and reflex critical focus eyepiece. Spring motor, 8-64 fps. Interchangeable lenses. Model 3 for single lens: Wollensak Cine Velostigmat f3.5/1" fixed focus. Models 4 and 5 have a 3-lens turret with focusing lenses: Wollensak f2.7/17mm, Cooke f3.5/2", and f1.9/1". With 3 lenses: $75-110. With single lens: $35-45.

Victor Ultra Cine Camera - 1924. 16mm battery-driven version of the 1923 Victor Cine Camera. Thomas Willard, of the Willard Storage Battery Co., is credited with designing this rare modification of the hand-cranked Victor. Compartment for re-chargeable battery at rear of camera, powering small electric motor placed in forward bottom part of camera. Less than 100 of these cameras were produced. $500-550.

Victor Projectors:
Victor Animatograph - 1914. 35mm semi-theatre projector, hand-cranked, upright construction. 1000' reel enclosures top and bottom, chain drive to Geneva intermittent. $75-125.

Safety Cinema - 1917. 28mm "safety film", 3 perforations per frame each side. Failed commercially for lack of suitable film. Rare. $125-150.

Home Cinema - 1920. 28mm Pathe safety film, 3 perforations on one side, one on the other. Victor's last attempt to keep the 28mm format alive in this country. Rare. $125-150.

Cine Projector - 1923. 16mm EKC direct reversal film. Victor's first projector for the new EKC 16mm film system. Marketed simultaneously with the Victor Cine Camera. Hand-cranked, co-axial 400' reels. 32cp, 12v lamp. $125-150.

Cine Projector Model 3 - c1928. 16mm motor-driven, single sprocket. 400' reels on retractable arms. $25-50.

VITAGRAPH COMPANY OF AMERICA (New York)

Vitagraph - 1915. This wood body, hand crank camera was a ruggedly built in-house design of the Vitagraph Studios. It is a fine looking camera with lots of external brass. The design is complex and it is somewhat unique for this type of camera in that it is loaded from its right camera side rather than the left. Range: $700-2000.

Vitalux Camera

VITALUX CAMERA CO. (Milwaukee, WI) *The Vitalux system was invented in 1918 by a German immigrant to New York City*

named Herman C. Schlicker. It was manufactured by a company formed by the prominent motion picture executive John R. Freuler.
The Vitalux Camera - 1922. Takes a spiral of 1664 images (each slightly larger than present day Super 8) on an endless loop of film 5" wide by 17½" long. The film was Eastman Safety negative, and was loaded in a steel magazine. The camera was die-cast aluminum. Hand-cranked. Goerz Hypar f3.5/20mm lens. Only 2 of these are known to exist. Estimate: $800-1200.

Vitalux Projector - 1922. Companion projector to the Vitalux camera (above). 5x17½" loop of EKC safety negative film. Hand-cranked, with optional motor drive; 250w lamp, cast-iron frame. Weight of motor, 25lbs. $200.

VITASCOPE CORP. (Providence, RI)
Movie Maker - c1931. 16mm movie camera, taking 50' spools. Hand crank, one rotation per 8 frames. Black crinkle finish metal body. Small waist level finder. Simple lens. $10-20.

WILLIAMSON LTD. (London, England)
Williamson 35mm Motion Picture Camera - 1909. This wood body camera uses internal 400' magazines, one above the other. The patented Williamson film transport movement and a variable shutter are used. Critical focusing is accomplished by viewing the image through the film. 200' models were also made. A 100' basic design camera, similar to Empire was made. Some Williamson cameras are called tropical models and have numerous brass inlays to reduce expansion and shrinkage in the wood body. Range: $450-750.
(Illustrated top of next page.)

WITTNAUER CAMERA CO. (NYC)
Automatic Zoom 800 - 1959. 8mm battery drive spool load camera/projector

Williamson 35mm Motion Picture Camera

combination like the Cine-Twin. Wittnauer f1.6 zoom lens, front-mounted coupled electric eye. $65-85.

Cine-Simplex - c1958. 8mm battery-drive spool load camera, without the projector conversion that the Cine-Twin has. Made in two models: 4-lens turret with optional screw-in EE exposure meter, or single Elgeet f1.8/13mm Synchronex lens with "wrap-around" electric eye for automatic exposure control. $30-50.

Wittnauer Cine-Twin - 1957. Battery powered 8mm spool load movie camera/ projector. Die cast body. Electric eye exposure meter. 4-lens turret holding standard, WA, and Tele camera lenses plus projector lens. 5-position telescope finder. Camera contains the reel arms and bulb. It is mounted on a base containing the electric motor and blower for projector operation. $50-75. *This is the original model,*

invented and patented in 1959 by J.W. Oxberry, inventor of the fames Oxberry Animation Stand.

WOLLENSAK OPTICAL CO. (Chicago)
Model 8 - Grey and black 8mm movie camera. Eye-level finder. Elgeet f1.9/½" focusing lens. $3-7.

Model 23 - c1956. 8mm magazine camera. 3-lens turret. Eye-level finfer. Spring motor, 5 speeds. Matte aluminum and black. $4-8.

Model 42 - 1957. 8mm spool load with spring motor. f1.9 lens, waterhouse stops, aperture adjustment. $5-15.

Model 43, 43-D - Like the Model 42, but with 3-lens turret. Model 43-D has 5 speeds. $5-15.

Model 46 - c1958. 8mm spool load movie. Electric eye. 3-lens turret with Raptar f1.8 normal, tele, and wide angle lenses. $5-10.

Model 46 Eye-Matic - 1958. 8mm spool load with spring motor. Coupled EE. f-stop visible in viewfinder. Footage counter. Hammertone gray lacquered finish. $5-15.

Model 57 Eye-Matic - 1958. 8mm magazine camera similar to Model 46 Eye-Matic, but with Wollensak f1.8 zoom lens which is powered by camera motor. Also featured "heart-beat" device to assure operator that film was advancing properly, a feature shared by several similar Revere magazine cameras of the period. Some are marked inside "Made for Wollensak Optical Co. by Revere Camera Co." and probably mark the take-over of Wollensak by Revere. Revere was acquired by the 3M Company at about this time. $5-15.

YASHICA (Japan)

Yashica 8, T-8 - c1959. 8mm spool load

movie cameras. Grey and black die-cast aluminum bodies. Spring motor, 16 fps on model 8, 8-64 fps on model T-8. Zoom-type viewfinder for 6.5-38mm lenses. Model 8 has a single interchangeable Yashikor f1.9/13mm lens. T-8 has a 2-lens turret for Yashinon f1.4/13mm normal, 38mm tele, or 6.5mm wide angle lenses. $5-10.

ZEISS

Kinamo S10 - c1928. 16mm movie camera taking a 10m special Zeiss magazine. Black leather covered metal body. Optical eye-level finder. Spring motor, 16 fps. Very small body compared to other 16mm movie cameras. Zeiss Tessar f2.7/15mm fixed focus lens. $40-55.

Movikon 8 - c1952. 8mm movie camera taking 25' spools. Interesting horizontal body design. Brown or grey crinkle finish metal body. Eye-level finder. Spring motor. Early version only 16 fps; later for 16-48 fps. Focusing Zeiss Movitar f1.9/10mm lens. $45-60.

Movikon 16 - c1936. 16mm spool load movie camera. Black leather covered metal body. Eye-level and waist-level finders, and separate critical focus sight.

Spring motor, 12-64 fps. Interchangeable Sonnar f1.4/25mm lens. $175-225.

ZENIT (USSR)
Zenit - c1960's. Spring wind 8mm, 12,64 fps. Built-in meter. Jupiter f1.9 lens. $20-30.

ZIX COMPANY (Detroit, MI)

Zix - 1920. The Zix is a wood body, leather covered, hand crank 35mm motion picture camera for amateur use. It is unusual in that the shutter is mounted forward of the lens, the lens is mounted midpoint in the camera box and the film plane is at the rear of the camera. The lens is focused by a knob on the side. The film transport is Geneva Cross. The camera can be used as a projector. Range: $250-500.

This section of the book lists items which look like cameras but actually serve a different purpose. Funcional cameras are in the main section of this guide. Many of these are recent items. Their "collectible" value is generally not based on rarity or demand, but more realistically is the retail price at which they currently are or recently were available. On these items, we have listed their approximate retail price. Items which have not been available new for some time have prices which reflect the current market value rather than the original price.

They are grouped by function, and the functional types are in alphabetical order, as shown in the following list.

CATEGORIES
Air Freshener
Albums
Bags (Handbags, Shoulder bags)
Banks
Belt Buckles
Candle
Candy & Gum
Cigarette Lighters
Clocks
Coasters
Compacts & Vanities
Containers
Convertors
Dart & Pellet Shooters
Decanters & Flasks
Dishes & Tableware
Dolls with Cameras
Jewelry
Keychains, Key Ring Fobs
Lights
Masks
Mouse, Worm, & Surprise Cameras
Music Box
Ornamental
Pencil Erasers, Sharpeners, Stationery
Phonographs
Planters
Printing Frames
Puzzles & Games
Radios
Rubber Stamps
Salt & Pepper Shakers
Soap
Squirt Cameras
Statuettes & Figurines
Toy Cameras
Toys & Games, unspecified
Vehicles
Viewing Devices

This list is only a sampling of the many camera-like novelites which have been produced. Readers contributions are welcomed to expand this section.

AIR FRESHENER

SOLIDEX INC. (Los Angeles, CA)

Minera Air Freshener - c1984. Room air freshener disguised as a zoom lens. Perfect for the high-tech bathroom, or to keep your camera bags smelling nice. About $5.

ALBUMS

ALBUM - Photo album shaped like 35mm SLR. Holds 24 prints 3¼x5". $4.

BAGS (HANDBAGS, SHOULDER BAGS)

LEADWORKS

Shoulder Bag - c1985. Rigid plastic carrying bag with shoulder strap. Shaped like a large camera. Lens and back are transparent plastic tinted in magenta or pale green. Retail about $11.

BANKS

EASTMAN KODAK CO.

Kodak Disc Bank - c1983. Black plastic bank shaped like Kodak Disc camera. Aluminum-colored covering. $2-5.

INSTAMATIC CAMERA BANK - c1967-1970. Given free to customers who purchased two rolls of Kodak color film. Several style variations:front identical to Instamatic 100 Camera (1967-68), or, styled like Instamatic 124 Camera (1968-1969). Black plastic body. Printed front behind clear plastic. Kodak logo on front. Molded into the back is "Instant Savings for Instamatic Cameras". Originally purchased by dealers for $5.00 per carton of 25. $1-2.

KODAK BANK - Early cast metal type. Shaped like a Brownie box camera. The door reads "Kodak Bank". This bank was not made by Kodak. Manufacturer unknown. Marked "Patent Pending 1905". It was offered for sale as late as 1914 by Butler Brothers, a toy distributor. $75-100.

PICCOLETTE CAMERA BANK - Ceramic coin bank shaped like Piccolette camera. $10-15.

POCKET COIN BANK - Black plastic coin bank shaped like 110 pocket camera. "Pocket Coin Bank" on aluminum-colored top. $1-3.

ROLLEICORD - Ceramic bank styled like Rolleicord TLR. White iridescent glaze with gold trim. Clear plastic lenses. $30-50. *(Illustrated on back cover.)*

TUPPERWARE - Black plastic bank with grey plastic knobs and lens. Lettered rings around lens set combination "tumblers" to open lens. "Tupper Toys" on front of top housing. $3-6.

BELT BUCKLES

LEWIS BUCKLES (Chicago)
Camera Buckles - c1980's. Cast metal belt buckles shaped like cameras or with bas-relief cameras as the major design. Available in various styles for different brands of cameras. About $5. *(Illustrated top of next page.)*

Lewis Belt Buckles

CANDLE

CAMERA CANDLE - Black wax candle shaped like small 35mm SLR. Aluminum-colored trim. $15-20.

CANDY & GUM

AKUTAGAWA CONFECTIONERY CO. LTD. (Tokyo)
Chocolate Camera - c1981. A well-detailed scaled-down chocolate model of the Canon AE-1 camera. A perfect gift for the man who wants to have his camera and eat it too. Retail price: $3.75

DONRUSS CO. (Memphis, TN)

Hot Flash Chewing Gum - c1984. Red or yellow plastic container shaped like SLR. "Hot Flash" on front of prism. Lens removes to open. Contains small pellets of chewing gum. Retail: $0.50

CIGARETTE LIGHTERS

AKW (Ankyu Workshop, Tokyo)

Perfect-Lighter - Lighter shaped like

35mm camera. Metal covering with stamped cherry tree design. Tree trunk and branches on back. Some traces of Leica styling include slow speed knob and focus lever. "Perfect" engraved on top, along with model number DI or DII. Actuator button is marked "pushing". "AKW Tokyo" on bottom. Another variation is leatherette covered, and marked "ANKYU WORKSHOP IN TOKYO" on bottom. With tripod: $30-40.

BROWN & BIGELOW (St. Paul, MN)
Kodak Film - Lighter in shape of small red roll of film on a film spool. Pulls apart to reveal "Redilite" lighter. $60-80.

CONT-LITE TABLE LIGHTER - Bakelite-bodied cigarette lighter styled like 35mm camera with cable release and tripod. "CONT-LITE" on back; "Cont-Lite Table Lighter" on original box. $10-15.

CONTINENTAL CAMERA-LIGHTER - Bakelite-bodied lighter, styled like 35mm camera. "CONTINENTAL NEW YORK" around lens. Made in Occupied Japan. With tripod and cable release: $10-15.

K.K.W.
Camera-Lighter - Lighter styled like 35mm camera. Bakelite body with no name on back. Compass built into front. "Made in occupied Japan" on bottom. "K.K.W. CAMERA LIGHTER" on lens rim. Some have "Photo-Flash" molded in back. With tripod: $15-25.

KYOEI TRADING CO. (Tokyo)

Mino Flex Snap Lite - Cigarette lighter styled in the form of a small TLR, 5cm high. Made in Occupied Japan. With tripod and cable release. $30-40.

LUCKY-LITE CAMERA-LIGHTER - Cigarette lighter/telescope shaped like 35mm camera. Bakelite body. "Lucky-Lite"

Lucky-Lite

black or brown bakelite lighter styled like Piccolette camera. Speed dial is marked "Triumpf". Made in Germany. $20-25.

NST
Phenix camera-lighter (bakelite body) - Lighter styled like 35mm camera. Black bakelite body. "NST" on focus ring. "Phenix" molded in back. Compass built into front. Made in Occupied Japan. With tripod: $9-15.

Phenix camera-lighter (metal covering) - Lighter styled like 35mm camera. Thin metal covering with stamped flower pattern on front. Back engraved with dragon design. Made in Occupied Japan. "NST" on focus scale. $15-20.

molded in back. Telescope through center of camera in lens position. Front lens focus. Made in Occupied Japan. $20-30.

LUMIX CAMERA-LIGHTER - Small cigarette lighter styled like Leica IIIc camera. "Winding knob" with numbered skirt functions as shutter release lock. Top housing profile is definitely Leica-styled (unlike other lighters). "Slow speed dial" on front. Viewfinder window and two round rangefinder windows on front. Side by side eyepieces on back. Focus lever on "Excellent Cherry" lens. Metal covering in either cherry blossom or leopard spot pattern. Made in Occupied Japan. $20-30.

MATCH KING - Lighter styled like small Piccolette camera. Top knob unscrews and withdraws attached "match" from the wicking where it has soaked up a small amount of fluid. Match is then struck on the side of the case. Speed dial is marked "Falcon". $20-25.

PEACE-GAS CAMERA-LIGHTER - Gas lighter styled like 35mm camera. "Peace-Gas" molded in back of bakelite body. No compass on front. With tripod and cable release: $15-25.

PENGUIN TRY CAMERA-LIGHTER - c1986. Small rectangular gas lighter with front and back plates printed to resemble a camera. $5.

MUGETTE CAMERA-LIGHTER - Small

PERFEOT LIGHTER - Cigarette lighter styled as 35mm camera. "PERFEOT (sic)

LIGHTER" on lens rim. No other identification. Thin metal covering stamped with cherry blossom pattern. "Made in Occupied Japan" on back. $20-25.

PHOTO-FLASH CAMERA-LIGHTER - Lighter styled like 35mm camera. "Photo-Flash" molded in back of bakelite body. Compass inset in front. "K.K.W. P.P 13449 Japan" on bottom. With tripod: $10-15.

S.M.R. (Japan)

PENTAX ME Cigarette Lighter - Cast metal table model cigarette lighter, styled after the Pentax ME camera. The lighter insert is the refillable gas type. Retail price in 1983 about $35.00.

View Camera Cigarette Lighter - Cast metal table model cigarette lighter, styled after a folding-bed view camera. Refillable gas lighter insert. Current value $10-20.

SUN ARROW (Japan)

KadocK-II Personal Gaslighter - Lighter disguised as a 120 film roll. Styling imitates Kodak packaging. One version even imitates Kodak trade dress in yellow, red and black colors. Another version is in silver and black. $15-30.

WOND-O-LITE - TLR-shaped lighter and cigarette case. About 50mm square by 92mm high. Fill point is marked "Fluid lens". Back opens to hold cigarettes. $40-50.

CLOCK

COPAL CO. LTD. (Japan)
Asanuma Clock - Brown plastic scale model of a studio camera on a stand. A mechanical digital clock is in the stand below the camera. The lens of the camera is marked "Asanuma & Co. Established in 1871". $30-40.

COASTERS

FRIENDLY HOME PARTIES INC. (Albany, NY)

Camera Coaster Set - Set of six wooden coasters with cork inserts. Storage rack designed like view camera on tripod. Chamfered edges of coasters resemble bellows. About $5.

COMPACTS & VANITIES

In addition to the camera-shaped compacts below, there are some real cameras which are built into makeup boxes, compacts, etc. These are listed in the main part of the book, under such diverse names as Ansco Photo Vanity, Vanity Kodak cameras, and Kunik Petie Vanity.

Compact, Change Purse, Cigarette Case - Unidentified manufacturer. Suede covered compact with comb, lipstick, cigarette case and lighter, and change purse. $25-35.

GIREY
Kamra-Pak Vanity - Small metal compact shaped like a folding camera. Front door conceals mirror and makeup. Winding knob is a lipstick. Various colored coverings, including colored leatherettes and imitation mother-of-pearl. Metal parts in brass or chrome. Often found with U.S. Navy emblem. Some collectors have expressed the opinion that the resemblance to a camera is coincidental. The name "Kamra-Pak" used by Girey confirms their

intentional design as camera look-alikes. That name is found on the original box, however, and not on the compact itself which has only the Girey name. $20-30.

Vanity kits - Several variations of same basic style. Vanity case is shaped like a large folding rollfilm camera in the folded position. The interior houses a makeup set including compact, lipstick, rouge, and comb. Several different exterior coverings, and some have ornamental lens or small mirror in red window position. $50-60.

Purse, Compact, & Lipstick - Unidentified manufacturer. Suede covered purse with round compact in lens position, lipstick in winding knob position. Top flap opens to small purse. $35-45.

Unidentified compact - Slightly larger than the common Girey Kamra-Pak. This compact has a door on each side. A mirror and makeup powder are on one side; a manicure set or cigarette case on the other. The winding key conceals the lipstick tube. Available in several finishes, including suede leather and brightly colored leather patterns. Complete: $30-40.

VENUS-RAY COMPACT - Brass-lacquered chrome compact with horizontal ribs. Shaped like a miniature Ikonta 6x6. Battery-powered lighted mirror in the door of the makeup compartment. The winding knobs conceal the batteries at the rounded ends of the body. $30-40.

CONTAINERS

GIBSON (C.R.) CO. (Norwalk, CT)
Camera Note Box - Cardboard box with note cards and envelopes. Exterior is extremely realistic lithograph of No. 2 Brownie. Design Copyright 1983 by Philip Sykes. Retail price $8.50. *(Illustrated top of next page.)*

Gibson Camera Note Box

IAN LOGAN LTD. (England)
Foto-File - Cardboard box for storing photographs. Styled to look like an Agfa box camera. $5-10.

Kodak Disc 4000 Photokina '82 - Shallow covered ceramic dish, shaped and decorated to resemble the Kodak Disc camera. Nameplate is actually the same as used on the real camera. Given as a promotional item at the 1982 Photokina. Could be used as a cigarette box, etc. $5-20.

MYSTERY MUG - c1920's? Leatherette covered wooden box "camera" is actually a disguised storage box for an enameled metal mug. The mug is shaped like a miniature chamber pot and has a mirror in the bottom. Perhaps it was designed for use as a cuspidor which could be hidden from view. Rare. Estimate: $75-100.

CONVERTORS

For those who don't understand this modern science-fiction terminology, "convertors" are robot-like people who convert to mechanical objects. Ask your kids.

CAVALIER/Camera A-1 - Toy camera converts to ray-gun and flashlight. Battery operated light and sound effects. $10-15.

CHIEN HSIN PLASTIC FAC. CO. LTD. (Taiwan)
Camera Pistol 116 - Toy disguised as a camera. Opens to become a cap gun. "Camera Pistol 116" on back. $4-8.

COMWISE INDUSTRY CO. LTD.

Camera Laser Gun 3-in-1 - c1982. This toy is shaped like a camera, but with a flashlight in the lens position. Converts to a toy laser gun. Retail price about $15.00

DAH YANG TOYS (Taiwan)
Cap gun camera - Disguised as a camera, it opens to become a cap gun. $4-8.

GALOOB (Lewis Galoob Toys, Inc., San Francisco)
Beddy-Bye Bear - c1984-85. A small pink and blue plastic charm which converts from a camera to a teddy bear in bed. One of a series of nine "Sweet Secrets" charms. Retail about $4. *(Illustrated top of next page.)*

519

red, blue, and yellow variations. Even more interesting is that the body has holes for a speaker, and "volume" and "tuning" molded near the edge. This indicates that a radio-equipped version may also exist. $12-18.

MARK

Galoob Beddy-Bye Bear

LI PING CO. LTD. (Taiwan)

Mark MA-1 as camera and robot. Film can in upper photo gives a size reference.

MA-1 camera-robot - Small SLR-type camera converts to robot. Copyright 1984 by Select, New York and Mark, Japan. Retail about $2.50.

Cambot Wonderful Slide Robot - c1985. Robot converts to camera shape and functions as a viewer for 35mm slides. In the absence of exhaustive research, we can only report that the package illustrates

MICROX ROBOT-TO-CAMERA - c1984. Three robots combine to make Microx camera. It does not function as a camera, but can be used as a telescope. Retail about $8-10.

SHELCORE INC. (So. Plainfield, NJ)

Change-A-Toy - c1985. A children's toy which converts from a camera to a car with a few simple motions. White, blue, yellow, and red plastic. Retail about $8.

Snap-Shot Secret Gun CH-337 - Toy disguised as a camera. Opens to become a cap gun. "Snap Shot" on front. "Secret Gun" on back. $4-8.

TAIFONG

Camera Shooter NIKO Nikosound 112XL - c1983. Toy styled like movie camera. Features include gun, flashlight, telescope 3.5x, laser gun. Provisions for built-in radio, but the only example we have seen did not have one. Retail about $12.00

DART & PELLET SHOOTERS

JA-RU
Pellet Shooting Camera - Small camera-shaped pellet shooter. Comes with box of pellets which resembles film box. Retail in 1980: $1.25

LINDSTROM TOOL & TOY CO. INC.
(Bridgeport, Conn.)
Candid Camera Target Shot - Masonite target, 9" square. Blue, aqua, green, yellow, and red sections, with photos of various

planes. One plane (in 9:00 position) is inverted. Metal "Candid Camera Gun" camera, spring-loaded to shoot darts. Set with darts and boards: $40-50. Camera only, without darts: $10-15.

DECANTERS & FLASKS

CAMERA-FLASK, Folding Camera Style (American) - Several different styles, shaped like a folding rollfilm camera in the closed position. Glass flask bottle inside leatherette covered wood body or leather covered aluminum body. $40-60.

CAMERA-FLASK, Folding Camera Style (German) - Very well made, all metal with genuine leather covering. Winding knob conceals set of four nested metal shot glasses. Corner of camera body twists off to pour contents. Beautifully crafted. $100-150.

CANDID SHOT - Ceramic decanter styled like 35mm. Winding knob is cork stopper. Two shot glasses in pouch on strap. $10-20.

MOVIE CAMERA (no name) - Ceramic decanter shaped like movie camera. Black glaze with gold trim. Two shot glasses for lenses. $10-20.

MOVIE CAMERA (three-lens) - Nameless ceramic decanter, very similar to Relco

Movie Shot, but non-removable lenses. $10-20.

RELCO (Japan)

Movie Shot - Ceramic decanter shaped like three-lens turret movie camera. The lenses are actually removable and usable as shot glasses. Black glazing with gold trim. $10-20.

REFLEX SHOT - Ceramic decanter shaped like TLR. Black glaze with gold trim. Cork stopper in top. Two shot glasses for lenses. $10-20.

SWANK
Camera Flask - Plastic flask shaped like 35mm SLR. Winding knobs conceal spout and air vent. Clear slot on back and clear lens are useful to gauge level of contents. Comes with a small plastic funnel. $8-12.

Schnapps-O-Flex - Ceramic decanter shaped like a TLR with a flash attachment on the left side. Black glazed with silver trim. The flash reflector removes to reveal the pouring spout for your favorite beverage. Complete outfit includes black

ceramic shotglass in box resembling Kodak 35mm film box. Outfit: $20-30. Flask w/flash only: $10-15.

UNIVEX MERCURY DECANTER - Ceramic decanter shaped like Univex Mercury camera. Glazed in all black, or black body with white shutter housing, lens, speed knobs, and VF window. $10-20.

DISHES & TABLEWARE

Champagne glass - From 1911 Shriners convention. Shows man with view camera

on a stand and a factory building in Rochester, NY. $75-100.

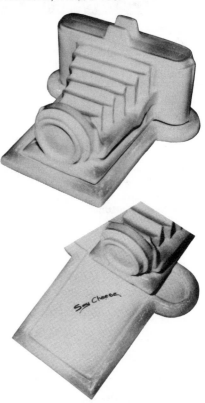

CHEESE DISH - Ceramic tray with cover shaped like folding camera. "Say Cheese" printed in bottom of dish. $40-50.

KODAK MUG "You press the button We do the rest" - Ivory colored coffee mug with brown printing. Drawing of woman photographing young girl with original Kodak Camera. Made in Korea for Kodak Australasia. $10-15.

**McDONALDS
Great Muppet Caper drinking glass -** c1981. Two different glasses with pictures featuring Gonzo with his camera. One depicts Gonzo in a hot air balloon, the other in a bus. New in 1981. $.60 each.

**WILTON (Columbia, PA)
Kodak 1880-1980 Centennial Plate -** Cast metal plate, 10" diameter. "A 100-year start on tomorrow" on rim. Center area has bas-relief scene of woman with the original Kodak Camera, photographing a young girl as a boy watches. Dealers ask up to $65.

DOLLS WITH CAMERAS

**KNICKERBOCKER TOY CO.
(Middlesex, NJ)**
Snoopy The Astronaut - Snoopy doll with space suit, helmet, and camera. Also includes moon shoes, life support system, vehicle, flag, and Woodstock. $20.

MATTEL
Fashion Photo Barbie - Imitation camera for fashion photography, connected to doll by a tube. Turning camera lens causes doll to change positions. Copyright 1977. $7.

JEWELRY

**AMERICAN GREETINGS CO.
Mr. Weekend Button** - c1985. A whimsical decorative button illustrating a man with a camera. About $1.00.

Charms: Happy (left) and JAS 300 (right)

CAMERA CHARM - c1986. Small blue, red, or white plastic charms shaped like 35mm rangefinder or SLR cameras. Usually with small bell and plastic clip attached. Occasionally with name such as "Happy" on front of lens. About 3 for $1.

CAMERA-CHARM JAS 300 - Small plastic charm for charm bracelet. Styled like 35mm RF camera. "JAS 300" on back. $0.25 *(Illustrated above.)*

CANON AE-1 PROGRAM LAPEL PIN - Small brass lapel pin inlaid with black & white enamel. About $1.

FILM NECKLACE - Tiny reproduction of 35mm cartridge of Kodacolor II, Agfa, or Fuji film. Only one inch tall. Comes with neck chain and matching box. $2.00

**KRUGENER DELTA-CAR LAPEL PIN
DVPCA 10th Anniv.** - Tiny replica of the Krugener trademark (Delta camera on wheels with rear cab). Fashioned in sterling silver for the Delaware Valley Photographic Collectors Assn. in 1984. About $20.

KEYCHAINS, KEY RING FOBS

CAMERA KEYCHAIN - c1986. Small plastic and metal camera with attached keychain. Levers and knobs are movable. Retail $1.50.

**GOLD HORSE (Taiwan)
Enjicolor F-II
Keepcolor I** - Key fobs shaped as 35mm cassettes, and with the same paper wrapper as the pencil erasers of the same name. To further confuse the issue, they are marked "pencil eraser" even though they are key chain fobs. Retail under $1.

LIGHTS

CAMERA KEYCHAIN FLASHLIGHT - c1986. Small black plastic flashlight shaped like camera. Rear button pushes miniature watch battery against bulb contacts. Keychain attached to strap lug. $1-2.

FLASH-IT CORP. (Miami, Florida) Switchplate cover (photographer) - Ivory plastic cover for electric light switch. Features "flasher" photographer with two cameras around his neck and another on a tripod. His trousers are around his ankles and the light switch is in an embarrassing position. $4-6.

Switchplate cover (tourist) - Ivory plastic cover for electric light switch. This one features a tourist photographer with a Hawaiian patterned shirt standing in front of the ocean with a sailboat in the background. He has a camera around his neck, a drink in one hand, and a shopping bag in the other. His trousers are around his ankles, and the light switch is in an obvious position. $4-6.

Spearhead Camera Mask

MOUSE, WORM, & SURPRISE CAMERAS

BICOH 36 - Painted metal body with Kiken Bicoh "lens". Shutter latch releases pink worm. Made in Japan. No. 6817612. $2-3.

COMMONWEALTH PLASTICS CORP. Jack-in-the Camera Sr. - Small black plastic "camera". When release lever is pressed, a small smiling face springs through the front of the lens. $1-5.

FRIEND BOY'S CAMERA - Eye-level style Mouse camera. $2.

HIT-SIZE - Miniature worm camera about the size of a Hit-type novelty camera. $2.

FOTOX - Reddish-brown bakelite flashlight styled like Piccolette. Unusual bulb with solid glass front in lens position. Made in Saxony. $20-35.

SASPARILLA DECO DESIGNS LTD. (New York, NY) Camera-lamp - White ceramic night-light designed like 35mm camera. Made in Japan. Copyright 1980. $22-27.

MASK

SPEARHEAD INDUSTRIES, INC. (Minneapolis)
Camera Mask - c1983. Rubber face mask shaped like SLR camera and hands holding it. Retail price about $6. *(Illustrated top of next column.)*

KING FLEX - Minature TLR-style worm camera. $1-5.

Wonderflex Comet Special Camera

PANOMATIC 126 - Mouse camera shaped like 126 cartridge camera. Same old mouse in a new package. $3-6.

PRINCE FLEX - Miniature worm camera. $2

SNAKE CAMERA (folding bellows style)

- Small cardboard bodied folding camera with bellows. Behind the shutter door lurks a green fabric-covered coiled spring with a snake-like head. Fabulous, fragile, and rare. $40-60.

WONDER SPECIAL CAMERA - Eye-level style mouse camera. $3.

WONDERFLEX COMET SPECIAL CAMERA - TLR styled mouse camera. Also sold under the name "Wonderflex Wonder Special Camera". Made in Japan. $4. *(Illustratd top of previous column.)*

MUSIC BOX

Girl holding camera - Ceramic figurine with music box in base. Girl holding camera. Cat seated on nearby chair. Music box plays "Everything Is Beautiful". Retail in 1983: $12.

ILLCO TOY CO. (Illfelder Toy Co. Inc., New York City.)
Cabbage Patch Kids Musical Toy Camera - ©1984. A music box shaped like a camera. Available in two styles: Lavender body with white trim (plays "Farmer in the Dell") and cream body with lavender trim (plays "Old MacDonald".) About $6.

Mickey Mouse Musical Toy Camera - Music box shaped like a camera. Turning lens winds the mechanism. Pressing the release plays "Rock-a-bye-Baby", and a small Mickey Mouse or Donald Duck head turns around on top. Red camera has Mickey head on top, Donald face on lens. Yellow camera has Donald head on top, Mickey face on lens. Retail about $6.

Pound Puppies Musical Toy Camera - c1986. Music box shaped like camera. Tan plastic with red trim. Plays "Turkey in the Straw". Retail $6.

Smurf Musical Toy Camera - Blue plastic camera-shaped music box toy. Plays "Rock-a-bye-Baby". Smurf head turns around on top. ©1982. Retail: about $5.

SANKYO SEIKI MFG. CO. LTD. (Tokyo)

Snap-Me-Happy Musical Camera Toy - c1976. Music box shaped like camera. Red plastic body with yellow trim. Pressing release button plays "Frere Jacques" and yellow bear's head rotates in flashcube position. Made in Hong Kong for Sankyo. Retail about $11.

ORNAMENTAL

These are decorative non-functional items.

CAMERA WITH BIRDIE - Miniature cast metal camera on tripod. Birdie on stick above lensboard. About $5.

DURHAM INDUSTRIES INC. (New York, NY)
Holly Hobbie Doll House Camera - Small cast metal view camera with tripod. About $3-4.

HASSELBLAD PLUSH TOY - Oversized stuffed Hassie. Black velour and gray terry-cloth. $5-10.

LIMOGES MINIATURE CAMERA - Tiny ceramic view camera with cobalt-blue or white glazing. Gold trim and gold tripod. Blue: $17. White: $15.

SHACKMAN (B.) & CO.
Glass Camera on Tripod - Small novelty glass camera on metal tripod. ©1981. $6.

PENCIL ERASERS, SHARPENERS, STATIONERY ITEMS

EASTMAN KODAK CO.
Kodacolor VR 200 - Pencil sharpener shaped like oversized 35mm cartridge. Made in Hong Kong. $1-2.

GOLD HORSE
Enjicolor F-11 Eraser - Rubber eraser shaped like small 35mm film cartridge. Green and white mimics Fujicolor film. $1-2.

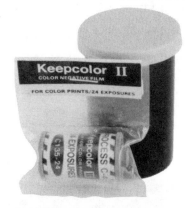

Keepcolor II Eraser - Rubber eraser shaped like small 35mm film cartridge. Black & yellow label for "Keepcolor II" film, "Process C-41", imitates Kodak trade dress. $1-2

HALL & KEANE DESIGN LTD.
Camera Kit - Consists of a pencil sharpener and eraser. In the same series as the Memo set below. Retail about $1.50.

HELIX LTD. (England)
Camera pencil box - Molded plastic in grey and black, shaped to resemble a 35mm SLR camera. The shutter release button is actually a yellow pencil eraser; the lens removes for use as a magnifying glass; a 35mm cassette inside the camera removes for use as a pencil sharpener; the camera back contains a school timetable. The inside of the camera is suitable for holding pencils, crayons, etc. Retail price about $6.

MEMO SET - Contains eraser, notebook, pencil sharpener and pencil stylized to relate to photography. Eraser is covered by paper to look like an Instamatic camera; sharpener is shaped and covered to look like two 35mm cassettes and the notebook is called "Photographers Notebook". Retail price about $2.25.

PENCIL SHARPENER ENJICOLOR F-II - Plastic pencil sharpener shaped like a film can. Red, green, and white label mimics Fujicolor. Retail $1.50.

PENCIL SHARPENER KEEPCOLOR II - Plastic pencil sharpener shaped like a film can. Yellow black label mimics Kodacolor. Retail $1.50.

PENCIL SHARPENER LANTERN PROJECTOR - Heavy metal construction, shaped like an old-fashioned lantern slide projector. $4.

PENCIL ERASER - c1985. Pencil eraser shaped like tiny 35mm SLR. Made of green rubber-like substance. Neck strap at top; hole in bottom to mount on pencil. $1-2.

PENCIL-SHARPENER CAMERA (Hong Kong) - Cast metal pencil sharpener shaped like a view camera. Bellows made of plastic. "Made in Hong Kong" on side of bellows. Retail about $2.

PHONOGRAPHS

PETER PAN GRAMOPHONE - Portable hand-cranked 78 rpm phonograph which resembles a box camera when closed. Black leather covered. $125-150.

PENCIL-SHARPENER CAMERA (Spain) - Cast metal pencil sharpener shaped like view camera. Bellows are also cast metal (unlike Hong Kong copies). Play/Me trademark and "Made in Spain" on bottom. Retail about $3-4.

PENCIL SHARPENER EGFECOLOR 400 - Plastic pencil sharpener shaped like a film can. Red, blue, and yellow label mimics Agfacolor. Retail $1.50. *(Illus. next column.)*

THORENS EXCELDA - A portable hand-cranked 78 rpm phonograph which packs neatly into a metal case shaped like a folding rollfilm camera. Available in black, blue, brown, or green enamel finish. $100-150.

PLANTER

NAPCO PLANTER - Ceramic plater shaped like Mamiya RB-67 camera. Black with silver trim. $8.

PRINTING FRAME

ELVIN (Japan)

jigsaw puzzle, 52x52 cm, with over 550 pieces. Full-color photo of photographic accessories & memorabilia. Retail about $5.

RADIOS

AMICO - Transistor radio shaped like Olympus OM-1 camera. Speaker is in lens mount. $15-25.

Magic Sun Picture Camera - A small cardboard box with a hinged glass back. Printed design resembles either a 35mm or TLR-style camera. Box contains "printing-out" paper for making prints from negatives by two-minute exposure to sunlight. $5-10.

PUZZLES & GAMES

EASTMAN KODAK CO.
Kolorcube - Everybody has heard of Rubik's cube. This is a special version with the Kodak logo on each square of each side. $8-15.

KAMERA - Small transistor radio shaped like a movie camera. Volume and tuning knobs in lens positions. Requires one AA battery. Made in Hong Kong. $10.

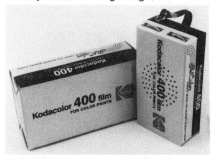

KODAK DICE CUP - Red plastic dice cup with Kodak logo. Five yellow dice with Kodak logo included. $10-15.

WARREN COMPANY (Lafayette, Indiana)
Click! Jigsaw Puzzle - c1986. Square

KODACOLOR 400 FILM RADIO - Transistor radio shaped and colored like Kodak film box. Radio box also mimics

Kodak film packaging. Made in Hong Kong. $15-25.

TOUR PARTNER - Styled like a large camera. Includes radio, lamp, horn and fittings for attaching to bicycle. About $10.

KODAK INSTANT COLOR FILM PR10 - Transistor radio shaped and colored like a box of Kodak's now defunct instant film. Operates on one 9v battery. Made in Hong Kong. $10-15.

SHIRASUNA DENKI MFG. CO. LTD.

Silver Pocket Radio - Vacuum tube radio in leather case designed to look like a camera case. Uses one "B" battery and one "A" battery. Small "filter case" on strap contains earphone and antenna wire. $40-50.

STEWART RADIO-LIGHT-MIRROR - Transistor radio shaped like a 110 pocket camera. Built-in flashlight. Battery compartment door has mirror inside. Made in Hong Kong. $5-10.

RUBBER STAMPS

BUTTERFLY ORIGINALS LTD. (Cherry Hill, NJ)
Cabbage Patch Kids Figurine Stamper - c1984. Small figurine of Cabbage Patch Doll holding a camera. The base has a rubber stamp (Smile!) and ink pad. Retail $2.50.

KODACLONE SLIDE - Cute rubber-stamp which mimics Kodak's logo on a 35mm slide mount. "Processed by clones" adds an interesting touch. $8-10.

SALT & PEPPER SHAKERS

Book & Camera - Set includes one small open book and one bellows camera. $10-20.

Movie Camera & Projector - Made of wood. $20-25. *(Illustrated top of next page.)*

Rollfilm Camera - The "camera" is in two parts. Body is pepper; bellows & front standard is salt. $15-25.

Salt & Pepper Movie Outfit

SASPARILLA DECO DESIGNS LTD.
Camera Salt & Pepper - Set of two miniature 35mm-styled ceramic shakers. One is black, the other is white. Retail $6.

Avon "Watch the Birdie" Soap

WF
Camera-screwdriver-keychain - Small red plastic "camera" with screwdriver bit in lens position. Interchangeable bits store in body. Keychain attached to strap lug. "WF" molded in back. $5-10.

AVON PRODUCTS, INC. (New York, NY)
"Watch the Birdie" Soap - c1962-64. A cake of soap on a rope with a 'birdie' on the lens. "Avon" on back. $30-40 with box. *(Illustrated in previous column.)*

WOLFF PRODUCTS (Long Island City, NY)
Camera Soap-on-a-rope - A six-ounce bar of soap shaped like a camera. $7-10.

BATTLESTAR GALACTICA - Small plastic squirt camera with Battlestar Galactica emblem on front. $3.

COHEN - c1986. Black plastic squirt camera from Hong Kong. Copy of the Shiba Aqua Camera. Retail $2.

DeMOULIN BROS & CO. (Greenville, IL)
Trick Camera - An early wooden box squirt camera. Cubical wooden box, 20cm on a side, with a brass lens tube on the

TRICK CAMERA
DIRECTIONS
Remove rubber tubing from nozzle of bulb; fill bulb with water and replace tubing.

When candidate is seated to be "photographed" the "photographer" places camera about eight or ten feet from him and takes focus by sighting through peep hole of lense. To make the "exposure" press the bulb.

DeMoulin Bros. & Co.,
Mfrs. of Lodge Supplies, Burlesque and Side Degree Paraphernalla, Uniforms, Banners, Badges, Etc.

Greenville, Illinois.

front. Some later models appear to have an aluminum disk with a lens mounted. The squirt tube runs along the bottom of the lens tube and is attached to a rubber hose and bulb outside the rear of the box, which is covered with a black focusing cloth. The rubber bulb is filled with water and then attached to the squirt tube. The subject is sighted through a tube which runs from the back to the front through the lens tube. The instructions say "To make the 'exposure', press the bulb." $350-450.

DICK TRACY SQUIRT GUN CAMERA - Square plastic squirt camera in Dick Tracy motif. $4.

FOTOMAT

Squirt Camera - Well-made squirt camera

shaped and sized like a 126 cartridge camera. Made in Hungary. No relation to Fotomat film stores in the U.S.A. $5-10.

GUCKI - c1986. Black plastic squirt camera made in W. Germany. Retail $2.

JA-RU Trick Squirt Camera No. 803 - Retail $1.

JAK PAK INC. (Milwaukee, Wisconsin)

Squirt Camera X-315 - c1986. Black plastic squirt camera made in Hong Kong. Back of body has "WK Toys" molded in, which is probably the actual manufacturer. Retail about $1.

PREMIER PLASTICS CO. (Brooklyn, NY)
Squirt Pix - Automatic water shooting camera. With original box: $10-15. Camera only: $3-5. *(Illustrated top of next page.)*

SHIBA

Aqua Camera Flash Shiba - c1984.

Premier Squirt Pix

Small "camera" which squirts water from the "winding knob". Knob rotates to allow squirting in a different direction. The instructions suggest that after squirting somebody by taking their picture, you give them the chance to do the same to you (but only after you reverse the direction of the knob!) This double-trouble toy comes in white, red, or black. Retail about $3.

"Instamatic" style water camera - No. 314A. Made in Hong Kong. $1-2.

T.H.
Water Camera No. 402 - Black or red plastic water camera. Chrome trim on front. "T.H." trademark and "No. 402" on back. Mushroom top on shutter release. Cloth strap. Retail: under $1.

T.K.

Squirt Camera "Diana Style" No. 686TK - This "camera" looks exactly like the cheap "Diana-type" cameras for 120 rollfilm, but squirts water. Made in Hong Kong. $2.

Water Camera No. 677 - Black plastic squirt camera. Chrome trim on front. "Made

in Hong Kong" on back. Thin shutter button. Plastic strap. Retail: under $1.

VOHO

Squirt Camera - Small rubber squirt camera styled like a Hit camera. Cream colored body with aluminum paint on top, front, and "latch". "Made in Occupied Japan" molded into bottom. Also available in a black model. $3-5.

WATER CAMERA, Leica-styled - Black rubber squeeze-type squirt camera made in Occupied Japan. Styling resembles Leica camera. Squirts from "slow-speed dial". Trimmed with aluminum and gold colored paints. $3-5.

WATER CAMERA - Black plastic squirt camera. White top and bottom. Chrome lens rim. Made in Hong Kong. $1-3.

WATER CAMERA No. 014 - Simple plastic squeeze-type squirt camera. Made in Hong Kong. Retail $.30.

STATUETTES & FIGURINES

ALDON PHOTOGRAPHER - Wooden figurine 30cm (12") tall. Man holds one camera to his face. Two other cameras hang at his sides. Made in China. Retail: $15.00 *(Illustrated on next page.)*

GIRL WITH CAMERA - Painted ceramic figurine. Girl with view camera. Camera rests on the face of a cat on a chair. Made in Taiwan. $10. *(Illustrated on next page.)*

HIPPOPOTAMUS WITH CAMERA - Soft plastic hippo stands 18cm tall. Advertising figure for East German "Pentacon" company. It holds a small "Praktica" camera and a trumpet. $15-25.

LEFTON CHINA
Man with camera - Hand painted ceramic figurine. Man with camera on tripod. Powder flash unit in left hand. Box of plates at his feet. Made in Taiwan. Retail: about $30.

LUCY RIGG

Teddy Bear Photographers - c1985. A set of two small figurines, 8.5cm tall. One is a girl and one a boy teddy bear, each holding a camera. Retail about $5 each.

Left: Royal Crown Boy holding camera
Right: Girl with Camera

ROYAL CROWN (Taiwan)
Boy Holding Camera - Figurine of boy seated on stump holding camera. Retail in 1983: $12.

SCHLEICH
Super Smurf Photographer - Small rubbery Smurf toy. Box camera camera on tripod. Copyright 1981. $12.

Aldon Photographer

SHUTTER BUG - Comical furry figure holding camera. Large eyes, nose, and sandaled feet protrude from furry body. "Nikon" SLR camera in left hand. "SHUTTER BUG" placard between feet. $10.

SQUIRREL HOLDING CAMERA - Multicolored ceramic figurine, 4" tall. Made in Taiwan. $15.

TOY CAMERAS

These are kid's toys that are made to look like and imitate the functions of real cameras.

20 CRAZE - Black, pink, & green toy shaped like a camera. Front pops out when shutter is pressed. Picture of comic character on front. $3-7.

AMBI TOYS

Focus Pocus - c1985. Yellow plastic toy shaped like camera. Front springs open and little man pops out. Retail about $10.

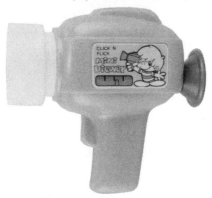

Click-N-Flick Mini Viewer

Turn-N-Click Mini Camera

ARCO INDUSTRIES LTD. (New York, NY)

Take-A-Picture - Toy camera styled after Kodak Colorburst 250 camera. Includes 12 pre-printed photos which eject when shutter is depressed. Made in Hong Kong. Copyright 1982. Retail: $3.

BLUE BOX TOY (New York, NY)
Click-N-Flick Mini Viewer - c1986. Toy shaped like movie camera. Hand crank flickers shutter for movie effect in viewfinder. Retail about $2. *(Illustrated in previous column.)*

Turn-N-Click Mini Camera - Childrens toy shaped like 35mm camera. Lens clicks when turned. Pushing the shutter raises "flashcube" with smiling sun. $1-5. *(Illustrated in previous column.)*

BRIGHT STAR - Black plastic toy camera made in Hong Kong. Shutter button clicks; winding knob turns. No other functions. A 'no frills' toy. $3-7.

IRWIN

Grand Camera - Black plastic toy camera which holds a quantity of printed pictures. Sliding a lever on the back ejects pictures one by one. $5-10.

KENNER
Picture-Quick - Toy camera styled like Kodak EK-4 Instant Camera. Knob ejects pre-printed pictures through bottom slot. Dated 1977 on back. $7.

MERRY MATIC FLASH CAMERA - Small black plastic camera-shaped toy. Pressing shutter makes clicking sound and lights flashlight bulb. Operates on one AA battery. $3-7.

SCHAPER MFG. CO. (Minneapolis, MN)

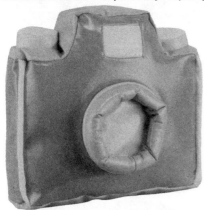

Tendertoys Camera - c1986. Child's stuffed toy shaped like a camera. Red, blue, yellow, and white vinyl fabric covering. Squeaks when squeezed. Retail $8.

SHELCORE INC. (So. Plainfield, NJ)
Clicker Bear - c1985. One of a series of "Squeeze-A-Mals", soft vinyl infant toys. This is a small teddy bear holding a camera. Tan, green, magenta & white. Squeaks when squeezed. Retail about $3. *(Illustrated on back cover.)*

TOMY
Ring-a-dingy Camera - Child's toy shaped like a camera. Lens turns with clicking sound. Film advance lever clicks and returns. Shutter button rings bell. ©1982. Other Ring-a-dingy toys are Telephone, Typewriter, and Cash Register. $5.

TOYPOWER MFG. CO. LTD.
Just Like Daddy's Camera - Toy camera with "simulated working flash". Detachable Kaleidoscope and zoom lenses. ©1983. $5.

TOYS & GAMES NOT OTHERWISE SPECIFIED

BEAR WITH FLASH CAMERA - Mechanical bear with camera. Wind-up mechanism raises camera to bear's eye and battery operated flash fires. Made in China. About $20.

EASTMAN KODAK CO.

Walking film box - Spring-operated mechanism with walking feet is mounted in Kodacolor 400 film box. $5-10.

EFS (Burlingame, CA)
Camp Out - Set of small toy camping items. Includes wrist compass, camera, canteen, flashlight, walkie-talkie, lantern, and radio. $1.50.

LEGO

Fabuland Patrick Parrot - Toy parrot with flash camera. Also has motorcycle and pipe wrench. Made to interlock with Lego building blocks. ©1982. Retail: $3.

TOMY

Roving Eye Camera - A clockwork mechanism allows the camera to walk around; the eye moves around, and the maginfying glass moves up and down. Retail about $3.

WINNER TOY (New York, NY)

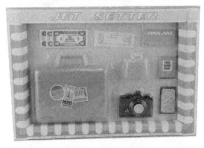

Jet Setter - Doll-size travel kit. Includes camera, suitcase, purse, passport, money, etc. About $1.

VEHICLES

LLEDO

Kodak Van - c1983. Small toy Model T Ford truck with Kodak Film advertising. Cast metal with enameled exterior; plastic trim. Made in England. Part of Lledo's "Models of Days Gone" series. Retail price around $4, but generally selling now among collectors for $8-12.

PHOTOING ON CAR - c1950's. Battery operated toy automobile, made in China. Horn sounds and headlights flash when it starts. Upon stopping, girl passenger turns with camera and flashbulb lights. New in box, these have sold for as much as $75-100.

TOYCRAFTER

Wooden Kodak Truck/whistle - c1985. Wooden whistle shaped like a truck. "Products by Kodak" logo on side of truck. $4-6.

WINROSS (Rochester, NY)

Kodak Truck 1880-1980 - Toy truck issued for the Kodak Centennial in 1980. Detachable semi-trailer with operable rear doors. Metal construction, white enameled with yellow trim. Dealers were asking $40-50 for these, but probably not selling many. More recent asking prices have been about $20.

Child Guidance Big Bird's 3-D Camera

VIEWING DEVICES

Camera-Viewers: Key chain type (left)
Vepla-Venezia Capri (center)
Small scenic viewer (right)

CAMERA-VIEWER - Small viewer shaped like a camera with 18 views of the Canadian Rockies or some other scenic spot. $2.

CAMERA-VIEWER KEY CHAIN - Small SLR-shaped, with views of New York City, Toronto, other major cities, zoo animals, undressed ladies, etc. Made in Hong Kong. $2. *(Illustrated above.)*

**CHILD GUIDANCE PLAYTHINGS INC.
(Subsid. of Gabriel Industries, Inc. Bronx, NY)**
Sesame Street Big Bird's 3-D Camera - Three-dimensional viewer shaped like a camera. 24 different pictures with alphabet letters. ©1978. Retail: $5. *(Illustrated top of next column.)*

DU ALL PRODUCTS CO. (New York)
Camera Scope - Kaleidoscope shaped like a rigid bodied rollfilm camera. Trapezoidal front; back has rounded ends. Cardboard construction with red leatherette covering. $100-150.

EAGLE VIEW 88 CAMERA - c1985. Plastic viewer shaped like a 35mm SLR. Shutter button changes 24 transparency views of zoo animals. Several variations of colors, caption language, etc. $3-5.

EPOCH LIGHTED SLIDE VIEWER -
Stamped metal slide viewer in shape of camera, complete with neck strap. Leatherette trim panels. $10-15.

FISHER-PRICE TOYS (East Aurora, NY)
Movie Viewer - Hand-cranked toy viewer for 8mm films in special interchangeable cartridges. $1-5.

Pocket Camera - Viewer shaped like 110 pocket camera with flashcube. Shutter advances 27 photos of zoo animals. $3-6.

HASBRO INDUSTRIES, INC. (Pawtucket, RI)

Romper Room Snoopy Counting Camera - Children's viewer shaped like a camera. Snoopy on front, Woodstock on top. Teaches children to count. Number of characters in scene matches film counter digit. Retail in 1981: $6.

JA-RU (Jacksonville, Florida)
Home Movie Super-8 Auto-matic -
c1984. Toy film viewer shaped like a movie camera. Includes interchangeable cylinders with translucent illustrations. New in package: $1-3.

"LEICA" VIEWER - Black and grey plastic viewer shaped like a Leica camera. With 18 "Views of beautiful Rhein". "Made in Germany, US-Zone, BPa. DBGM. St. & Co." For the Leica collector who has everything. One sold at 10/86 auction for about $100.

STEVEN MFG CO. (Herman, MO)
Talking Vue Camera - Viewer shaped like a camera. 16 animal cartoon pictures. Six voice messages play when string is pulled. $8.

VEPLA-VENEZIA
Camera-Viewer Capri - A detailed SLR-shaped viewer. 14 views of the island of Capri. Made in Italy. $3-5.
(Illustrated at the beginning of the VIEWING DEVICES section on the previous page.)

This section on accessories is a totally new addition to the Price Guide. We are indebted to Mr. Fred Waterman for his efforts in compiling this listing. The initial compiling of such a list is a time-consuming and frustrating task, since collectors and dealers are not accustomed to using "standardized" names for many of these items. In addition to the organizational problems encountered, Mr. Waterman also had to deal with the widely varying prices which are common in a field without an established pricing guide. For this reason, we would caution our readers to consider these prices not as established averages or normal prices, but rather as a sampling of specific items encountered for sale in recent months. In time, this section of the book will take a more firm shape as the accessories market stabilizes and as our base of data expands to allow for better overall tracking of prices in this segment of the market. As with any part of this book, we welcome your comments, criticisms, and suggested additions to make this section better or more useful.

For this edition, we have divided accessories into the following categories:

BELLOWS for CLOSE-UP
CLOSE-UP ATTACHMENTS
DARKROOM DEVELOPING
   CHEMICALS
   DRYING RACKS
   OUTFITS
   SCALES
   TANKS
   THERMOMETERS
   TIMERS
   TRAYS
DARKROOM PRINTING
   ENLARGERS
   MASKS, MOUNTS
   PRINTERS
   RETOUCHING
   MISC.
DARKROOM SAFELIGHTS
EXPOSURE METERS
FILMPACK & ROLLFILM HOLDERS
FINDERS
FLASHES
LENSES without Shutters
LENSES in Shutters
MICROSCOPE ADAPTERS
PLATES/ ROLLFILM
RANGEFINDERS
SELF-TIMERS
SHUTTERS
STEREO VIEWERS
TRIPODS

Please note that the intent of this section is not to list the types of accessories in common use among photographers today, but rather to list those accessories whose main attractions are collectibility and historical interest.

■ BELLOWS for CLOSE-UP ■
ACCURA close-up bellows
- for Exakta: $35. for Canon: $50.

ASAHI KOGAKU
- single rail bellows, universal screw-mount. $20.
Bellows II - Universal screw-mount. With slide copier attachment. $65.

IHAGEE KAMERAWERK
- Large dual track bellows assembly for Exakta larger focal length lenses. Has external and internal bayonet mounts. $25.

KOPIL - folding single track bellows assembly for Exakta: $10.

MIRANDA CAMERA CO. LTD.
- dual track bellows. Has internal screw-mount and external bayonet mount. With IB: $20.
Focabell II Deluxe Bellows Outift - Early style dual step assembly with matching slide copier and extension tube attachment set; all in fitted case. $35.

NOVOFLEX
- bellows outfit for universal screw-mounts. Includes bellows, shade, slide copy attachment. $65.
- dual track bellows assembly for Exakta. $15.
- Model II bellows. $65.

PIESKER - single track folding bellows assembly for Exaktas. $10.

PRINZ - double track bellows for Miranda. $15.

TOPCON
- bellows-type microscope attachment for Topcon. $50.
Bellows II - includes shade, slide copier, copy stage. $45.

■ CLOSE-UP ATTACHMENTS ■
ARGUS
Macro Kit - for C1, C2, C3. Rare. $50.
Macro Kit - for C, C2. Includes copy stand, extension tubes, two stages with ground glass for focusing, case, instructions. $30.
Techniscope - Sliding, focusing device for C and C2, with instructions. $25.

EASTMAN KODAK CO.
- close-up rangefinder for Retina. With two lenses, case, box, instructions. $45.
- Prismatic close-up attachment for Kodak Stereo. Rare. $35.
Instamatic Reflex Close-Up Set Type N/29.5 - with instructions. $15.
Kodak Close-Up Stand 1:1 - for Retina I and II. With stage. $60.
Kodak Table Copy Stand - for Retina Reflex. With ball head. $65.
Retina 1:1 tripod copy stand - $15.
Retina Close-Up Kit B - $20.
Close Range and View Finder Kit B - for Retina cameras. $28.

Retina Close-Up Lenses I, II, III - in leather case. $10.
Retina Close-Up Lens Set Type N - $10.
Retina Close-Up Lens N 60/I, 60/II - $15.
Retina Close-Up Lens Set Type R - $18.

MINOX - copy stand. $40.

■ **DARKROOM DEVELOPING** ■
● **CHEMICALS** ●
ARGO - Developing powder in tube. $1.00

BURKE & JAMES
Rexo Metol Quinol Developer - Box of 6 tubes, for paper plates and films. Original price was $0.25. $4.

DEFENDER Sepia Toner - glass tube. $2.

EASTMAN KODAK CO.
- Eastman bottle. $5.
- Eastman brown glass bottle, with complete graphic label. $12.
- Kodak 5 gallon ceramic chemical jug, with trademark on side. $250.
- 8 oz glass graduate. $10.
- Ammonium Bichromate in glass bottle marked "EKC". $5.
- Kodelun in 1 oz brown Kodak-embossed bottle. Has lead-foil Kodak-embossed top. $8.
- Nepera solution in 4 oz brown Kodak-embossed bottle. Has lead-foil Kodak-embossed top. In original box. c1910. $10.
- Potassium Meta-Bisulphite in 1 oz brown Kodak-embossed bottle. Has wax-covered cork. $8.
- Potassium Ferricyanide, glass bottle. $4.
Eastman Developing Powders - 6 envelopes in a box. $5.
Eastman MQ Developer - in glass tube. Original price was $0.05. $1.00
Eastman Spectal Developing Powders - 4 glass tubes in a box. $7.
Eastman Universal Developing Powders - in 5 glass tubes. $9.
Eastman Intensifier - in glass tube. $2.
Kodak Chromium Intensifier - 6 packs. $5.
Eastman Kodak Pyro - 5 pair in a box. $14.
Kodak Reducer and Stain Remover - in glass tube marked "EKC". $3.

SENECA M.Q. Developer - glass tube. $1.

TABLOID - developing tablets in glass bottle. $4.
■ **DARKROOM DEVELOPING** ■
● **DRYING RACKS** ●
- unidentified 4x5" folding wooden drying rack for glass plates. $10.

■ **DARKROOM DEVELOPING** ■
● **OUTFITS** ●
BURKE & JAMES
Ingento Developing & Printing Outfit

No. 1 - c1909. 3 developing trays, 2 tubes of M.Q. developer, 1 printing frame, Rexo/Acid Hypo, 4 oz graduate, Rexo paper, ruby candle lamp. Original price: $1.00. $20.

EASTMAN KODAK CO.
A-B-C Photo Lab Outfit, Model A - Steel print box, 3 trays, thermometer, graduate, tong, developer, fixer, safelight, instructions. $15.

A-B-C Darkroom Outfit - 3¼x5½" trays, glass graduate, film clips, print frame, stirring rod, instructions. $20.

■ **DARKROOM DEVELOPING** ■
● **SCALES** ●
BAUSCH & LOMB - darkroom scales. $50.

EASTMAN KODAK CO. - nickel darkroom scale. $38.
Eastman Studio Scale - Black and brass, double pan, wooden base. $60.

■ **DARKROOM DEVELOPING** ■
● **TANKS** ●
- unidentified brass developing tank for glass plates. Has a dial. $15.
- unidentified nickel-plated daylight developing tank for 120 film. Has orange transparent apron and 2 winding handles. Uncommon. $30.

AMATO - 45x107mm processing tank, nickel. $12.

BURKE & JAMES
- glass plate developing tank. Nickel, rectangular box for 4x5" plates, with wire rack, rectangular funnel and hook. $15.
Rexo developing tank - stainless steel. $12.

DALLON Cut Film Tanks
- for 4.5x6cm film. $10.
- for 9x12cm film. Nickel-silver. $20.

EASTMAN KODAK CO.
- Kodak stainless steel tank, 4x5". $40.
- nickel tank, 5x7". $12.
Brownie Developing Box - brass. $65.

Developing Tank Model E - c1904. Metal with turning handles and 2 rounded compartments for rollfilm up to 5" wide. $15.

Kodak Film Tank - c1905-37. Consists of a wooden "winding box" in which the film is wound in combination with a light-proof apron onto a reel. The reel is then placed into a nickel-plated cylindrical tank for development. The complete outfit includes the wooden box with two cranks, apron, reel, and tank. Made in sizes for 2½", 3½", 5", and 7" films. $20-40.

Premo Film Pack Tank - $6.

FR CORP. Special Adjustable Roll Film Developing Tank Model 2 - c1950. Bakelite, for 35mm to 116 film. Original price: $3.95. $3.

GENNERT Auto Tank - c1905. $10.

GOERZ Tenax Developing Tank - Brass with chrome finish. $12.

MINOX Developing Tank - $12.

■ DARKROOM DEVELOPING ■
• THERMOMETERS •
ANSCO - stirring rod/thermometer. $5.

BURKE & JAMES
Ingento #3 Thermometer - metal. $5.
Ingento #4 Thermometer - 5½" long. $7.

EASTMAN KODAK CO.
- 5" thermometer, curved metal with hook at top. In a cardboard box. $5.
- 9" stirring rod/thermometer in wooden tube. $14.

■ DARKROOM DEVELOPING ■
• TIMERS •
BURKE & JAMES Perle Audible Timer - $6.

EASTMAN KODAK - red key wind timer. $9

FR CORP. Interval Timer - art-deco. $4.

■ DARKROOM DEVELOPING ■
• TRAYS •
- unidentified amber glass developing tray, 5½x8½". $10.
- enameled or hard rubber trays. Common. $3-6.

BURKE & JAMES
Ideal Jr. Hypo Fixing Box No. 2A - for 3¼x5½" plates. Original Price: $0.50. $15.
EASTMAN KODAK - Eastman tray siphon, c1934. $7.

NASSBAUM - glass film developing tray. Amber with red on the bottom. $20.

ZEISS IKON A.G. - 5x7" glass developing tray with "Zeiss Ikon" in the bottom. $25.

■ DARKROOM PRINTING ■
• ENLARGERS •
EASTMAN KODAK
Brownie #2 Enlarging Camera - Black cloth-reinforced cardboard, for 2¼x3¼" to 5x7" negatives. $35.
Kodak Enlarging Outfit Camera - Bausch & Lomb RR f4 lens. $80.
No. 1 Kodak Enlarging Camera - 6½x8½". Red bellows. $100.
Home Enlarger - wooden. $80.
Miniature Enlarger - Ektar f4.5/50mm lens. $75.

Kodak Easel, 11x14" - masking paper board, 2 blade. $35.

■ DARKROOM PRINTING ■
• MASKS, MOUNTS •
BURKE & JAMES Morrison Vignetter - $5.

EASTMAN KODAK CO. - mounts for panoramic photos, c1900. $2.50 per dozen.

GENNERT Montauk Post Card Masks - For 3¼x5½" negatives. Original price: $0.15 per dozen. $1.50

MANNING, A.B. (Chicago)
Manning's Masks - Package of 10 masks with 2 center pieces for 4x5" printing frames. Original price: $0.25. $1.50

■ DARKROOM PRINTING ■
• PRINTERS •
- unidentified wooden contact printer for 5x7" prints, with electric light. $35.
EASTMAN KODAK CO. - wooden printing frames. 2¼x3¼, 3¼x4¼, or 3½x5½", 4x5". $2-3.
Auto Mask - 4x5" wooden print frame $12.
Kodak Amateur Printer - dovetailed oak box, 10x7x8". $15
Eastman Printer No. 8, Model 2 - A contact printer. $40.

■ DARKROOM PRINTING ■
• RETOUCHING •
- unidentified retouching easel for 8x10" or smaller glass plates. With mirror and swivel reflector in base, sliding hand rest, adjustable hood. $25.

ANTHONY & SCOVILL - retouching easel. Wooden, adjustable ground glass easel with drawer for utensils. $30.

BURKE & JAMES Ingento Retouching Desk No. 2 - Oak with black interior, 16x12". $30-35.

EASTMAN KODAK - retouching desk, dark wood. $25-30.

FLEXICHROME COLORS - retouching desk, c1940's. $25-50.

■ DARKROOM PRINTING ■
• MISC •
BURKE & JAMES Print Burnisher - c1900. $18.

EASTMAN KODAK CO.
Eastman Print Straightener, Model A - c1924. $35.
Kodak Paper Trimmer - Wooden, 12x12". $18.

■ DARKROOM SAFELIGHTS ■
- unidentified red kerosene safelight. $13.

AETNA No. 4 Kerosene lantern - c1890. With 4x5" glass. $17.

AGFA Safelight - Brown metal box with rounded corners. Bulb base sticks out back. Amber glass on front. $2.

BURKE & JAMES
Ingento Darkroom Light - Large black metal kerosene lantern with large red glass front, small round red glass on one side, square white glass on the other (covered by a door). Movable reflector inside. $20.
Ingento #6 Kerosene Safelight - Red with hinged door. $15.
Ingento #9 Oil Safelight - $15.
Ingento Ruby Candle Lamp No. 17 - Rectangular red metal box with red glass that pulls out the top when you lift the flap to light the candle. Orig. price: $0.40. $9.

EASTMAN KODAK CO.
Brownie Darkroom Lamp A - paper. $5.
Brownie Darkroom Lamp B - Round plastic cover on a black bakelite base that screws into a scoket. 7w bulb. Plastic covers were red, yellow, or green. $3.
Brownie Darkroom Lamp Series 2 - A red Dixie cup-like device with cover on the wide end. 7½w lamp inside. Lamp base protrudes out narrow end. $5.
Brownie Safelight - c1930's. Green. $9.
Brownie Safelight Lamp Model D - $7.
Kodak Candle Lamp - Red canvas on folding wire frame. Metal bottom holds candle; metal top has vent. $15.
Kodak Kerosene Lamp - c1890. 4x5" glass. $20.
Kodak Kerosene Safelight - Red with top hinged door and red and amber glass. $16.

POCKET TIM Kerosene Darkroom Lamp - $18.

ROCHESTER OPTICAL CO. Universal No. 1 Darkroom Kerosene Lamp - $15.

■ EXPOSURE METERS ■
AGFA Lucimeter S - $6.

ANSCO Light Meter - Extinction. Circular with square at top. While aimed at the light source, a wheel is turned to match a red dot with the red dot above it. $10.

ARGUS
CM-2 Meter - For C33 or C44R. $15.
Model L-3 - Hand-held selenium. $6.
Model L44 - Shoe mount. $6.
Model LC3 - for Match-Matic. $16.
Model LS-3 - for C3 Standard. $18.

ASAHI KOGAKU - Clip-on meter for very early Pentax models. $30.

BERTRAM
- 1950's Amateur model. Shaped like a

pocket watch. Opening the lid automatically opens the two doors in front of the cell. Scales for still and cine. $10-15.
Chrolon - Junior version of Chronos. $10.
Chronos - $25.   **Chronstar** - $17.

BEWI
Automat N.G. - $6.
Bewi Jr. - $16.
Electro - 1940 selenium meter with DIN scale and extinction meter in center. $10.
Super L - CdS. $25.

BROCKWAY Studio model - $20.

BURROUGHS-WELLCOME *Began making exposure calculator tables in 1903, later incorporating them in the Diary and producing them until the 1970's.*
Photo Exposure Calculator, Handbook, and Diary - Leather folder containing exposure hints and tables, a calculator wheel, info on the company's chemicals, diary pages for recording pictures taken and a pencil.
1909: $25.   1935: $15.
1915: $20.   1939: $13.

CALUMET Flashmeter - $18.

CANON - Supplemented CdS meter, models for FP and FT. $11.

CHOU
Promatic 1 - Blue selenium meter. $3.
Promatic Auto-Dial - Hand-held selenium meter. ASA, DIN, and EVS scales. $4.
COMBI Combi-meter - Combination rangefinder and extinction meter, DIN scale. With camera shoe. $10.

CONTAX Helius #1325/3 - Brown bakelite selenium meter. Rare. $125.

CORONET Model B - $7.

DEJUR ANSCO CORP. *All the meters listed below are selenium meters.*
Model 5B - $5.
Model 6A - c1946-47. $11.
Model 40 - Large metal pre-WWII meter. Weston scale. $8.
Model LM-46A - Made under contract for the U.S. Air Force. USA scale. $17.
Model 50 - c1945. ASA scale. $10.
Model SD - $7.
Dual Professional - $7.

DIRECTOR PRODUCTS CORP.
Norwood Director - Selenium meters.
- Model B - The top professional meter before the popularity of the Luna Pro. $15.
- Model C - Precursor to Sekonic L28C2. $18.
- Model E - $15.   - M2 - $17.
Norwood Super Director - Selenium. $20.
Norwood Flashrite - Selenium. $12.

DREM Extinction meters
Cinephot - $14.
Dremophot - Telescoping type, black with nickel finish. $13.
Instoscope - $10.
Justophot - Telescoping type, all nickel finish. $13.

EASTMAN KODAK Kodalux L - for Retina cameras. $20.

FEDERAL Ideal - Direct reading selenium meter. $4.

FRANKE & HEIDECKE
Rollei Diaphot - 1932-34. Combination extinction meter and depth of field previewer, calibrated for 6x6cm models. All black. $38.
Rolleiflex Diaphot - 1934. Iris diaphragm and extinction meter that attaches to the viewing lens of the Old or New Standard Rolleiflexes. $38.
Rolleiphot - Later version of the Diaphot for 4x4cm or 6x6cm cameras. Chrome and black. Rare. $40.

GENERAL ELECTRIC Selenium meters
DW-40 - $5.
DW-47 - First type. $11.
DW-47 - Hexagonal-shaped. 1938 forerunner of DW series. $22.
DW-48 - $12.   **DW-58** - $10.
DW-68 - All-metal version of the DW-58. $10.
PC-1 Color Control Meter Kit - 1956 with filter kit and case. $25.
PR-1 - $7.   **PR-2** - $9.
PR-3 - $11.
PR-3 Golden Crown - $22.
PR-23 - $6.
PR-30, PR-30.35 - $6.
PRI-2 - $7.   **PRI-3** - $14.
Model 213 - foot candle meter. $7.
Junior Model - $12.
Mascot - $8.
Mascot II, Type PR-35 - $5.
Skan - Square, in black or gray. $8.

GOSSEN
C-Mate - $18.
Dual-Sixon - c1935. Selenium meter with roller-blind. $13.
Ombrux - c1936. Selenium. $13.
Pilot, Pilot 2 - Selenium. $14.
Retina Meter - Selenium. $13.
Scout - Selenium incident-reflected light meter. $10.
Scout 2 - Selenium. $15.
Sixon - Selenium. $10.
Sixtino - Selenium, ASA 6400. $8.
Sixtomat - CdS meter with white roll-top blind that covered the photo-cell for measuring incident light. $20.
Sixtus - In self-contained plastic case. $13.
Super Pilot - CdS. $22.
Trisix - with color temperature scale. $11.

HYDES Aktina Photo Meter - $28.

HONEYWELL - Coupled CdS meter for Pentax models H1-H3r. $12.

IHAGEE
Exakta Lightmeter IIa - Selenium. $50.
Examat Meter Prism - Exakta CdS. $80.

KALIMAR Selenium meters
Models A-1, B-1 - $7.
Model K-420 - Miniature selenium meter that fits in an accessory shoe. $12.

KINOX Model 3 - Selenium. $3.

KNIGHT meter - $5.

KONICA - Shoe-mount selenium meter for Konica III, IIIa. $8.

LEITZ (Ernst Leitz GmbH) Leica Meter #650 - $40.

LENTAR meter - $4.

LIOS Aktinometer - 1925-28. Telescoping cine meter. $18.

MAXIUM INSTRUMENT CO. (N.J.)
Pierce Exposure Meter - Rectangular plastic extinction meter with dials. $9.

METRAWATT Selenium Meters
Models M, MC - for Leicas. $18.
Metraphot - Clip-on selenium meter. $23.
Metraphot 2 - Leica-mount. $15.
Metraphot 3 - Shoe-mount. $20.

MIMOSA AMERICAN CORP. Extinction meters
Leudi - American model with no cine scale intro. 1934.: $5. European model with cine scale c1940: $5.
Leudi 3 - c1930's. Extinction meter. $5.

MINOLTA Selenium meter - $18.
SR meter - $40.

MINOX Meter - $13.
Minosix - $23.

MIRANDA
Models F, FV, G - Clip-on CdS meters. $13
Meter Prism - Cell in face. For Models C-F. $10.

PHAOSTRON CO. (Alahambra, CA)
Phaostron - pre-WWII. Square, bakelite, battery-operated comparison meter. Knob in center varies brightness of inside bulb to match that of outside light. Both are seen through a little window on top. $13.

PIERCE meter - $8.

RIKEN Ricoh meter - Camera foot mount. $5.

SEARS
Tower selenium meter - Shoe mount, ASA 10-200. $14.
Tower meter - Made in West Germany. $25.

SEDIC PR-60 - Jeweled movement, shock proof. $5.

SEIKO Sekonic meters
86 - $10.
246 - Foot candle meter. $25.
Auto Leader, Auto Leader II - $8.
Auto Leader III - $12.
Auto-Lumi, Auto-Lumi 86 - Selenium. $8.
Delux, Model I - $12.
LC-2 - $8.
L6 - $8.
L8 - Selenium. Miniature version of the Weston Master V. ASA 1600. $8.
L398 - $30.
L428 - Silicon cell incident or reflected meter. $30.
Leader #32, #38 - $11.
Micro - Clip-on CdS meter. $14.
Micro Leader - $7.

SOLIGOR Selector - CdS. $5.

SPECTRA Combi 500 - $25.
Universal - $23.

UNITTIC meter - $6.

UNIVERSAL Univex extinction meters - Chromed aluminum. For Mercury I: $10. For Mercury II: $7.
Cine - 1938. Telescoping style. $8.

VIVITAR Model 35 - Selenium. $16.

VOTAR Hyper VIII - $6.

WALZ Coronet B - $5.

WATKINS *Bee Meters were patented in 1902, and remained on sale until 1939.*
Bee Actinic Plate - 1905-1910. Shape of a pocket watch. Calibrated in HD and US stops. $20.
Bee Colour Plate - Similar, but with a different glass face. $23.
Bee Filmo Cine - Similar, but has scales for cine work. $23.
Bell & Howell Cine Bee (or Filmo) - c1920. For 35mm cine cameras. $20.

WELCH Model 3588 - Foot candle meter. $8.

WESTON
Model 617 - 1932. First meter in which selenium cell's output alone was used. Streamlined, pocket-type with two photocells, one on each side of the meter. $10.
Model 617, Type 2 - 1933. Rectangular with rounded ends, one photocell. $11.
Model 617 Photronic - c1936. Early version of the Cadet. $10.

Model 627, Type 2 Cine - Selenium. $16.
Model 650 - 1935 octagonal version was the first popular model: $10.
1936 rectangular selenium meter: $8.
Model 717 Master I - c1940. Selenium. First successful meter of the Master series; about twice as thick as later models. $11.
Model 735 Master II - 1945. Sliver and dark gray selenium meter. $12.
Model 736 Master II Cine - $11.
Model 737 Master III - $13.
Model 745 Master IV - Stainless steel case; needle lock. Easy to read. $25-35.
Model 748 Master V - Selenium. $14.
Master VI - $17.
Model 756 Illumination Meter - $18.
Model 819 Cine - 1937. Selenium. $12.
Model 852 - $10.
Model 853 Cadet - Selenium. Direct read F-stop, LV, or Pol. $8.
Director Reading CDR - $7.
Euro-Master - $20.
Pixie - $11.   **Ranger** - $15.
Ranger 9 - $60.
Ranger 9 Model 348 - $70.
Universal - $8.

WYNNE
Wynne's Infallible Exposure Meter - 1898-1905 Actinic meter in shape of silver pocket watch. US stops for plates. $20.
Wynne's Infallible Hunter - Pat. 1914. Extinction meter with hinged cover over face. $23.

ZEISS IKON A.G.
Contameter - for Continas, Contessas, and late Tenaxs (28.5mm lens diameter). $40.
Diaphot - c1930. Selenium. $30.
Ikophot - c1950. Selenium. $18.

■ **FILMPACK / ROLLFILM HOLDER** ■
CALUMET C2 rollfilm holder - for 4x5" cameras. $90.

EASTMAN KODAK CO.
- 5x7" film pack adapter, black and nickel, c1910. $20.
- early wood and brass rollholder. $50.
Bantam 828 adapter - $12.
Bantam 9x12cm adapter - Adapter made for German 9x12cm cameras, making them capable of taking 828 rollfilm. With reflex finder and ground glass. $35.
Recomar to Bantam 828 plate back adapter - Replaces ground glass back on Recomar or Avus 9x12cm cameras. $30.
No. 3A Folding Pocket Kodak Combination Back - With ground glass, 6 holders, dark cloth. Rare. $50.
No. 3A Folding Pocket Kodak Plate Holder - 3¼x5½". Rare. $5.
Premo Film Pack Adapters - Wooden. 3x4", 4x5": $2-4. 5x7": $3-5.

GRAFLEX
- roll back with 828 Bantam adapter. $20.

Graflex 22 rollfilm holder. $65.
No. 51 - For 122 film: $15. With 828 Bantam adapter: $20.
No. 53 - For 5" film. $15.

RADA Rollholders
- 2¼x3¼" for 6x9cm cameras. $55.
- 120 film for 9x12cm plate cameras. $28.

SUYDAM - 120 rollfilm adapter for 4x5" Graphic backs. $28.

ZEISS IKON A.G. Super Ikonta B/BX Bantam adapter - $15.

■ FINDERS ■

ALPEX
Multi-Focal Zoom Finder - Identical to the Tewe and Nikon finders, but with a scale range of 3.5, 5, 7.3, 8.5, 9, 10, 13.5, 15, 18, and 20cm focal lengths. Parallax base. $45.
135mm Brightline finder - Nikon SP style, parallax base. Black. $13.

ARGUS Multi-focal or Turret Viewfinder - 30/50/100mm. $20.
Viewfinder for 35 and 100mm - fits in shoe. Black plastic. $7.
Zoom finder - with flash connection. $35.

ASAHI Pentax Folding Sportsfinder - Fits onto accessory shoe. $20.

EASTMAN KODAK CO.
35/80mm Optical Multifinder - for Retina Models Ib, IIc, IIIc. $22.
Right Angle Optical Finders - Models for Kodak Ektra or Retina Reflex. $40.
35/80mm Sportsfinder - $14.
50/80mm Sportsfinder - for Retina II, IIa. $18.
Retina Folding Sports Finder - for 50mm Retina. $17.
Retina Sports Finder, Model C - for all rangefinder and Retina Reflexes. $22.

FRANKE & HEIDECKE
Rollei Eye-Level Prism Finder - Fits all Rolleicords, and Rolleiflex E2, 3F. $150.
Rollei Sports Finder - Hasselblad-style sportsfinder. Fits on the hood of all Rolleicords and Rolleiflex Automats below #1,100,XXX. $13.

GRAFLEX - flip-up optical viewfinder for early 4x5" Graphic. $18.

HEINEMAN, O.G.
Auxiliary Sportsfinder - Slips over hood of all Rolleiflexes below #1,099,XXX (1937-1946), and non-Rollei cameras. Has parallax correction. $15.

IHAGEE KAMERAWERKE
Exa Waist-level finder - Early, original model with non-removeable ground glass, magnifier, long sword-like extension. $10.

Exakta Eye-level finder
- Chrome, early style for Exakta. $20.
- With RF grid. $25.
- Later style, for Exakta Varex. $15.
Magnear finder - $35.
Right Angle Magnifying Viewer - with diopter adjustment. $40.
Waist-level finders
- Original style with non-removeable ground glass, flip-out magnifier, and sportsfinder cover. $11.
- Early style with safety foot. $15.
- Later styles. Chrome: $10. With leather top and rangefinder glass. $18.

ILOCA Folding Sportsfinder - Chrome, for Pentax. Offset dual shoe, a level in the folding joint. $18.

K.W. (KAMERA WERKSTATTEN A.G.)
Praktina waist-level finder - $16.
Praktisix waist-level finder - $20.

MAMIYA TLR waist-level finder - $18.

MINOLTA 35mm Optical finder - Rare. $25.

MIRANDA
Eye-level Prism Finder
- black or chrome, for Models C-G. $9.
- chrome, for Models F, G. $9.
- chrome, for Models T, S, A-D. $9.
Sensorex Eye-level Finder - Black and chrome. With accessory shoe: $10. No accessory shoe: $8.
Sensorex II Eye-level Finder - Black and chrome, with hot shoe. $12.
Waist-level Finder
- for Automex and Sensorex. $7.
- for Models S, A-G. $6.
- for Models T, S, A-D, black. $8.
- for Models T, S, A-D, chrome. $7.
- for Sensorex. $9.
VF-3 Finder - Early style critical magnifier finder. $10.

NIHON SHOKAI Walz Universal Finder - $22.

SANDMAR Zoom-Vue Finder, 35-135mm - For Argus. $22.

TANAKA OPTICAL CO. Tanack 35mm finder - $10.

TELEX - distance finder. $18.

TEWE
Multi-focal Zooming Finder - original, with 35, 38, 45, 50, 85, 90, 135 range. $50.
35-200mm Universal Finder - parallax corrected. $50.

TOKYO KOGAKU
- Right angle finder for Topcon. $35.
- Waist-level finder for Topcon Super D, DM, etc. $20.

VOIGTLANDER
Kontur 35mm Viewfinder - $15.
Right angle finder, #344/45 - $40.
Turnit 3 Finder 35/50/100 - Black, for Prominent. $25.

■ FLASHES ■

- Unidentified German Pocket Magnesium Flasholder, c1920's. Hinged case, (similar in style to a cigarette case), holds a roll of magnesium ribbon threaded through a flat tube. The tube flips up vertically when the case is opened. Silver finish. $30.

AGFA KAMERAWERKE
Agfalux-C - for cubes. $2.
Agfalux-K - for AG-1. $2.
Tully-K - for AG-1. $2.

ALPEX Pocket Flash, Type BC - fan, slips on accessory shoe. $3.

ARGUS Flashes
- Argus C: $8. Argus C3. $4.
- Argus C4 or C44. $5.
- Argus F, for hot shoe. $6.
- Argus 75. $4.
#760 folding flash unit - for hot shoe. $6.
Flash Bracket, #799 - for C4 or C44. $6.

BOLSEY - Flashes for Bolsey or Jubilee. $6.

BURKE & JAMES
Ingento Flash Pan No. 1 - 12" metal trough on a metal rod, with a wooden handle. Spring-activated pin, released by thumb, strikes paper cap in trough and ignites powder. $22.

CANON Flash - for Canon VT. $13.
- Flash unit, a coupler for early RF models. $15.

EASTMAN KODAK
Brownie Flasholder - for 620 flash. $2.
Brownie Flasholder, Type 2 - $2.
Ektamite flasholder - $5.
Flashgun - for Ektra. $15.
Flasholder Model B - $3.
Flash sheet holder - $30.
Generator Flasholder Type 1, No. 771 - Fires M2 or No. 5 bulb without batteries for cameras with screw-in flasholder fittings. $10.
Generator Flasholder Type 2, No. 772 - Has shoe bracket and cord for most flash synched cameras. $10.
Hawkeye Flashgun - $2.
Kodablitz - for Retina. $2.
Kodak Flash Cartridges - in tin box. $15.
Kodak Handy Reflector, Model C - Cardboard reflectors that unfold and fit (with metal rings) around bulbs in floor lamps. Come 2 in a box. $20.
Kodak Magnesium Ribbon Holder - Metal, teardrop-shaped holder. Roll of magnesium ribbon dispenses out top. $30.

Retina Flasholder - Bracket with midget flash holder. $15.
Rotary Flasholder, Type 2 - Holds 6 bulbs that are manually moved into position. $3.
Spreader Cartridge Flash Pistol - c1902. $35.
Standard Flasholder - $2.

EDISON Mazda foil flash lamp - $3.

FRANKE & HEIDECKE Rollei Flash - Fold-up clamp, cord. I has single arm bayonet. II has dual arm bayonet. $7.

GRAPHLEX Graflite flash - with reflector. $3.

KALART CO.
Kalart "Safety First" Deluxe Speed Flash - Combination battery case and reflector. Kalabrack extension bracket, test lamp, and passive synchronizer unit for cameras with self-setting auto shutters. $7.
Exakta Flash Unit - Pre-WWII. In soft case. Rare. $12.

MINOX
AG-1 flasholder - For Minox B: $10. For Minox C/III: $15.
C4 Cube Flash - $18.   **FL4 Flash** - $4.
FC Flash - $15.   **TC Flash** - $30.

NICHOLS, CHARLES H.
Portrait Flash Lamp - Flash powder ignites by blowing the flame from the kerosene lamp through a hole in the metal back plate. It could be raised to 10'. $160.

NIPPON KOGAKU
BC6 Flash - for Nikon RF's. $7.
M-B-C-5 Flash - $4.   **Model V** - $11.

REVERE - flash for Stereo 33. $15.

RIKEN OPTICAL
Ricoh Fan Flash - $1-5.
Ricohlite V Flash - Holds 5 bulbs. $3-6.

SMITH (J.H.) & SONS
Actino Cartridge Holder - 5x8" metal reflector on cardboard handle. The round wooden cartridge sits on a small shelf, with a fuse running through a hole in the back. Original price: $0.50. $20.
Actino #12 Flash Cartridges - box of 6. $14.

TOKYO KOGAKU
Accessory shoe R - Slightly angled flash shoe that slides under the rewind of the Topcon B. $9.

UNIVERSAL CAMERA CORP.
Mercury Photoflash Unit - with separate calculator wheel, IB, box: $12. Flash only: $6
Minute 16 Flash Unit - $7.
Univex Photoflash Reflector Unit - $8.

ACCESSORIES: FLASHES - LENSES without Shutters

VOIGTLANDER
Flash-Case - Front cover of leather case flops down to reveal flash reflector. For Prominent and Vitessa. Takes #5 bulbs. Original price: $30. $10.

VICTOR Flash Powder, Normal Grade - Glass bottle inside cardboard can. $12.

WESTPHALEN Little Sunny - Hand-held carbon arc sun gun. $17.

WITTNAUER BC Flash - $8.

ZEISS IKON A.G. Ikoblitz Flash - $7.

■ **LENSES (without Shutters)** ■
- 5" Carte-de-Visite 4-lens set. Brass tubes mounted on 5x6¼" brass plate. c1860's. $275.

ANTHONY (E & HT) & CO.
Single Achromatic 254mm - Brass barrel, rotating diaphragm with 5 stops. $80.
Anthony Achromatic 260mm - Brass barrel, Daguerrotype style, rotating diaphragm with 4 stops. $90.

BAUSCH & LOMB
f18 Zeiss Anastigmat, Series V - $25.
120mm/f20 Zeiss Anastigmat - Brass. $36.
150mm/f12.5 Zeiss Anastigmat - Brass barrel, rotating diaphragm with 6 stops. $79.
150mm Bausch & Lomb Optical Co. - Brass barrel, geared focusing. $40.
165mm/f8 Planatograph - Brass. $15.
254mm Bausch & Lomb Optical Co. - Brass barrel, geared focusing. $35.
265mm/f20 Zeiss Protar, Series V - 11x14", brass barrel. $40.
f18 Protar, Series V - 8x10", brass barrel, internal diaphragm. $60.
355mm Bausch & Lomb Optical Co. - Mfr. for Lubin Mfg. Co. Brass barrel, geared focusing. $20.
375mm/f4.5 Zeiss Protrait Unar No. 9 - Brass barrel, adjustable soft focusing. $100.
5x7"/f4.5 Tessar - Brass barrel, for Graflex. $50.
8x10" Tessar Ic - coated. $95.
4⅝"/f6.3 Tessar - Black barrel mount, round flange. $20.

BECK, R.J. Brass barrel lenses
4¼x3¼" Rapid Rectilinear - Waterhouse stops. Leather cap. $75.
254mm/f8 Beck Symmetrical - $50.

BURKE & JAMES 230mm No. 1 Ajax -
Brass barrel, geared focusing. $20.

BURKHOLDER, J.H. (Mansfield, Ohio)
8x10 Wide Angle - Waterhouse stops. Mounted on 6x6" board. $35.

DAGOR Brass barrel lenses
10¾"/f6.8 - $220.   **12"/f6.8** - $260.

DALLMEYER, J.H.
455mm 12x10" Rapid Rectilinear - Brass barrel, f stops stamped f8-64. $45.
25x21 Rapid Rectilinear - Pat. June 30, 1868. Brass barrel, waterhouse stops. 8" long, 5½" dia. $110.
5" Triple Achromatic - Brass barrel, flange and slot for waterhouse stops. $50.
Daguerreotype lens - 3¼" long, 2¼" dia. Brass barrel, brass sunshade. Sleeve focus, waterhouse stops. $175.

DARLOT OPTICIEN Brass barrel lenses
90mm No. 2 - built-in 3 lever stops. $95.
200mm - built-in 3 lever stops. $175.
255mm - built-in 3 lever stops. $135.
430mm - geared focus. $70.
4 Gem Lenses - Brass tubes, mounted on brass board. No stops. Possibly for CDV wet plate. $550.
Wide Angle - waterhouse stops. With flange. $50.
3" Wide Angle Landscape - c1870's. 3 lever-activated internal stops. Flared rear element. With flange. $70.

DEKER & Co. (Chicago) Convertible
8x10 Wide Angle Rectilinear - Brass barrel, waterhouse stops. $50.

EASTMAN KODAK
7"/f2.5 Aero Ektar - $80.
7½"/f4.5 Anastigmat - in barrel. $30.
8½"/f4.5 Anastigmat - in barrel. $65.
10"/f4.5 Anastigmat - in barrel. Correct size for 5x7" Graflex. With front cap. $105.
12" Portrait - in barrel. $85.
21"/f10 Anastigmat - in barrel. $150.
280mm/f8 Hawkeye Portrait Rapid Rectlinear 8x10 - Brass barrel. $50.
f4 Hawkeye Portrait Series A, No. 3 - Brass barrel, difusing focus. $150.

ENTERPRISE OPTICAL MFG. CO.
125mm Enterprise - Brass barrel, geared focusing. $20.

FRENCH (Benjamin French & Co., Boston) 6"/f5** - Brass barrel, 2¼" long. Rack and pinion focusing, waterhouse stops. $126.

GOERZ, C.P.
160mm/f4 Rapid Rectilinear - Brass barrel. $40.
500mm/f4.5 Dogmar - coated. On large lensboard. $200.

GRAF-BISHOP
Doublet - soft focus, for view camera. With flange. $60.
455mm/f8 Anastigmat - Brass barrel. $70.

GUNDLACH
5x7" Wide Angle - Brass barrel, rotating diaphragm with 6 stops. $60.
8x10" Wide Angle - Brass barrel, waterhouse stops. $80.

6½x8½" Wide Angle - Early wet-plate lens in brass barrel. Waterhouse stops. $50.

HARRISON, C.C. *These are American Daguerreian lenses, in brass barrels.*
- 5½" long, 2½" dia., rack and pinion focus, waterhouse stops, no flange. $150.
- 6" long, 2¾" dia., rack & pinion focus, waterhouse stops. $275.
- 7" focal length. Radial drive, slotted for stops. With shade, no flange. $240.
- 12" focal length. Radial drive. With flange, no focusing knob or shaft. $300.

HOLMES, BOOTH & HAYDEN (N.Y.)
170mm - Brass barrel, geared focus. $60.
Daguerreian lenses - brass barrels:
- 6" focal length, radial drive. With shade. $210.
- 7" focal length, rack and pinion focus. With mounting ring, original board. $275.
- 12" focal length, radial drive, slot for waterhouse stops. $300.
- 12" focal length, radial drive. c1850's. Slightly flared front rim and flange. 7½" long, 4" dia. $300.
- 5¾" long, 2¾" dia. Rack and pinion focus, waterhouse stops. Leather cap. $275.

KOEHLER 210mm/f16 Commercial 8x10 Wide Angle - Brass barrel, rotating diaphragm with 5 stops. $60.

LAVERNE (A.) & CO. Panorthoscopic Obis 200mm/f8 - Brass barrel. $22.

LONDON STEREOSCOPIC
125mm/f11 Coy's Wide Angle - Brass barrel, rotating diaphragm with 5 stops. $65.

MANHATTAN OPTICAL CO.
240mm/f4 Extra Rapid Rectilinear Lens No. 3 - Brass barrel. $25.

MARION & CO. (London) Soho 15x12 lens - $60.

MEYER 14½/f4 Double Plasmat - in barrel. $120.

NEHRING (N.Y.) 8x10 Convertible Rectilinear - Brass barrel, single waterhouse stop. $45.

OKOLI GESELLSCHAFT 240mm/f4.5 Okolinar Series T - Brass barrel. $75.

PECK Co. 10x12 to 12x14/f8 Rapid Rectilinear Portrait, Series 770. - $35.

RODENSTOCK 240mm/f6.8 Doppel Anastigmat Eurynar - Brass barrel. $70.

ROSS (London)
120mm Actinic Doublet - Brass barrel, rotating diaphragm with 5 stops. $65.
255mm/f5 Unar - Brass barrel, internal diaphram. $60.

5"/f4 Xpress 5x7 Wide Angle - Brass barrel - $60.
7"/f7.7 Double Anastigmat - Brass barrel, internal diaphragm. With flange. $40.
8½"/f4.5 Xpress - in barrel. $70.
10"/f6.3 Homocentric - Brass barrel. With flange. $60.
14"/f8.5 Rapid Symmetrical 9x7 - Brass barrel, waterhouse stops. 3¼" long, 1⅞" dia. With leather cap. $55.
18"/f5.6 Homocentric - in barrel. $100.

SCHNEIDER-KREUZNACH
90mm/f6.8 Angulon - Brass barrel, on 2⅝" metal board. $35.
180mm/f5.5 Tele-Xenar - For Bertram Press camera. Very Rare. $130.
210mm/f4.5 Xenar - $50.
240mm/f4.5 Xenar - coated. $120.

SCIENTIFIC LENS CO.
200mm/f8, 8x10 Wide Angle - Brass barrel, rotating diaphragm with 5 stops. $50.
7"/f16, 8x10 Wide Angle - $40.
12"/f8 No. 2 Portrait - Brass barrel. $85.

SCOVILL & ADAMS Morrison Wide Angle - Brass barrel. For 8x10" view. $75.

SENECA CAMERA CO. 5x7 Rapid Convertible - $50.

SIMPKINSON & MILLER 355mm/f8, 8x10 Premier Rapid Rectilinear - Brass barrel. $20.

SOMERVILLE (J.C.) (St. Louis) 8x10"/ f8 No. 3A - Brass barrel. $55.

STERLING 200mm/f16 8x10 Improved Wide Angle - Brass barrel. $45.

ST. LOUIS PHOTO SUPPLY CO.
335mm Rapid Rectilinear 8x10 Portrait - Brass barrel. $70.

STEINHEIL
150mm/f12 Orthostigmat - $45.
360mm/f4 Cassar Speed Portrait - $100.

TAYLOR HOBSON COOKE Brass barrel lenses
325mm/f4.5 Anastigmat Series II - $68.
325mm/f5.6 Anastigmat Series IV - $68
330/f8 Anastigmat, Series V - $115.
6½"/f6.5 Wide Angle - on lensboard. $49.

TURNER-REICH Lens Set, Series II - 14", 18", 24", 28" lenses that are used in different combinations in one barrel to give 9 different focal lengths. $150-300.

VEGA 3" Stereo Lenses - Adjustable internal diaphrams. With mounting flanges. $250-350.

VOIGTLANDER & SOHN
No. 5 - 5½" long, 4¼" dia. Waterhouse stops. $140.

18" Euryscope No. 5 - Brass barrel, slot for waterhosue stops. $85.
Portrait No. 6 - Brass barrel, 9" long, 5½" dia. 5 waterhouse stops. $150.
14" lens - Brass barrel, 6 aperture discs in holder. $95.
280mm Landschafts No. 4 - in barrel. Rotating diaphragm with 4 stops. $49.
14" Wet-plate lens - Brass barrel, rack and pinion focus, slot for waterhouse stops. With flange and shade. $120.
18" Wet-plate lens - Slot for waterhouse stops. $220.

WILLARD & CO. 430mm lens - Brass barrel, geared focus. $120.

WOLLENSAK OPTICAL
162mm/f4.5 Raptar - in barrel. $45.
5x7" Rapid Convertible - $35.
6½"/f4.5 Velostigmat - in barrel. $35.
6½"/f12.5, 8x10 Wide Angle - in barrel. $35.
7½" Velostigmat - in barrel. $30.
8¼"/f4.5 Velostigmat, Series II - $75.
f3.8 Vitax Portrait Lens No. 3 - 11" long, 6" dia. $175.
18"/f4 Diffused Focus Verito - in barrel, on 9x9 board. With Packard shutter. $125.

WRAY (London) 9½" focal length, 8x10 - 3" long. $75.

ZEISS IKON A.G.
180mm/f4.5 Jena Tessar - $40.
210mm/f4.5 Tessar - in barrel, no diaphragm. $30.
5½" Protar, Series V - Brass barrel. $65.

■ **LENSES in Shutters** ■
BAUSCH & LOMB
135mm/f8 Symmetrical - Brass, in double piston shutter. $12.
5x7"/f4.5 Tessar Ic - in Ilex Acme. $125.

CONLEY 250mm/f6.8 Anastigmat - in Conley Auto Shutter. $30.

EASTMAN
305mm/f4.8 12" Portrait - in #5 Ilex MX Synchro shutter, coated: $285. On 6x6 board, in Universal Synchro Shutter: $255.

GOERZ, C.P. 75mm Hypergon Doppel-Anastigmat Series X, No. 000a - without star. Scarce. $325.

GUNDLACH
Korona Triple Convertible Anastigmat - 8½"- 15"- 18". Rapax shutter. $175.
130mm/f11 - Brass. Single piston. $18.
5x7" Symmetrical - single piston shutter. $15.

ILEX
77mm/f4.5 Paragon - in 00 Acme 1/300 shutter, on 2⅝" square metal board. $25.

5½"/f4.5 Paragon - coated, in Acme #3 shutter. $60.

MEYER
120mm/f6.3, Wide Angle Aristostigmat
5x7 - Dial Compur shutter. $115.
3⅛"/f6.3, Wide Angle Aristostigmat
4x5 - Compur shutter. $115.

PROSCH MFG. CO.
Stereo Triplex Wide Angle lenses - pre-1900 shutter. $575.
125mm Triplex - Brass, 5 rotating stops in external shutter mechanism. $105.
290mm Triplex - Similar, $125.

SEROCO 5x7 Rapid Rectilinear - in Unicum shutter. $40.

ROCHESTER OPTICAL CO.
150mm/f6.8 Victor - Brass, Bausch & Lomb shutter. $16.
155mm/f8, 4x5 Rapid Rectilinear - Brass, double piston Unicum shutter. $12.

SCHNEIDER-KREUZNACH
80mm/f2.8 Xenotar - MX Compur. $100.
90mm/f6.8 Angulon - uncoated, in unsynched shutter. $75.
120mm/f6.8 Angulon - Compur S, 1/200 shutter. $90.
135mm/f4.7 Xenar - coated, in Compur MX shutter. $115.
150mm/f2.8 Xenotar - coated, in Compur shutter. Leather cap. $300.
150mm/f5.6 Symmar-S - Copal shutter, front cap. $190.

VOIGTLANDER 330mm/f7.7, 13" Collinear - Compound-type shutter. $300.

WOLLENSAK
6¼"/f12.5 Wide Angle Series IIIa - in Betax #3 shutter, for 8x10 camera. $175.
6½"/f6.3 Velostigmat, Series IV - in Betax, X sync. $60.
162mm/f4.5 Raptar - coated, in Alphax shutter. $95.
210mm/f4.5 Rapter - in Betax, X sync. $150.
12"/f4.5 Velostigmat - in Studio shutter: $65. Coated, in Betax, X sync. $300.

ZEISS IKON A.G. 300mm/f4.5 Tessar - in Alphax shutter. $200.

■ **MICROSCOPE ADAPTERS** ■
EASTMAN KODAK CO.
Instamatic Reflex Adapter - $30.
Retina Reflex Adapter - $36.
Adapter Kit Model B - for Retina Ib, IIc, IIIc. $30.
Microscope Attachment and Camera Holder Model D - for Retina cameras. $36.

IHAGEE - Adapter Type I. $18.

YASHICA - Adapter for Pentax. $8.

■ PLATES/ ROLLFILM ■
BERNING Robot Film Cassettes - $13.

EASTMAN KODAK CO.
Dry Plates - Box of 3¼x4¼": $5. 4x5": $6.
Glass Plate Negatives - Box, 6½x8½". $8.
Daylight Film Loader - bakelite, 35mm. $7.
Verichrome Film Pack - dated 1941,
unopened 12 pack. $7.
Verichrome Pan VP130 - unopened. $4

ILFORD Compass Film plates -
unopened package, 35x43mm. $7.

**PHOTAVIT-WERK Photavit Film
Cassette** - $7.

SAKURA SEIKI CO. Petal Film Cartridge
- Round or octagonal version. $14-20.

■ RANGEFINDERS ■
BALDA Distanzer - $17.
DEJUR Rangefinder - $10.

EASTMAN KODAK
Pocket Rangefinder - Clip-on. $20.
Service Rangefinder - Chrome. $15.
Split-image Rangefinder - Mounts
vertically. $20.

FRANKE & HEIDECKE Rolleimeter f2.8
- Prismatic focusing rangefinder for the
f2.8 non-removable hood cameras. $40.

HEYDE Pocket Rangefinder. $7.
Photo-Telemeter - Pocket split-image
rangefinder. $17.

HUGO MEYER Pocket Rangefinder- $11.
IDEAL Rangefinder Federal - $8.
KI SET Rangefinder - Chrome. $8,
KOMBI Combi-Meter - Combination
rangefinder/extinction meter. c1946. $10.

POLLUX Rangefinder - $4.
SAYMOUNT Rangefinder - $10.
TELEX Rangefinder - $4.
UNITY Rangefinder - Clip-on style. $8.
VOTAR Rangefinder - clip-on with feet. $7.
WATAMETER II - $6.

ZEISS IKON A.G.
Rangefinder - Hand-held rangefinder for
early folding camras. $35.

■ SELF-TIMERS ■
AGFA Self-Timer - $3

EASTMAN KODAK CO.
- piston-type. $6.
- 1933 self-timer in art-deco box. $9.

HAKA
Autoknips I - $5. **Autoknips II** - $6.

HANSA Self-timer - $6.
KOPI - Self-timer for Argus. $6.
WALZ Self-Timer Assembly - $6.

■ SHUTTERS ■
GRAFLEX Focal Plane - for 8x10".$120.

ILEX
00 Acme - 1/300 shutter, chrome. $15.
#3 Ilex - X-sync. Marked for 5"/f4.5 Ilex
Paragon lens. $50.

LANCASTER - Adjustable rubber-band
activated shutter. $15.

PACKARD - sync. shutter. $15.

■ STEREO VIEWERS ■
- 1930's, hand-held. Black metal. $25.
- c1890's tabletop viewer. Light wood. 17"
high. Viewing hoods on both sides. $325.
- Portable Combination Graphoscope -
For viewing stereo cards with a pair of
lenses, or cabinet cards with a single lens.
5½x9" wood base. $80.

BAIRD, ANDREW H.
The Lothian Stereoscope - c1875. Brass
and wood. Separates into 4 pieces when
handle is removed, for easy storage in a
box. Adjustable viewing lenses. $250.

**BATES, Joseph (Boston) Holmes Bates
Stereoscope** - Pedestal-mounted,
Holmes-style viewer. All wood. $125.

BECKER, ALEXANDER (N.Y.)
Tabletop Stereo Viewer - c1859.
Rosewood. Holds 36 paper or glass
views. $400.

BREWSTER-Style Stereoscope - c1890.
Wooden viewer on a stand, 15" high. Black
laquered base, brass center post. $260.

KEYSTONE - c1900. Hand-held stereo
viewer. Wood with aluminum hood. $25.

ROWSELL Parlor Graphoscope - c1875.
Folding table model, 23x12" walnut base.
$200.

■ TRIPODS ■
EASTMAN KODAK CO.
Bulls-Eye, Models B and C - Double
extension wooden tripod. $10.
Bullet, Model H - $10.
Flexo, Model C - $10.
Kodapod - $5.

FOLMER GRAFLEX
Crown Tripod #1 - 1920's. Wooden
tripod extends to 6'. $18.
Crown Tripod #2 - $20.
Crown Tripod #4 - $30.
Tripod for #10 Cirkut Camera -
including turntable head. $150.

FRANKE & HEIDECKE Rolleifix Q.D.
Tripod Adapter - $15.

SUNART PHOTO CO. - double extension
wooden tripod. $12.

INDEX

Agfa Opal Luxus: 22
Agfa Optima: 22
Agfa Optima Parat: 22
Agfa Optima Rapid 125C: 22
Agfa Optima Reflex: 22
Agfa PD-16: 22
Agfa Paramat: 22
Agfa Parat: 22
Agfa Pioneer: 23
Agfa Plate cameras: 23,24
Agfa Plenax: 23
Agfa Preis-Box: 23
Agfa Record I,II: 23
Agfa Rollfilm models: 23
Agfa Schul-Praemie Box: 23
Agfa Selecta: 23
Agfa Selecta-M: 23
Agfa Selectaflex: 23
Agfa Shurflash: 23
Agfa Shurshot: 23
Agfa Silette: 23
Agfa Silette L,LK: 23
Agfa Silette Rapid,I,F,L: 23
Agfa Silette SL,SLE: 23
Agfa Solinette: 24
Agfa Speedex: 24
Agfa Speedex 0: 24
Agfa Speedex B2: 24
Agfa Speedex Jr.: 24
Agfa Standard: 24
Agfa Super Silette,L,LK: 23
Agfa Super Solinette: 24
Agfa Superior: 24
Agfa Synchro-Box: 24
Agfa Trolita: 25
Agfa Trolix: 25
Agfa Ventura: 25
Agfa Ventura 66, 69: 25
Agfa Ventura Deluxe: 25
Agfa View cameras: 25
Agfa Viking: 25
Agiflash 35 (Agilux): 25
Agfaflex: 19
Agiflex (Agilux): 25
Agifold (Agilux): 25
Agilux Auto Flash Super 44: 25
AGILUX LTD.: 25
Ahi: 25
Aidex (Adams & Co.): 16
Aiglon (subminiature): 25
Aiglon (TLR) (Atoms): 48
Aiglon Reflex (Atoms): 48
Air Force Bolsey: 68
AIR FRESHENER (Non-Camera): 513
Air King Camera Radio: 26
AIR KING PRODUCTS: 26
AIRES CAMERA IND. CO. LTD.: 26
Aires Penta 35: 26
Aires 35-III: 26
Aires 35-IIIC: 26
Aires 35-IIIL: 26
Aires 35LM: 26
Aires 35-V: 26
Aires Viscount: 26
Airesflex: 26
AIVAS: 26
Aivas Beginners Camera: 26

Ajax (Coronet): 103
Akarelle (Apparate & Kamerabau): 41
Akarette (Apparate & Kamerabau): 41
Akarex (Apparate & Kamerabau): 42
Akarex III (Apparate & Kamerabau): 42
Akeley: 484
AKELEY CAMERA INC. (Movie): 484
AKUTAGAWA CONFECTIONERY CO.
  LTD. (Non-Camera): 515
AKW (Non-Camera): 515
Al-Vista Cameras Wanted: ADV
Al-Vista Model 3B (Multiscope): 330
Al-Vista Model 4B (Multiscope): 330
Al-Vista Model 4G (Multiscope): 330
Al-Vista Model 5B (Multiscope): 330
Al-Vista Model 5C (Multiscope): 330
Al-Vista Model 5D (Multiscope): 330
Al-Vista Model 5F (Multiscope): 330
Al-Vista Model 7D (Multiscope): 330
Al-Vista Model 7E (Multiscope): 330
Al-Vista Model 7F (Multiscope): 330
Al-Vista Panoramic (Multiscope): 330-331
Albert (Shincho): 395
ALBUMS (Non-Camera): 513
Aldon Photographer (Non-Camera): 533
Alethoscope (Joux): 254
Alfa 2 (Varimex): 430
Alfax Model I: 27
ALIBERT: 27
Alibert Kauffer Photo-Sac a Main: 27
Alka Box (Vredeborch): 440
All Distance Ensign (Houghton): 234
ALLIED: 27
Allied Carlton Reflex: 27
Alpa (I) (Pignons): 355
Alpa 4 (Pignons): 356
Alpa 4b (Pignons): 356
Alpa 5 (Pignons): 356
Alpa 5b (Pignons): 356
Alpa 6 (Pignons): 356
Alpa 6b (Pignons): 356
Alpa 6c (Pignons): 356
Alpa 7 (Pignons): 356
Alpa 7b (Pignons): 356
Alpa 7s (Pignons): 356
Alpa 8 (Pignons): 356
Alpa 8b (Pignons): 356
Alpa 9d (Pignons): 356
Alpa 9f (Pignons): 356
Alpa 10d (Pignons): 356
Alpa 10f (Pignons): 356
Alpa 10s (Pignons): 356
Alpa 11e (Pignons): 356
Alpa 11el (Pignons): 357
Alpa 11fs (Pignons): 357
Alpa 11si (Pignons): 357
Alpa 11z (Pignons): 357
Alpa Prisma Reflex (III) (Pignons): 356
Alpa Reflex (II) (Pignons): 356
Alpha (Watson): 442
Alpin (Voigtlander): 432
Alpin Stereo-Panoram (Voigtlander): 432
ALSAPHOT: 27
Alsaphot Dauphin: 27
Alsaphot Maine I,IIc,IIIa: 27
Alta Automatic (Reichenbach): 367
Alta D (Reichenbach): 367

B Daylight Kodak (EKC): 133
B Ordinary Kodak (EKC): 148
B & R MANUFACTURING CO.: 49
B & R Mfg. Photoette #115: 49
B & W MANUFACTURING CO.: 49
B & W Mfg. Press King: 49
Babette: 49
Baby (Yen-Kame): 456
Baby Al-Vista (Multiscope): 330
Baby BB Semi First (Kuribayashi): 271
Baby Bessa (Voigtlander): 434
Baby Box Tengor (Zeiss): 458
Baby Brownie (EKC): 124
Baby Brownie (EKC- Kodak Ltd.): 124
Baby Brownie New York World's Fair
  Model (EKC): 124
Baby Brownie Special (EKC): 124
Baby Camera: 49
Baby Hawk-Eye (EKC): 141
Baby Deardorff: 112
Baby Deckrullo (Zeiss): 458
Baby Finazzi: 49
Baby Flex: 49
Baby Hawk-Eye (Blair): 63
Baby Ikonta (Zeiss): 458
Baby Lyra (Fuji): 199
Baby Makina (Plaubel): 358
Baby-Max (Tougodo): 418
Baby Minolta (Minolta): 314
Baby Pearl (Konishiroku): 263
Baby Powell (Rex): 368
Baby Reflex (Yen-Kame): 456
Baby Ruby (Ruberg): 381
Baby Semi First (Kuribayashi): 271
Baby Sibyl (Newman & Guardia): 336
Baby Special (Yen-Kame): 456
Baby Sports (Yen-Kame): 456
Baby Standard (Vicam Photo): 509
Baby Wizard (Manhattan): 304
Babysem (S.E.M.): 390
BACO ACCESSORIES: 49
Baco Press Club: 49
BAGS (Non-Camera): 513
BAIRD: 49-50
Baird Single lens stereo camera: 49
Baird Tropical Field Camera: 50
Bakelite (Gallus): 200
Baky (Wirgin): 449
Balda Baldalette: 50
Balda Baldalux: 50
Balda Baldamatic: 50
Balda Baldax: 50
Balda Baldaxette: 45
Balda Baldessa,Ib: 50
Balda Baldi: 50
Balda Baldina: 50
Balda Baldinette: 50
Balda Baldini: 50
Balda Baldix: 50
Balda Baldixette: 51
Balda Doppel-Box: 51
Balda Erkania: 51
Balda Fixfocus: 51
Balda Gloria: 51
Balda Hansa 35: 51
Balda Jubilette: 51
Balda Juwella: 51

Balda Mickey Rollbox: 51
Balda Piccochic: 51
Bakina Rakina (Fototechnica): 194
Balda Pierrette: 52
Balda Poka: 52
Balda Pontina: 52
Balda Rigona: 52
Balda Rollbox 120: 52
Balda Springbox: 52
Balda Super Baldax: 52
Balda Super Baldina: 52
Balda Super Baldinette: 52
Balda Super Pontura: 52
BALDA-WERK: 50-52
BALDALETTE (Balda): 50
Baldalux (Balda): 50
Baldamatic (Balda): 50
Baldax (Balda): 50
Baldaxette (Balda): 50
Baldessa,Ib (Balda): 50
Baldi (Balda): 50
Baldina (Balda): 50
Baldinette (Balda): 50
Baldini (Balda): 50
Baldix (Balda): 50
Baldixette (Balda): 51
Baldur Box (Zeiss): 458
Baldwinflex (National): 332
Balnet Baby (Fuji): 199
Banco Perfect (Kaftanski): 255
Bandi (Fototechnica): 194
Banier: 53
BANKS (Non-Camera): 514
Banner: 53
Banquet (Folmer & Schwing): 191
Bantam (EKC): 122-123
Bantam Colorsnap (EKC): 122
Bantam f4.5 (EKC): 122
Bantam f4.5 Military Model (EKC): 122
Bantam f5.6 (EKC): 122
Bantam f6.3 (EKC): 122
Bantam f8 (EKC): 122
Bantam RF (EKC): 122
Bantam Special (EKC): 122
Baoca BC-9: 53
Barbie (Non-Camera): 524
Barbie Cameramatic (Vanity Fair): 430
Barco: 53
BARON CAMERA WORKS: 53
Baron Six (Baron): 53
BARTHELEMY: 53
Barthelemy Stereo Magazine Camera: 53
BARKER BROS. (Movie): 484
Battlestar Galactica (Non-Camera): 531
BAUCHET: 53
Bauchet Mosquito: 53
BAUDINET INTERNATIONAL: 53
Baudinet Pixie Slip-On: 53
Bauer: 53
BAUER (Movie): 485
Bauer 88B: 485
BAZIN & LEROY: 53
Bazin & Leroy Le Stereocycle: 53
BB Semi First (Kuribayashi): 271
Beacon (Whitehouse): 447
Beacon II (Whitehouse): 447
Beacon 225 (Whitehouse): 447

Bear Camera (Kiddie Camera): 259
BEAR PHOTO CO.: 53
Bear Photo Special: 53
Bear with Flash Camera (Non-Camera): 536
Beau Brownie (EKC): 124
Beaurline Imp: 53
BEAURLINE INDUSTRIES INC.: 53
Beaurline Pro: 54
Beauta Miniature Candid (Rolls): 379
Beauty (Taiyodo): 409
Beauty 35 Super II (Taiyodo Koki): 410
Beauty Super L (Taiyodo Koki): 410
Beautycord (Taiyodo Koki): 410
Beautyflex (Taiyodo Koki): 410
Bebe (Ica): 241
Bebe (Zeiss): 458
Bebe (Zulauf): 481
Beby Pilot (Tachibana): 409
BECK: 54
Beck Cornex: 54
Beck Frena: 54
Beck Frena Deluxe: 54
Beck Zambex: 54
Beddy-Bye Bear (Non-Camera): 519
Bedfordflex: 54
Bee Bee (Burleigh Brooks): 75
Beginners Camera (Aivas): 26
Beica: 54
BEIER: 54-55
Beier Beier-Flex: 54
Beier Beiermatic: 54
Beier Beira: 54
Beier Beirax: 55
Beier Beirette: 55
Beier Beirette K,VSN: 55
Beier Edith II: 55
Beier-Flex (Beier): 54
Beier Folding sheet film cameras: 55
Beier Lotte II: 55
Beier Precisa: 55
Beier Rifax: 55
Beier Voran: 55
Beiermatic (Beier): 54
BEIL & FREUND: 56
Beil & Freund Plate Camera: 56
Beira (Beier): 54
Beirax (Beier): 55
Beirette (Beier): 55
Beirette K,VSN (Beier): 55
Bel-Park Photo: ADV
Belca Belfoca,II: 56
Belca Belplasca: 56
Belca Beltica: 56
BELCA-WERKE: 56
Belco: 56
Belco (Idam): 247
Belfoca,II (Belca): 56
Bell 14: 56
BELL & HOWELL: 56-57
BELL & HOWELL (Movie): 485-487
Bell & Howell 200EE: 486
Bell & Howell 220: 487
Bell & Howell 240 Electric Eye: 487
Bell & Howell 252: 487
Bell & Howell 319: 487
Bell & Howell Cine Camera #2709: 485
Bell & Howell Colorist: 56

Bell & Howell Dial 35: 56
Bell & Howell Double Run Eight
(Sporster): 486
Bell & Howell Electric Eye 127: 56
Bell & Howell Eyemo 35mm: 485
Bell & Howell Filmo 127-A: 486
Bell & Howell Filmo 141-A: 486
Bell & Howell Filmo 141-B: 486
Bell & Howell Filmo 70A: 485
Bell & Howell Filmo 70AC: 485
Bell & Howell Filmo 70AD: 485
Bell & Howell Filmo 70C: 485
Bell & Howell Filmo 70DR: 485
Bell & Howell Filmo 70HR: 485
Bell & Howell Filmo 70J: 485
Bell & Howell Filmo 75: 485
Bell & Howell Filmo 75 A-5: 486
Bell & Howell Filmo Aristocrat Turret 8: 486
Bell & Howell Filmo Auto Load: 486
Bell & Howell Filmo Companion: 486
Bell & Howell Filmo Sportster: 486
Bell & Howell Filmo-121-A: 486
Bell & Howell Foton: 56
Bell & Howell Infallible (Electric Eye): 56
Bell & Howell Magazine Camera-172: 486
Bell & Howell Magazine Camera-200: 486
Bell & Howell Projectors 57A,B,C: 487
Bell & Howell Projectors 112-A: 487
Bell & Howell TDC Stereo Vivid: 57
Bell & Howell Vivid: 57
BELL CAMERA CO.: 57
Bell Kamra: 57
BELL MFG. CO. (Movie): 487
Bell Model 10: 487
Bell's Straight-Working Panorama: 57
Bella (Bilora): 62
Bella 35 (Bilora): 62
Bella 44 (Bilora): 62
Bella 46 (Bilora): 62
Bella 66 (Bilora): 62
Bella D (Bilora): 62
Bellcraft Can-Tex: 57
BELLCRAFT CREATIONS: 57
BELLIENI: 57
Bellieni Jumelle: 57
Bellieni Stereo Jumelle: 57
Bellina 127 (Bilora): 62
Bellows for Close-Up: 540
Bellows replacement: ADV
Belmira (Pentacon): 348
Belplasca (Belca): 56
BELT BUCKLES (Non-Camera): 514-515
Beltica (Belca): 56
Ben Akiba (Lehmann): 281
BENCINI: 57-58
Bencini Animatic 600: 57
Bencini Comet: 57
Bencini Cometa: 57
Bencini Eno: 57
Bencini Gabri: 57
Bencini Koroll: 57
Bencini Koroll 24: 57
Bencini Koroll S: 58
BENETFINK: 58
Benetfink Lightning Detective: 58
Benetfink Lightning Hand: 58
Benetfink Speedy Detective: 58

BENSON DRY PLATE & CAMERA CO.: 58
Benson Street Camera: 58
Benson Victor: 58
Bentley BX-3: 58
BENTZIN: 58-60
Bentzin Astraflex II (Primarflex II): 59
Bentzin Folding Focal Plane Camera: 58
Bentzin Plan Primar: 59
Bentzin Planovista: 58
Bentzin Primar: 59
Bentzin Primar Folding Reflex: 59
Bentzin Primar Reflex: 59
Bentzin Primarette: 59
Bentzin Primarflex: 59
Bentzin Rechteck Primar: 59
Bentzin Stereo-Fokal Primar: 59
Bentzin Stereo Reflex: 60
Bentzin Stereo Reflex Primar: 60
Bera (Mashpriborintorg Vega): 306
Bera 2 (Mashpriborintorg Vega): 306
Bergheil (Voigtlander): 432
Bergheil Deluxe (Voigtlander): 433
BERMPOHL & CO. K.G.: 60
Bermpohl Miethe/Bermpohl: 60
Bermpohl's Naturfarbenkamera: 60
Bernard Faultless Miniature: 60
BERNER: 60
BERNARD PRODUCTS CO.: 60
BERNING: 60-61
Berning Robot I: 60
Berning Robot II: 60
Berning Robot IIa: 60
Berning Robot Junior: 60
Berning Robot Luftwaffe: 61
Berning Robot Royal: 61
BIAL & FREUND: 61
Bial & Freund Magazine Camera: 61
BIANCHI: 61
Bianchi Tropical Stereo Camera: 61
Berning Robot Star: 61
BERTRAM: 61
Bertram-Kamera: 61
BERTSCH: 61
Bertsch Chambre Automatique: 61
Bessa 46 (Voigtlander): 434
Bessa 66 (Voigtlander): 434
Bessa I (Voigtlander): 434
Bessa II (Voigtlander): 434
Bessa folding rollfilm (Voigtlander): 433
Bessa RF (Voigtlander): 434
Bessamatic (Voigtlander): 434
Bessamatic Deluxe (Voigtlander): 434
Best (Minolta): 314
Besta: 61
Bettax (Zeh): 456
Bicoh 36 (Non-Camera): 525
Biflex 35: 61
Big Bird 3-D Camera (Non-Camera): 538
Big Shot (Polaroid): 361
Bijou (Kern): 258
Bijou (Voigtlander): 435
Bilux (Iso): 253
Billy (Agfa): 19
Billy-Clack (Agfa): 19
Billy Compur (Agfa): 19
Billy I (Luxus) (Agfa): 19
Billy Optima (Agfa): 19

Billy Record (Agfa): 19
BILORA: 62-63
Bilora Bella: 62
Bilora Bella 35: 62
Bilora Bella 44: 62
Bilora Bella 46: 62
Bilora Bella 66: 62
Bilora Bella D: 62
Bilora Bellina 127: 62
Bilora Blitz Box: 62
Bilora Bonita 66: 62
Bilora Box Camera: 62
Bilora Boy: 62
Bilora Cariphot: 63
Bilora Radix: 63
Bilora Stahl Box: 63
Bilora Standard Box: 63
BING: 63
Bing Fita: 63
Binoca Picture Binocular: 63
Binocular camera (London Stereoscopic):
   298
Bioflex: 63
Bioflex (Tokiwa): 416
Bioscope (Caillon): 79
Bioscope (Darling): 489
Birdland (Sanders & Crowhurst): 382
BIRDSEYE CAMERA CORP.: 63
Birdseye Flash Camera: 63
BIRMINGHAM PHOTOGRAPHIC CO.: 63
Birmingham Photographic Criterion: 63
BISCHOFF: 63
Bischoff Detective Camera: 63
Blair '95 Hawk-Eye Box: 65
Blair Baby Hawk-Eye: 63
BLAIR CAMERA CO.: 63-66
Blair Century Hawk-Eye: 63
Blair Columbus: 64
Blair Combination Camera: 64
Blair Combination Hawk-Eye: 64
Blair English Compact Reversible Back: 64
Blair Focusing Weno Hawk-Eye: 64
Blair Folding '95 Hawkeye: 64
Blair Folding Hawk-Eye: 64
Blair Hawk-Eye: 65
Blair Hawk-Eye Box: 65
Blair Hawk-Eye Detective: 65
Blair Hawk-Eye Junior: 65
Blair Kamaret: 65
Blair Lucidograph: 65
Blair No. 2 Weno Hawk-Eye: 66
Blair No. 3 Combination Hawk-Eye: 64
Blair No. 3 Folding Hawk-Eye: 64
Blair No. 3 Weno Hawk-Eye: 66
Blair No. 4 Folding Hawk-Eye: 64
Blair No. 4 Folding Weno Hawk-Eye: 65
Blair No. 4 Weno Hawk-Eye: 66
Blair No. 6 Weno Hawk-eye: 66
Blair No. 7 Weno Hawk-eye: 66
Blair Petite Kamarette: 66
Blair Stereo Hawk-Eye: 66
Blair Stereo Weno: 66
Blair Tourist Hawk-Eye: 66
Blair Tourist Hawk-Eye Special: 66
BLAIR TOUROGRAPH CO. (Blair): 63
Blair View cameras: 66
Blair Weno Hawk-Eye: 66

BLAND & CO.: 66
Blitz (Adox): 18
Blitz Box (Bilora): 62
Bloc-Metal 41,45 (Pontiac): 362-363
BLOCH: 66-67
Bloch Photo-Bouquin Stereoscopique: 66
Bloch Photo Cravate: 66
Bloch Physio-Pocket: 66
Bloch Physiographe: 67
Bloch Stereo Physiographe: 67
Block-Notes (Gaumont): 202
Block-Notes Stereo (Gaumont): 202
Blockmaster (Eves): 186
BLUE BOX TOY (Non-Camera): 535
Bo-Peep (Manhattan): 304
Bob (Zeiss): 458
Bob 0 (Ernemann): 175
Bob 00 (Ernemann): 175
Bob I (Ernemann): 175
Bob II (Ernemann): 176
Bob III (Ernemann): 176
Bob IV, V (Zeiss): 459
Bob IV (Ernemann): 176
Bob V (Ernemann): 176
Bob V (stereo) (Ernemann): 176
Bob X (Ernemann): 176
Bob XV (Ernemann): 176
Bobby: 67
Bobette I (Ernemann): 176
Bobette I (Zeiss): 459
Bobette II (Ernemann): 176
Bobette II (Zeiss): 459
Bochod: 67
Bolca I (Pignons): 355
Bolca (Standard) (Pignons): 355
Bolex B8 (Paillard): 502
Bolex B8L (Paillard): 502
Bolex C8 (Paillard): 502
Bolex C8SL (Paillard): 502
Bolex D8L (Paillard): 502
Bolex G-816 Projector (Paillard): 503
Bolex H8 (Paillard): 502
Bolex H-16 (Paillard): 503
Bolex H-16 Leader (Paillard): 503
Bolex H-16 Reflex (Paillard): 503
Bolex L8V (Paillard): 502
Bolex L8 (Paillard): 502
BOLLES & SMITH: 67
Bolles & Smith Patent Camera Box: 67
Bolsey 8: 69
Bolsey Air Force Model (B2): 68
Bolsey B: 67
Bolsey B2: 68
Bolsey B3: 68
Bolsey B22: 68
Bolsey C: 68
Bolsey C22: 68
BOLSEY CORP. OF AMERICA: 67-69
Bolsey Explorer: 68
Bolsey Explorer "Treasure Chest": 68
Bolsey Jubilee: 68
Bolsey La Belle Pal: 68
Bolsey PH324A: 68
Bolsey Reflex: 69
Bolsey Uniset 8: 69
Bolseyflex (Bolsey): 68
BOLTA-WERK: 69-70

Bolta Photavit: 69
Boltavit (Bolta): 69
Boltax (Miyagawa): 326
Bonita 66 (Bilora): 62
Bonny Six (Yamato): 453
Book Camera (Scovill): 385
BOOTS: 70
Boots Special (Boots): 70
BOREUX: 70
Boreux Nanna: 70
BORSUM CAMERA CO.: 70
Borsum 5x7 New Model Reflex: 70
Borsum 5x7 Reflex: 70
Boston Bull's-Eye: 70
BOSTON CAMERA CO.: 70
BOSTON CAMERA MFG. CO.: 70
Boston Hawk-Eye Detective: 70
Boucher (Macris-Boucher): 301
BOUMSELL: 70-71
Boumsell Azur: 70
Boumsell Box Metal: 70
Boumsell Longchamp: 71
Boumsell Photo-Magic: 71
BOWER: 71
Bower 35: 71
Bower-X: 71
Box cameras: see Manufacturers' names
Box Kolex (Kolar): 263
Box Metal (Boumsell): 70
Box Scout No. 2,2A,3,3A (Seneca): 393
Box Tengor (Goerz): 206
Box Tengor (54) (Zeiss): 459
Box Tengor (54/2) (Zeiss): 459
Box Tengor (54/14) (Zeiss): 459
Box Tengor (54/15) (Zeiss): 459
Box Tengor (55/2) (Zeiss): 459
Box Tengor (56/2) (Zeiss): 459
Boy (Bilora): 62
Boy Holding Camera (Non-Camera): 534
Boy Scout Brownie (EKC): 123
Boy Scout Camera (Herbert George): 230
Boy Scout Kodak (EKC): 123
Boy Scout Memo (Ansco): 35
BRACK & CO.: 71
Brack Field camera: 71
BRADAC: 71
Bradac Kamarad I, MII: 71
Brass Bound Instantograph (Lancaster): 277
BRAUN: 72-73
Braun Gloria: 72
Braun Gloriette: 72
Braun Imperial 6x6: 72
Braun Imperial Box 6x6: 72
Braun Imperial Box 6x9: 72
Braun Norca: 72
Braun Pax: 72
Braun Paxette: 72
Braun Paxette IIM: 72
Braun Paxette Electromatic I,Ia,II: 72
Braun Paxiflash: 72
Braun Paxina: 72
Braun Super Colorette: 72
Braun Super Paxette I,IB,IIB,IIBL: 72
Braun Super Vier: 73
Brenda Starr (Seymore): 394
Briefmarken Camera (Ica): 241
Bright Star (Non-Camera): 535

Brillant (Voigtlander): 435
Brin's Patent Camera: 73
BRIOIS: 73
Briois Thompson's Revolver Camera: 73
Briskin 8: 487
BRISKIN MFG. CO. (Movie): 487
British (Chapman): 92
BRITISH FERROTYPE CO.: 73
British Ferrotype Co. Telephot Button: 73
Brooklyn Camera: 73
BROOKLYN CAMERA CO.: 73
Brooks Veriwide (Burleigh Brooks): 75
BROWN & BIGELOW (Non-Camera): 515
BROWNELL: 73
Brownell Stereo Camera: 73
Brownie (Original) (EKC): 123
Brownie 44A (EKC): 124
Brownie 127 (EKC): 124
Brownie Auto 27 (EKC): 124
Brownie box cameras (EKC): 123-126
Brownie Bull's-Eye (EKC): 125
Brownie Bullet (EKC): 125
Brownie Bullet II (EKC): 125
Brownie Chiquita (EKC): 125
Brownie Fiesta (EKC): 125
Brownie Flash (EKC): 125
Brownie Flash IV (EKC): 125
Brownie Flash 20 (EKC): 125
Brownie Flash B (EKC): 126
Brownie Flash Six-20 (EKC): 126
Brownie Flashmite 20 (EKC): 126
Brownie Fun Saver (EKC): 491
Brownie Hawkeye (EKC): 127
Brownie Holiday (EKC): 127
Brownie Junior 620 (EKC): 127
Brownie Model I (EKC): 127
Brownie Movie Camera (EKC): 491
Brownie Portrait (EKC): 127
Brownie Reflex (EKC): 127
Brownie Reflex 20 (EKC): 127
Brownie Scout (Herbert George): 230
Brownie Six-20 (EKC): 127
Brownie Starflash (EKC): 128
Brownie Starflex (EKC): 128
Brownie Starlet (Kodak Ltd.) (EKC): 129
Brownie Starlet (USA) (EKC): 129
Brownie Starluxe II (EKC): 129
Brownie Starmatic (EKC): 129
Brownie Starmeter (EKC): 129
Brownie Starmite (EKC): 129
Brownie Super 27 (EKC): 129
Brownie Target Six-16 (EKC): 129
Brownie Target Six-20 (EKC): 129
Brownie Turret Movie Camera (EKC): 491
Brownie Twin 20 (EKC): 129
Brownie Vecta (EKC): 130
BRUECKNER : 73
Brueckner Field Camera: 73
Brueckner Schueler-Apparat: 73
BRUMBERGER (Movie): 487
Brumberger 8mm-E3L: 487
Brumberger 8mm-T3L: 487
Brumberger 35: 73
BRUNS: 73
Bruns Detective camera: 73
Buccaneer (Universal): 424
Buckeye (American Camera Mfg.): 28

Buckeye (Anthony): 38
Buckeye (Cardinal): 88
Buckeye (EKC): 130
Buckeye Special (American Camera): 28
Buckles (Non-Camera Belt Buckles):
    514-515
Buddy 8 Mod. 532A (Stewart-Warner): 507
Buena 35-S (Tougodo): 418
BUESS: 73-74
Buess Multiprint: 73
Bugs Bunny (Helm): 228
Buick: 74
BULL: 74
Bull Detective: 74
Bull's-Eye (Boston): 70
Bull's-Eye (EKC): 130
Bull's-Eye Special (EKC): 130-131
BULLARD CAMERA CO.: 74
Bullard Folding Magazine Camera: 74
Bullard Folding Plate Camera: 74
Bullet (EKC): 131
Bullet (plastic) (EKC): 131
Bullet New York World's Fair (EKC): 131
Bullet Special (EKC): 131
BURKE & JAMES: 74-75
Burke & James Cub: 74
Burke & James Folding Rexo: 75
Burke & James Grover: 74
Burke & James Ingento: 74
Burke & James No. 1A Folding Rexo: 75
Burke & James No. 1A Ingento Jr.: 74
Burke & James No. 1A Rexo Jr.: 75
Burke & James No. 2C Rexo Jr.: 75
Burke & James No. 3 Folding Rexo: 75
Burke & James No. 3 Rexo Jr.: 75
Burke & James No. 3A Folding Ingento:
    74
Burke & James No. 3A Folding Rexo: 75
Burke & James No. 3A Ingento Jr.: 74
Burke & James PH-6-A: 75
Burke & James Panoram 120: 75
Burke & James Press: 75
Burke & James Press/View: 75
Burke & James Rexo: 75
Burke & James Rexoette: 75
Burke & James Vest Pocket Rexo: 75
Burke & James Watson Press: 75
Burke & James Watson-Holmes
    Fingerprint Camera: 75
BURLEIGH BROOKS, INC.: 75
Burleigh Brooks Bee Bee: 75
Burleigh Brooks Veriwide: 75
BURR: 75-76
Burr Stereo camera: 75
Burr Wet plate camera: 76
BUSCH (Emil): 76
BUSCH CAMERA CORP.: 76
Busch Folding plate camera: 76
Busch Pressman: 76
Busch Verascope F-40: 76
Busch Vier-Sechs: 76
Buster Brown (Ansco): 32
Buster Brown Junior (Ansco): 32
Buster Brown Special (Ansco): 32
Busy Bee (Seneca): 391
BUTCHER: 76-78
BUTCHER (Movie): 487

Butcher Cameo: 76
Butcher Cameo Stereo: 76
Butcher Carbine: 76-77
Butcher Clincher: 77
Butcher Dandy Automatic Camera: 77
Butcher Empire: 487
Butcher Klimax: 77
Butcher Little Nipper: 77
Butcher Maxim No. 1, No. 2: 77
Butcher Midg: 77
Butcher Popular Pressman: 78
Butcher Reflex Carbine: 78
Butcher Royal Mail Postage Stamp: 78
Butcher Stereolette: 78
Butcher Watch Pocket Carbine: 78
BUTLER: 78
BUTLER BROS.: 78-79
Butler Bros. Pennant Camera: 78
Butler Patent Three-Colour Separation: 78
BUTTERFLY ORIGINALS LTD.
   (Non-Camera): 530
Button tintype camera (Mountford): 329
C Daylight Kodak (EKC): 133
C Ordinary Kodak (EKC): 148
Cabbage Patch Kids 110 Camera
   (Playtime Products): 359
Cabbage Patch Kids Figurine Stamper
   (Non-Camera): 530
Cabbage Patch Kids Musical Toy Camera
   (Non-Camera): 526
Cadet (Agfa): 20
Cadet (Ansco): 32
Cadet (Soho): 400
Cadet Flash (Ansco): 32
CADOT: 79
Cadot Scenographe Panoramique: 79
CAILLON: 79
Caillon Bioscope: 79
Caillon Kaloscope: 79
Caillon Megascope: 79
Caillon Scopea: 79
Calypso (Spirotechnique): 404
CAM-O (United States Cam-O): 423
CAM-O CORP.: 79
Cam-O Ident: 79
Cambinox (Moeller): 327
Cambot Wonderful Slide Robot: 520
Cambridge (Marion): 305
Camel Model II (Tohokoken): 416
Cameo (Butcher): 76
Cameo (Coronet): 104
Cameo (Houghton Ensign): 234
Cameo Stereo (Butcher): 76
Cameo Stereo (Ica): 241
Cameo Ultrix (Ihagee): 250
Camera: 79
Camera (Yen-Kame): 456
Camera Buckles(Non-Camera): 514-515
Camera-Cap Gun (Non-Camera): 519
Camera Charm (Non-Camera): 524
Camera City View (Seneca): 391
Camera Coaster Set (Non-Camera): 517
Camera Collectors Books: ADV
CAMERA CORP. OF AMERICA (Chrislin):
   93
CAMERA CORP. OF AMERICA (Perfex):
   79-80

Camera Corp. Perfex Cee-Ay: 79
Camera Corp. Perfex DeLuxe: 80
Camera Corp. Perfex Fifty-Five: 80
Camera Corp. Perfex Forty-Four: 79
Camera Corp. Perfex One-O-One: 80
Camera Corp. Perfex One-O-Two: 80
Camera Corp. Perfex Speed Candid: 79
Camera Corp. Perfex Thirty-Three: 80
Camera Corp. Perfex Twenty-Two: 80
Camera-Flasks (Non-Camera): 521-523
Camera keychain (Non-Camera): 531
Camera Kit, Wonderful Camera (Multiple
   Toymakers): 329
Camera Kit sharpener (Non-Camera): 527
Camera-Lamp (Non-Camera): 525
Camera Laser Gun 3-in-1 (Non-Camera):
   519
Camera-Lighter (Non-Camera): 515
Camera-Lite (Suzuki): 408
Camera-Lite Seastar (Suzuki): 409
CAMERA MAN, INC.: 80
Camera Man Champion: 80
Camera Man President: 80
Camera Man Silver King: 80
Camera Mask (Non-Camera): 525
Camera Note Box (Non-Camera): 518
Camera Obscura: 80
Camera pencil box (Non-Camera): 527
Camera Pistol (Non-Camera): 519
CAMERA PROJECTOR LTD. (Movie): 487
Camera Projector Midas: 487
Camera Repair: ADV
Camera-Robot (Non-Camera): 520
Camera Salt & Pepper Shakers
   (Non-Camera): 530-531
Camera Scope (Non-Camera): 538
Camera-screwdriver-keychain
   (Non-Camera): 531
Camera Shooter NIKO Nikosound: 521
Camera Soap-on-a-Rope (Non-Camera):
   531
Camera-Viewer (Non-Camera): 538-539
Camera-Viewer Keychain: 538
Camera with Birdie (Non-Camera): 527
Cameradio (Universal Radio): 428
Cameragraph (Power): 505
CAMERAS LTD. (Movie): 488
Cameras Ltd. Dekko: 488
Camerette: 81
Camerette (Yen-Kame): 456
Camex Reflex 8 (Ercsam): 494
Camex Six (Mamiya): 302
Camflex (National): 333
CAMOJECT: 81
Camp Fire Girl's Kodak (EKC): 131
Camp out (Non-Camera): 537
CAMPBELL (Movie): 48
Campbell Cello: 488
Campro: 488
Campro Cine Camera-Projector: 488
CAMPRO LTD. (Movie): 488
Camro 28 (Argus): 45
Can Camera 110 TX Coca-Cola (Tizer): 416
Can Cameras (Eiko): 173
Can-Tex (Bellcraft): 57
CANADIAN CAMERA CO.: 81
Canadian Camera Co. Glenco: 81

Candex Jr. (General Products): 202
CANDID CAMERA CORP. OF AMERICA
   (Camera Corp. of America): 79
CANDID CAMERA CORP. OF AMERICA
   (Movie): 488
Candid Camera Corp. Cine Perfex Double
   Eight: 488
CANDID CAMERA SUPPLY CO.: 81
Candid Camera Supply Minifoto Junior: 81
Candid Camera Target Shot: 521
Candid Flash (Flash Camera Co.): 191
Candid Shot (Non-Camera): 522
CANDLE (Non-Camera): 515
CANDY & GUM (Non-Camera): 515
Canon IIA: 84
Canon IIAF: 84
Canon IIB: 84
Canon IIC: 84
Canon IID: 84
Canon IID1: 85
Canon IID2: 85
Canon IIF: 85
Canon IIF2: 85
Canon III: 85
Canon IIIA: 85
Canon IIIA Signal Corps.: 85
Canon IIS: 85
Canon IIS2: 85
Canon IV: 85
Canon IVBS: 86
Canon IVF: 85
Canon IVS: 85
Canon IVSB2: 86
Canon 7: 87
Canon 7s: 87
Canon 7sZ: 87
Canon AE-1 Program Lapel Pin
   (Non-Camera): 524
CANON CAMERA CO.: 81-88
CANON CAMERA CO. (Movie): 489
Canon Canonet: 88
Canon Canonex: 88
Canon Canonflex: 87
Canon Demi: 88
Canon Dial 35: 88
Canon Eight-T: 489
Canon EX-EE: 88
Canon FP: 88
Canon FT: 88
Canon FX: 88
Canon Hansa: 82
Canon J: 83
Canon J-II: 83
Canon JS: 83
Canon Kwanon: 82
Canon L-1: 86
Canon L-2: 86
Canon L-3: 86
Canon NS: 83
Canon Original: 82
Canon P: 87
Canon Pellix: 88
Canon Pellix QL: 88
Canon S: 83
Canon S-I (Canon S): 83
Canon S-II: 84
Canon Seiki S-II: 83

Canon TL: 88
Canon VI-L: 87
Canon VI-T: 87
Canon VL: 86
Canon VL-2: 86
Canon VT: 86
Canon VT-Deluxe: 86
Canon VT-Deluxe-M: 86
Canon VT-Deluxe-Z: 86
Canon X-Ray Cameras: 84
Canonet (Canon): 88
Canonex (Canon): 88
Canonflex (Canon): 87
Canter Beauty (Taiyodo Koki): 410
Capital MX-II: 88
Capitol 120: 88
Capri (Keystone): 498
Capri Camera-Viewer (Non-Camera): 539
Capta, Capta II, Super Capta: 88
Captain (Agfa): 20
Carbine (Butcher): 76-77
Carbine (Houghton Ensign): 235
Carbine, Tropical (Houghton Ensign): 235
Cardinal: 88
Cardinal Buckeye: 88
Cardinal Cinex: 88
CARDINAL CORP.: 88
Cardinal Photo-Champ: 88
CARENA S.A. (Movie): 489
Carena Zoomex: 489
Cariphot (Bilora): 63
CARL ZEISS OPTICAL CO. (Zeiss): 457
Carlton (London Stereoscopic): 298
Carlton (Rochester Optical): 374
Carlton (Utility): 429
Carlton Reflex (Allied): 27
Carlton Reflex (Utility): 428
Carmen: 88
CARPENTIER: 88
Carpentier Photo Jumelle: 88
Cartridge Hawk-Eye (EKC): 141
Cartridge Kodak (EKC): 132
Cartridge Premo (EKC): 152
Casca I (Steinheil): 405
Casca II (Steinheil): 405
Cavalier/Camera A-1 (Non-Camera): 519
Cello (Campbell): 488
Century 35 (Graflex): 220
CENTURY CAMERA CO.: 88-89
Century Copy Camera: 89
Century Field cameras: 89
Century Grand: 89
Century Grand Sr.: 89
Century Graphic (Graflex): 216
Century Hawk-Eye (Blair): 63
Century Long Focus Grand: 89
Century of Progress (Ansco): 32
Century of Progress, World's Fair
   Souvenir (EKC): 132
Century Stereo plate camera: 89
Certix (Certo): 89
Certo Certix: 89
Certo Certo-phot: 89
Certo Certonet: 89
Certo Certoplat: 89
Certo Certoruf: 89
Certo Certosport: 89

Cinklox Model 3-S (Cincinnati Clock): 489
Cinoscope (Industrial Syndicate): 498
Cirkut Camera (EKC): 132-133
Cirkut Cameras Wanted: ADV
Cirkut Outfits (EKC): 132-133
Ciro 35 (Ciro): 94
Ciro 35 (Graflex): 220
CIRO CAMERAS, INC.: 94
Ciroflex: 94
Citonette (Rodenstock): 378
Citoskop (Zeiss): 460
Citoskop Stereo (Contessa): 100
CITY SALE & EXCHANGE: 94
City Sale & Exchange Field camera: 94
Civica PG-1: 94
Clack (Agfa): 20
Clack (Rietzschel): 369
Clarissa (Contessa): 100
Clarissa (Lorenz): 299
Clarovid,II (Rodenstock): 378
Clartex 6/6 (Olbia): 343
CLARUS CAMERA MFG. CO.: 95
Clarus MS-35: 95
Classic II: 95
Classic III: 95
Classic IV: 95
Classic 35: 95
Classic 35 (Craftmen's): 106
Classic 35 IV (Fujita): 200
Classic Cameras Wanted: ADV
Clic (Idam): 247
Click I,II (Agfa): 20
Click (Tougodo): 418
Click-N-Flick Mini Viewer (Non-Camera): 535
Clicker Bear (Non-Camera): 536
Clifton (Anthony): 38
Climax Detective (Anthony): 38
Climax Portrait (Anthony): 38
Clincher (Butcher): 77
Clipper (Ansco): 32
Clipper PD-16 (Agfa): 20
Clipper Special (Agfa): 20
Clipper Special (Ansco): 32
Clix 120 (Metropolitan): 310
Clix Deluxe (Metropolitan): 310
Clix-Master (Metropolitan): 310
Clix Miniature (General Products): 202
Clix Miniature (Metropolitan): 310
Clix-O-Flex (Metropolitan): 310
CLOCKS (Non-Camera): 517
Clopic "Reporter": 95
CLOSE & CONE: 95
Close & Cone Quad: 95
Close Focus Camera (Kugler): 269
Close-Up Attachments: 540
CLOSTER: 96
Closter C60: 96
Closter IIa: 96
Closter Olympic: 96
Closter Princess: 96
Closter Sport: 96
Closter Sprint: 96
Clover (Hagi): 223
Clover Six (Hagi): 223
Clown Camera (Kiddie Camera): 259
Club (Adams & Co.): 16

CMC: 96
Cnopm (Sport) (GOMZ): 210
CNYTHNK (Sputnik): 404
COASTERS (Non-Camera): 517
Coat Pocket Tenax (Goerz): 207
Coca-Cola (Eiko): 173
Coca-Cola Can Camera (Tizer): 416
Cocarette (Contessa): 100
Cocarette (Zeiss): 460
Cocarette Luxus (Zeiss): 460
Cogan Collection: ADV
Cohen (Non-Camera): 531
Coke Happy Times (EKC): 140, 144
Colibri: 96
Colis Postal (Enjalbert): 174
Collectible Cameras for sale: ADV
Collections Wanted: ADV
College (Thornton-Pickard): 413
Collegiate (Yen-Kame): 456
Collegiate Camera No. 3: 96
COLLINS: 96
Collins "The Society": 96
Columbus Camera Group: ADV
Colly (Koeda): 263
Colly (Tougodo): 418
Colonel (National): 333
Color Clipper (Ansco): 32
Color-flex (Monroe Sales): 328
Color Master (Curtis): 107
Color Scout (Curtis): 107
Colora (Zeiss): 460
Colora F (Zeiss): 460
Colorado (S.E.M.): 391
Colorburst Instant Cameras (EKC): 144
Colorcamera (Argus CC): 43
Colorflash Deluxe: 96
Colorflex I,II (Agfa): 20
Colorist (Bell & Howell): 56
Colorsnap 35 (EKC): 133
Colt 44 (Kalimar): 256
COLUMBIA OPTICAL & CAMERA CO.: 96
Columbia Optical Pecto: 96
Columbus (Blair): 64
Combat Graphic (Graflex): 216
Combination Camera (Blair): 64
Combination Hawk-Eye (Blair): 64
Combined ¼-plate, Postcard, Stereo, Plate & Rollfilm Camera (Ernemann): 176
Combined Postcard and Stereo, Model VI (Ernemann): 177
Combined Stereo and Half-Plate Focal-Plane Camera (Ernemann): 177
Comet (Bencini): 57
Comet (Zenith): 480
Comet Flash (Zenith): 480
Cometa (Bencini): 57
Comex (Fuji): 199
C.O.M.I.: 97
C.O.M.I. Luxia, Luxia II: 97
Commander (Ansco): 32
Commando (Houghton Ensign): 235
Commercial Cameras (Deardorff): 112
COMMONWEALTH PLASTICS CORP. (Non-Camera): 525
Compact (Pearsall): 347
Compact Camera (Anthony): 38
Compact Graflex: 213

Contina (Zeiss): 466
Contina I (522/24) (Zeiss): 465
Contina Ia (526/24) (Zeiss): 466
Contina II (Zeiss): 465
Contina IIa (Zeiss): 466
Contina III (Zeiss): 466
Contina III Microscope (Zeiss): 466
Contina III lenses (Zeiss): 466
Contina L (Zeiss): 466
Contina LK (Zeiss): 466
Continental (Wittnauer): 452
Continental Camera-Lighter
  (Non-Camera): 515
Continette (Zeiss): 466
Contura (Stereo Corp.): 406
CONVERTORS (Non-Camera): 519-521
Conway (Standard Cameras): 404
COPAL CO. LTD. (Non-Camera): 517
Coquette (EKC): 133
CORD: 102
Cord Box 6x9 (Cord): 102
CORFIELD: 102
Corfield 66: 102
Corfield Periflex: 102
Cornex (Beck): 54
CORNU CO.: 103
Cornu Fama: 103
Cornu Ontobloc: 103
Cornu Ontoflex: 103
Cornu Ontoscope: 103
Cornu Ontoscope 3D: 103
Cornu Reyna II: 103
Cornu Reyna Cross III: 103
Coro-Flash F-20 (Coronet): 104
Corona (K.S.K.): 269
CORONET (Movie): 489
Coronet 3-D Stereo Camera: 105
Coronet 66: 104
Coronet Ajax: 103
Coronet Ambassador: 104
Coronet Box cameras: 103
Coronet Cameo: 104
CORONET CAMERA CO.: 103-106
Coronet Consul: 104
Coronet Coroflash F-20: 104
Coronet Cub: 104
Coronet Cub Flash: 104
Coronet Eclair Lux: 104
Coronet F-20 Coro-Flash: 104
Coronet Fildia: 105
Coronet Flashmaster: 105
Coronet Midget: 105
Coronet Model A, B: 489
Coronet Polo: 105
Coronet Rapide: 105
Coronet Rex: 105
Coronet Victor: 105
Coronet Vogue: 106
Corrida (Ica): 241
Corsair I, II (Universal): 424
Cosmic: 106
Cosmograph Model 16-R (Maggard-
  Bradley): 500
Cosmopolite (Francais): 195
Cowi (Widmar): 448
Craftex Hollywood Reflex: 106
CRAFTEX PRODUCTS: 106

Craftsman (Ansco): 32
Craftsman Cinex Candid Camera: 106
CRAFTSMAN SALES CO.: 106
CRAFTSMEN'S GUILD: 106
Craftsmen's Guild Classic 35: 106
Cristallos (Jumeau & Jannin): 255
Criterion (Appleton): 42
Criterion (Birmingham Photographic): 63
Criterion View (Gundlach): 222
Croma Color 16: 106
CROWN CAMERA CO.: 106
Crown Camera Dandy Photo Camera: 106
Crown View (Graflex): 220
Crusier: 106
CRUSIER CAMERA CO.: 106
CRUVER-PETERS: 107
Cruver-Peters Palko: 107
Crystar: 107
Crystarflex: 107
Cub (American Advertising & Research): 27
Cub (Burke & James): 74
Cub (Coronet): 104
Cub Flash (Coronet): 104
Cub Scout Camera (Herbert George): 230
Cubex IV (Imperial): 251
Cupid (Houghton Ensign): 235
Cupido (Huttig): 240
Cupido (Ica): 242
Curlew I,II,III (Kershaw): 258
CURTIS: 107
Curtis Color Master: 107
Curtis Color Scout: 107
Cycle Graphic Cameras (Graflex): 218
Cycle Pocos (Rochester Camera): 373
Cycle Wizard (Manhattan): 304
Cyclographe a foyer fixe (Damoizeau): 109
Cyclone: 107
Cyclone Cameras (Rochester Optical): 374
Cyclone Jr. (Western): 446
Cyclone Junior (Rochester Optical): 374
Cyclone Senior (Rochester Optical): 374
Cyclone Sr. (Western): 446
Cyclops (Tokyo Kogaku): 416
Cyko Reko (Rochester Optical): 374
Da-Brite (Herold): 231
Daci, Daci Royal (Dacora): 107
Daco, Daco II (Dacora): 107
Dacora I: 107
Dacora Daci, Daci Royal: 107
Dacora Daco, Daco II: 107
Dacora Dacora-Matic 4D: 107
Dacora Digna: 108
Dacora Dignette: 108
Dacora Instacora E: 108
DACORA KAMERAWERK: 107-108
Dacora-Matic 4D (Dacora): 107
Dacora Royal: 108
Dacora Subita: 108
Dacora Super Dignette: 108
Daguerreotype camera (Lewis): 293
Daguerreotype cameras: 108
Daguerreotype cannon (replica)
  (Voigtlander): 435
Daguerreian Cameras Wanted: ADV
DAH YANG TOYS (Non-Camera): 519
DAIDO SEIKI CO.: 108
Daido Six (Daido): 108

Detective Camera (Lamperti & Garbagnati): 277
Detective Camera (Smith): 399
Detective Camera (Watson): 442
Detective Cameras: 114
Detrola 400: 115
Detrola A: 114
Detrola B: 115
DETROLA CORP.: 114-115
Detrola D: 115
Detrola E: 115
Detrola G: 115
Detrola GW: 115
Detrola H: 115
Detrola HW: 115
Detrola K: 115
Detrola KW: 115
DEVIN COLORGRAPH CO.: 115
Devin Tri-Color Camera: 115
DEVRY (QRS DeVry Corp.): 115
DEVRY CORP. (Movie): 490
DeVry 16mm: 490
DeVry 16mm Deluxe: 490
DeVry Cinetone Projector: 490
DeVry Home Movie Camera: 490
DeVry Portable Motion Picture Proj.: 490
DeVry QRS-DeVry Home Movie Camera: 490
DeVry Standard: 490
DeVry Type ESF Projector: 490
Devus: 115
DEYROLLE: 115
Deyrolle Scenographe: 115
Dial 35 (Bell & Howell): 56
Dial 35 (Canon): 88
Diamond Gun Ferrotype (International Metal): 253
Diamond Jr.: 115
Diana: 115
Diana (Mozar): 329
Diana (Welta): 443
Diana Deluxe: 115
Diana-style squirt camera (Non-Camera): 533
Diax (Voss): 439
Diaxette (Voss): 440
Dice Cup (Non-Camera): 529
Dick Tracy (Laurie): 280
Dick Tracy (Seymore): 394
Dick Tracy (Seymour): 394
Dick Tracy Squirt Gun Camera (Non-Camera): 532
Digna (Dacora): 108
Dignette (Dacora): 108
Dionne F2: 115
Diplomat: 115
Direct Positive Camera (Mourfield): 329
Direct Positive Camera (Wabash): 440
Direct Positive Street Camera (Glossick): 204
Direct Positive Street Camera (Thompson): 413
DISHES (Non-Camera): 523
Dispatch Detective (London Stereoscopic): 298
DITMAR (Movie): 490
Ditmar 9.5mm: 490

Ditto 99 (Finetta): 191
Diva (Phoba): 352
Dog Camera (Kiddie Camera): 259
Dolca 35 (Tokyo Koken): 417
Dollar Box (Ansco): 32
Dollina (Certo): 90
Dollina "O" (Certo): 90
Dollina II (Certo): 90
Dollina III (Certo): 90
Dolly 3x4 (Certo): 90
Dolly Vest-Pocket (Certo): 90
Dominant (King): 260
Donald Duck (Herbert George): 229
Donald Duck (Toy's Clan): 420
Donata (Contessa): 101
Donata (Zeiss): 466
DONRUSS CO. (Non-Camera): 515
Doppel-Box (Balda): 51
Doppel Box (Certo): 91
Dories: 115
Doris (Tokyo Seiki): 418
DORYU CAMERA CO.: 116
Doryu 2-16: 116
Dossert Detective Camera: 116
DOSSERT DETECTIVE CAMERA CO.: 116
Double-8 (Houghton Ensign): 235
Double Run Eight (Bell & Howell Filmo Sportster): 486
Double Shutter Camera (Ernemann): 177
DOVER FILM CORP.: 116
Dover 620 A: 116
Dralowid Reporter 8: 491
DRALOWID-WERK (Movie): 491
Drepy (Pierrat): 355
DRGM: 116
Drinking glass, Muppet (Non-Camera): 523
Drive (Fuji): 200
Drying Racks: 541
DRP: 116
DRUCKER: 116
Drucker Ranger: 116
DRUOPTA: 116
Druoflex (Druopta): 116
Druopta Druoflex: 116
Druopta Vega II, III: 116
DU ALL (Non-Camera): 538
Duaflex (EKC): 134
Dubla (Welta): 443
DUBRONI: 116-117
Duca (Durst): 117
DUCATI: 117
Ducati Wet-plate Tailboard camera: 117
Duchess: 117
Duchessa (Contessa): 101
Duchessa Stereo (Contessa): 101
Duex (EKC): 134
DUFA: 117
Dufa Pionyr: 117
Duflex (Gamma): 201
Duo (Seneca shutter): 392
Duo Six-20 (EKC): 134
Duo Six-20 Series II (EKC): 134
Duo Six-20 Series II w/ RF (EKC): 134
Duovex (Universal): 425
Duplex (Ihagee): 247
Duplex 120 (Iso): 253
Duplex Novelette (Anthony): 40

EKC No. 0 Brownie: 123
EKC No. 0 Folding Pocket Kodak: 138
EKC No. 0 Premo Junior: 153
EKC No. 00 Cartridge Premo: 152
EKC No. 1 Autographic Kodak Junior: 121
EKC No. 1 Autographic Kodak Special: 121
EKC No. 1 Brownie: 123
EKC No. 1 Cone Pocket Kodak: 133
EKC No. 1 Film Premo: 152
EKC No. 1 Folding Pocket Kodak: 138
EKC No. 1 Kodak: 119
EKC No. 1 Kodak Junior: 145
EKC No. 1 Kodak Series III: 146
EKC No. 1 Panoram Kodak: 149
EKC No. 1 Pocket Kodak: 150
EKC No. 1 Pocket Kodak Junior: 150
EKC No. 1 Pocket Kodak Series II: 151
EKC No. 1 Pocket Kodak Special: 151
EKC No. 1 Premo Junior: 153
EKC No. 1 Premoette: 154
EKC No. 1 Premoette Junior: 155
EKC No. 1 Premoette Junior Special: 155
EKC No. 1 Premoette Special: 155
EKC No. 1A Autographic Kodak: 120
EKC No. 1A Autographic Kodak Junior: 121
EKC No. 1A Autographic Kodak Special: 121
EKC No. 1A Folding Hawk-Eye: 141
EKC No. 1A Folding Pocket Kodak: 139
EKC No. 1A Folding Pocket Kodak Special: 139
EKC No. 1A Gift Kodak: 140
EKC No. 1A Kodak Junior: 145
EKC No. 1A Kodak Series III: 146
EKC No. 1A Pocket Kodak: 150
EKC No. 1A Pocket Kodak Junior: 150
EKC No. 1A Pocket Kodak Series II: 151
EKC No. 1A Pocket Kodak Special: 151
EKC No. 1A Premo Junior: 153
EKC No. 1A Premoette: 154
EKC No. 1A Premoette Junior: 155
EKC No. 1A Premoette Junior Special: 155
EKC No. 1A Premoette Special: 155
EKC No. 1A Special Kodak: 165
EKC No. 1A Speed Kodak: 165
EKC No. 2 Brownie: 123
EKC No. 2 Bull's-Eye: 130
EKC No. 2 Bull's-Eye Special: 130
EKC No. 2 Bullet: 131
EKC No. 2 Bullet Special: 131
EKC No. 2 Cartridge Hawk-Eye: 141
EKC No. 2 Cartridge Premo: 152
EKC No. 2 Eureka: 135
EKC No. 2 Eureka Jr.: 135
EKC No. 2 Falcon: 136
EKC No. 2 Film Pack Hawk-Eye: 141
EKC No. 2 Flexo Kodak: 136
EKC No. 2 Folding Autographic Brownie: 126
EKC No. 2 Folding Brownie: 126
EKC No. 2 Folding Bull's-Eye: 130
EKC No. 2 Folding Cartridge Hawk-Eye: 142
EKC No. 2 Folding Cartridge Premo: 153
EKC No. 2 Folding Film Pack Hawk-Eye: 142
EKC No. 2 Folding Hawk-Eye Special: 142

EKC No. 2 Folding Pocket Brownie: 127
EKC No. 2 Folding Pocket Kodak: 139
EKC No. 2 Folding Rainbow Hawk-Eye: 142
EKC No. 2 Folding Rainbow Hawk-Eye Special: 142
EKC No. 2 Hawk-Eye Special: 143
EKC No. 2 Hawkette: 141
EKC No. 2 Kodak: 119
EKC No. 2 Rainbow Hawk-Eye: 142
EKC No. 2 Stereo Brownie: 129
EKC No. 2 Stereo Kodak: 166
EKC No. 2 Target Hawk-Eye: 143
EKC No. 2 Target Hawk-Eye Junior: 143
EKC No. 2 Weno Hawk-Eye: 143
EKC No. 2A Brownie: 124
EKC No. 2A Cartridge Hawk-Eye: 141
EKC No. 2A Cartridge Premo: 152
EKC No. 2A Film Pack Hawk-Eye: 141
EKC No. 2A Folding Autographic Brownie: 126
EKC No. 2A Folding Cartridge Hawk-Eye: 142
EKC No. 2A Folding Cartridge Premo: 153
EKC No. 2A Folding Hawk-Eye Special: 142
EKC No. 2A Folding Pocket Brownie: 127
EKC No. 2A Folding Rainbow Hawk-Eye: 142
EKC No. 2A Folding Rainbow Hawk-Eye Special: 142
EKC No. 2A Hawk-Eye Special: 143
EKC No. 2A Rainbow Hawk-Eye: 142
EKC No. 2A Target Hawk-Eye: 143
EKC No. 2C Autographic Kodak Junior: 121
EKC No. 2C Autographic Kodak Special: 121
EKC No. 2C Brownie: 124
EKC No. 2C Cartridge Premo: 152
EKC No. 2C Folding Autographic Brownie: 126
EKC No. 2C Folding Cartridge Premo: 153
EKC No. 2C Kodak Series III: 146
EKC No. 2C Pocket Kodak: 150
EKC No. 2C Pocket Kodak Special: 151
EKC No. 3 Autographic Kodak: 120
EKC No. 3 Autographic Kodak Special: 121
EKC No. 3 Brownie: 124
EKC No. 3 Bull's-Eye: 130
EKC No. 3 Cartridge Kodak: 132
EKC No. 3 Film Premo: 152
EKC No. 3 Flush Back Kodak: 136
EKC No. 3 Folding Brownie: 126
EKC No. 3 Folding Hawk-Eye Special: 142
EKC No. 3 Folding Hawk-Eye: 142
EKC No. 3 Folding Kodet: 146
EKC No. 3 Folding Pocket Kodak: 139
EKC No. 3 Folding Pocket Kodak, Deluxe: 140
EKC No. 3 Kodak: 119
EKC No. 3 Kodak Jr.: 119
EKC No. 3 Kodak Series III: 146
EKC No. 3 Pocket Kodak Special: 151
EKC No. 3 Premo Junior: 153
EKC No. 3 Special Kodak: 165
EKC No. 3 Zenith Kodak: 170

Eho-Altissa Altiflex: 172
Eho-Altissa Altiscop: 172
Eho-Altissa Altissa,II: 172
Eho-Altissa Altix I,II: 172
Eho-Altissa Altix IV: 172
Eho-Altissa Altix-N: 172
Eho-Altissa Altix NB: 172
Eho-Altissa Eho Baby Box: 172
Eho-Altissa Eho Box: 172
Eho-Altissa Eho Stereo Box: 173
Eho-Altissa Juwel: 173
Eho-Altissa Mantel-Box 2: 173
Eho Baby Box (Eho-Altissa): 172
Eho Box (Eho-Altissa): 172
EHO KAMERAFABRIK (Eho-Altissa): 172
Eho Stereo Box (Eho-Altissa): 173
Eight-20 Penguin (Kershaw): 258
Eiko Budweiser: 173
Eiko Can Cameras: 173
EIKO CO. LTD.: 173
Eiko Coca-Cola: 173
Eiko Mickey Mouse: 173
Eiko Pepsi-Cola: 173
Eiko 7-up: 173
Eiko Snoopy: 173
EK4, EK6, EK8, Instant Cameras (EKC): 144
Eka (Krauss): 267
Ektra (EKC): 135
Ektra 1 (EKC): 135
Ektra 2 (EKC): 135
Ektra II (EKC): 135
Ektra 200 (EKC): 135
Elbaflex VX1000 (Ihagee): 247
E.L.C.: 173
E.L.C. l'As: 173
Elca (Elop): 173
Elca II (Elop): 173
Electric Eye 127 (Bell & Howell): 56
Electro Shot (Minolta): 321
Electronic: 173
Electus (Krugener): 269
Elega-35 (Nitto): 342
Elegante (Zeiss): 466
Elettra I (Sirio): 399
Elettra II (Sirio): 399
Elf (Spiegel): 404
Elgin: 173
ELGIN LABORATORIES: 173
Elgin Miniature: 173
Elioflex (Ferrania): 189
Elite: 173
Elite (Merkel): 309
Elite-Fex (Fex): 190
Eljy (Lumiere): 300
Eljy Club (Lumiere): 300
Ellison Kamra: 173
ELLISON KAMRA COMPANY: 173
ELMO CO. LTD: 173
ELMO CAMERA CO. (Movie): 494
Elmo Honeywell Dual-Filmatic: 494
Elmo Honeywell Tri-Filmatic: 494
Elmoflex (Elmo): 173
Elop Elca: 173
Elop Elca II: 173
ELOP KAMERAWERK: 173
ELVIN (Non-Camera): 529
Elvo (Ro-To): 372

EMEL (Movie): 494
Emel C83: 494
EMMERLING & RICHTER: 173
Emmerling & Richter Field Camera: 173
Empire (Butcher): 487
Empire 120: 174
Empire-Baby: 174
Empire Scout: 174
Empire State (EKC): 135
Empire State (Rochester Optical): 374
Empress (Houghton): 234
Emson: 174
ENCORE CAMERA CO.: 174
Encore De Luxe Camera: 174
Encore Hollywood Camera: 174
English Compact Reversible Back (Blair): 64
Enica-Six (Nikoh): 338
ENJALBERT: 174
Enjalbert Colis Postal: 174
Enjalbert Photo Revolver de Poche: 174
Enjicolor (Non-Camera): 524
Enjicolor F-II Eraser (Non-Camera): 527
Enjicolor F-II pencil sharpener
  (Non-Camera): 528
Enlargers: 542
Eno (Bencini): 57
Enolde (Kochmann): 262
Enolde I,II,III (Kochmann): 262
ENSIGN, LTD.: 174
Ensign Autokinecam (Houghton): 497
Ensign Auto-Kinecam 16 Type B
  (Houghton): 497
Ensign Autospeed (Houghton): 234
Ensign box cameras (Houghton): 234
Ensign Cameo (Houghton): 234
Ensign Carbine (Houghton): 235
Ensign Carbine, Tropical (Houghton): 235
Ensign Commando (Houghton): 235
Ensign Cupid (Houghton): 235
Ensign Deluxe Reflex (Houghton): 237
Ensign Double-8 (Houghton): 235
Ensign folding rollfilm cameras
  (Houghton): 235
Ensign Ful-Vue (Houghton): 235
Ensign Ful-Vue Super (Houghton): 235
Ensign Greyhound (Houghton): 235
Ensign Junior Box (Houghton): 235
Ensign Mascot (Houghton): 235
Ensign Mickey Mouse (Houghton): 235
Ensign Midget (Houghton): 236
Ensign Midget Silver Jubilee (Houghton):
  236
Ensign Multex (Houghton): 236
Ensign Pocket (Houghton): 236
Ensign Popular Pressman Reflex
  (Houghton): 237
Ensign Popular Reflex (Houghton): 237
Ensign Ranger (Houghton): 237
Ensign Reflex (Houghton): 237
Ensign Roll Film Reflex (Houghton): 237
Ensign Roll Film Reflex, Tropical
  (Houghton): 237
Ensign Selfix 12-20, 16-20 (Houghton): 237
Ensign Selfix 20, 220, 320, 420, 820
  (Houghton): 237
Ensign Special Reflex, Tropical
  (Houghton): 237

Franke & Heidecke Rollei 35: 195
  Rollei 35B: 195
  Rollei 35C: 195
  Rollei 35LED: 196
  Rollei 35S: 196
  Rollei 35T: 196
  Rollei A26: 196
  Rolleicord I: 196
  Rolleicord Ia: 196
  Rolleicord II: 196
  Rolleicord IIa (II): 196
  Rolleicord III: 196
  Rolleicord IV: 196
  Rolleicord V: 196
  Rolleicord Va: 196
  Rolleicord Vb: 197
  Rolleidoscop: 197
  Rolleiflex I: 197
  Rolleiflex 2.8D: 198
  Rolleiflex 2.8C: 198
  Rolleiflex 2.8B: 198
  Rolleiflex 2.8A: 197
  Rolleiflex 4x4 (original): 199
  Rolleiflex 4x4, Grey Baby: 199
  Rolleiflex 4x4, Post-war Black: 199
  Rolleiflex Automat (1937): 197
  Rolleiflex Automat (1939): 197
  Rolleiflex Automat (MX-EVS): 197
  Rolleiflex Automat (MX-sync): 197
  Rolleiflex Automat (X-sync): 197
  Rolleiflex E: 198
  Rolleiflex E2: 198
  Rolleiflex E3: 198
  Rolleiflex F2.8 Aurum: 198
  Rolleiflex New Standard: 198
  Rolleiflex Old Standard: 198
  Rolleiflex SL26: 198
  Rolleiflex Studio: 198
  Rolleiflex T: 198
  Rolleiflex Tele: 198
  Rolleiflex Wide-Angle: 198
  Rolleimagic: 199
  Rolleimagic II: 199
  Sports Rolleiflex: 199
  Tele Rolleiflex: 198
  Wide-Angle Rolleiflex: 198
Franklin Magazine 8: 496
FRANKLIN PHOTOGRAPHIC
  INDUSTRIES (Movie): 496
Fred Flintstone (Hanna-Barbera): 225
Frena (Beck): 54
Frena Deluxe (Beck): 54
FRENNET: 199
Frennet Stereoscopic Reflex: 199
Friend Boy's Camera (Non-Camera): 525
FRIENDLY HOME PARTIES INC.
  (Non-Camera): 517
FT-2: 199
Fuji Baby Balnet: 199
Fuji Baby Lyra: 199
Fuji Balnet Baby: 199
Fuji Comex: 199
Fuji Drive: 200
Fuji Fujica Mini: 200
Fuji Fujica Single-8 P1: 496
Fuji Fujicaflex: 200
Fuji Fujipet: 200

FUJI KOGAKU SEIKI: 199-200
Fuji Lyra: 199
Fuji Lyra Six: 199
Fuji Lyra Six III: 199
Fuji Lyraflex: 200
Fuji Lyrax: 200
Fuji Pet 35: 200
FUJI PHOTO FILM CO.: 200
FUJI PHOTO FILM CO. (Movie): 496
Fuji Semi-Lyra: 199
Fujica Single-8 P1 (Fuji): 496
Fujica Mini (Fuji): 200
Fujicaflex (Fuji): 200
FUJIMOTO MFR. CO.: 200
Fujimoto Semi-Prince,II: 200
Fujipet (Fuji): 200
Fujita 66SL: 200
Fujita 66SQ: 200
Fujita 66ST: 200
Fujita Classic 35 IV: 200
FUJITA OPT. IND. LTD.: 200
Ful-Vue (Houghton Ensign): 235
Ful-Vue Super (Houghton Ensign): 235
Full-Vue (Spartus): 402
Fulvueflex (Ross Ensign): 380
Furet (Guerin): 222
FUTURA KAMERA WERK, A.G.: 200
Futura-S: 200
Futuro (Ruberg): 382
Gabri (Bencini): 57
GAF Ansco Autoset CdS (Minolta): 320
Galileo Condor I: 200
Galileo Gami 16: 200
GALILEO OPTICAL: 200
GALLUS: 200-201
Gallus Bakelite: 200
Gallus Derby: 201
Gallus Derlux: 201
Gallus Folding Rollfilm camera: 201
Gallus Stereo camera: 201
GALOOB (Non-Camera): 519
Galter Hopalong Cassidy Camera: 201
Galter Majestic: 201
Galter Pickwik: 201
GALTER PRODUCTS: 201
Galter Regal: 201
Galter Sunbeam 120: 201
Gami 16 (Galileo): 200
GAMMA: 201
Gamma (35mm): 201
Gamma (subminiature): 201
Gamma Duflex: 201
Gamma Pajtas: 201
GANDOLFI: 201
GAP Box 3x4 (Paris): 347
GAP Box 6x9 (Paris): 347
GARLAND: 202
Garland Wet Plate camera: 202
Gaudin Daguerreotype (Lerebours): 292
GAUMONT: 202
Gaumont Block-Notes: 202
Gaumont Block-Notes Stereo: 202
Gaumont Klopic: 202
Gaumont Reporter: 202
Gaumont Spido: 202
Gaumont Spido Stereo: 202
Gaumont Stereo cameras: 202

G.E. Toppers Club (Universal Univex AF): 427
GEC: 202
Gec Transistomatic Radio Camera: 202
Gelto D III (Toakoki): 416
Gem 16 Model II (Morita): 329
Gem Apparatus (Lancaster): 277
Gem Box (Anthony): 39
Gem Poco (Rochester Camera): 374
Gemflex (Showa): 396
Gemmy (Okada): 343
General (Rocket): 377
GENERAL PRODUCTS: 202
General Products Candex Jr.: 202
General Products Clix Miniature: 202
Genesee Outfit (EKC): 140
Genie: 202
GENIE CAMERA CO.: 202
GENNERT: 202-203
Gennert Folding Montauk: 202
Gennert Golf Montauk: 202
Gennert Long Focus Montauk: 203
Gennert Montauk: 202
Gennert Montauk rollfilm camera: 203
Gennert Penny Picture camera: 203
Gennert Stereoscopic Montauk: 203
Genos: 203
GENOS K.G.: 203
Genos Fix: 203
Genos Rapid: 203
George Washington Bicentennial Camera (EKC): 140
GERMAN-AMERICAN CINEMATOGRAPH AND FILM CO.: 496
German-American Everhard Schneider 35mm: 497
GERSCHEL: 203
Gerschel le Mosaic: 203
Gevabox (Gevaert): 203
GEVAERT: 203-204
Gevaert Gevabox: 203
Gevaert Ofo: 204
Gewir (Wirgin): 450
Gewirette (Wirgin): 450
GEYMET & ALKER: 204
Geymet & Alker Jumelle de Nicour: 204
GF 81, GF 82 Ring Camera (Ferro): 190
GIBSON (C.R.) CO. (Non-Camera): 518
Gift Kodak (EKC): 140
Gilbert (Hunter): 239
GILLES-FALLER: 204
Gilles-Faller Studio camera: 204
GINREI KOKI: 204
Ginrei Vesta: 204
GIREY (Non-Camera): 517
Girl Guide Kodak (EKC): 140
Girl Holding Camera
    (Non-Camera Music Box): 526
    (Non-Camera Statuette): 533
Girl Scout Camera (Herbert George): 230
Girl Scout Falcon (Utility): 429
Girl Scout Kodak (EKC): 140
Girl Scout Official Camera (Trusite): 421
Glass Camera on Tripod (Non-Camera): 527
Glenco (Canadian Camera Co.): 81
Global: 204
Global 35 (OMO): 345

Globus (Ernemann): 178
Gloria (Balda): 51
Gloria (Braun): 72
Gloriette (Braun): 72
GLOSSICK MFG. CO.: 204
Glossick Direct Positive Street Camera: 204
GLUNZ: 204-205
Glunz Folding plate camera: 204
Glunz Folding rollfilm cameras: 205
Glyphoscope (Richard): 369
Gnco: 205
Gnoflex: 205
Gnom (Huttig): 240
GNOME PHOTOGRAPHIC PRODUCTS.: 205
Gnome Pixie: 205
Go Bots 110 Camera (Playtime Products): 359
GOEKER: 205
Goeker field camera: 205
GOERZ: 205-208
Goerz Ango: 205
Goerz Ango Stereo: 206
Goerz Anschutz: 206
Goerz Anschutz Stereo: 206
Goerz Box Tengor: 206
Goerz Coat Pocket Tenax: 207
Goerz Folding Reflex: 206
Goerz Folding rollfilm camera: 207
Goerz Manufoc Tenax: 208
Goerz Minicord: 207
Goerz Minicord III: 207
Goerz Roll Tenax: 208
Goerz Roll Tenax Luxus: 208
Goerz Roll Tengor: 207
Goerz Stereo Photo Binocle: 207
Goerz Stereo Tenax: 208
Goerz Taro Tenax: 208
Goerz Tenax: 207
Goerz Tengor (Box Tengor): 206
Goerz Vest Pocket Rollfilm Tenax: 208
Goerz Vest Pocket Tenax: 207
GOLD HORSE (Non-Camera): 524,527
Golda (Goldammer): 208
GOLDAMMER: 208-209
Goldammer Golda: 208
Goldammer Goldeck 16: 208
Goldammer Goldix: 208
Goldammer GuGo: 209
Goldeck 16 (Goldammer): 208
Golden Ricoh 16 (Riken): 370
Golden Steky (Riken): 371
Goldi (Zeh): 456
Goldix (Goldammer): 208
GOLDMANN: 209
Goldmann Amateur Field camera: 209
Goldmann Field camera: 209
Goldmann Press camera: 209
Goldmann Universal Stereo camera: 209
GOLDSTEIN: 209
Goldstein Goldy: 209
Goldy (Goldstein): 209
Golf (Adox): 18
Golf IA Rapid (Adox): 18
Golf IIA (Adox): 18
Golf IIIA (Adox): 18
Golf Montauk (Gennert): 202

HALL & KEANE DESIGN (Non-Camera): 527
HALL CAMERA CO.: 224
Hall Mirror Reflex Camera: 224
Hall Pocket Camera: 224
Halloh (Ica): 242
Halma-Flex: 224
HAMAPHOT KG: 224-225
Hamaphot Modell P56L, P56M: 224
Hamaphot Modell P66: 225
Hamco: 225
Hamilton Super-Flex: 225
HANAU: 225
Hanau le Marsouin: 225
Hanau Passe-Partout: 225
Hand Camera (Chadwick): 91
HANDBAGS (Non-Camera Bags): 513
Handle (EKC): 144
Handy (Rochester Optical): 374
HANEEL TRI-VISION CO.: 225
Haneel Tri-Vision Stereo: 225
HANIMEX: 225
Hanimex Holiday, Holiday II: 225
Hanken (Riken): 371
HANNA-BARBERA: 225-226
Hanna-Barbera Fred Flintstone: 225
Hanna-Barbera Huckelberry Hound: 225
Hanna-Barbera Yogi Bear: 225
Hansa (Canon): 82
Hansa 35 (Balda): 51
HANSEN: 226
Hansen Norka: 226
Hapo (Photo-Porst): 354
Haponette B (Photo-Porst): 354
Happi-Time (Herbert George): 229
Happy: 226
Happy (K.W.): 273
Happy (Minolta): 313
Happy Times Instant Camera (EKC): 140
HARBOE: 226
Harboe Wood box camera: 226
HARE: 226
Hare Stereo camera: 226
Hare Tailboard camera: 226
Hare Tourist camera: 226
Hare Tropical wet-plate stereo: 226
Hare Wet-plate stereo camera: 226
Harmony: 226
Hartex: 226
HARUKAWA: 226
Harukawa Septon Pen Camera: 226
Harukawa Septon Penletto: 226
Harvard camera (Mason): 307
HASBRO INDUSTRIES (Non-Camera): 539
HASSELBLAD: 226-227
Hasselblad 500C: 227
Hasselblad 1000F: 227
Hasselblad 1600F: 227
Hasselblad Aerial Camera HK7: 226
Hasselblad Plush Toy (Non-Camera): 527
Hasselblad Super Wide Angle: 227
Hat Detective Camera (Adams & Co.): 16
Hawk-Eye (Blair): 65
Hawk-Eye (EKC): 141-143
Hawkeye Ace (EKC): 141
Hawk-Eye Box (Blair): 65
Hawk-Eye Detective (Blair): 65

Hawk-Eye Detective (Boston): 70
Hawk-Eye Flashfun (EKC): 141
Hawk-Eye Flashfun II (EKC): 141
Hawk-Eye Junior (Blair): 65
Hawk-Eye Special (EKC): 142-143
Hawkette (EKC): 141
Heag (Ernemann): 179
Heag (tropical) (Ernemann): 184
Heag 0 (Ernemann): 179
Heag 00 (Ernemann): 179
Heag I (Ernemann): 179
Heag I Stereo (Ernemann): 179
Heag II (Ernemann): 179
Heag III (Ernemann): 179
Heag IV (stereo) (Ernemann): 179
Heag IX Universal (Ernemann): 180
Heag V (Ernemann): 180
Heag VI (Ernemann): 180
Heag VI (stereo) (Ernemann): 180
Heag VII (Ernemann): 180
Heag XI (Ernemann): 181
Heag XII (Ernemann): 181
Heag XII Model III stereo (Ernemann): 181
Heag XIV (Ernemann): 181
Heag XV (plate type) (Ernemann): 181
Heag XV (rollfilm type) (Ernemann): 181
Heag XVI (Ernemann): 181
HEALTHWAYS: 227-228
Healthways Mako Shark: 227
Heidescop (Franke & Heidecke): 195
HEILAND PHOTO PRODUCTS: 228
Heiland Premiere: 228
Heli-Clack (Rietzschel): 369
Heli-Clack Universal I, II (Rietzschel): 370
Heliar Reflex (Voigtlander): 435
HELIN-NOBLE INC.: 228
Helin-Noble Noble 126: 228
Heliomatic 8 S2R (Nizo): 502
Helios (Huttig): 240
HELIX (Non-Camera): 527
Hello Kitty (Sanrio): 383
Helm Bugs Bunny: 228
Helm Mickey Mouse: 228
Helm Mickey Mouse Head: 228
Helm Punky Brewster: 228
Helm Snoopy-Matic: 228
HELM TOY CORP.: 228
HENDREN ENTERPRISE: 228
Hendren Octopus "The Weekender": 228
HENNING: 228
Henning Rhaco: 228
Henning Rhaco Monopol: 228
Henry Clay (American Optical): 29
Henso Reporter (Hensoldt): 229
Henso Standard (Hensoldt): 229
HENSOLDT: 228-229
Hensoldt Henso Reporter: 229
Hensoldt Henso Standard: 229
Herbert George Boy Scout Camera: 230
Herbert George Brownie Scout: 230
HERBERT GEORGE CO.: 229-230
Herbert George Cub Scout Camera: 230
Herbert George Davy Crockett: 229
Herbert George Donald Duck: 229
Herbert George Flick-N-Flash: 229
Herbert George Girl Scout Camera: 230
Herbert George Happi-Time: 229

HERBERT GEORGE HERCO - HOUGHTON ENSIGN BOX

Ilford Sportsman: 251
Ilford Sprite: 251
Ilford Sprite 35: 251
Ilford Witness: 251
ILLCO TOY CO. (Non-Camera): 526
Iloca I, Ia, II, IIa (Witt): 451
Iloca Quick A, B (Witt): 451
Iloca Rapid (Witt): 451
Iloca Reporter (Witt): 451
Iloca Stereo (original) (Witt): 451
Iloca Stereo I, II (Witt): 451
Iloca Stereo Rapid (Witt): 451
Imp (Beaurline): 53
Impera (Fex): 190
Impera 4x4 (Indo): 252
Imperial 6x6 (Braun): 72
Imperial Box 6x6 (Braun): 72
Imperial Box 6x9 (Braun): 72
IMPERIAL CAMERA & MFG. CO.: 252
IMPERIAL CAMERA CORP.: 251-252
IMPERIAL CAMERA CORP. (HERBERT
  GEORGE): 229
Imperial Cinex: 251
Imperial Cubex IV: 251
Imperial Debonair (Herbert George): 229
Imperial Delta: 251
Imperial Deltex: 251
Imperial Deluxe Six-Twenty Twin Lens
  Reflex: 251
Imperial Lark: 251
Imperial Magazine Camera: 252
Imperial Mark 27: 251
Imperial Mark XII Flash: 251
Imperial Mark XII Flash (Herbert George):
  229
Imperial Matey 127 Flash: 251
Imperial Mercury Satellite 127: 251
Imperial Nor-Flash 127: 251
Imperial Pocket (Thornton-Pickard): 413
Imperial Rambler Flash Camera: 251
Imperial Reflex: 251
Imperial Reflex (Herbert George): 229
Imperial Satellite II: 251
Imperial Satellite 127 (Herbert George): 229
Imperial Satellite Flash (Herbert George):
  229
Imperial Savoy: 251
Imperial Scout cameras: 251
Imperial Six-Twenty: 251
Imperial Six-Twenty Reflex: 251
Imperial Stereo (Thornton-Pickard): 413
Imperial Triple Extension
  (Thornton-Pickard): 413
IMPULSE LTD.: 252
Impulse Voltron Starshooter 110: 252
Incredible Hulk (Vanity Fair): 430
INDO: 252
Indo Impera 4x4: 252
INDRA: 252
Indra Indra-Lux: 252
Indra-Lux (Indra): 252
INDUSTRIAL SYNDICATE OF
  CINOSCOPE (Movie): 498
Industrial Syndicate Cinoscope: 498
INDUSTRIEA BRASILEIRA: 252
Industriea Brasileira Plik: 252
Inette: 252

Infallible (Bell & Howell Electric Eye 127):
  56
Inflex: 252
Infra (Oehler): 343
Ingento (Burke & James): 74
INGERSOLL: 252
Ingersoll Shure-Shot: 252
Ingo (Ica): 243
Inos (Voigtlander): 435
Inos II (Voigtlander): 435
Inos II, Two-format (Voigtlander): 436
Inspectograph Camera (Graflex): 221
Insta-Flash (Herbert George): 229
Instacora E (Dacora): 108
Instamatic (EKC): 143-144
Instamatic Camera Bank (Non-Camera):
  514
Instamatic Reflex (EKC): 144
Instamatic S-10, S-20 (EKC): 144
Instamatic-style water camera
  (Non-Camera): 533
Instanto (Underwood): 423
Instantograph (Lancaster): 278
INTERNATIONAL METAL & FERROTYPE
  CO.: 253
International Metal Diamond Gun
  Ferrotype: 253
International Patent (Lancaster): 278
INTERNATIONAL PROJECTOR CORP.
  (Movie): 498
International Projector Simplex Pockette:
  498
INTERNATIONAL RESEARCH CORP.
  (Argus): 42
Invincibel (Mader): 301
Invisible Camera (Talbot): 411
Iris, Iris Deluxe (Universal): 425
Irving (Scovill): 385
IRWIN: 253
IRWIN (Non-Camera): 535
IRWIN CORP. (Movie): 498
Irwin Kandor: 253
Irwin Kandor Komet: 253
Irwin Magazine Model 16,21,24: 498
Irwin Reflex: 253
ISE: 253
Ise Edelweiss Deluxe: 253
ISING: 253
Ising Isoflex I: 253
Ising Puck: 253
Ising Pucky: 253
Ising Pucky I,Ia,II: 253
ISO: 253
Iso Bilux: 253
Iso Duplex 120: 253
Iso Rapid (Agfa): 20
Iso Standard: 253
Iso Super Duplex 120: 253
Isoflash Rapid (Agfa): 20
Isoflex I (Ising): 253
Isola I,II (Agfa): 21
Isolar (Agfa): 21
Isolar Luxus (Agfa): 21
Isolette (Agfa): 21
Isolette L (Agfa): 21
Isolette Super (Agfa): 21
Isolette V (Agfa): 21

Klopic (Gaumont): 202
KN35 (Certo): 91
Knack Detective (Scovill): 385
Kneb (Mashpriborintorg Kiev): 307
KNICKERBOCKER TOY CO.
 (Non-Camera): 524
KNIGHT & SONS: 261
Knights No. 3 Sliding-box camera: 251
Knox (Wuensche): 453
KOBLIC: 261
Koblic Epifoka: 261
KOCH: 261
Koch Stereo wet-plate camera: 261
KOCHMANN: 262-263
Kochmann Enolde: 262
Kochmann Enolde I,II,III: 262
Kochmann Korelle: 262
Kochmann Korelle K: 262
Kochmann Korelle P: 262
Kochmann Master Reflex: 262
Kochmann Meister Korelle: 262
Kochmann Reflex Korelle: 262
Kodaclone Slide (Non-Camera): 530
Kodacolor 400 Film Radio (Non-Camera):
 529
Kodacolor VR 200 sharpener
 (Non-Camera): 527
Kodak (original) (EKC): 119
Kodak 35 (EKC): 146
Kodak 35 (Military PH-324) (EKC): 146
Kodak 35 w/ Rangefinder (EKC): 146
Kodak 1880-1980 Centennial Plate
 (Non-Camera): 523
Kodak Bank (Non-Camera): 514
Kodak Box 620 (EKC): 145
Kodak Cine Automatic (EKC): 493
Kodak Cine Scopemeter (EKC): 493
Kodak Dice Cup (Non-Camera): 529
Kodak Disc 4000 Photokina
 (Non-Camera): 519
Kodak Disc Bank (Non-Camera): 514
Kodak Ektra (EKC): 135
Kodak Ektra 1 (EKC): 135
Kodak Ektra 2 (EKC): 135
Kodak Ektra II (EKC): 135
Kodak Ektra 200 (EKC): 135
Kodak Electric 8 Automatic (EKC): 493
Kodak Ensemble (EKC): 135
Kodak Escort 8 (EKC): 493
Kodak Film-Lighter (Non-Camera): 515
Kodak Instant Color Film PR10 Radio
 (Non-Camera): 530
Kodak Junior (EKC): 145
Kodak Junior Six-16 (EKC): 145
Kodak Junior Six-16 Series II (EKC): 145
Kodak Junior Six-16 Series III (EKC): 145
Kodak Junior Six-20 (EKC): 145
Kodak Junior Six-20 Series II (EKC): 145
Kodak Junior Six-20 Series III (EKC): 145
Kodak Medalist (EKC): 147
Kodak Medalist II (EKC): 147
Kodak Monitor Six-16 (EKC): 147
Kodak Monitor Six-20 (EKC): 147
Kodak Mug (Non-Camera): 523
Kodak Recomar 18 (EKC): 156
Kodak Recomar 33 (EKC): 156

Kodak Reflex (EKC): 145-146
Kodak Reflex IA (EKC): 145
Kodak Reflex II (EKC): 146
Kodak Senior Six-16 (EKC): 163
Kodak Senior Six-20 (EKC): 163
Kodak Series II (EKC): 146
Kodak Series III (EKC): 146
Kodak Six-16 (EKC): 164
Kodak Six-16 (Improved) (EKC): 164
Kodak Six-20 (EKC): 164
Kodak Six-20 (Improved) (EKC): 164
Kodak Special Six-16 (EKC): 165
Kodak Special Six-20 (EKC): 165
Kodak Startech (EKC): 166
Kodak Stereo (35mm) (EKC): 166
Kodak Suprema (EKC): 167
Kodak Tele-Ektra (EKC): 167
Kodak Tele-Instamatic (EKC): 167
Kodak Tourist (EKC): 167
Kodak Tourist II (EKC): 167
Kodak Trimlite Instamatic (EKC): 167
Kodak Truck 1880-1980 (Non-Camera):
 538
Kodak Truck/Whistle (Non-Camera): 537
Kodak Van (Non-Camera): 537
Kodak Winner Pocket (EKC): 170
Kodak Zoom 8 Reflex (EKC): 493
Kodamatic Instant Cameras (EKC): 144
Kodascope Eight (EKC): 494
Kodascope, A,B,C (EKC): 493
KODEL ELEC. & MFG. CO. (Movie): 499
Kodel Kemco Homovie: 499
Kodet (EKC): 146-147
KOEDA: 263
Koeda Colly: 263
KOEHNLEIN: 263
Koehnlein Wiko Standard: 263
KOGAKU: 263
KOGAKU SEIKI (NICCA): 337
Kokka Hand (Kuribayashi): 271
Kola (Kolar): 263
Kola Diar (Kolar): 263
KOLAR: 263
Kolar Box Kolex: 263
Kolar Kola: 263
Kolar Kola Diar: 263
Kolar Kolex: 263
Kolex (Kolar): 263
Kolibri (Zeiss): 471
Kolorcube (Non-Camera): 529
Kolt (Okada): 343
Komaflex-S (Kowa): 266
Kombi (Kemper): 257
Komlosy: 263
Konair Ruby (Yamato): 453
Konan 16 (Chiyoda): 93
Konan 16 (Minolta): 323
Konica (Konishiroku): 264
Konica II (Konishiroku): 264
Konica III (Konishiroku): 264
Konica IIIA (Konishiroku): 264
Konica IIIM (Konishiroku): 264
Konica Autoreflex (Konishiroku): 264
Konica F (Konishiroku): 264
Konilette 35 (Konishiroku): 264
Konishiroku Baby Pearl): 263
KONISHIROKU KOGAKU: 263-265

Kuribayashi Petri Color 35, 35E: 273
Kuribayashi Petri Compact: 272
Kuribayashi Petri Compact 17: 272
Kuribayashi Petri Compact E: 272
Kuribayashi Petri Computor 35: 272
Kuribayashi Petri EBn: 272
Kuribayashi Petri Eight: 500
Kuribayashi Petri ES Auto 1.7: 272
Kuribayashi Petri ES Auto 2.8: 272
Kuribayashi Petri FA-1: 273
Kuribayashi Petri Flex: 272
Kuribayashi Petri Flex Seven: 273
Kuribayashi Petri Flex V: 273
Kuribayashi Petri Fotochrome: 273
Kuribayashi Petri FT: 273
Kuribayashi Petri FT-II: 273
Kuribayashi Petri FT 500: 273
Kuribayashi Petri FT 1000: 273
Kuribayashi Petri FT EE: 273
Kuribayashi Petri FTE: 273
Kuribayashi Petri FTX: 273
Kuribayashi Petri Grip Pak 110: 273
Kuribayashi Petri Half: 272
Kuribayashi Petri Hi-Lite: 272
Kuribayashi Petri Instant Back: 273
Kuribayashi Petri Junior: 272
Kuribayashi Petri M 35: 272
Kuribayashi Petri MFT 1000: 273
Kuribayashi Petri Micro Compact: 273
Kuribayashi Petri Micro MF-1: 273
Kuribayashi Petri Penta: 273
Kuribayashi Petri Penta V2: 273
Kuribayashi Petri Penta V3: 273
Kuribayashi Petri Penta V6: 273
Kuribayashi Petri Penta V6-II: 273
Kuribayashi Petri Pocket 2: 273
Kuribayashi Petri Power Eight: 500
Kuribayashi Petri Prest: 272
Kuribayashi Petri Pro Seven: 272
Kuribayashi Petri Push-Pull 110: 273
Kuribayashi Petri Racer: 272
Kuribayashi Petri RF, RF 120: 272
Kuribayashi Petri Semi: 272
Kuribayashi Petri Seven: 272
Kuribayashi Petri Seven S: 272
Kuribayashi Petri Seven S-II: 272
Kuribayashi Petri Super: 272
Kuribayashi Petri Super Eight: 500
Kuribayashi Petri Super V: 272
Kuribayashi Plate cameras: 271
Kuribayashi Romax Hand: 271
Kuribayashi Semi First: 271
Kuribayashi Tokiwa Hand: 271
K.W.: 273-276
K.W. Happy: 273
K.W. Jolly: 274
K.W. Kawee: 274
K.W. Patent Etui: 274
K.W. Patent Etui Luxus: 274
K.W. Pilot 6: 274
K.W. Pilot Reflex: 274
K.W. Pilot Super: 274
K.W. Pocket Dalco: 274
K.W. Praktica: 275
K.W. Praktica FX: 275
K.W. Praktica FX2: 275
K.W. Praktica FX3: 275

K.W. Praktica Nova: 275
K.W. Praktiflex: 275
K.W. Praktiflex II: 276
K.W. Praktiflex FX: 276
K.W. Praktina IIa: 276
K.W. Praktina FX: 276
K.W. Praktisix: 276
K.W. Praktisix II: 276
K.W. Reflex-Box: 276
K.W. Rival Reflex: 276
Kwanon (Canon): 82
KYOEI TRADING CO. (Non-Camera): 515
Kyoto Lovely: 276
KYOTO SEIKO CO.: 276
L.A. 35mm Movie camera: 500
L.A. MOTION PICTURE CO. (Movie): 500
L'As (E.L.C.): 173
La Belle Pal (Bolsey): 68
LA CROSSE CAMERA CO.: 277
La Crosse Snapshot: 277
LA ROSE: 277
La Rose Rapitake: 277
LAACK: 277
Laack Ferrotype camera: 277
Laack Merkur: 277
Laack Padie: 277
Laack Tropical camera: 277
Laack Wanderer: 277
Lacon C: 277
LACON CAMERA CO. INC.: 277
Ladies Cameras (Lancaster): 278-279
Ladies Gem Camera (Lancaster): 278
Lady Carefree (Argus): 45
Lafayette 35 (Tokiwa): 416
Lamp (Non-Camera): 525
LAMPERTI & GARBAGNATI: 277
Lamperti & Garbagnati Detective: 277
Lamperti & Garbagnati Wet-plate: 277
LANCART: 277
Lancart Xyz: 277
LANCASTER: 277-280
Lancaster Brass Bound Instantograph: 277
Lancaster Gem Apparatus: 277
Lancaster Instantograph: 278
Lancaster International Patent: 278
Lancaster Kamrex: 278
Lancaster Ladies Cameras: 278-279
Lancaster Ladies Gem Camera: 278
Lancaster Meritoire: 279
Lancaster Merveilleux: 279
Lancaster Omnigraph: 279
Lancaster Postage Stamp Cameras: 279
Lancaster Rover: 279
Lancaster Special Brass Bound
    Instantograph: 279
Lancaster Stereo Instantograph: 279
Lancaster Watch Camera: 280
Lancer (Ansco): 34
Lantern slide projector pencil sharpener
    (Non-Camera): 528
Lapel pin (Non-Camera Krugener
    Delta-Car): 524
Lark (Imperial): 251
Laurelflex (Tokyo Kogaku): 416
Laurie Dick Tracy: 280
LAURIE IMPORT LTD.: 280
Laurie Miniature Novelty Camera: 280

Minolta 24 Rapid: 320
Minolta 35, Model I: 315
Minolta 35 (I) (Type A): 315
Minolta 35 (I) (Type B): 315
Minolta 35 (I) (Type C): 315
Minolta 35 (I) (Type D): 315
Minolta 35, Model II: 316
Minolta 35, Model E: 315
Minolta 35, Model F: 315
Minolta A: 316
Minolta A2: 316
Minolta A3: 316
Minolta A5: 316
Minolta Aerial camera: 315
Minolta AL: 318
Minolta AL-2: 318
Minolta AL-F: 319
Minolta AL-S: 319
Minolta Ansco Autoset: 320
Minolta Anscoset III: 318
Minolta Auto Minolta: 314
Minolta Auto Press: 315
Minolta Auto Semi-Minolta: 313
Minolta Auto Wide: 317
Minolta Autocord: 321-322
Minolta Autocord CdS I,II,III: 321
Minolta Autocord L: 322
Minolta Autocord LMX: 322
Minolta Autocord RA: 322
Minolta Automat: 322
Minolta Baby Minolta: 314
Minolta Best: 314
Minolta ER: 320
Minolta Electro Shot: 321
Minolta GAF Ansco Autoset CdS: 320
Minolta Happy: 313
Minolta Hi-Matic: 319
Minolta Hi-Matic 7: 320
Minolta Konan 16: 323
Minolta Marble: 314
Minolta Maxxum: 324
Minolta Memo: 315
Minolta Miniflex: 321
Minolta Minoltacord: 321
Minolta Minoltacord Automat: 322
Minolta Minoltaflex (I): 322
Minolta Minoltaflex II: 322
Minolta Minoltaflex IIB: 322
Minolta Minoltaflex III: 322
Minolta Minoltina P: 320
Minolta Minoltina-S: 320
Minolta Nifca-Dox: 312
Minolta Nifca-Klapp: 312
Minolta Nifca-Sports: 312
Minolta Nifcalette: 312
Minolta Repo: 319
Minolta Repo-S: 319
Minolta Sales & Service: ADV
Minolta SR-1: 317
Minolta SR-1S: 317
Minolta SR-2: 317
Minolta SR-3: 318
Minolta SR-7: 319
Minolta SR-M: 321
Minolta Semi-Minolta: 313
Minolta Semi-Minolta I: 313
Minolta Semi-Minolta II: 313

Minolta-Six: 314
Minolta Sky: 316
Minolta Sonocon 16mm MB-ZA: 323
Minolta Super A: 316
Minolta Uniomat: 318
Minolta Uniomat III: 318
Minolta V2: 318
Minolta V3: 318
Minolta XD: 321
Minolta XD-7: 321
Minolta XD-11: 321
Minoltacord (Minolta): 321
Minoltacord Automat (Minolta): 322
Minoltaflex (I) (Minolta): 322
Minoltaflex II (Minolta): 322
Minoltaflex IIB (Minolta): 322
Minoltaflex III (Minolta): 322
Minoltina P (Minolta): 320
Minoltina-S (Minolta): 320
MINOX: 324-325
Minox, original: 324
Minox A: 324
Minox B: 324
Minox BL: 325
Minox C: 325
Minox II: 324
Minox III: 324
Minox III, Gold-plated: 324
Minox III-S: 324
Minox "Made in USSR": 324
Minute 16 (Universal): 425
M.I.O.M. Lec Junior: 325
M.I.O.M. Loisir: 325
M.I.O.M. Miom: 325
M.I.O.M. Photax: 325
Miom (M.I.O.M.): 325
Miracle: 325
Miraflex (Compco): 97
Mirage: 325
Miranda A: 325
Miranda C: 325
MIRANDA CAMERA CO. LTD.: 325-326
Miranda D: 325
Miranda F: 325
Miranda G: 325
Miranda S: 325
Miranda Standard: 326
Miranda T: 326
Miranda T II: 326
Miroflex (Contessa): 101
Miroflex A (Zeiss): 472
Miroflex B (Zeiss): 472
Mirror Reflex Camera (Hall): 224
MISUZU TRADING CO.: 326
Misuzu Midget Jilona: 326
Misuzu Midget Jilona Model III: 326
Misuzu Midget Jilona No. 2: 326
MITCHELL CAMERA CORP. (Movie): 501
Mitchell: 501
Mithra 47: 326
Mity: 326
MIYAGAWA SEISAKUSHO: 326
Miyagawa Boltax: 326
Miyagawa Picny: 326
MIZUHO KOKI: 326
Mizuho-Six: 326
Mockba 5: 327

MOELLER: 327
Moeller Cambinox: 327
MOLLIER: 327
Mollier Le Cent Vues: 327
MOLTENI: 327
Molteni Detective camera: 327
MOM (MAGYAR OPTIKAI MUVEK): 327
MOM Fotobox: 327
MOM Mometta: 327
MOM Mometta II: 327
MOM Momikon: 327
Momehm (Moment): 327
Moment: 327
Mometta (MOM): 327
Mometta II (MOM): 327
Momikon (MOM): 327
MONARCH MFG. CO.: 327
Monarch 620: 327
Monarch Flash-Master: 327
Monarch Fleetwood: 327
Monarch Flex-Master: 327
Monarch Kando Reflex: 327
Monarch Photo-Master Twin 620: 327
Monarch Pickwick: 327
Monarch Remington: 327
MONARCK MFG. CO.: 327
Monarck: 327
Monitor (Rochester Optical): 375
Monitor Six-16 (EKC): 147
Monitor Six-20 (EKC): 147
MONO-WERK: 328
Mono-Trumpf: 328
Monobloc (Jeanneret): 254
Monobloc (Liebe): 294
Monopol (Huttig Magazine): 240
MONROE CAMERA CO.: 328
MONROE RESEARCH (Webster): 442
MONROE SALES CO.: 328
Monroe Folding plate cameras: 328
Monroe Model 7: 328
Monroe Sales Color-flex: 328
Montana (Montanus): 328
MONTANUS: 328
Montanus Montana: 328
Montanus Montiflex: 328
Montanus Rocca Super Reflex: 328
Montauk (Gennert): 202
Montauk rollfilm camera (Gennert): 203
Monte 35 (Shinsei): 395
Monte Carlo (Monti): 329
Monte Carlo Special (Monti): 329
MONTGOMERY WARD & CO.: 328-329
Montgomery Ward Model B: 328
Montgomery Ward MW: 328
Montgomery Ward Thornwood Dandy: 328
Montgomery Ward Wardflex: 328
Montgomery Ward Wards 35: 328
Montgomery Ward Wards xp400: 328
MONTI: 329
Monti Monte Carlo: 329
Monti Monte Carlo Special: 329
Montiflex (Montanus): 328
MOORE & CO.: 329
Moore Aptus Ferrotype Camera: 329
MOORSE: 329
Moorse Single-lens Stereo: 329
Morita Gem 16 Model II: 329

Morita Kiku 16 Model II: 329
MORITA TRADING CO.: 329
MORLEY: 329
Morley Wet-plate camera: 329
Morley Wet-plate stereo camera: 329
Mosaic (Gerschel): 203
Moscow: 329
Moskwa (Moscow): 329
Mosquito (Bauchet): 53
Motion Picture Cameras Wanted: ADV
Moto-Rapid C (Agfa): 22
Motoca (Kashiwa): 257
Motor-Kamera (Agfa): 22
Motormatic 35 (EKC): 148
Motormatic 35F (EKC): 148
Motormatic 35R4 (EKC): 148
MOUNTFORD: 329
Mountford Button tintype camera: 329
Mounts (Darkroom): 542
MOURFIELD: 329
Mourfield Direct Positive Camera: 329
Moviegraph (Keystone): 499
MOZAR: 329
Mozar Diana: 329
MOUSE CAMERAS (Non-Camera): 525
MOVETTE CAMERA CORP. (Movie): 501
Movette 17½mm: 501
Movex 8 (Agfa): 482
Movex 8L (Agfa): 483
Movex 16-12B (Agfa): 483
Movex 16-12L (Agfa): 483
Movex 30B, 30L (Agfa): 483
Movex 88 (Agfa): 483
Movex 88L (Agfa): 484
Movex Automatic I (Agfa): 484
Movex Reflex (Agfa): 484
Movexoom (Agfa): 484
Movie Camera Decanter (Non-Camera): 522
MOVIE CAMERAS: 482-512
Movie Maker (Vitascope): 510
Movie Shot (Non-Camera): 522
Movie viewer (Non-Camera): 539
Moviematic: 501
MOVIEMATIC CAMERA CORP. (Movie): 501
Movikon 8 (Zeiss): 512
Movikon 16 (Zeiss): 512
MOY (Movie): 501
Moy and Bastie's: 501
M.P.C. (Vive): 431
Mr. Weekend Button (Non-Camera): 524
MUELLER: 329
Mueller Noris: 329
Mug (Non-Camera Kodak Mug): 523
Mugette Camera-Lighter (Non-Camera): 516
Multex (Houghton Ensign): 236
Multi-Speed Precision Camera (Linhof): 295
Multicolore (Rochechovard): 373
MULTIPLE TOYMAKERS: 329-330
Multiple Toymakers Camera Kit, Wonderful Camera: 329
Multiplying Camera (Smith): 399
Multiplying View Camera (Wing): 449
Multiprint (Buess): 73

NEW YORK FERROTYPE CO.: 335
New York Tintype camera: 335
New York World's Fair Baby Brownie
 (EKC): 124
New York World's Fair Bullet (EKC): 131
Newgold (Ihagee): 249
NEWMAN & GUARDIA: 335
Newman & Guardia Baby Sibyl: 336
    Deluxe: 335
    Excelsior: 336
    Folding Reflex: 335
    New Ideal Sibyl: 336
    New Special Sibyl: 336
    Nydia: 336
    Sibyl: 336
    Sibyl Deluxe: 336
    Sibyl Stereo: 337
    Trellis: 337
    Twin Lens Reflex: 337
    Universal Pattern B: 337
    Universal Special Pattern B: 337
NEWMAN & SINCLAIR (Movie): 501
Newman Auto Kine Camera, Model E: 501
Newness Express (Murer): 331
Newton New Vue: 337
NEWTON PHOTO PRODUCTS: 337
NIAGARA CAMERA CO.: 337
Niagara No. 2: 337
NICCA CAMERA WORKS: 337
Nicca IIIA: 337
Nicca IIIB: 337
Nicca 3F: 337
Nicca IIIL: 337
Nicca IIIS: 337
Nicca 3S: 337
Nicca 4: 337
Nicca 5: 337
Nicca 33: 337
Nicca L-3: 337
Nicca Nippon: 337
Nicca Original: 337
Nicca Type 3: 337
Nichibei (Yen-Kame): 456
Nichiryo Nicnon Binocular Camera: 337
NICHIRYO TRADING CO.: 337-338
Nicnon Binocular Camera (Nichiryo): 337
NIELL & SIMONS: 338
Niell & Simons Lopa: 338
NIEZOLDI & KRAMER (NIZO): 502
Nifca-Dox (Minolta): 312
Nifca-Klapp (Minolta): 312
Nifca-Sports (Minolta): 312
Nifcalette (Minolta): 312
Night Exakta (Ihagee): 248
Night Hawk Detective (Manhattan): 304
NIHON KOKI: 338
Nihon Nescon 35: 338
NIHON PRECISION INDUSTRY: 338
NIHON SEIKI: 338
Nihon Well Standard: 338
Nihon Zany: 338
Nikette (Fischer): 191
Nikkorex (Nippon): 339
Nikkorex 8, 8F (Nippon): 501
Nikkorex Zoom 8 (Nippon): 501
Niklas (Ica): 244
Niko: 338

NIKOH CO. LTD.: 338
Nikoh Enica-Six: 338
Nikoh Minimax-Lite: 338
Nikoh Supra Photolite: 338
Nikon I (Nippon): 339
Nikon Accessories (Nippon): 341
Nikon Historical Society: ADV
Nikon M (Nippon): 339
Nikon RF Wanted: ADV
Nikon S (Nippon): 339
Nikon S2 (Nippon): 339
Nikon S3 (Nippon): 340
Nikon S3M (Nippon): 340
Nikon S4 (Nippon): 340
Nikon SP (Nippon): 340
Nil Melior Stereo (Macris-Boucher): 301
Ninoka: 338
Nippon (Nicca): 337
NIPPON CAMERA WORKS (NICCA): 337
NIPPON KOGAKU (Movie): 501
NIPPON KOGAKU K.K.: 338-341
Nippon Nikkorex 8, 8F: 501
Nippon Nikkorex Zoom 8: 501
NISHIDA KOGAKU: 341-342
Nishida Mikado: 341
Nishida Westar Autorol: 342
Nitor (Agfa): 22
NITTO SEIKO: 342
Nitto Elega-35: 342
Nixe (Ica): 244
Nixe (Zeiss): 473
NIZO (Movie): 502
Nizo Exposomat 8R: 502
Nizo Heliomatic 8 S2R: 502
No Name Contax (Zeiss): 464
No Need Dark Room (Yen-Kame): 456
No. 0 Brownie (EKC): 123
No. 0 Buster Brown (Ansco): 32
No. 0 Folding Pocket Kodak (EKC): 138
No. 0 Graphic (Graflex): 216
No. 0 Premo Junior (EKC): 153
No. 00 Cartridge Premo (EKC): 152
No. 1 Ansco Junior: 33
No. 1 Autographic Kodak Junior (EKC): 121
No. 1 Autographic Kodak Special (EKC):
 121
No. 1 Brownie (EKC): 123
No. 1 Cone Pocket Kodak (EKC): 133
No. 1 Film Premo (EKC): 152
No. 1 Folding Ansco: 33
No. 1 Folding Buster Brown (Ansco): 32
No. 1 Folding Pocket Kodak (EKC): 138
No. 1 Goodwin Jr. (Ansco): 33
No. 1 Kodak (EKC): 119
No. 1 Kodak Junior (EKC): 145
No. 1 Kodak Series III (EKC): 146
No. 1 Panoram Kodak (EKC): 149
No. 1 Pocket Kodak (EKC): 150
No. 1 Pocket Kodak Junior (EKC): 150
No. 1 Pocket Kodak Series II (EKC): 151
No. 1 Pocket Kodak Special (EKC): 151
No. 1 Premo Junior (EKC): 153
No. 1 Premoette (EKC): 154
No. 1 Premoette Junior (EKC): 155
No. 1 Premoette Junior Special (EKC): 155
No. 1 Premoette Special (EKC): 155
No. 1 Seneca Junior (Seneca): 392

No. 1 Special Folding Ansco: 33
No. 1 Tourist Buckeye (American Camera Mfg.): 28
No. 1A Ansco Junior: 33
No. 1A Autographic Kodak (EKC): 120
No. 1A Autographic Kodak Junior (EKC): 121
No. 1A Autographic Kodak Special (EKC): 121
No. 1A Folding Ansco: 33
No. 1A Folding Goodwin (Ansco): 33
No. 1A Folding Hawk-Eye (EKC): 141
No. 1A Folding Pocket Kodak (EKC): 139
No. 1A Folding Pocket Kodak Special (EKC): 139
No. 1A Folding Rexo (Burke & James): 75
No. 1A Gift Kodak (EKC): 140
No. 1A Ingento Jr. (Burke & James): 74
No. 1A Kodak Junior (EKC): 145
No. 1A Kodak Series III (EKC): 146
No. 1A Pocket Kodak (EKC): 150
No. 1A Pocket Kodak Junior (EKC): 150
No. 1A Pocket Kodak Series II (EKC): 151
No. 1A Pocket Kodak Special (EKC): 151
No. 1A Premo Junior (EKC): 153
No. 1A Premoette (EKC): 154
No. 1A Premoette Junior (EKC): 155
No. 1A Premoette Junior Special (EKC): 155
No. 1A Premoette Special (EKC): 155
No. 1A Rexo Jr. (Burke & James): 75
No. 1A Special Kodak (EKC): 165
No. 1A Speed Kodak (EKC): 165
No. 2 Brownie (EKC): 123
No. 2 Buckeye (American Camera Mfg.): 28
No. 2 Bull's-Eye (EKC): 130
No. 2 Bull's-Eye Special (EKC): 130
No. 2 Bullet (EKC): 131
No. 2 Bullet Special (EKC): 131
No. 2 Buster Brown (Ansco): 32
No. 2 Cartridge Hawk-Eye (EKC): 141
No. 2 Cartridge Premo (EKC): 152
No. 2 Eureka (EKC): 135
No. 2 Eureka Jr. (EKC): 135
No. 2 Falcon (EKC): 136
No. 2 Film Pack Hawk-Eye (EKC): 141
No. 2 Flexo Kodak (EKC): 136
No. 2 Folding Autographic Brownie (EKC): 126
No. 2 Folding Brownie (EKC): 126
No. 2 Folding Bull's-Eye (EKC): 130
No. 2 Folding Cartridge Hawk-Eye (EKC): 142
No. 2 Folding Cartridge Premo (EKC): 153
No. 2 Folding Film Pack Hawk-Eye (EKC): 142
No. 2 Folding Hawk-Eye Special (EKC): 142
No. 2 Folding Pocket Brownie (EKC): 127
No. 2 Folding Pocket Kodak (EKC): 139
No. 2 Folding Rainbow Hawk-Eye (EKC): 142
No. 2 Folding Rainbow Hawk-Eye Special (EKC): 142
No. 2 Goodwin (Ansco): 33
No. 2 Hawk-Eye Special (EKC): 143
No. 2 Hawkette (EKC): 141

No. 2 Kewpie (Conley): 98
No. 2 Kodak (EKC): 119
No. 2 Rainbow Hawk-Eye (EKC): 142
No. 2 Stereo Brownie (EKC): 129
No. 2 Stereo Kodak (EKC): 166
No. 2 Target Hawk-Eye (EKC): 143
No. 2 Target Hawk-Eye Junior (EKC): 143
No. 2 Weno Hawk-Eye (Blair): 66
No. 2 Weno Hawk-Eye (EKC): 143
No. 2A Brownie (EKC): 124
No. 2A Buster Brown (Ansco): 32
No. 2A Cartridge Hawk-Eye (EKC): 141
No. 2A Cartridge Premo (EKC): 152
No. 2A Film Pack Hawk-Eye (EKC): 141
No. 2A Folding Autographic Brownie (EKC): 126
No. 2A Folding Buster Brown (Ansco): 32
No. 2A Folding Cartridge Hawk-Eye (EKC): 142
No. 2A Folding Cartridge Premo (EKC): 153
No. 2A Folding Hawk-Eye Special (EKC): 142
No. 2A Folding Pocket Brownie (EKC): 127
No. 2A Folding Rainbow Hawk-Eye (EKC): 142
No. 2A Folding Rainbow Hawk-Eye Special (EKC): 142
No. 2A Folding Scout (Seneca): 393
No. 2A Goodwin (Ansco): 33
No. 2A Hawk-Eye Special (EKC): 143
No. 2A Kewpie (Conley): 98
No. 2A Rainbow Hawk-Eye (EKC): 142
No. 2A Target Hawk-Eye (EKC): 143
No. 2C Ansco Junior: 33
No. 2C Autographic Kodak Junior (EKC): 121
No. 2C Autographic Kodak Special (EKC): 121
No. 2C Brownie (EKC): 124
No. 2C Buster Brown (Ansco): 32
No. 2C Cartridge Premo (EKC): 152
No. 2C Folding Autographic Brownie (EKC): 126
No. 2C Folding Cartridge Premo (EKC): 153
No. 2C Folding Scout (Seneca): 393
No. 2C Kewpie (Conley): 98
No. 2C Kodak Series III (EKC): 146
No. 2C Pocket Kodak (EKC): 150
No. 2C Pocket Kodak Special (EKC): 151
No. 2C Rexo Jr. (Burke & James): 75
No. 3 Ansco Junior: 33
No. 3 Autographic Kodak (EKC): 120
No. 3 Autographic Kodak Special (EKC): 121
No. 3 Brownie (EKC): 124
No. 3 Buckeye (American Camera Mfg.): 28
No. 3 Bull's-Eye (EKC): 130
No. 3 Buster Brown (Ansco): 32
No. 3 Cartridge Kodak (EKC): 132
No. 3 Combination Hawk-Eye (Blair): 64
No. 3 Eclipse (Horsman): 233
No. 3 Film Premo (EKC): 152
No. 3 Flush Back Kodak (EKC): 136
No. 3 Folding Ansco: 33
No. 3 Folding Brownie (EKC): 126
No. 3 Folding Buster Brown (Ansco): 32

No. 3 Folding Hawk-Eye (Blair): 64
No. 3 Folding Hawk-Eye (EKC): 142
No. 3 Folding Hawk-Eye Special (EKC): 142
No. 3 Folding Kodet (EKC): 146
No. 3 Folding Pocket Kodak (EKC): 139
No. 3 Folding Pocket Kodak, Deluxe
  (EKC): 140
No. 3 Folding Rexo (Burke & James): 75
No. 3 Folding Scout (Seneca): 393
No. 3 Goodwin (Ansco): 33
No. 3 Kewpie (Conley): 98
No. 3 Kodak (EKC): 119
No. 3 Kodak Jr. (EKC): 119
No. 3 Kodak Series III (EKC): 146
No. 3 Pocket Kodak Special (EKC): 151
No. 3 Premo Junior (EKC): 153
No. 3 Rexo Jr. (Burke & James): 75
No. 3 Special Kodak (EKC): 165
No. 3 Weno Hawk-Eye (Blair): 66
No. 3 Zenith Kodak (EKC): 170
No. 3A Ansco Junior: 33
No. 3A Autographic Kodak (EKC): 120
No. 3A Autographic Kodak Junior (EKC):
  121
No. 3A Autographic Kodak Special (EKC):
  121
No. 3A Folding Ansco: 33
No. 3A Folding Autographic Brownie
  (EKC): 126
No. 3A Folding Brownie (EKC): 126
No. 3A Folding Buster Brown (Ansco): 32
No. 3A Folding Cartridge Hawk-Eye
  (EKC): 142
No. 3A Folding Cartridge Premo (EKC): 153
No. 3A Folding Hawk-Eye (EKC): 142
No. 3A Folding Ingento (Burke & James): 74
No. 3A Folding Pocket Kodak (EKC): 140
No. 3A Folding Rexo (Burke & James): 75
No. 3A Folding Scout (Seneca): 393
No. 3A Ingento Jr. (Burke & James): 74
No. 3A Kewpie (Conley): 98
No. 3A Kodak Series II (EKC): 146
No. 3A Kodak Series III (EKC): 146
No. 3A Panoram Kodak (EKC): 149
No. 3A Pocket Kodak (EKC): 150
No. 3A Signal Corps Model K-3 (EKC): 121
No. 3A Special Kodak (EKC): 165
No. 3B Quick Focus Kodak (EKC): 156
No. 4 Autographic Kodak (EKC): 120
No. 4 Bull's-Eye (EKC): 130
No. 4 Bull's-Eye Special (EKC): 131
No. 4 Bullet (EKC): 131
No. 4 Bullet Special (EKC): 131
No. 4 Cartridge Kodak (EKC): 132
No. 4 Eureka (EKC): 136
No. 4 Folding Ansco: 33
No. 4 Folding Hawk-Eye (Blair): 64
No. 4 Folding Hawk-Eye (EKC): 142
No. 4 Folding Kodak (EKC): 137
No. 4 Folding Kodet (EKC): 147
No. 4 Folding Kodet Junior (EKC): 147
No. 4 Folding Kodet Special (EKC): 147
No. 4 Folding Pocket Kodak (EKC): 140
No. 4 Folding Weno Hawk-Eye (Blair): 65
No. 4 Kodak (EKC): 120
No. 4 Kodak Jr. (EKC): 120
No. 4 Kodet (EKC): 146

No. 4 Panoram Kodak (EKC): 149
No. 4 Premo Junior (EKC): 153
No. 4 Screen Focus Kodak (EKC): 163
No. 4 Weno Hawk-Eye (Blair): 66
No. 4 Weno Hawk-Eye (EKC): 143
No. 4A Autographic Kodak (EKC): 120
No. 4A Folding Kodak (EKC): 138
No. 4A Speed Kodak (EKC): 165
No. 5 Cartridge Kodak (EKC): 132
No. 5 Cirkut Camera (EKC): 132
No. 5 Folding Ansco: 33
No. 5 Folding Kodak (EKC): 137
No. 5 Folding Kodet (EKC): 147
No. 5 Folding Kodet Special (EKC): 147
No. 5 Weno Hawk-Eye (EKC): 143
No. 6 Cirkut Camera (EKC): 133
No. 6 Cirkut Outfit (EKC): 133
No. 6 Folding Ansco: 33
No. 6 Folding Kodak (EKC): 137
No. 6 Weno Hawk-eye (Blair): 66
No. 7 Folding Ansco: 33
No. 7 Weno Hawk-Eye (EKC): 143
No. 7 Weno Hawk-eye (Blair): 66
No. 8 Cirkut Outfit (EKC): 133
No. 8 Folding Buckeye (American Camera
  Mfg.): 28
No. 9 Ansco Model B: 33
No. 10 Ansco: 33
No. 10 Cirkut Camera (EKC): 133
No. 16 Cirkut Camera (EKC): 133
Noble 126 (Helin-Noble): 228
Nodark Tintype Camera (Popular
  Photograph Co.): 363
Nomad 127 (Sawyers): 384
Nomad 620 (Sawyers): 384
Nomar No. 1: 342
NON-CAMERAS: 513-539
  AIR FRESHENER: 513
  ALBUMS: 513
  BAGS (Handbags, Shoulder Bags): 513
  BANKS: 514
  BELT BUCKLES: 514-515
  CANDLE: 515
  CANDY & GUM: 515
  CIGARETTE LIGHTERS: 515-517
  CLOCKS: 517
  COASTERS: 517
  COMPACTS & VANITIES: 517-518
  CONTAINERS: 518-519
  CONVERTORS: 519-521
  DART CAMERAS: 521
  DECANTERS: 521-523
  DISHES & TABLEWARE: 523
  FIGURINES: 533-534
  FLASKS: 521-523
  DOLLS: 524
  JEWELRY: 524
  KEYCHAINS: 524
  LIGHTS: 524-525
  MASKS: 525
  MOUSE CAMERAS: 525
  MUSIC BOX: 526
  ORNAMENTAL: 527
  PELLET SHOOTERS: 521
  PENCIL ERASERS, SHARPENERS,
    STATIONERY: 527-528
  PHONOGRAPHS: 528

ORNAMENTAL (Non-Camera): 527
Ortho Jumelle Duplex (Joux): 254
O.T.A.G.: 346
O.T.A.G. Amourette: 346
O.T.A.G. Lutin: 346
OTTEWILL: 346
Ottewill Sliding-box camera: 346
OTTICO MECCANICA ITALIANA (OMI): 344
OWLA KOKI: 346
Owla Stereo: 346
Oxford Minicam (Shaw): 394
Pacemaker Crown Graphic (Graflex): 218
Pacemaker Speed Graphic (Graflex): 219
Pacific: 346
Pacific Lynx PPL-500XL: 346
PACIFIC PRODUCTS: 346
Pack 126 (Viennaplex): 431
Padie (Laack): 277
PAILLARD (Movie): 502
Pajtas (Gamma): 201
Palko (Cruver-Peters): 107
Palmer (Rocket): 377
PALMER & LONGKING: 346
Palmer & Longking Lewis-style
  Daguerreotype: 346
Palmos Klapp-Stereo (Ica): 245
Palmos-O (Zeiss): 473
Panax: 346
Panda (Ansco): 35
Panomatic 126 (Non-Camera): 526
PANON CAMERA CO. LTD.: 346-347
Panon Wide Angle Camera: 346
Panon Widelux: 347
Panoram 120 (Burke & James): 75
Panoram Kodak (EKC): 149
Panoramic camera (Conley): 99
Panoramic camera (Turret): 421
Panta (Rodehueser): 377
PAPIGNY: 347
Papigny Jumelle Stereo: 347
PARAGON CAMERA CO. (Movie): 503
Paragon Model 33: 503
Paramat (Agfa): 22
Parat (Agfa): 22
Parcel Detective (Marion): 305
PARIS: 347
Paris GAP Box: 347
PARK: 347
Park Tailboard camera: 347
Parker: 347
PARKER PEN CO.: 347
Partytime Instant Cameras (EKC): 144
Parva (San Giorgio): 382
Parvo Interview (Debrie): 489
Parvola (Ihagee): 249
Pascal (Japy): 254
Passe-Partout (Hanau): 225
Patent camera (Rouch): 381
Patent Camera Box (Bolles & Smith): 67
Patent Etui (K.W.): 274
Patent Etui Luxus (K.W.): 274
Patent Klapp Reflex (Ihagee): 249
Patent Reflex Hand camera (Reflex
  Camera Co.): 366
Patent Stamp Camera (Hyatt): 241
Patent Three-Colour Separation Camera
  (Butler): 78

PATHE FRERES (Movie): 503
PATHE S.A. (Movie): 503-505
Pathe 28mm: 503
Pathe 35mm: 503
Pathe Baby: 504
Pathe Baby with Camo motor: 504
Pathe Baby with motor: 504
Pathe-Baby Projector: 504
Pathe Kid Projector: 504
Pathe Kok Home Cinematograph: 504
Pathe Mondial B: 504
Pathe Motocamera: 503
Pathe Motocamera 16: 503
Pathe Motocamera Luxe: 503
Pathe National I: 504
Pathe National II: 504
Pathe New Premier Pathescope: 504
Pathfinder (Polaroid 110, 110A): 361
Pax (Braun): 72
Pax (Yamato): 453
Pax Golden View (Yamato): 454
Pax Jr. (Yamato): 454
Paxette (Braun): 72
Paxette IIM (Braun): 72
Paxette Electromatic I,Ia,II (Braun): 72
Paxiflash (Braun): 72
Paxina (Braun): 72
PD-16 (Agfa): 22
PDQ (Anthony): 40
PDQ CAMERA CO.: 347
PDQ Mandel Automatic PDQ: 347
PDQ Photo Button Camera: 347
PDQ Street Camera (Chicago Ferrotype
  Co.): 93
Peace: 347
Peace (reflex): 347
Peace Baby Flex: 347
Peace III: 347
Peace-Gas Camera-Lighter
  (Non-Camera): 516
Pearl I (Konishiroku): 265
Pearl II (Konishiroku): 265
Pearl IV (Konishiroku): 265
Pearl No. 2 (Konishiroku): 265
Pearlette (Konishiroku): 265
PEARSALL: 347
Pearsall Compact: 347
PECK: 348
Peck Ferrotype: 348
Peck Wet-plate camera: 348
Peckham Wray (Wray): 452
Pecto (Columbia Optical): 96
Peer 100: 348
Peer 100 (EKC): 149
Peerflekta (Welta): 443
Peerless (Rochester Optical): 375
Peerless Box camera: 348
PEERLESS MFG. CO.: 348
Peggy I (Krauss): 267
Peggy II (Krauss): 267
Pelar-Camera (Lehman): 280
PELLET SHOOTERS (Non-Camera): 521
Pellix (Canon): 88
Pen (Olympus): 344
Pen D (Olympus): 344
Pen F (Olympus): 344
Pen FT (Olympus): 344

Press Graflex: 214
Press King (B & W Mfg.): 49
Press Reflex (Dallmeyer): 109
Press Van (Suzuki): 409
Press/View (Burke & James): 75
Pressman (Busch): 76
Presto (Magic Introduction): 302
PRESTWICH MFG. CO. (Movie): 505
Prestwich 35mm: 505
Primar (Bentzin): 59
Primar Folding Reflex (Bentzin): 59
Primar Reflex (Bentzin): 59
Primarette (Bentzin): 59
Primarflex (Bentzin): 59
Primo Jr. (Tokyo Kogaku): 417
Prince: 363
Prince Flex (Non-Camera): 526
Princess (Closter): 96
Princess May (London & Paris Optic): 298
Princess of Power She-Ra (HG Toys): 232
Printers (Darkroom): 542
Printex: 363
PRINTEX PRODUCTS: 363
PRINTING FRAMES (Non-Camera): 529
Prismac (Deloye): 113
Prismotype (Fallowfield): 188
Pro (Beaurline): 54
Pro Camera: 364
Projecting Kinetoscope (Edison): 494
Prominent (6x9) (Voigtlander): 436
Prominent (35mm) (Voigtlander): 436
Prominent II (Voigtlander): 436
Prontoklapp (Rodenstock): 378
Proud Chrome Six III (Sumida): 407
Puck (Ising): 253
Puck Special (Thornton-Pickard): 414
Pucky (Ising): 253
Pucky I,Ia,II (Ising): 253
Pullman Detective (Levi): 293
Punky Brewster (Helm): 228
Pupille (EKC): 155
Pupille (Nagel): 332
Purma Plus (Hunter): 239
Purma Special (Hunter): 239-240
PUTNAM: 364
Putnam Marvel: 364
PUZZLES & GAMES (Non-Camera): 529
Pygmee (Carmen): 88
PYNE: 364
Pyne Stereoscopic Camera: 364
Q.P.: 364
Q.R.S. (Movie): 505
Q.R.S. Kamra: 364
Q.R.S. Model B: 505
Q.R.S. Projector: 505
Q.R.S.-DeVRY CORP.: 364
Q.R.S.-DeVry Home Movie Camera (DeVry): 490
Quad (Close & Cone): 95
Quick Focus Kodak (EKC): 156
Quigley Photographic Services: ADV
Raaco: 364
Radial Hand camera (Marion): 305
RADIOS (Non-Camera): 529-530
Radix: 364
Radix (Bilora): 63
Rainbow Hawk-Eye (EKC): 142

RAJAR: 364
Rajar No. 6 (APeM): 41
Rakso: 364
Raleigh: 364
Rambler Flash Camera (Imperial): 251
Ramera (Kowa): 266
Ranca (EKC): 156
Ranca (Nagel): 332
Randorflex: 364
Rangefinders: 551
Ranger (Drucker): 116
Ranger (Houghton Ensign): 237
Rank (Rankolor): 364
RANKOLOR LABORATORIES: 364
Rankolor Rank: 364
Rapide (Coronet): 105
Rapide (Yashica): 455
Rapitake (La Rose): 277
Ray Box camera: 365
RAY CAMERA CO.: 365
Ray Jr.: 365
Ray No. 1: 365
Ray No. 2: 365
Ray No. 4: 365
Ray No. 6: 365
Rayelle: 365
Rayflex (Fototechnica): 194
Raylo Color Camera (American Raylo): 30
R.B. Graflex Junior: 214
R.B. Graflex Series B: 215
R.B. Graflex Series C: 215
R.B. Graflex Series D: 215
R.B. Super D Graflex: 215
R.B. Tele Graflex: 215
RCA Sound Cameras: 506
RCA VICTOR CO. (Movie): 506
Ready Ranger Tele-photo Camera Gun (Aurora): 48
Readyflash (Ansco): 35
Readyset (Ansco): 35
Readyset Royal (Ansco): 35
Readyset Traveler (Ansco): 35
Real Camera: 365
Realist 35, 45 (White): 447
Rechteck Primar (Bentzin): 59
Recomar (Nagel): 332
Recomar 18 (EKC): 156
Recomar 33 (EKC): 156
Record (Ica): 245
Record Camera: 365
Record I,II (Agfa): 23
Record Stereo Camera (Huttig): 241
RECTAFLEX: 365-366
Rectaflex Junior: 365
Rectaflex Rotor: 365
Rectaflex Standard: 365
Recto (Contessa): 102
Red Flag 20: 366
REDDING: 366
Redding's Patent Luzo: 366
Rediflex (Ansco): 36
Reflecta, Reflekta (Welta): 444
Reflekta II, III (Welta): 444
Reflex (Compco): 97
Reflex (Ernemann): 183
Reflex (Houghton Ensign): 237
Reflex (Ica): 245

Rex Baby Powell: 368
Rex Kayson: 368
REX MAGAZINE CAMERA CO.: 368
Rex Magazine Camera: 368
Rex Miniature (Utility): 429
Rexo (Burke & James): 75
Rexoette (Burke & James): 75
REYGONAUD: 368
Reygonaud Stand camera: 368
Reyna II (Cornu): 103
Reyna Cross III (Cornu): 103
Reyna Cross III (Royet): 381
REYNOLDS & BRANSON: 368
Reynolds Field camera: 368
Rhaco (Hendren): 228
Rhaco Monopol (Hendren): 228
RHEINMETALL: 368
Rheinmetall Perfekta: 368
Rheinmetall Perfekta II: 368
Rich-Ray: 368
Rich-Ray Richlet 35: 368
RICH-RAY TRADING CO.: 368
RICHARD (F.M.): 368
RICHARD (Jules): 369
Richard Detective: 368
Richard Glyphoscope: 369
Richard Homeos: 369
Richard Homeoscope: 369
Richard Verascope: 369
Richard Verascope F40: 369
Richlet 35 (Rich-Ray): 368
Ricoh 16 (Riken): 371
Ricoh 35 (Riken): 371
Ricoh Six (Riken): 371
Ricoh Super 44 (Riken): 371
Ricoh Teleca 240 (Riken): 371
Ricoh TLS-401 (Riken): 371
Ricohflex (Riken): 371
Ricohmatic 44 (Riken): 371
Ricolet (Riken): 371
Ricsor: 369
RIDDELL: 369
Riddell Folding plate camera: 369
RIETZSCHEL: 369-370
Rietzschel Clack: 369
Rietzschel Heli-Clack: 369
Rietzschel Heli-Clack Universal Type I, II
  & III: 370
Rietzschel Kosmo-Clack Stereo: 370
Rietzschel Miniatur-Clack: 370
Rietzschel Reform-Clack: 370
Rifax (Beier): 55
Rigona (Balda): 52
Riken Golden Ricoh 16: 370
Riken Golden Steky: 371
Riken Hanken: 371
RIKEN OPTICAL: 370-372
Riken Ricoh 16: 371
Riken Ricoh 35: 371
Riken Ricoh Six: 371
Riken Ricoh Super 44: 371
Riken Ricoh Teleca 240: 371
Riken Ricoh TLS-401: 371
Riken Ricohflex: 371
Riken Ricohmatic 44: 371
Riken Ricolet: 371
Riken Roico: 371

Riken Steky: 371
Riken Super Ricohflex: 372
Rilex Press (Riley): 372
RILEY RESEARCH: 372
Riley Rilex Press: 372
Rilo: 372
Ring Camera (Ferro): 190
Ring-a-dingy Camera (Non-Camera): 536
Rio (Orion): 346
RISDON MFG. CO. (Movie): 506
Risdon Model A: 506
Risdon Model A (Ansco): 484
Ritacon F (Pentacon): 350
Rittreck IIa (Mushashino): 331
Rival 35: 372
Rival 120: 372
Rival Reflex (K.W.): 276
RO-TO: 372
Ro-To Elvo: 372
Ro-To Nea Fotos: 372
Roamer I (Universal): 426
Roamer II (Universal): 426
Roamer 63 (Universal): 426
ROBBIN PRODUCTS: 372
Robbin Reflex: 372
Robin (Neoca): 334
ROBINSON: 372
Robinson Luzo: 372
ROBOT FOTO & ELECTRONIC GmbH &
  CO. K.G. (Berning): 60
Robot I (Berning): 60
Robot II (Berning): 60
Robot IIa (Berning): 60
Robot Junior (Berning): 60
Robot Luftwaffe (Berning): 61
Robot Royal III (Berning): 61
Robot Royal 24 (Berning): 61
Robot Royal 36 (Berning): 61
Robot Star (Berning): 61
Robra (Rodenstock): 378
Roc (Idam): 247
Rocamco: 373
Rocamco No. 3 Daylight Loading Rollfilm
  Camera: 373
ROCAMCO PRODUCTS: 373
Rocca Super Reflex (Montanus): 328
ROCHECHOVARD: 373
Rochechovard Le Multicolore: 373
ROCHESTER CAMERA & SUPPLY CO.:
  373
Rochester Camera Cycle Poco: 373
Rochester Camera Favorite: 373
Rochester Camera Folding Rochester: 373
Rochester Camera Gem Poco: 374
Rochester Camera King Poco: 374
ROCHESTER CAMERA MFG.: 373-374
Rochester Camera New Model View: 375
Rochester Camera Pocket Poco: 373
Rochester Camera Poco: 373
Rochester Camera Telephoto Cycle
  Poco: 374
Rochester Camera Telephoto Poco: 374
Rochester Camera Tuxedo: 374
ROCHESTER OPTICAL & CAMERA CO.:
  373
Rochester Optical Carlton: 374
ROCHESTER OPTICAL CO.: 373,374-377

Shur-Flash (Ansco): 36
Shur-Shot (Ansco): 36
Shure-Shot (Ingersoll): 252
Shurflash (Agfa): 23
Shurshot (Agfa): 23
Shutter Bug (Non-Camera Stattuette): 534
Shutter Repairs: ADV
Shutters: 551
SIAF: 397
Siaf Amiga: 397
Sibyl (Newman & Guardia): 336
Sibyl Deluxe (Newman & Guardia): 336
Sibyl Stereo (Newman & Guardia): 337
Sico (Simons): 398
Sida: 397
Sida Extra: 397
SIDA GMBH: 397
Sida Sidax: 397
Sida Standard: 397
Sidax (Sida): 397
SIEMENS & HALSKE (Movie): 507
Siemens B: 507
Siemens C: 507
Siemens C II: 507
Siemens F: 507
Signal Corps Combat Camera (Simmon): 398
Signet 30 (EKC): 163
Signet 35 (EKC): 164
Signet 35 (Signal Corp.) (EKC): 164
Signet 40 (EKC): 164
Signet 50 (EKC): 164
Signet 80 (EKC): 164
SIGRISTE: 397
Sigriste Stereo: 397
Sil-Bear: 397
Silar (Meyer): 310
Silette (Agfa): 23
Silette L,LK (Agfa): 23
Silette Rapid,I,F,L (Agfa): 23
Silette SL,SLE (Agfa): 23
Siluro (Nemrod): 334
Silver King (Camera Man): 80
Silver Pocket Radio (Non-Camera): 530
Simco Box: 397
SIMDA: 397
Simda Panorascope: 397
Simili Jumelle (Zion): 481
SIMMON BROTHERS, INC.: 397-398
Simmon Omega 120: 397
SIMONS: 398
Simons Sico: 398
Simplex (112/7) (Zeiss): 474
Simplex (511/2) (Zeiss): 474
Simplex Ernoflex (Ernemann): 183
Simplex Magazine (Krugener): 269
Simplex Pockette (International Projector): 498
Simplex Snapper (Lava-Simplex): 280
Simplex-Ernoflex (Zeiss): 474
SIMPRO CORP. of AMERICA: 398
SIMPRO INTERNATIONAL LTD.: 398
Simpro Slip-on: 398
Simpro-X: 398
SINCLAIR: 398
Sinclair Traveller Roll-Film Camera: 398

Sinclair Traveller Una: 398
Sinclair Tropical Una: 398
Sinclair Una: 398
Sinclair Una Cameo: 398
Sinclair Una Deluxe: 398
Sinemat Duplex 17½mm: 507
SINEMAT MOTION PICTURE CO. (Movie): 507
Sing 88,388: 398
Single lens stereo (Baird): 49
Single lens stereo (Derogy): 114
Single-lens Stereo (Moorse): 329
Sinnox (Jougla): 254
Sinox (Lumiere): 300
Siraton: 398
SIRCHIE FINGER PRINT LABORATORIES INC.: 399
Sirchie Finger Print Camera: 399
Sirene (Ica): 245
Sirene (Zeiss): 474
SIRIO: 399
Sirio Elettra I: 399
Sirio Elettra II: 399
SITACON CO. LTD.: 399
Sitacon ST-3: 399
Six-Three Kodak No. 1A (EKC): 164
Six-Three Kodak No. 3 (EKC): 164
Six-Three Kodak No. 3A (EKC): 164
Six-16 Brownie (EKC): 127
Six-16 Brownie Junior (EKC): 128
Six-16 Brownie Special (EKC): 128
Six-16 Folding Hawk-Eye (EKC): 142
Six-16 Target Hawk-Eye (EKC): 143
Six-20 Boy Scout Brownie (EKC): 123
Six-20 Brownie (EKC): 127-128
Six-20 Brownie Junior (EKC): 128
Six-20 Brownie Special (EKC): 128
Six-20 Bull's-Eye Brownie (EKC): 128
Six-20 Flash Brownie (EKC): 128
Six-20 Folding Hawk-Eye (EKC): 142
Six-20 Target Hawk-Eye (EKC): 143
Six-Twenty (Imperial): 251
Six-Twenty Reflex (Imperial): 251
SKAIFE: 399
Skaife Pistolgraph: 399
Sky (Minolta): 316
Sky Scraper (Folmer & Schwing): 192
Skyflex: 399
Skylark (Mansfield): 305
SKYVIEW CAMERA CO.: 399
Skyview Aerial: 399
SL-706 (Zeiss): 474
Sliding-box Daguerreotype (Kranz): 267
Sliding-box wet-plate camera (Dallmeyer): 109
Sliding-box wet-plate camera (Piggott): 355
Slip-on (Simpro): 398
Slomexa (Vredeborch): 440
Smena (Mashpriborintorg): 370
Smena Symbol (Mashpriborintorg): 307
SMITH: 399
SMITH (James H.): 399
Smith Detective Camera: 399
Smith Multiplying Camera: 399
S.M.R. (Non-Camera): 517
Smurf Musical Toy Camera (Non-Camera): 527

Snake Camera (Non-Camera): 526
Snap 16: 399
Snap-Me-Happy Musical Camera Toy (Non-Camera): 527
Snap No. 2 (Conley): 99
Snap-Shot Secret Gun CH-337 (Non-Camera): 521
Snappa (Rochester Optical): 377
Snapper (Ross): 380
Snappy (Konishiroku): 265
Snapshooter (Plastics Development): 357
Snapshot (Dallmeyer): 109
Snapshot (La Crosse): 277
Snoopy (Eiko): 173
Snoopy Counting Camera (Non-Camera): 539
Snoopy The Astronaut (Non-Camera): 524
Snoopy-Matic (Helm): 228
SOAP (Non-Camera): 531
SOCIETA CONSTRUZIONI-ARTICOLI-TECHNICI (S.C.A.T.): 384
SOCIETA GAMMA (Gamma): 201
SOCIETE d'APPAREILS MECANIQUES IDAM (Idam): 247
SOCIETE DE PHOTOGRAPHIE ET D'OPTIQUE (S.P.O.): 404
Society (Collins): 96
Society of Cinema Olikos: 507
SOCIETY OF CINEMA PLATES (Movie): 507
SOENNECKEN & CO.: 399
Soennecken Field camera: 399
Soennecken Folding camera: 399
Soho Altrex: 399
Soho Cadet: 400
SOHO LTD.: 399-400
Soho Model B: 400
Soho Myna Model SK12: 400
Soho Pilot: 400
Soho Pilot (Marion): 306
Soho Precision: 400
Soho Reflex (Marion): 306
Soho Stereo Reflex (Marion): 306
Soho Tropical Reflex (Marion): 306
Soho Vest Pocket: 400
Sokol Automat: 400
Sola (Schatz): 384
SOLAR MATES: 400
Solar Mates Sunpet 826: 400
Solida I,II,III (Franka-Werk): 195
Solida (Welta): 444
Solida Jr. (Franka-Werk): 195
SOLIDEX Minera Air Freshener (Non-Camera): 513
SOLIGOR: 401
Soligor 35: 401
Soligor 45: 401
Soligor 66: 401
Soligor Reflex I: 401
Soligor Reflex II: 401
Solinette (Agfa): 24
Solograph, Stereo (Anthony): 41
Sonnar (Contessa): 102
Sonnet (Contessa): 102
Sonnet (Nettel): 334
Sonnet (Zeiss): 474
Sonny (Certo Dolly Vest Pocket): 90

Sonocon 16mm MB-ZA (Minolta): 323
SONORA INDUSTRIAL: 401
Sonora Love: 401
Sound Kodascope Special (EKC): 494
SOUTHERN (E.J.) IND.: 401
Southern Mykro-Fine: 401
Souvenir Camera (Vive): 431
Spartacord (Herold): 231
Spartacord (Spartus): 403
Spartaflex: 403
Spartus 35 (Herold): 231
Spartus 35, 35F: 402
Spartus 120 Flash Camera (Herold): 231
Spartus box cameras: 402
Spartus Cinex: 402
Spartus Co-Flash (Herold): 231
SPARTUS CORP.: 401-403
Spartus folding cameras: 402
Spartus Full-Vue: 402
Spartus Junior: 402
Spartus Miniature (Utility): 429
Spartus Press Flash: 402
Spartus Rocket: 402
Spartus Spartacord: 403
Spartus Super R-I: 403
Spartus Vanguard: 403
Spartus Vest Pocket: 402
SPEARHEAD INDUSTRIES. INC. (Non-Camera): 525
Special Brass Bound Instantograph (Lancaster): 279
Special Camera: 403
Special Camera (Yen-Kame): 456
Special King (Yen-Kame): 456
Special Kodak (EKC): 165
Special Reflex, Tropical (Houghton Ensign): 237
Special Ruby Reflex (Thornton-Pickard): 415
Spectator Flash (Pho-Tak): 352
Spectra Super II: 403
Speed Camera (Dallmeyer): 109
Speed Film Reflex (Houghton Ensign): 237
Speed Film Reflex, Tropical (Houghton Ensign): 237
Speed Graphic (early) (Graflex): 218
Speed Graphic, Anniversary (Graflex): 219
Speed Graphic, Miniature (Graflex): 219
Speed Graphic, Pacemaker (Graflex): 219
Speed Graphic, Pre-anniversary (Graflex): 218
Speed Kodak (EKC): 165
SPEED-O-MATIC CORP.: 403
Speed-O-Matic: 403
Speedex (Agfa): 24
Speedex (Ansco): 36
Speedex (subminiature): 403
Speedex 0 (Agfa): 24
Speedex B2 (Agfa): 24
Speedex Jr. (Agfa): 24
Speedliner (Polaroid 95B): 361
Speedy Detective (Benetfink): 58
Spektareta (Optikotechna): 345
SPENCER CO.: 403-404
Spencer Flex-Master: 403
Spencer Majestic: 404
Spider-Man (Vanity Fair): 430

Super Paxette I,IB,IIB,IIBL (Braun): 72
Super Pontura (Balda): 52
Super Regent (Ansco): 36
Super Ricohflex (Riken): 372
Super Rolls (Rolls): 379
Super Rolls Seven Seven (Rolls): 379
Super Silette,L, LK (Agfa): 23
Super Smirf Photographer (Non-Camera): 534
Super Solinette (Agfa): 24
Super Speed Cameo (Houghton Ensign): 237
Super Speed Graphic (Graflex): 220
Super Speed Graphic, Military KE-12(2): 220
Super Star (Vanity Fair): 430
Super Vier (Braun): 73
Superb (Voigtlander): 437
Superfekta (Welta): 444
Superfex (Fex): 190
Superflex Baby (Kiko-Do): 259
Superior (Agfa): 24
Superior (Fex): 190
Superior Flash Camera 120: 408
Supersport Dolly (Certo): 91
Supra No.2 (Kenngott): 258
Supra Photolite (Nikoh): 338
Supre-Macy (Macy): 301
Suprema (EKC): 167
Supreme (Keystone): 499
SURPRISE CAMERAS (Non-Camera): 525
Suruga Mihama Six IIIA: 408
SURUGA SEIKI CO.: 408
SUTER: 408
Suter Detective magazine cameras: 408
Suter Stereo Detective: 408
Suter Stereo Detective, Magazine: 408
Suter Stereo Muro: 408
Sutton Panoramic Camera (Ross): 380
SUZUKI OPTICAL CO.: 408-409
Suzuki Camera-Lite: 408
Suzuki Camera-Lite Seastar: 409
Suzuki Echo 8: 409
Suzuki Press Van: 409
Swallow: 409
SWANK (Non-Camera): 522
Swank Camera Flask (Non-Camera): 522
Swiftshot (Foster): 192
Swinger Model 20 (Polaroid): 361
Swinger Sentinel M15 (Polaroid): 362
Switchplate covers (Non-Camera):
    (photographer): 525
    (tourist): 525
SX-70 (Polaroid): 362
Symbol (Welta): 444
Symbolica (Zeiss): 478
Synchro-Box (Agfa): 24
T & W Detective Camera (Tisdell): 415
Tachibana Beby Pilot: 409
TACHIBANA TRADING CO.: 409
TAHBES: 409
Tahbes Populair: 409
TAIFONG (Non-Camera): 521
Tailboard camera (Fallowfield): 188
Tailboard camera (Hare): 226
Tailboard camera (Park): 347
Tailboard stereo (London Stereoscopic): 299

TAISEI KOKI: 409
Taisei Koki Welmy 35: 409
Taisei Koki Welmy M-3: 409
Taisei Koki Welmy Six: 409
Taisei Koki Welmy Wide: 409
TAIYODO KOKI: 409-411
Taiyodo Koki Beauty: 409
Taiyodo Koki Beauty 35 Super II: 410
Taiyodo Koki Beauty Super L: 410
Taiyodo Koki Beautycord: 410
Taiyodo Koki Beautyflex: 410
Taiyodo Koki Beauty Canter: 410
Taiyodo Koki Epochs: 410
Taiyodo Koki Meteor: 410
Taiyodo Koki Reflex Beauty: 410
Taiyodo Koki Vestkam: 411
TAIYOKOKI CO. LTD.: 411
Taiyokoki Viscawide-16: 411
Takahashi Arsen: 411
TAKAHASHI OPTICAL WORKS: 411
Take-A-Picture (Non-Camera): 535
TakIV (Walker): 441
Takyr (Krauss): 267
TALBOT (Romain): 411
TALBOT (Walter): 411
TALBOT & EAMER CO.: 411
Talbot & Eamer Talmer: 411
Talbot Errtee button tintype camera: 411
Talbot Errtee folding plate camera: 411
Talbot Errtee folding rollfilm camera: 411
Talbot Invisible Camera: 411
Talking Vue Camera (Non-Camera): 539
Talmer (Talbot & Eamer): 411
Tanack (Tanaka): 412
TANAKA OPTICAL CO. LTD.: 412
Tanaka Tanack, Type IV-S: 412
Tanit (Ferrania): 190
Tanks (Darkroom): 541
TARGET: 412
Target Brownie Six-16 (EKC): 129
Target Brownie Six-20 (EKC): 129
Target Hawk-Eye (EKC): 143
Target New Folding Stereo: 412
Taro Tenax (Goerz): 208
TARON CO.: 412
Taron Chic: 412
Taschenbuch-Camera (Krugener): 269
Tauber: 412
Taxo (Contessa): 102
Taxo (Zeiss): 478
Taxona (Pentacon): 350
TAYLOR: 412
Taylor View camera: 412
TDC Stereo Vivid (Bell & Howell): 57
Techni-Pak 1 (Technicolor): 412
TECHNICOLOR CORP.: 412
TECHNICOLOR CORP. (Movie): 507
Technicolor Automatic 8: 507
Technicolor Techni-Pak 1: 412
Technika I (Linhof): 295
Technika III (Linhof): 295
Technika Press 23 (Linhof): 295
Teddy (Ica): 246
Teddy Bear Photographer (Non-Camera): 534
TEDDY CAMERA CO.: 412
Teddy Model A: 412

TOSEI OPTICAL: 418
Tosei Optical Frank Six: 418
Toska (Huttig): 241
Toska (Ica): 246
Tougo (Tougodo): 419
Tougo Camera (Yen-Kame): 456
TOUGODO: 418-420
Tougodo Baby-Max: 418
Tougodo Buena 35-S: 418
Tougodo Click: 418
Tougodo Colly: 418
Tougodo Hit: 418
Tougodo Hobiflex: 418
Tougodo Hobix: 418
Tougodo Hobix Junior: 418
Tougodo Kino-44: 418
Tougodo Leader: 418
Tougodo Meikai: 418
Tougodo Meikai EL: 419
Tougodo Meisupi: 419
Tougodo Meisupi II, IV: 419
Tougodo Meisupii Half: 419
Tougodo Metraflex II: 419
Tougodo Stereo Hit: 419
Tougodo Tougo: 419
Tougodo Toyoca 16: 419
Tougodo Toyoca 35: 419
Tougodo Toyocaflex: 419
Tougodo Toyocaflex 35: 419
Tour Partner (Non-Camera): 530
Tourist (EKC): 167
Tourist (Hare): 226
Tourist II (EKC): 167
Tourist Buckeye (American Camera): 28
Tourist Graflex: 216
Tourist Hawk-Eye (Blair): 66
Tourist Hawk-Eye Special (Blair): 66
Tourist Multiple (New Ideas): 335
Tower 16 (Sears): 387
Tower 18B (Sears): 388
Tower 22 (Asahi Asahiflex IIA): 47
Tower 22 (Sears): 388
Tower 23 (Sears): 388
Tower 24 (Sears): 388
Tower 26 (Sears): 388
Tower, 35mm (Sears): 388
Tower 51 (Sears): 388
Tower 127 EF (Sears): 388
Tower Automatic 127 (Sears): 388
Tower Bonita (Sears): 388
Tower Camflash 127 (Sears): 388
Tower Camflash II 127 (Sears): 388
Tower Companion (Sears): 389
Tower Flash (Sears): 388
Tower Flash 120 (Sears): 388
Tower Hide Away (Sears): 389
Tower Junior (Sears): 389
Tower No. 5 (Sears): 387
Tower One-Twenty (Sears): 388
Tower One-Twenty Flash (Sears): 388
Tower Pixie 127 (Sears): 389
Tower Pixie II 127 (Sears): 389
Tower Reflex (Sears): 389
Tower Reflex Type (Sears): 389
Tower Skipper (Sears): 389
Tower Snappy (Sears): 389
Tower Stereo (Sears): 389

Tower Type 3 (Sears): 388
Town: 420
TOY CAMERAS (Non-Camera): 534-535
TOY'S CLAN: 420
Toy's Clan Donald Duck: 420
TOYCRAFTER (Non-Camera): 537
TOYO KOGAKU: 420
Toyo Kogaku Mighty: 420
Toyo Kogaku Tone: 420
Toyoca: 420
Toyoca 16 (Tougodo): 419
Toyoca 35 (Tougodo): 419
Toyocaflex (Tougodo): 419
Toyocaflex 35 (Tougodo): 419
TOYPOWER MFG. CO. (Non-Camera): 536
TOYS & GAMES, UNSPECIFIED
  (Non-Camera): 536-537
Trade-in Service (Adorama): ADV
TRAID CORPORATION: 420
Traid Fotron: 420
Traid Fotron III: 420
Trailblazer 120 (Pho-Tak): 352
TRAMBOUZE: 421
Trambouze Plate Camera: 421
Transistomatic Radio Camera (Gec): 202
Traveler: 421
Traveler 120 (Pho-Tak): 352
Traveller: 421
Traveller Roll-Film Camera (Sinclair): 398
Traveller Una (Sinclair): 398
Trays (Darkroom): 542
Treble Patent Camera (McKellen): 308
Trellis (Newman & Guardia): 337
Tri-Color Camera (Devin): 115
Tri-Color Camera (Jos-Pe): 254
Tri-Vision Stereo (Haneel): 225
Triad Detective (Scovill): 386
Triamapro (Deardorff): 112
Trick Squirt Camera (Non-Camera): 531,532
Trilby (Ica): 246
Trimlite Instamatic (EKC): 167
Trio (Seneca shutter): 393
Trio (Welta): 444
Trioflex: 421
Triomphant (Mendel): 308
Triple Victo (Houghton): 239
Tripods: 551
Trivision Camera (Keys): 258
Trix (Ica): 246
Trokonet (Photo Materials): 353
Trolita (Agfa): 25
Trolix (Agfa): 25
Trona (Ica): 246
Trona (Zeiss): 479
Tropen Adoro (Zeiss): 479
Tropen Rio (Orion): 346
Tropica (Ica): 246
Tropica (Zeiss): 479
Tropical camera (Laack): 277
Tropical Deckrullo Nettel (Nettel): 334
Tropical Field Camera (Baird): 50
Tropical Hand Camera (Adams & Co.): 17
Tropical Heag VI (Ernemann): 184
Tropical Heag XI (Ernemann): 184
Tropical Klapp (Ernemann): 185
Tropical plate camera (Huttig): 241
Tropical plate cameras (Contessa): 102

Universal Stereo camera (Goldmann): 209
Universal Studio Camera (Schiansky): 385
Universal Twinflex: 426
Universal Uniflash: 426
Universal Uniflex I, II: 426
Universal Univex A: 427
Universal Univex AF: 427
Universal Univex AF Special models: 427
Universal Univex AF-2: 427
Universal Univex AF-3: 427
Universal Univex AF-4: 427
Universal Univex AF-5: 427
Universal Univex G.E. Toppers Club: 427
Universal Univex Hollywood: 427
Universal Univex Model A Century of
 Progress: 427
Universal Univex Official Girl Scout: 427
Universal Vitar: 428
Universal Zenith: 428
Universelle (Saint-Etienne): 382
Univex A (Universal): 427
Univex AF (Universal): 427
Univex AF Special models (Universal): 427
Univex AF-2 (Universal): 427
Univex AF-3 (Universal): 427
Univex AF-4 (Universal): 427
Univex AF-5 (Universal): 427
Univex G.E. Toppers Club (Universal): 427
Univex Hollywood (Universal): 427
Univex Mercury Decanter (Non-Camera):
 523
Univex Model A Century of Progress
(Universal): 427
Univex Official Girl Scout (Universal): 427
Uno (Seneca shutter): 393
Ur-Leica (Original) (Leitz): 282
Ur-Leica (Replica) (Leitz): 282
Uriu Cinemax 85E: 509
URIU SEIKI (Movie): 509
U.S. CINEMATOGRAPH CO. (Movie): 508
U.S. Cinematograph 35mm: 508
USC 35 (United States Camera Corp.): 424
Used Photo Equipment: ADV
Utility Carlton: 429
Utility Carlton Reflex: 428
Utility Falcon: 428
Utility Falcon-Abbey Electricamera: 429
Utility Falcon-Flex: 429
Utility Falcon Junior: 428
Utility Falcon Midget: 429
Utility Falcon Minette: 429
Utility Falcon Miniature: 428
Utility Falcon Minicam Junior: 429
Utility Falcon Minicam Senior: 428
Utility Falcon Model Four: 428
Utility Falcon Model F,FE: 428
Utility Falcon Model G,GE: 428
Utility Falcon Model V16: 428
Utility Falcon Press Flash: 429
Utility Falcon Special: 429
Utility Girl Scout Falcon: 429
UTILITY MFG. CO.: 428-429
Utility Rex Miniature: 429
Utility Spartus Miniature: 429
UYEDA CAMERA: 429
Uyeda Vero Four: 429
Vag (Voigtlander): 437

Vagabond (United States Camera): 423
Valiant 620 (Shaw-Harrison): 394
Van Albada Stereo (Schapp): 384
Van Dyke Bitters Camera: 429
Vanguard: 429
Vanguard (Spartus): 403
VANITIES (Non-Camera): 517-518
VANITY FAIR: 430
Vanity Fair Barbie Cameramatic: 430
Vanity Fair Holly Hobbie: 430
Vanity Fair Incredible Hulk: 430
Vanity Fair Spider-Man: 430
Vanity Fair Sunny-Bunch: 430
Vanity Fair Super Star: 430
Vanity Kodak (EKC): 167
Vanity Kodak Ensemble (EKC): 168
Vanneck (Watson): 442
VARIMEX: 430
Varimex Alfa 2: 430
VARSITY CAMERA CORP.: 430
Varsity Model V: 430
Vauxhall: 430
VEB ALTISSA-CAMERA-WERK
 (Eho-Altissa): 172
VEB PRIMAR (Bentzin): 58
Vega: 430
Vega 2 (Mashpriborintorg): 306
Vega II, III (Druopta): 116
VEGA S.A.: 430
Vega Telephot Vega: 430
VEHICLES (Non-Camera): 537-538
Velo Klapp (Ernemann): 185
Velocigraphe (Hermagis): 230
Velocigraphe Stereo (Hermagis): 230
Velox Magazine Camera (Hurlbut): 240
VENA: 430
Vena Venaret: 430
Venaret (Vena): 430
Ventura (Agfa): 25
Ventura 66, 69 (Agfa): 25
Ventura Deluxe (Agfa): 25
Venus-Ray Compact (Non-Camera): 518
VEPLA-VENEZIA (Non-Camera): 539
Verascope (Richard): 369
Verascope F40 (Busch): 76
Verascope F40 (Richard): 369
Verax (Unger & Hoffman): 423
Verax Gloria (Unger & Hoffman): 423
Veriwide 100 (Plaubel): 359
Vero Four (Uyeda): 429
Vest Camera (Gray): 221
Vest Olympic (Olympic): 344
Vest Pocket Ansco Junior: 37
Vest Pocket Ansco Model A: 36
Vest Pocket Ansco No. 0: 36
Vest Pocket Ansco No. 1: 36
Vest Pocket Ansco No. 2: 37
Vest Pocket Autographic Kodak (EKC): 168
Vest Pocket Autographic Kodak Special
 (EKC): 168
Vest Pocket Ensign (Houghton): 237
Vest Pocket Focal Plane (Ernemann): 185
Vest Pocket Hawk-Eye (EKC): 143
Vest Pocket Kodak (EKC): 168-169
Vest Pocket Kodak Model B (EKC): 168
Vest Pocket Kodak Series III (EKC): 168
Vest Pocket Kodak Special (EKC): 168

DATING CAMERAS BY UNITED STATES PATENT NUMBERS

Patent dates can often be helpful in dating cameras, shutters or other accessories. One must be careful, however, not to conclude that the item was manufactured in the year the patent was issued. This is usually not the case. The patent date serves to indicate the year *after* which the item was made. Often the patents had been issued for five years or more before an item was produced bearing the patent number. Many products continued to carry the patent numbers for many years after the patent was issued. Thus a camera manufactured in 1930 could have a 1905 patent date.

The first numbered patents were issued in 1836, just before the advent of photography. Originally the law required that the patent date (but not the number) be put on the product. The present requirement to place the patent number on the item or its container began on April 1, 1927. Many earlier products, however, bore the patent number even though it was not required by law.

The following table lists the first patent number for the indicated year.

YEAR	NUMBER	YEAR	NUMBER	YEAR	NUMBER
1836	1	1887	355,291	1938	2,104,004
1837	110	1888	375,720	1939	2,142,080
1838	546	1889	395,305	1940	2,185,170
1839	1,061	1890	418,665	1941	2,227,418
1840	1,465	1891	443,987	1942	2,268,540
1841	1,923	1892	466,315	1943	2,307,007
1842	2,413	1893	488,976	1944	2,338,081
1843	2,901	1894	511,744	1945	2,366,154
1844	3,395	1895	531,619	1946	2,391,856
1845	3,873	1896	552,502	1947	2,413,675
1846	4,348	1897	574,369	1948	2,433,824
1847	4,914	1898	596,467	1949	2,457,797
1848	5,409	1899	616,871	1950	2,492,941
1849	5,993	1900	640,167	1951	2,536,016
1850	6,891	1901	664,827	1952	2,580,379
1851	7,865	1902	690,385	1953	2,624,046
1852	8,622	1903	717,521	1954	2,664,562
1853	9,512	1904	748,567	1955	2,698,434
1854	10,358	1905	778,834	1956	2,728,913
1855	12,117	1906	808,618	1957	2,775,762
1856	14,009	1907	839,799	1958	2,818,567
1857	16,324	1908	875,679	1959	2,866,973
1858	19,010	1909	908,436	1960	2,919,443
1859	22,477	1910	945,010	1961	2,966,681
1860	26,642	1911	980,178	1962	3,015,103
1861	31,005	1912	1,013,095	1963	3,070,801
1862	34,045	1913	1,049,326	1964	3,116,487
1863	37,266	1914	1,083,267	1965	3,163,865
1864	41,047	1915	1,123,212	1966	3,226,729
1865	45,085	1916	1,166,419	1967	3,295,143
1866	51,784	1917	1,210,389	1968	3,360,800
1867	60,658	1918	1,251,458	1969	3,419,907
1868	72,959	1919	1,290,027	1970	3,487,470
1869	85,503	1920	1,326,899	1971	3,551,909
1870	98,460	1921	1,364,063	1972	3,631,539
1871	110,617	1922	1,401,948	1973	3,707,729
1872	122,304	1923	1,440,362	1974	3,781,914
1873	134,504	1924	1,478,996	1975	3,858,241
1874	146,120	1925	1,521,590	1976	3,930,271
1875	158,350	1926	1,568,040	1977	4,000,520
1876	171,641	1927	1,612,790	1978	4,065,812
1877	158,813	1928	1,654,521	1979	4,131,952
1878	198,733	1929	1,696,897	1980	4,180,167
1879	211,078	1930	1,742,181	1981	4,242,757
1880	223,211	1931	1,787,424	1982	4,308,622
1881	236,137	1932	1,839,190	1983	4,366,579
1882	251,685	1933	1,892,663	1984	4,423,523
1883	269,820	1934	1,941,449	1985	4,490,855
1884	291,016	1935	1,985,878		
1885	310,163	1936	2,026,516		
1886	333,494	1937	2,066,309		

DATING CAMERAS BY SHUTTER TYPE

Dating cameras by shutter type is a rather unreliable guide to dating, since shutters and lenses are easily interchanged, and photographers over the years have often made these changes. However, if the shutter has been determined to be original equipment, then the following dates serve the purpose of estimating a date AFTER WHICH the camera would have been made. Shutters are listed by manufacturer, either in alphabetical order by shutter name, or chronologically.

We are indebted to Dr. Rudolf Kingslake for the research on these shutters, particularly the Bausch & Lomb, Kodak, and Wollensak brands.

BAUSCH & LOMB (Rochester, NY)
Bausch & Lomb began as an optical company, at first making eyeglass lenses, then in 1883 adding photographic lenses. In 1888 they made their first shutters, and continued making shutters until 1935.

Iris Diaphragm Shutter - 1890-1904. Shutter blades act as diaphragm. *(Illustrated in previous column.)*

"Star" - 1893. Has rotating disc with waterhouse stops. Pneumatic release cylinder added in 1894. *(Illustrated in previous column.)*

Bausch & Lomb Iris Diaphragm shutter

Victor (Unicum with air retard cylinder) - 1894-1897. Iris diaphragm.

Bausch & Lomb "Star" shutter

Unicum - 1897-past 1907. Iris diaphragm.

Vici - c1892.

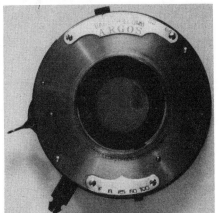

Argos - Patented 1900.

Bausch & Lomb Auto

Victor (1901 type) - 1901. Flat top with speed dial on it.

Volute - Patented 1902, continued until 1935.

AUTOMATIC SHUTTERS
All B&L Shutters made after 1901, except for the Volute, were of the automatic type which did not require cocking.

Auto - Patented Dec. 1900. Speed lever on bottom. Inverted a couple years later so speed dial was on top. *(Illustrated in previous column.)*

Automat (1901 type) - Introduced late 1901, but not patented until December 1904. Speed control lever in a curved slot just below the lens.

Bausch & Lomb Gem (above)
Bausch & Lomb Simplex (below)

Gem - c1902 (Patented Feb. 1901). First model had TBI lever on left (viewed from front) and air retard cylinder on right. In 1903, the mechanism was reversed, so the positions of the TBI lever and air cylinder were also reversed. This was called the "Simplex". *(Illustrated in previous column.)*

Simplex - c1903. See "Gem" above. *(Illustrated in previous column.)*

Automat (1906 type) - c1906-1913. This popular style has a circular control lever at the top.

FPK Automatic - 1903-1913. Made for the Eastman Kodak Co. for use on the Folding Pocket Kodak cameras.

Automatic (1910) - Three distinct types.

- IBT. Two-blade shutter

- 1-100, BT controlled by lever at top

- Same speeds as previous shutter: 1, 2,

5, 25, 50, 100, BT but this version is controlled by dial at top.

Compound - c1907 or 1908 on. Made under license from Deckel. *See Deckel Compound shutter.*

- c1907-1910. Speed dial has flat face with markings on face.

- c1910. Speed dial is conic section with markings on the edge.

- c1914. Pneumatic piston replaced by cable release.

B&L STEREO SHUTTERS

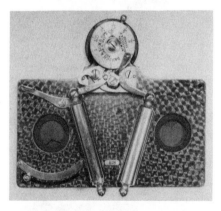

Iris Diaphragm Stereo - Intro. 1893. Two air cylinders between lenses.

Automat Stereo (slot below lens) - Intro. 1901.

Simplex Stereo - Intro. 1902. Air valve and TBI lever on left face of shutter (viewed from front.)

Automat Stereo (top dial) - Intro. 1904.

Single Valve Stereo - 1907.

Stereo Compound - 1911

DECKEL (Friedrich Deckel, Munich)
Bruns & Deckel founded 1903. F. Deckel firm established 1905. Following are major shutter types with approximate dates of introduction.

Compound - Introduced c1903.

Compur (Dial-set) - Introduced 1912.

Compur (Rim-set) - Introduced c1930.

Synchro Compur - c1951.

GAUTHIER (Alfred Gauthier, Calmbach)

Koilos (original with leather brake) - c1904.

Koilos (air piston) - c1906.

Ibso - c1908.

Ibsor - c1926. Gear control.

Prontor S - c1948.

Prontor SV - c1950. Full synchronization.

Prontor SKL - 1957. Meter-coupled

Prontormat-S - Fully automatic meter-controlled.

KODAK SHUTTERS - *This list includes only those shutters made by Kodak. They are listed in alphabetic order by shutter name.*
Automatic - 1904-17. 5-speed, bulb release.

Automatic Flash - 1960-. Single-speed. For Automatic and Motormatic Cameras.

Kodak Ball Bearing shutter

Ball Bearing Shutters: *3-speed shutter illustrated bottom of previous page.*
- #0 - 1914-26. 2-speed. For Vest Pocket cameras.
- #1 - 1909-24. 3-speed. Bulb or cable release.
- #2 - 1909-33. 3-speed. Bulb or cable release.
- Stereo Ball Bearing - 1919-24. 3-speed. Similar to the #2.

Brownie Automatic - 1904-15. Single-speed.

Brownie Automatic Stereo - 1905-15. Single-speed. For bulb operation.

Diomatic top dial shutters - 4-speed.
- #0 - 1924-35.
- #1 - 1924-33.

Diomatic ring set shutters - These are similar to the Kodamatic #1 and #2 shutters.
- #1 - 3-speed version 1940-48. 4-speed version 1938-48.
- #2 - 1938-39. 4-speed.

Eastman Automatic - 1898-1906. Single-speed.

Flash 200 - 1949-59. 4-speed.

Flash 200 Stereo - 1954-59. 4-speed.

Flash 250 - 1957-61. 4-speed.

Flash 300 - 1953-58. 4-speed.

Flash Dakon - 1947-48. 3-speed

Flash Diomatic - 1946-52. 3 and 4-speed versions.

Dak - 1940-1948. Single-speed.

Dakar #1 - 1935-36. 4-speed.

Dakon - 2-speed version 1940-48. 3-speed version 1946-48. *(Illustrated next page.)*

Diodak - 4-speed.
- #1 - 1932-35.
- #2 - 1932-33.
- #2A - 1936-41.

Flash Kodamatic - 1946-53, 5-speed version. 1946-54, 7-speed version for the Kodak Reflex Camera.

EKC Dakon shutter

Flash Kodon - 1948-58. Single-speed, TBI. This is the "Dak" shutter with flash sync.

Flash Supermatic #1 - 1946-48. 9-speed.

Flash Supermatic #2 - 1946-52. 9-speed.

Hawk-Eye - 1923. Single-speed. A simplified Ball Bearing #0, T and I only.

Kodal #0 - 1932. Single-speed. Octagonal. T & I only.

Kodal #1 - 1932-40. Single-speed. Octagonal, B & I only.

Kodamatic (old style) - 1921-34. 7-speed. Small version was called the #1 or #1A. Large version was called #2 or #3A.

Kodamatic (ring set) #1 - 1937-48. 5-speed.

Kodamatic (ring set) #2 - 1937-47. 5-speed.

Kodex #0 - 1924-34. 2-speed.

Kodex #1 - Old style 1925-33; 2-speed. New style 1935-45; 3-speed.

Kodo #0 - 1929-40. Single-speed.

Kodo #1 - 1929-40. Single-speed.

Kodon #0 - 1932-40. 3-speed. Octagonal.

Kodon #1 - 1932-40. 3-speed. Octagonal.

Supermatic #0 - 1941-48. 9-speed. For the Bantam Special.

Supermatic #1 - 1939-48. 9-speed.

Supermatic #2 - 1939-47. 9-speed.

Supermatic #3 - 8-speed.

Supermatic X - 8-speed. Same as the #3 but with X sync.

Synchro 80 - 1959-. 2-speed. For the Automatic 35 Camera.

Synchro 250 - 1957-60. 7-speed. For the Signet 30 and 50 Cameras.

Synchro 300 - 1951-58. 4-speed. For the Signet 35 Camera.

Synchro 400 - 1956-59. 7-speed. For the Signet 40 Camera.

Synchro-Rapid 800 - 1949-56. 10-speed.

Triple Action - 1897-03. 3-speed. Made in small and large versions.

WOLLENSAK SHUTTERS

Actus - 1912-14. 3-speed, T,B.

Alphax - 1946-56. 5-speed, T,B.

Autex - 1908-13. 6-speed, T,B.

Auto A - 1913-18. 6-speed, T,B.

Auto B - 1918-22. 7-speed, T,B.

Automatic A - 1901-02. 8-speed, T,B.

Automatic B - 1902-08. 6-speed, T,B.

Automatic s.v. - 1900-02. 3-speed, T,B.

Betax - 1922-48. 6-speed, T,B.

Ballard Unique - 1901?. Single-speed, T,B.

Conley Safety - 1911?. 6-speed, T,B.

Deltax - 1922-42. 3-speed, T,B.

Gammax - 1922-42. 4-speed, T,B.

Graphex - 1946?. 9-speed, T,B.

Junior - 1901-11. Single-speed, T,B.

Optimo #0 - 1916-22. 7-speed, T,B.

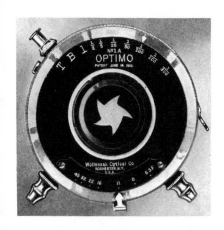

Studio - 1906-40.

TIB - 1911-14. Single-speed, T,B.

Ultro A - 1914-19. Single-speed, T,B.

Ultro B - 1919-22. Single-speed, T,B.

Optimo (Velosto) - 1909-30. 8-speed, T,B.

Rapax - 1946-56. 9-speed, T,B.

Victo A - 1914-18. 4-speed, T,B.

Regno A - 1908-11. 6-speed, T,B.

Victo B - 1918-22. 4-speed, T,B.

Regno B - 1911-18. 6-speed, T,B.

Victus - 1908-12. 3-speed, T,B.

(Original) - 1900-01. 8-speed, T,B.

Winner A - 1901-02. 4-speed, T,B.

Regular A - 1901-02. 8-speed, T,B.

Winner B - 1902-08. 3-speed, T,B.

Regular B - 1902-08. 6-speed, T,B.

Senior - 1903-07. Single-speed, T,B.

Skyshade - 1906-13. 6-speed, T,B.

METRIC/ENGLISH EQUIVALENTS of camera image sizes

The sizes in this table are not always exact measurements, but are the equivalents used in popular parlance among collectors.

METRIC	ENGLISH	COMMENTS
5x8mm		Echo 8
8x11mm		Minox
10x14mm		many 16mm subminiatures
13x17mm		110 cassette
14x14mm		many 16mm subminiatures
16x22mm	⅝x⅞"	Expo watch camera
18x24mm	¾x15/16"	single frame 35mm
18x28mm	¾x1⅛"	Expo police camera
2x3cm	¾x1⅛"	
22x31mm	¾x1¼"	
22x33mm	⅞x1¼"	
22x35mm	⅞x1⅜"	
24x24mm	1x1"	35mm square format
24x30mm	15/16x1-3/16"	many 35mm stereo cameras
24x36mm	1x1⅜"	35mm standard format
25mm dia.	1" round	
28x28mm	1⅛x1⅛"	126 cassette
28x40mm	1⅛x1½"	828 full frame, 8 exp.
3x4cm	1-3/16x1½"	127 half frame, 16 exp.
32x45mm	1¼x1¾"	Cartridge Premo #00
35x45mm	1⅜x1¾"	
4x4cm	1⅝x1⅝"	127 square format, 12 exp.
4x5cm	1½x2"	
4x6cm	1½x2¼"	
4x6.5cm	1⅝x2½"	127 full frame, 8 exp.
4.5x6cm	1¾x2¼"	120/620 half frame, 16 exp.
4.5x6cm	1¾x2-5/16"	
4.5x6cm	1¾x2⅜"	Premo Jr. #0
4.5x6.5cm	1¾x2½"	
4.5x10.7cm	1¾x4¼"	popular stereo plate size
5x5cm	2x2"	
5x6.5cm	2x2½"	
5x7.5cm	2x3"	Houghton Ensignette #2
5x8cm	2x3⅛"	
5.5x6.5cm	2-1/16x2½"	116/616 half frame, 16 exp.
6x6cm	2¼x2¼"	120/620 square format, 12 exp.
6x6.5cm	2¼x2½"	National Graflex, 10 exp on 120
6x7cm	2¼x2¾"	1/9 plate, "Ideal format": 10 exp. on 120 or 21 exp. on 220
6x8.5cm	2¼x3¼"	
6x9cm	2¼x3¼", 2¼x3½"	120/620 full frame, 8 exp.
6x13cm	2¼x5⅛"	common stereo plate size
6x17cm	2¼x6¾"	Baby Al Vista
6x18cm	2¼x7"	panoramic
6.5x6.5cm	2½x2½"	
6.5x7.5cm	2½x3"	
6.5x9cm	2½x3½"	
6.5x11cm	2½x4¼"	1A or 116/616 full frame
7x8.4cm	2¾x3¼"	1/6 plate, or "A" Daylight or Ordinary Kodak
71x93mm	2¾x3⅝"	Kodak instant film (68x91mm actual)
7.25x12.5cm	2⅞x4⅞"	2C or 130 film
7.5x10cm	3x4"	
8x8cm	3⅛x3-3/16"	each image of stereo pair
8x10.5cm	3¼x4¼"	¼ plate (popular approximation), lantern slide
8x14cm	3¼x5½"	3A or 122 film, postcard size

METRIC	ENGLISH	COMMENTS
8x16cm	3⅛x6¼"	stereo pair
8x26cm	3¼x10⅜	panoram
8x46cm	3¼x18"	panoram
8.2x10.7cm	3¼x4¼"	literal measurement (The approxmiation 8x10.5cm is usually used.)
8.5x14.5cm	3⅜x5¾"	stereo format
9x9cm	3½x3½"	
9x10cm	3½x4"	"B" Daylight or Ordinary Kodak
9x12cm	3½x4¾"	popular European plate size
9x13cm	3½x5"	
9x14cm	3½x5½"	
9x15cm	3½x6"	stereo format
9x16cm	3½x6¼"	stereo format
9x18cm	3½x7"	stereo format
9x23cm	3½x9"	Al Vista 3B
9x30cm	3½x12"	#4 Panoram Kodak
9.5x12cm	3¾x4¾"	
10x13cm	4x5"	common plate and film size
10x15cm	4x6"	sometimes used as a metric equivalent for 4x5"
10x25cm	4x10"	
10x30cm	4x12"	
11x11cm	4¼x4¼"	
11x16.5cm	4¼x6½"	half plate
11.5x14cm	4½x5½"	
11.5x21.5cm	4½x8½"	Stock stereo wet-plate
12x16.5cm	4¾x6½"	
12x17cm	4¾x6¾"	
13x18cm	5x7"	popular plate and film size
13x19cm	5x7½"	
13x20cm	5x8"	popular size before 1900
13x30cm	5x12"	
14x16.5cm	5½x6½"	⅔ plate
16.5x21.5cm	6½x8½"	full plate
18x24cm	7x9½"	
18x25cm	7x10"	
18x28cm	7x11"	
18x43cm	7x17"	"banquet" cameras
19x24cm	7½x9½"	
20x25cm	8x10"	
20x50cm	8x20"	"banquet" cameras
24x30cm	9½x12"	
25x30cm	10x12"	
28x35.5cm	11x14"	large studio size

KODAK & ANSCO FILM NUMBERS AND IMAGE SIZES

KODAK	ANSCO	INCHES	METRIC
101	8A	3½x3½	9x9cm
103	10A	4x5	10x13cm
105	5A	2¼x3¼	6x9cm
116	6A,6B	2½x4¼	6.5x11cm
117	3A	2¼x2¼	6x6cm
118	7A	3¼x4¼	8x10.5cm
120	4A	2¼x3¼	6x9cm
122	18A	3¼x5½	8x14cm
124	7C	3¼x4¼	8x10.5cm
125	18C	3¼x5½	8x14cm
127	2C	1⅝x2½	4x6.5cm
130	26A	2⅞x4⅞	7.25x12.5cm

COLLECTORS' ORGANIZATIONS

Organization	DUES (n=non-profit, S=single, F=family, I=internat'l, C=corresponding)	SHOW DATES	MEMBERSHIP	MEETING (M=monthly, B=bi-monthly, A=annual)	PUBLICATION (N=newsletter, J=journal, S="semi-ann'l, Q="quarterly, P=Photographica Journal)		
AMERICAN PHOTOGRAPHIC HISTORICAL SOCIETY P.O. Box 1775 Grand Central Station New York, NY 10163	$22.50 n	May Nov	600	M	N		P
AMERICAN SOCIETY OF CAMERA COLLECTORS, Inc. 4918 Alcove Ave. North Hollywood, CA 91607 (818) 769-6160	$20.00 n	March Sept	283	M	N		
ATLANTA PHOTOGRAPHIC COLLECTORS CLUB P.O. Box 98291 Atlanta, GA 30345	$10.00	Nov	30				
BAY AREA PHOTOGRAPHICA ASSN. (BAPA) 2538 34th Ave. San Francisco, CA 94116 (415) 664-6498	$16.00 n	none	40	B			
C.A.M.E.R.A. Camera and Memorabilia Enthusiasts Regional Association c/o William J. Tangredi, Sec'y 15 Turner Lane Loudonville, NY 12211	$12.00	March Nov	17	M			
CHICAGO PHOTOGRAPHIC COLLECTORS SOCIETY P.O. Box 375 Winnetka, IL 60093	$18.00	Spring Fall	110	M	N		P
CLUB DAGUERRE-DARRAH 2562 Victoria Wichita, KS 67216 (316) 265-0393	$12.00	Feb	18	M	N		
CLUB NIEPCE LUMIERE 35 rue de la Mare a l'Ane F93100 Montreuil FRANCE	325 FF n	Oct	200	M			Q
DELAWARE VALLEY PHOTOGRAPHIC COLLECTORS ASSN. P.O. Box 74 Delanco, NJ 08075	$15.00 n	Feb June Aug Nov	90	M	N		P
DUTCH SOCIETY OF FOTOGRAFICA COLLECTORS (Formerly: Camera Oldtimer Club) P.O. Box 4262 2003 EG HAARLEM NETHERLANDS	$25.00 I	March Nov	800				Q
INTERNATIONAL KODAK HISTORICAL SOCIETY P.O. Box 21 Flourtown, PA 19031	$20.00	none	73			J	

	DUES n=non-profit S=single F=family I=internat'l C=corresponding	SHOW DATES	MEMBERSHIP	MEETING M=monthly B=bi-monthly A=annual	PUBLICATION N=newsletter J=journal S="semi-ann'l Q="quarterly P=Photographica Journal
INTERNATIONAL PHOTOGRAPHIC HISTORICAL ORGANIZATION P.O. Box 16074 **(InPHO)** San Francisco, CA 94116 (415) 681-4356	$16.00	none	77	B	
LEICA HISTORICAL SOC. of AMERICA 10590 N.W. 27th St. #101 Miami, FL 33172 (305) 477-7300 or (305) 223-9233	$25.00 n	Oct	987	A	NJ
MICHIGAN PHOTOGRAPHIC HISTORICAL SOCIETY Box 202 Wayne, MI 48184 (313) 721-5126	$ 2.50 S $10.00 I n	Nov	70	B	NJ
MIDWEST PHOTOGRAPHIC HISTORICAL SOCIETY 19 Hazelnut Ct. Florissant, MO 63033	$10.00 n	April Oct	80	M	N ... P
NATIONAL STEREOSCOPIC ASSN. Box 14801 Columbus, OH 43214	$22.00 S $30, 1stCl	Aug	1700		J
NIKON HISTORICAL SOCIETY c/o Robert Rotoloni P.O Box 3213 Munster, IN 46321 USA (312) 895-5319	$20.00	none	110		Q
THE OHIO CAMERA COLLECTORS P.O. Box 282 Columbus, OH 43216 (614) 885-3224	$10.00 n	May	100	M	NJ
PENNSYLVANIA PHOTOGRAPHIC HISTORICAL SOC., Inc. P.O. Box 862 Beaver Falls, PA 15010-0862 (412) 843-5688	$15.00 S $20.00 F n	Aug Oct	55	B	N
PHOTOGRAPHIC COLLECTORS CLUB of GREAT BRITAIN 42 Tynedale Avenue Whitley Bay Tyne & Wear NE26 3BA 091 252-8486					
PHOTOGRAPHIC COLLECTORS of HOUSTON 1201 McDuffie #104 Houston, TX 77019	$15.00	April Oct	80	M	N
PHOTOGRAPHIC COLLECTORS of TUCSON P.O. Box 18646 Tucson, AZ 85731					

	DUES n=non-profit S=single F=family I=internat'l C=corresponding	SHOW DATES	MEMBERSHIP	MEETING M=monthly B=bi-monthly A=annual	PUBLICATION N=newsletter J=journal S=semi-ann'l Q=quarterly P=Photographica Journal
THE PHOTOGRAPHIC HISTORICAL SOCIETY P.O. Box 39563 Rochester, NY 14604	$12.00 n	Oct	60	M	N P
THE PHOTOGRAPHIC HISTORICAL SOCIETY of CANADA	$20.00 n	May Oct	250		J
PHOTOGRAPHIC HISTORICAL SOCIETY of METROPOLITIAN TORONTO P.O. Box 115, Postal Stn "S" Toronto, Ont, CANADA M5M 4L6 (416) 243-1439 (Evenings)	$ 8.00 n	Fall Wint	150	M	N
PHOTOGRAPHIC HISTORICAL SOCIETY of NEW ENGLAND, Inc. P.O. Box 189 Boston, MA 02165 (617) 277-0207	$15.00 S $30.00 I n	April Oct	350	M	N P
THE PHOTOGRAPHIC HISTORICAL SOCIETY of the WESTERN RESERVE P.O. Box 25663 Cleveland, OH 44125 (216) 382-6727 or 232-1827	$12.00 n	July -Aug	78	M	N Q
PUGET SOUND PHOTOGRAPHIC COLLECTORS SOCIETY 10421 Delwood Dr. S.W. Tacoma, WA 98498 (206) 582-4878	$10.00 n	May	65	M	N
TRI-STATE PHOTOGRAPHIC COLLECTORS SOCIETY 8910 Cherry Blue Ash, OH 45242 (513) 891-5266	$ 5.00 n	none	12	M	
WESTERN CANADA PHOTOGRAPHIC HISTORICAL ASSN. Box 33742 Vancouver, B.C. CANADA V6J 4L6 (604) 254-6778	$15.00 S $20.00 F $10.00 C	none	45	M	N
WESTERN PHOTOGRAPHIC COLLECTOR ASSN. Inc. P.O. Box 4294 Whittier, CA 90607 (213) 693-8421	$18.00 S $15.00 C $26.00 I n	May Nov	400	M	NJ +$8,P
ZEISS HISTORICA SOCIETY P.O. Box 631 Clifton, NJ 07012 (201) 472-1318	$20.00 n	none	200	A	N S

POCKET PRICE GUIDE TO CAMERAS !
The book you are holding in a pocket size? YES!
See the exciting details on the next page.

COLLECTORS GUIDE TO ROLLEI CAMERAS

By Arthur Evans. A complete, illustrated guide to all Rollei cameras from 1921 to 1986. This book includes descriptions of all models of Heidoscop, Rolleidoscop, Rolleiflex, Rolleicord, 35mm and 6x6cm SLRs, subminis, and compact 35s. 272pp. 5½x8½". 134 B&W photographs. $16.95. ISBN 0-931838-06-1

COLLECTORS GUIDE TO KODAK CAMERAS

Millions of Americans own antique Kodak cameras, and this is the first comprehensive guide which describes and illustrates most of these family heirlooms. Large, clear photos and easy to use index make it an ideal guide for the novice or expert alike. Identification features have been included for each camera model as well as technical specifications and original prices. Virtually all Kodak and Brownie cameras are listed along with the shutter and lens variations and the years of production for each variation.
176 pages, 5.5x8.5 inches. $12.95. ISBN 0-931838-02-9

Add $1.00 for postage for a single title, $2.00 for any multiple-book order. We will ship by 4th Class Book Rate in the USA and by Surface Mail to foreign countries. If other method of shipping is requested, please include an appropriate amount to cover the cost. Foreign orders, please pay in U.S. Dollars, preferably in currency to avoid excessive bank charges. We accept VISA and MasterCard. Include card number, expiration date, and name of cardholder.

OTHER TITLES ARE UNDER PREPARATION, including:
Collector's Guides to Union Cases, Olympus Cameras, Petri & Kuribayashi Cameras,
and others. Please send self-addressed stamped envelope for complete
list of books available.

Centennial Photo
Rt. 3, Box 1125
Grantsburg, WI 54840 USA

POCKET PRICE GUIDE

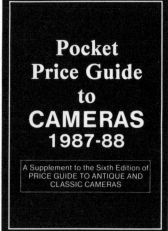
650

BURTON TILLEY BUYS CAMERAS!

TOLL FREE
1-800-525-0359
PLEASE CALL

We Will Buy The Following Cameras in Ex+ or Better Condition at Prevailing Prices.

JAPANESE CAMERAS

Acro 35 w/top viewer
Hansa Canon
Canon S or S-2 any cond.
Canon J or J2, any cond.
Canon Seiki Serenar Lenses
Canon VI or VIT w/Lens
Honor w/lens (Leica copy)
Nikon I Serial #609-1 to 609-759, any cond.
Nikon M Serial #M609-759 to M609-2000, any cond., no sync.
Nikon M Serial #M6092000 to M6094000, any cond. (factory sync) WL
Nikon 50mm lens only, for above, says "Tokyo" not "Japan", some are rare.
Nikon S2, S2 Black, w/lens. Exc+
Nikon S3 w/lens. like new
Nikon S3 Black, w/lens. Exc+
Nikon S4, SP w/lens. Mint
Nikon SP Black, w/lens. Exc++
Nikon S-3M Half frame
Nippon Kogaku "Tokyo" lenses
Nikon 21mm or 25mm lens w/finder for RF
Nikon 50/3.5 Macro, or 50/1.1 SM or BM for RF
Nikon RF any camera accessories
Nippon Camera (Leica copy)
Nippon Camera collapsible fixed lens, any cond.
Look, Leica copy
Peerless, Leica copy

EUROPEAN EQUIPMENT

Alpa-Reflex I, ca. 1947
Bertram (3 lens set) Mint
Casca (no rangefinder) or Casca II (w/RF)
Exakta 6x6 Pre or Post War
Gami (complete)
Kardon Military or Civilian
Leica copies
Minox B new type, Mint
Minx III or IIIS
Pilot TLR
Plaubel Makinette
Cart Bentzin Primarette
Roland
Rolleiflex 4x4 black or grey
Grey Rollei T
Rollei 2.8F or 3.5F, newest, truly Mint, 120/220 Planar
Rolleiwide w/case. Mint
Sept. Exc+
Sybil Baby and all other sizes
Vollenda w/Elmar lens. Exc++

LEICAS

Leitz plastic stereoviewer
Leica IIIc Wartime. Must be Exc+

Leica IIIf RD ST. Must be Mint
Leica Ig. Must be Exc+
Leica M2. Must be Mint
Leica M3 under SR #700200, any cond.
Leica M3 above #1,100,000. Mint
Leica M5 chrome, 3 lug. Mint
Leica Brightline finders 21, 28, 35
Leitz 15 Hologon w/finder
Leitz 28/5.6 Summaron or 28/6.3 Hektor
Leitz 33/2.5 Stemar Stereo. Set.
Leitz 35/2 Summicron. Germany or no eyes-SM
Leitz 50/2 Summicron Rigid, BM
Leitz 50/3.5 Red Dial, Elmar, SM
Leitz 90/2.8 Elmarit or 90/4 Elmarit
Leitz 90/4 Elmar collapsible or SM
Leitz 125/2.5 Hektor w/hood & caps
Leitz 135 Elmar
Leica All Viewfinders, many types
Other cameras - Please CALL

VOIGTLANDER

Bessas, many types, I, II, II Apo-Lanthar
Prominent II
Superb, Heliar or Skopar lens, like new

ZEISS

Contaflex Twin lens truly Mint
35/2.8 Biogon for above w/finder
Contarex Professional, Special, or SE Electronic Exc++
Contarex Super, new type
Contarex 16mm or 18/4 Distagon, black
Contarex 25/2.8 or 35/2 Distagon, black
Contarex 35/4 Curtagon, PA
Contarex 85/1.4 black
Contarex 180/2.8, black RARE
250/4 Sonnar w/knob focus black
Contarex 1000mm or 500mm Mirotar, Valuable
Contarex Vario Sonnar S. Valuable
Contax D, Contax F, Contax S
Contax IIa full sync Exc++, 50/1.5 "Carl Zeiss" lens
Contax IIIa full sync Exc+, 50/1.5
Contax 21mm lens w/finder
Contax 25mm Topogon
Contax 28mm Black Tessar
Contax 35mm Orthometer or Biometer
Contax 35mm Biogon (post war) or Planar
Contax 40mm or 75mm Biotar. Rare
Contax Long Lenses and Contax Reflex Housings
Icarex
Hologon w/grip filter
Baby Ikonta w/Tessar
Super Ikonta A or C w/MX Tessar
Zeiss plastic stereoviewer for Stereotar C

Burton Tilley's
World Cameras
1705 14th Street, Suite 222, Boulder, CO 80302
TOLL FREE 1-800-525-0359 or (303) 443-3097

THE KESSLER COLLECTION

Collectors and dealers in rare and unusual cameras and related
photographica; specializing in the cameras and history of
SIMON WING and fine **STANHOPES**. Mike and Gladys Kessler,
25749 Anchor Circle, San Juan Capistrano, California 92675
714•661•3320.